NEURONAL
INFORMATION TRANSFER

P & S BIOMEDICAL SCIENCES SYMPOSIA Series

HENRY J. VOGEL, Editor
College of Physicians and Surgeons
Columbia University
New York, New York

Henry J. Vogel (Editor). *Nucleic Acid–Protein Recognition,* 1977

Arthur Karlin, Virginia M. Tennyson, and Henry J. Vogel (Editors). *Neuronal Information Transfer,* 1978

NEURONAL INFORMATION TRANSFER

Edited by
ARTHUR KARLIN
VIRGINIA M. TENNYSON
HENRY J. VOGEL
College of Physicians and Surgeons
Columbia University
New York, New York

ACADEMIC PRESS

New York San Francisco London 1978

A Subsidiary of Harcourt Brace Jovanovich, Publishers

ACADEMIC PRESS, INC.
111 Fifth Avenue, New York, New York 10003

United Kingdom Edition published by
ACADEMIC PRESS, INC. (LONDON) LTD.
24/28 Oval Road, London NW1 7DX

Library of Congress Cataloging in Publication Data

Main entry under title:

Neuronal information transfer.

(P & S biomedical sciences symposia series)
Papers of a symposium held on the Harriman campus of Columbia University June 10–12, 1977.
Includes bibliographical references and index.
1. Neural transmission––Congresses. 2. Neurotrans–mitters––Congresses. I. Karlin, Arthur. II. Tennyson, Virginia M. III. Vogel, Henry James, Date
IV. Series.
QP364.5.N48 596'.01'88 77–25732
ISBN 0–12–398450–5

PRINTED IN THE UNITED STATES OF AMERICA

Contents

Regulation of Sensitivity to β-Adrenergic Stimulation in the Rat Pineal

MARTIN ZATZ AND JULIUS AXELROD

Molecular Properties and Regulation of Alpha- and Beta-Adrenergic Receptors

ROBERT J. LEFKOWITZ

Biochemical Characterization of Neurotransmitter Receptors in the Brain

IAN CREESE AND SOLOMON H. SNYDER

PART II CHOLINERGIC SYSTEM

The Cholinergic Electromotor System of *Torpedo:* Recent Biochemical and Morphological Findings

V. P. WHITTAKER

Studies on the Mechanism of Acetylcholine Release in Mammalian Tissues

B. COLLIER, P. BOKSA, AND D. ILSON

Nerve Excitability: From Descriptive Phenomenology to Molecular Interpretation

DAVID NACHMANSOHN

Acetylcholine Receptor-Mediated Ion Flux in Electroplax Membrane Microsacs

JOHN P. ANDREWS AND GEORGE P. HESS

Acetylcholine Receptor: Accelerated Dissociation of Receptor–Ligand Complexes

ALFRED MAELICKE AND MARJORIE McCONNELL

Elementary Chemical Reactions of Acetylcholine with Receptor and Esterase: Relationship to Neuronal Information Transfer

EBERHARD NEUMANN, TERRONE L. ROSENBERRY, AND HAI WON CHANG

PART III AMINO ACID SYSTEMS

Roles of GABA in Neurons in Information Processing in the Vertebrate CNS

EUGENE ROBERTS

An Evaluation of the Proposed Transmitter Role of Glutamate and Taurine

ROGER A. NICOLL AND EDGAR T. IWAMOTO

PART IV BRAIN PEPTIDES AND OPIATE SYSTEM

Biologically Active Peptides in the Brain

MICHAEL J. BROWNSTEIN

Opioid Peptides

JOHN HUGHES

On the Physiologic Role of Endorphins

B. M. COX AND AVRAM GOLDSTEIN

Discovery and Function of the Endorphins

L. TERENIUS

Recent Studies on Opiate Receptors and Analogs of Enkephalin

KENNETH A. BONNET, JACOB M. HILLER,
AND ERIC J. SIMON

PART V CYCLIC NUCLEOTIDES

Regulation of Cyclic AMP Metabolism by Neural Hormones in Brain

THEODORE W. RALL

Electrophysiological Assessment of Mononucleotides and Nucleosides as First and Second Messengers in the Nervous System

G. R. SIGGINS

PART VI NEURONAL STRUCTURE AND DEVELOPMENT

Development of Peripheral Monoaminergic Neurons

MICHAEL D. GERSHON, TAUBE P. ROTHMAN,
AND HOWARD HOLTZER

List of Participants

ANDREWS, JOHN, P., Institute for Cancer Research, The Fox Chase Cancer Center, Philadelphia, Pennsylvania 19111

AXELROD, JULIUS, Laboratory of Clinical Science, National Institute of Mental Health, Bethesda, Maryland 20014

BARKAI, AMIRAM, New York State Psychiatric Institute, Mail Box 54, New York, New York 10032

BARNES, ELIZABETH N., Department of Pathology, College of Physicians and Surgeons, Columbia University, New York, New York 10032

BAUGHMAN, ROBERT W., Department of Neurobiology, Harvard University, Boston, Massachusetts 02115

BLANC, WILLIAM A., Department of Pathology, College of Physicians and Surgeons, Columbia University, New York, New York 10032

BODICK, NEIL, Department of Biological Sciences, Columbia University, New York, New York 10027

BOKSA, P., Department of Pharmacology and Therapeutics, McGill University, Montreal H3G 1Y6, Canada

BONNET, KENNETH A., Department of Psychiatry, New York University Medical Center, New York, New York 10016

BROWNSTEIN, MICHAEL J., Laboratory of Clinical Science, National Institute of Mental Health, Bethesda, Maryland 20014

BURDEN, STEVEN J., Harvard Medical School, Boston, Massachusetts 02115

CASSANO, VICTORIA A., Department of Human Genetics and Development, College of Physicians and Surgeons, Columbia University, New York, New York 10032

CHANG, HAI WON, Departments of Neurology and Biochemistry, College of Physicians and Surgeons, Columbia University, New York, New York 10032

CHÉRAMY, A., Collège de France, 75231 Paris Cedex 05, France

CHESKIN, HOWARD, Department of Pathology, College of Physicians and Surgeons, Columbia University, New York, New York 10032

CHIANG, GRACE S., Department of Psychiatry, New York University Medical Center, New York, New York 10016

COLLIER, BRIAN, Department of Pharmacology and Therapeutics, McGill University, Montreal H3G 1Y6, Canada

CONSTANTINE-PATON, MARTHA, Department of Biology, Princeton University, Princeton, New Jersey 08540

COTÉ, LUCIEN J., Department of Neurology, College of Physicians and Surgeons, Columbia University, New York, New York 10032

COX, BRIAN M., Addiction Research Foundation, Palo Alto, California 94304

CRAIN, STANLEY M., Department of Neuroscience, Albert Einstein College of Medicine, Bronx, New York 10461

CREESE, IAN, Departments of Pharmacology and Experimental Therapeutics and Psychiatry and Behavioral Sciences, The Johns Hopkins University School of Medicine, Baltimore, Maryland 21205

CUNIN, RAYMOND, Laboratory of Microbiology, Free University of Brussels, Research Institute, C.E.R.I.A., B1070 Brussels, Belgium

DENNIS, MICHAEL J., Departments of Physiology and Biochemistry, University of California School of Medicine, San Franscisco, California 94143

DREYFUS, CHERYL, Department of Anatomy, College of Physicians and Surgeons, Columbia University, New York, New York 10032

EDELIST, TRUDY, Department of Pathology, College of Physicians and Surgeons, Columbia University, New York, New York 10032

FAHN, STANLEY, Department of Neurology, College of Physicians and Surgeons, Columbia University, New York, New York 10032

FINCK, DONALD, Department of Anesthesiology, College of Physicians and Surgeons, Columbia University, New York, New York 10032

FINE, ALAN, Department of Molecular Biology, University of Pennsylvania, Philadelphia, Pennsylvania 19174

FISCHBACH, GERALD D., Department of Pharmacology, Harvard Medical School, Boston, Massachusetts 02115

FREDERICKSON, ROBERT C. A., Pharmacology Department, Eli Lilly and Company, Indianapolis, Indiana 46206

FRIEDLANDER, DAVID, Department of Biological Sciences, Columbia University, New York, New York 10027

FRIEDMAN, EITAN, Department of Psychiatry, New York University Medical Center, New York, New York 10016

GERSHON, MICHAEL D., Department of Anatomy, College of Physicians and Surgeons, Columbia University, New York, New York 10032

GINTZLER, ALAN R., Department of Anatomy, College of Physicians and Surgeons, Columbia University, New York, New York 10032

GLOWINSKI, JACQUES, Collège de France, 75231 Paris Cedex 05, France

GODMAN, GABRIEL C., Department of Pathology, College of Physicians and Surgeons, Columbia University, New York, New York 10032

GOLDENSOHN, ELI S., Department of Neurology, College of Physicians and Surgeons, Columbia University, New York, New York 10032

GOLDSTEIN, AVRAM, Addiction Research Foundation, Palo Alto, California 94304

GOODRICH, JAMES T., Department of Anatomy, College of Physicians and Surgeons, Columbia University, New York, New York 10032

GORIO, ALFREDO, Department of Biophysics, The Rockfeller University, New York, New York 10021

GRAPPI, VINCENT, Department of Pharmacology, Rutgers Medical School, Piscataway, New Jersey 08854

GREENSPAN, RALPH, Biology Department, Brandeis University, Waltham, Massachusetts 02154

HALPERIN, A., Department of Biology, Princeton University, Princeton, New Jersey 08540

HARRINGTON, WILLIAM, Department of Pathology, College of Physicians and Surgeons, Columbia University, New York, New York 10032

HAYS, ARTHUR P., Department of Pathology, College of Physicians and Surgeons, Columbia University, New York, New York 10032

HESS, GEORGE P., Section of Biochemistry, Cornell University, Ithaca, New York 14850

HILLER, JACOB M., Departments of Psychiatry and Medicine, New York University School of Medicine, New York, New York 10016

HIRSCH, JAMES D., Department of Physiological Chemistry and Pharmacology, Roche Institute of Molecular Biology, Nutley, New Jersey 07110

HOFFER, BARRY J., Department of Pharmacology, University of Colorado School of Medicine, Denver, Colorado 80262

HOLCK, MARK I., Department of Pharmacology, School of Medicine, Wayne State University, Detroit, Michigan 48201

HOLTZER, HOWARD, Department of Anatomy, University of Pennsylvania School of Medicine, Philadelphia, Pennsylvania 19104

HSIAO, WENDY W. L., Department of Human Genetics and Development, College of Physicians and Surgeons, Columbia University, New York, New York 10032

HUGHES, JOHN, Department of Biochemistry, Imperial College of Science and Technology, London, SW7, England

ILSON, D., Department of Pharmacology and Therapeutics, McGill University, Montreal H3G 1Y6, Canada

IWAMOTO, EDGAR T., Departments of Pharmacology and Physiology, University of California School of Medicine, San Francisco, California 94143

JOH, TONG H., Department of Neurology, Cornell University Medical College, New York, New York 10021

JONAKAIT, G. MILLER, Department of Anatomy, College of Physicians and Surgeons, Columbia University, New York, New York 10032

KANDEL, ERIC R., Division of Neurobiology and Behavior, College of Physicians and Surgeons, Columbia University, New York, New York 10032

KARLIN, ARTHUR, Department of Neurology, College of Physicians and Surgeons, Columbia University, New York, New York 10032

KOE, B. KENNETH, Department of Pharmacology, Pfizer Inc., Groton, Connecticut 06340

KOWALIK, SHARON, Department of Pathology, College of Physicians and Surgeons, Columbia University, New York, New York 10032

KRAUTHAMER, GEORGE, Department of Anatomy, Rutgers Medical School, Piscataway, New Jersey 08854

KROOTH, ROBERT S., Department of Human Genetics and Development, College of Physicians and Surgeons, Columbia University, New York, New York 10032

KUSLANSKY, BERNARD, Department of Physiology, College of Physicians and Surgeons, Columbia University, New York, New York 10032

LAMPERT, MURRAY, Department of Electrical Engineering, Princeton University, Princeton, New Jersey 08540

LEEMAN, SUSAN, Department of Physiology, Harvard Medical School, Boston, Massachusetts 02115

LEFKOWITZ, ROBERT J., Departments of Medicine and Biochemistry, Duke University Medical Center, Durham, North Carolina

LEVINTHAL, CYRUS, Department of Biological Sciences, Columbia University, New York, New York 10027

LOVELACE, ROBERT E., Department of Neurology, College of Physicians and Surgeons, Columbia University, New York New York 10032

LOVELL, RICHARD A., Ciba-Geigy Corporation, Summit, New Jersey 07901

LUBIT, BEVERLY W., Department of Physiology, College of Physicians and Surgeons, Columbia University, New York, New York 10032

MAELICKE, ALFRED, Max-Planck-Institut, 46 Dortmund, Rheinlanddamm 201, West Germany

MAYLIÉ-PFENNINGER, MARIE-FRANCE, Sloan-Kettering Institute for Cancer Research, New York, New York 10021

MAZAITIS, ANTHONY J., Department of Pathology, College of Physicians and Surgeons, Columbia University, New York, New York 10032

MCCONNELL, MARJORIE, The Rockefeller University, New York, New York 10021

MERRIFIELD, R. BRUCE, The Rockefeller University, New York, New York 10021

MESA-TEJADA, RICARDO, Department of Pathology, College of Physicians and Surgeons, Columbia University, New York, New York 10032

MEYER, JERROLD S., The Rockefeller University, New York, New York 10021

MODEL, PAT G., Department of Neuroscience, Albert Einstein College of Medicine, Bronx, New York 10461

MORRIS, DEBORAH G., Department of Physiology, Harvard Medical School, Boston, Massachusetts 02115

NACHMANSOHN, DAVID, Departments of Neurology and Biochemistry, College of Physicians and Surgeons, Columbia University, New York, New York 10032

NEUMANN, EBERHARD, Max-Planck-Institut für Biochemie, D-8033 Martinsried-München, Federal Republic of Germany

NICOLL, ROGER A., Department of Pharmacology and Physiology, University of California School of Medicine, San Fransciso, California 94143

NIEOULLION, A., Collège de France, 75231 Paris Cedex 05, France

NORTON, GERARD, Lenox Hill Hospital, New York, New York 10021
O'DONOVAN, GERARD A., Department of Biochemistry and Biophysics, Texas A & M University, College Station, Texas 77843
OKAMOTO, MICHIKO, Department of Pharmacology, Cornell University Medical College, New York, New York 10021
OLSON, LARS, Department of Histology, Karolinska Institutet, S-10401 Stockholm, Sweden
PALUCH, EDWARD, Department of Pathology, College of Physicians and Surgeons, Columbia University, New York, New York 10032
PEARSE, ANTONIA, Department of Pathology, College of Physicians and Surgeons, Columbia University, New York, New York 10032
PFENNINGER, KARL H., Department of Anatomy, College of Physicians and Surgeons, Columbia University, New York, New York 10032
PRAKASH, OM, Department of Biochemistry, College of Physicians and Surgeons, Columbia University, New York, New York 10032
RALL, THEODORE W., Department of Pharmacology, University of Virginia School of Medicine, Charlottesville, Virginia 22903
RAPPORT, MAURICE M., Division of Neuroscience, New York State Psychiatric Institute, New York, New York 10032
RAYPORT, STEPHEN, Division of Neurobiology and Behavior, College of Physicians and Surgeons, Columbia University, New York, New York 10032
REIS, DONALD J., Department of Neurology, Cornell University Medical College, New York, New York 10021
RIEMAN, MARK W., The Rockefeller University, New York, New York 10021
ROBERTS, EUGENE, Division of Neurosciences, City of Hope National Medical Center, Duarte, California 91010
ROBSON, RONALD, Ciba-Geigy Corporation, Summit, New Jersey 07901
ROSENBERRY, TERRONE L., Departments of Neurology and Biochemistry, College of Physicians and Surgeons, Columbia University, New York, New York 10032
ROTHMAN, RICHARD, Department of Anatomy, School of Medicine, University of Pennsylvania, Philadelphia, Pennsylvania 19104
ROTHMAN, TAUBE P., Department of Anatomy, College of Physicians and Surgeons, Columbia University, New York, New York 10032
ROWLAND, LEWIS P., Department of Neurology, College of Physicians and Surgeons, Columbia University, New York, New York 10032
SABBATH, MARLENE, Department of Pathology, College of Physicians and Surgeons, Columbia University, New York, New York 10032
SACHAR, EDWARD J., Department of Psychiatry, College of Physicians and Surgeons, Columbia University, New York, New York 10032
SACKS, WILLIAM, Research Department, Rockland Psychiatric Center, Convent Road, Orangeburg, New York 10962
SCHECHTER, NISSON, Department of Biochemistry, State University of New York, Stony Brook, New York 11794
SCHENKER, CHRISTINA, LHRRB and Department of Physiology, Harvard Medical School, Boston, Massachusetts 02115

SCHMIDT, JAKOB, Department of Biochemistry, State University of New York, Stony Brook, New York 11794

SEIGER, ÅKE, Department of Histology, Karolinska Institutet, S-10401 Stockholm, Sweden

SIGGINS, GEORGE R., Salk Institute, San Diego, California 92112

SIMON, ERIC J., Departments of Psychiatry and Medicine, New York University School of Medicine, New York, New York 10016

SLOVIN, SUSAN, Department of Pathology, College of Physicians and Surgeons, Columbia University, New York, New York 10032

SNYDER, SOLOMON H., Departments of Pharmacology and Experimental Therapeutics and Psychiatry and Behavioral Sciences, The Johns Hopkins University School of Medicine, Baltimore, Maryland 21205

STEINACKER, ANTOINETTE, Department of Pharmacology, Rutgers Medical School, Piscataway, New Jersey 08854

TAMIR, HADASSAH, Department of Neuroscience, New York State Psychiatric Institute, New York, New York 10032

TAPLEY, DONALD F., Office of the Dean, College of Physicians and Surgeons, Columbia University, New York, New York 10032

TENNYSON, VIRGINIA M., Department of Anatomy, College of Physicians and Surgeons, Columbia University, New York, New York 10032

TERENIUS, LARS, Department of Medical Pharmacology, University of Uppsala, S-75123 Uppsala, Sweden

THOMSON, JEANNE, Department of Pathology, New York Medical College, Valhalla, New York 10595

TRUBATCH, JANETT, Department of Physiology, New York Medical College, Valhalla, New York 10595

VOGEL, HENRY J., Department of Pathology, College of Physicians and Surgeons, Columbia University, New York, New York 10032

VOGEL, RUTH H., Department of Pathology, College of Physicians and Surgeons, Columbia University, New York, New York 10032

VON EULER, U. S., Fysiologiska Institutionen I, Karolinska Institutet, S-10401 Stockholm, Sweden

WHITTAKER, V. P., Abteilung für Neurochemie, Max-Planck-Institut für Biophysikalische Chemie, D-3400 Göttingen, Federal Republic of Germany

WILLIAMS, MICHAEL, Neuropsychopharmacology Section, Merck Institute for Therapeutic Research, West Point, Pennsylvania 19486

WOODWARD, DONALD J., Department of Cell Biology, University of Texas Health Science Center, Dallas, Texas 75235

YIP, J. W., Departments of Physiology and Biochemistry, University of California School of Medicine, San Francisco, California 94143

ZATZ, MARTIN, Laboratory of Clinical Science, National Institute of Mental Health, Bethesda, Maryland 20014

ZEMLAN, FRANK P., The Rockefeller University, New York, New York 10021

ZUCKERKANDL, EMILE, Linus Pauling Institute of Science and Medicine, Menlo Park, California 94025

Preface

Neurotransmitter–receptor recognition and the ultrastructure of the environment in which it occurs are central concerns of neurobiology. Recent bursts of research activity have dramatically advanced our understanding of information transfer in this area and have thus provided insights, in molecular detail, into long-standing problems of neural function.

The progress achieved encouraged discussion of a number of systems showing defined receptor–effector interactions. The receptor concept recommended itself as a natural focus for relevant molecular, ultrastructural, and broader morphological considerations.

A symposium on "Neuronal Information Transfer" was held at Arden House, on the Harriman Campus of Columbia University, from June 10 through June 12, 1977. The meeting was the second of the P & S Biomedical Sciences Symposia. The proceedings are contained in this volume.

Dr. Donald F. Tapley, Dean of the Faculty of Medicine, welcomed the participants and spoke on the history of the neurosciences at the College of Physicians and Surgeons (P & S), which sponsors the symposia.

To Professor Ulf S. von Euler, we express our sincere gratitude for his delivery of the Opening Address and for his most generous helpfulness. The contributions of the session chairmen, Dr. Jacques Glowinski, Dr. Donald J. Reis, Dr. Victor P. Whittaker, Dr. David Nachmansohn, Dr. Eugene Roberts, Dr. John Hughes, Dr. Lars Terenius, Dr. Theodore W. Rall, Dr. Gerald D. Fischbach, and Dr. Lewis P. Rowland, are acknowledged with much appreciation.

Several colleagues from P & S, Dr. Philip E. Duffy, Dr. Michael D. Gershon, Dr. Eric R. Kandel, Dr. Lewis P. Rowland, Dr. Edward J. Sachar, and Dr. Edward B. Schlesinger, kindly agreed to serve as honorary hosts, and, as a group, provided much constructive advice, as did Dr. Nachmansohn and Dr. James H. Schwartz. A fruitful discussion with Dr. Cyrus Levinthal is also gratefully acknowledged. Special thanks go to Dr. Julius Axelrod, who devoted a good deal of his time to giving us most valued counsel. For his advice on the scope of the meeting, we are greatly indebted to Dr. Marshall W. Nirenberg.

Dr. Ruth H. Vogel has made much appreciated contributions to the organization of the symposium and to the preparation of this volume.

Welcome financial aid was provided by a grant from the National Science Foundation.

Arthur Karlin
Virginia M. Tennyson
Henry J. Vogel

OPENING ADDRESS

Opening Address

U. S. von EULER
Fysiologiska Institutionen I
Karolinska Institutet
Stockholm, Sweden

It is a great honor and pleasure for me to give the Opening Address at this Symposium where so many distinguished colleagues are gathered. While expressing my sincere thanks to Professor Vogel for his kind invitation to this attractive place, I may also express the hope that my fellow members of the Conference will bear with me if my presentation somewhat arbitrarily deals with various problems related to the general theme of this Symposium. Should it be felt that I refer too frequently to my stepchildren, Substance P and the prostaglandins the reason is simply that I have known them for many years and have tried over a long period of time to find a suitable role for them.

The developments in the nervous information transfer field in recent years suggest perhaps that the time is approaching for certain modifications of the classic neurotransmission concept developed and formulated some 50 years ago.

With your consent, I will briefly recapitulate some major points in the history of nervous signal transfer.

Chemical transmission of nerve impulses to the target cell, first suggested by DuBois Reymond 100 years ago (1), is still only incompletely understood, even if the classic experiments by Cannon, Loewi, and Dale did much to clarify the situation. The same can be said about the development of the receptor concept which is so intimately connected with chemical transmission. It is largely through the fundamental studies by Langley that the basis for thinking in terms of receptors was created.

Historically it is interesting to note how various alternatives have been considered with regard to active neurotransmitters and receptors. Noting that adrenaline exerted both stimulatory and inhibitory actions, Langley (2) in 1906 assumed that the target cells possessed "receptive substances" which could differentiate the action, in

ISBN 0-12-398450-5

other words, were supplied with different sets of receptors. This seems to be the first clearly expressed concept of specific receptors. Dale's (3) discovery that some but not all of the adrenaline effects were blocked by ergot alkaloids could readily be made to fit into this scheme. A complication arose when Barger and Dale (4) a few years later found that noradrenaline better mimicked the effects of sympathetic nerve stimulation than adrenaline, which was supposed to be the transmitter according to the proposal made by Elliott (5).

In pursuance of his receptor theory, Langley (6) postulated in 1909 a variety of receptors, responding more or less specifically to a large number of agonists and antagonists. Though this concept met with some opposition at the time, it gradually gained acceptance, and in analogy to the previously differentiated adrenaline receptors, Dale, some 25 years later, made his distinction between nicotinic and muscarinic receptors for acetylcholine.

The theory of two sympathins proposed by Cannon and Rosenblueth (7) was in fact a consequence of the assumption that adrenaline was the transmitter, which, however, did not fit in with the experimental facts.

Systematic studies by Ahlquist (8) and others have further contributed to the concept of differentiated receptors. Of special importance was the finding of a specific beta blocker (9), and in the last 10 years we have seen a fractionation of the adrenergic receptors or adrenoceptors into both $alpha_1$ and $alpha_2$ and $beta_1$ and $beta_2$ (cf. 10). Further subdivisions may well appear, and have in fact been suggested.

In the meantime it also became clear that noradrenaline like adrenaline had both excitatory and inhibitory actions, and around 1950 noradrenaline was generally accepted as the sympathetic or adrenergic neurotransmitter.

The isolation and characterization of receptors within several areas, which we have witnessed in recent years, have provided a solid basis for better understanding agonist–receptor interaction. Still there are many "dark" spots concerning the specificity of receptors and the nature of the binding, not to mention the transducer mechanism by which the target cell is activated.

The relatively simple system of cholinergic and adrenergic neurotransmission as formulated by Dale (11) in 1933 brought a much-needed element of order, and greatly assisted in the understanding of the mediation of nerve signals to the responding cells. It soon turned out, not unexpectedly perhaps, that these systems needed complementation. In the following 40 years a large number of factual and tentative neurotransmitters have been suggested or proposed. For some of them the transmitter function seems to be proved beyond doubt, such as for 5-HT, dopamine, and GABA, but also for some others the evidence must be regarded as strong.

Again, for a number of other naturally occurring bioactive substances with a clear relationship to nervous structures the transmitter function still remains uncertain. Various amino acids, peptides, a simple alkaloid like piperidine, and fatty acids like prostaglandins belong to this group. All of them seem to interfere with nervous activity in one way or another, and this is the reason why transmitter action sometimes has been attributed to them. Some of them seem to have a true transmitter action in certain animal species, often primitive ones.

In connection with this new situation the concept of moderators or modulators of nerve action has gradually developed. If it was not a transmitter, the active agent could at least serve as a modulator. Unfortunately many of them have no known antagonists, which otherwise could have been helpful in ascertaining their physiological function.

If we consider, for instance, Substance P, recent studies using immunofluorescence technique have confirmed its presence in nerve fibres and also shown a distribution within the nervous system which strongly suggests important functions both centrally and peripherally (12). The preponderance of substance P in the dorsal roots and dorsal horns of the spinal cord actually led Lembeck as early as 1953 to postulate that Substance P might serve as transmitter of the primary sensory neuron (13). This hypothesis has found strong support by Otsuka and his group (14) who were able to show its depolarizing effects on the spinal motor neurons of the frog and young rats. Krnjević (15) has confirmed the activity of Substance P on the spinal cord but seems to doubt its transmitter function on the grounds that it acts too slowly. However, it could still exert a facilitating or reinforcing modulator action, perhaps in a similar way as it seems to act on intestinal motor activity, including peristalsis. Substance P occurs in relatively large amounts in the autonomic nerve plexa in the intestine, and enhances the peristaltic reflex in isolated intestinal preparations. Similarly, it increases the nerve-induced twitch of vas deferens in the guinea pig, in concentrations which are less than $\frac{1}{100}$ of that necessary to evoke a contraction (16). Substance P (SP) occurs in peripheral nerves in subcellular granules like noradrenaline and other neurotransmitters (17). The active peptide can readily be released from the isolated granules by lysis or acid treatment. It remains to be shown whether the SP fibers exert their action on other autonomic fibers in the periphery or act directly on target cells.

The inhibitory effect of prostaglandins on nerve-induced contractions of the splenic capsule (18) or the vas deferens may also be referred to as a modulator effect on the transmission, though it is believed that PG is formed in the target cells. Actually, a large number of compounds seem to act on the release of transmitter from the nerve endings, thereby either facilitating or inhibiting the effect on the target cells.

The mechanism for this kind of effect is not known but it has been suggested that the agents induce alteration of the axon membrane at the nerve terminal, causing changes in ion movements, perhaps in the first place, Ca^{2+}. In other instances the release and uptake mechanisms in the transmitter storage granules may be affected.

A discovery of great significance was the finding by Paton and Vizi (19) that adrenergic agonists of the alpha type inhibited the transmitter release from nerves innervating intestinal smooth muscle. This meant that an established neurotransmitter like noradrenaline could regulate the release of another transmitter, presumably by acting on prejunctional receptors close to the site of transmitter liberation.

Soon afterward this phenomenon was shown to occur also for adrenergic nerves (cf. 10). In this case one could speak of a negative feedback system mediated by prejunctional α-receptors, since it appears that some of the released noradrenaline inhibits further liberation of the neurotransmitter. Interestingly, there is no increase in the twitch response in the rat vas deferens after blocking of the prejunctional α-receptors (20). In human blood vessels β_2-agonists increase the nerve-induced release of noradrenaline (21). Propranolol does not, however, decrease the release under normal conditions, which argues against a physiological positive feedback system. It was not so long ago that the old belief that various drugs acted on nerve endings was refuted as old-fashioned thinking and replaced by the then-modern concept of agonist and antagonist action only on the target cell. But now it must be seriously considered that the nerve ending is amply supplied with receptors of various kinds. It must also be remembered that, for instance, the adrenergic storage granules respond to a large number of drugs which more or less strongly alter their capacity or rate of uptake and release of transmitter. A few examples may serve to illustrate this point. Thus the release of noradrenaline from adrenergic nerve granules is inhibited by almost all adrenoceptor blockers which seem to have a special affinity for them. Radioactively labeled adrenergic blockers act as ligands to the granules, suggesting a kind of receptor function for them (22). This would also logically fit in with the specific uptake of noradrenaline in the granules, although the complex so formed does not have to exert a transducer action. A number of psychotropic drugs behave in a similar way, inhibiting both release and concomitant uptake in adrenergic nerve granules. A notable exception is haloperidol which is of interest since dopamine does not appear to bind as such to adrenergic nerve granules.

Particular interest has developed in recent years in the naturally occurring ligands to opiate receptors through the work of Snyder, Hughes, Kosterlitz, Terenius, Hökfelt, Guillemin, Goldstein, and others. Since this field will be covered extensively in this volume, I shall not go into any detail with regard to enkephalin, endorphins, and β-lipotropin. However it might be mentioned that Substance P exerts analgesic actions when injected intracerebroventricularly in mice (Krivoy *et al.*, 23) and that this peptide and enkephalin appear to be closely related spatially in some parts of the central nervous system. Snyder has commented on the occurrence of opiate receptor binding in some primitive animals like hagfish and the dogfish. It is perhaps of interest to recall that the central nervous system of these species also contains substance P in considerable quantities.

The pharmacologically induced actions on the nerve endings determining or modulating transmitter release are indeed not of a uniform type. As mentioned previously, α-receptors apparently invariably mediate inhibition of the transmitter release, whereas β-receptors tend to facilitate release. In the case of human blood vessels, such a facilitating effect is mediated by β_2-receptors (21), and an effect of the same kind is observed on the isolated cat spleen. These effects are consequently blocked by butoxamine. However this is not an absolute rule since in the guinea pig vas deferens, for instance, the prejunctional β_2-receptors mediate inhibition of the twitch.

This difference brings up the question of the nature of neurotransmission in the guinea pig vas deferens. It is well known that the vas deferens is amply supplied with adrenergic nerves and very sparsely with cholinergic nerves. The stimulating effect of noradrenaline on the organ is rather weak however. Moreover this amine usually inhibits the nerve-induced twitch. It has also been repeatedly noted that adrenergic blockers do not inhibit the nerve-induced twitch, not even an irreversible blocker like phenoxybenzamine administered over long periods of time. Ambache and Zar (24) therefore questioned the general belief that noradrenaline acts as a motor transmitter in this organ. It is true that prolonged nerve stimulation causes a tonic contraction which is abolished by α-adrenergic blockers, indicating that this form of contraction is mediated by the adrenergic neurotransmitter. The twitch remains, however, and can be abolished by neuronal blockers, such as guanethidine, tetrodotoxin, and lanthanum, which apparently blocks the calcium transfer necessary for contraction.

The inhibitory effect of noradrenaline on the twitch is partly an α-effect and partly a β_2-effect, since it is annulled only by combined action of α- and β_2-antagonists (25). We also found that tyramine or phenethylamine could inhibit the twitch, apparently by releasing noradrenaline. The picture is complicated by the fact that noradrenaline, in addition to its prejunctional inhibitory effect, also exerts a postjunctional stimulating action, and, in agreement with this, tyramine may sometimes enhance the twitch, an action which is abolished by α-blockers.

It thus seems unlikely that noradrenaline serves as motor transmitter for the twitch in the guinea pig vas deferens. The question as to the nature of the transmitter therefore has to be considered. It has already been shown that ACh possibly plays some part in the motor transmission (Birmingham, 26), but since the twitch is largely unaffected by atropine, ACh could hardly be the main transmitter. The same is true for 5-HT and for ATP. We then turned our attention to K^+ as a possible candidate, as proposed for neural transmission by Nachmansohn (27). Actually Eccles, before his "conversion," had proposed K^+ as ganglionic transmitter. We have no proof so far that K^+ triggers the twitch response in the guinea pig vas deferens, but some circumstances tend to support the idea that K^+ is somehow involved in the transmission. First, the isolated organ is extremely sensitive to K^+ and responds with a twitchlike contraction to K^+ concentrations in the bath, less than 10 m*M*. Second, the nerve endings are characteristically invaginated in the smooth muscle cells of the organ with a very narrow synaptic gap of the order of 20 nm (28). Moreover, the nerve-induced twitch, which had been abolished by lanthanum, could be revived, not only by addition of 10 m*M* Ca^{2+} but also by the same low concentration of K^+. The slow decrease of the twitch response after lanthanum might therefore be associated with a secondary depletion of available K^+ which could be restored by raising the K^+ concentration in the bath (29).

The twitchlike contractions caused by addition of K^+ to the bath, or replacement of the normal bath solution by one containing more K^+, are inhibited by noradrenaline as well as by tyramine in higher concentrations. In the latter case noradrenaline is probably released and causes inhibition. This response seems to indicate that K^+

produces the twitchlike response by activating the neuron. In fact the response to low concentrations of K^+ is totally prevented by tetrodotoxin. The K^+-induced twitch should therefore be subject to prejunctional inhibition. Low concentrations of tyramine, on the other hand, increase the twitch response to K^+, presumably by releasing some facilitating factor.

Low concentrations of ACh also elicit a twitchlike contraction of the isolated guinea pig vas deferens, although this seems to be due mainly to a direct effect on the smooth muscle since it is not abolished by TTX. This effect is enhanced by K^+ added in concentrations as low as 1 m*M* which do not exert an action on their own. In such a case it appears conceivable that K^+ acts postjunctionally in conjunction with ACh. Alternatively, K^+ and ACh might act together in activating the nerve.

It is clearly too early to make any definite statements as to the role of K^+ in neurotransmission in the nerve-induced twitch in the guinea pig vas deferens, but it is tempting to regard an ionic factor as important in this instance. Moreover, if this special case of rapid information transfer should prove to be mediated by ion effects, a similar mechanism might well be operating, for instance, in some parts of the central nervous system in agreement with the proposal made by Neumann *et al.* (27) for interneuronal transfer. The classical transmitters might under such conditions play the role of modulators rather than triggering the primary response.

The guinea pig vas deferens is not the only example of an organ in which the current concepts of transmitter mechanisms seem to require some modifications and, since ionic movements have already been implicated in the transmission processes, further disclosures along these lines do not seem unlikely.

REFERENCES

1. DuBois Reymond, E. (1877) *Gesammelte Abh. Allg. Muskel-Nervenphys.* **2,** 700.
2. Langley, J. N. (1906) *Proc. R. Soc. London, Ser. B* **78,** 183.
3. Dale, H. H. (1906) *J. Physiol. (London)* **34,** 163–206.
4. Barger, G., and Dale, H. H. (1910) *J. Physiol. (London)* **41,** 19–59.
5. Elliott, T. R. (1905) *J. Physiol. (London)* **32,** 401–467.
6. Langley, J. N. (1909) *J. Physiol. (London)* **39,** 235–295.
7. Cannon, W. B., and Rosenblueth, A. (1933) *Am. J. Physiol.* **104,** 557–574.
8. Ahlquist, R. P. (1948) *Am. J. Physiol.* **153,** 586–600.
9. Powell, C. E., and Slater, J. H. (1958) *J. Pharmacol. Exp. Ther.* **122,** 480–488.
10. Starke, K., Taube, H. D., and Borowski, E. (1977) *Biochem. Pharmacol.* **26,** 259–268.

11. Dale, H. H. (1933) *J. Physiol. (London)* **80,** 10P–11P.
12. Hökfelt, T., Kellerth, J. -O., Nilsson, G., and Pernow, B. (1975) *Science* **190,** 889–890.
13. Lembeck, F. (1953) *Naunyn-Schmiedebergs Arch. Exp. Pathol. Pharmakol.* **219,** 197–213.
14. Takahashi, T., Konishi, S., Powell, D., Leeman, S. E., and Otsuka, M. (1974) *Brain Res.* **73,** 59–69.
15. Krnjević, K. (1977) *In* "Substance P" (U. S. von Euler and B. Pernow, eds.), pp. 217–230. Raven Press, New York.
16. von Euler, U. S., and Hedqvist, P. (1974) *Acta Physiol. Scand.* **90,** 651–653.
17. von Euler, U. S. (1963) *Ann. N. Y. Acad. Sci.* **104,** 449–463.
18. Hedqvist, P. (1970) *Acta Physiol. Scand., Suppl.* **345.**
19. Paton, W. D. M., and Vizi, E. S. (1969) *Br. J. Pharmacol.* **35,** 10–28.
20. Drew, G. M. (1977) *Eur. J. Pharmacol.* **42,** 123–130.
21. Stjärne, L., and Brundin, J. (1976) *Acta Physiol. Scand.* **97,** 88–93.
22. von Euler, U. S. (1972) *J. Endocrinol.* **55,** i–ix.
23. Krivoy, W. A., Stewart, J. M., and Zimmerman, E. (1977) *In* "Substance P" (U. S. von Euler and B. Pernow, eds.), pp. 195–200. Raven Press, New York.
24. Ambache, N., and Zar, M. A. (1971) *J. Physiol. (London)* **216,** 359–389.
25. Hedqvist, P., and von Euler, U. S. (1976) *Eur. J. Pharmacol.* **40,** 153–162.
26. Birmingham, A. T. (1966) *Br. J. Pharmacol.* **27,** 145–156.
27. Neumann, E., Nachmansohn, D., and Katchalsky, A. (1973) *Proc. Natl. Acad. Sci. U.S.A.* **70,** 727–731.
28. Furness, J. B. (1974) *Br. J. Pharmacol.* **50,** 63.
29. von Euler, U. S., and Hedqvist, P. (1975) *Med. Hypothesis* **1,** 214–216.

PART I

BIOGENIC AMINE SYSTEMS

Genetic, Structural, and Molecular Mechanisms Governing the Long-Term Regulation of Tyrosine Hydroxylase, a Neurotransmitter Synthesizing Enzyme in the Brain

DONALD J. REIS AND TONG HYUB JOH
Department of Neurology
Cornell University Medical College
New York, New York

NEUROTRANSMITTER SYNTHESIZING ENZYMES IN THE BRAIN

It is now widely accepted that in brain, as in the periphery, the transfer of information from one nerve cell to another is largely mediated by chemical messengers. These are released from presynaptic terminals to act primarily upon the postsynaptic membrane. While it has long been recognized that the rate and duration of neuronal firing is essential in determining the availability of neurotransmitters, in recent years there has been increasing awareness that other cellular processes may also play an important role. These include the mechanisms governing their synthesis, storage, release, and metabolic inactivation.

One of the most important determinants of neurotransmitter economy is the activity of the enzymes which subserve their biosynthesis. The identity of these enzymes has been well characterized for several classes of chemical transmitters (1). Those neurotransmitter synthesizing enzymes which have been studied in the greatest detail include (1) the catecholamine synthesizing enzymes, tyrosine hydroxylase (TH), aromatic L-amino-acid decarboxylase (AADC), dopamine-β-hydroxylase (DBH), and phenylethanolamine-*N*-methyltransferase (PNMT); (2) tryptophan hydroxylase, the enzyme catalyzing the biosynthesis of serotonin; (3) choline acetyltransferase (CAT), the enzyme subserving the biosynthesis of acetylcholine; and (4) glutamic acid decarboxylase (GAD), the enzyme essential for the biosynthesis of GABA. It has been clearly shown that the activities and amounts of each or several of these enzymes are not fixed, but can be regulated by many factors including the concentration of substrates, the availability of cofactors, the concentration of end product, nerve impulse activity, axonal integrity, the hormonal and metabolic environment of the neuron, and the molecular form of the enzyme. The relative contribution of these factors to neurotransmitter biosynthesis varies between different enzymes and, even for the same enzyme, between different tissues.

It is evident that the principal biological function of the neurotransmitter synthesizing enzymes is to catalyze the biosynthesis of their respective chemical messengers. However, it is important to emphasize that in brain these macromolecules are neuron-specific proteins, restricted to chemically defined pathways. Because they can be easily characterized they have the potential to serve as useful probes in neurobiology, for example, as chemical markers for the biochemical and/or immunocytochemical identification of the pathways of chemically selective systems in the brain, or as model intraneuronal proteins useful, for example, in studying the cellular biology of protein biosynthesis in the CNS.

It is the objective of this presentation to illustrate some aspects of the long-term regulation of one of these neurotransmitter synthesizing enzymes in brain: tyrosine hydroxylase (TH). Until recently, studies of the molecular mechanisms involved in regulating the enzyme have been restricted to kinetic analysis. However, the purification of TH, and production of antibodies to it, have permitted a much more detailed analysis of the molecular events in its regulation. In this essay we shall demonstrate that there are several mechanisms which determine relatively static levels of TH activity in brain, including variations in accumulation of enzyme molecules, changes in its molecular form, and differences in the number of TH-containing neurons and/or their processes.

LONG-TERM REGULATION OF BRAIN TYROSINE HYDROXYLASE

BRAIN TYROSINE HYDROXYLASE

Distribution. In brain, as in periphery, TH catalyzes the initial and presumably rate-limiting step in the biosynthesis of the catecholamine neurotransmitters dopamine, norepinephrine, and epinephrine. The enzyme is contained preponderantly in intrinsic neurons of the brain. The only noncentral source is the sympathetic plexus, which accompanies the blood vessels penetrating into the depths of the brain, arising from peripheral sympathetic ganglion cells of the superior cervical ganglion.

The neuronal systems of the brain which contain TH have been well characterized. They consist of the central noradrenergic neurons whose cell bodies lie in the lower brainstem and whose processes traverse well-defined pathways to innervate specific regions of the forebrain, hypothalamus, brainstem, cerebellum, and spinal cord (2–4).

Of particular interest, with respect to the noradrenergic system, are the neurons of the nucleus locus coeruleus, a nucleus of the rostral pons, in which all of the constituent neurons appear to synthesize, store, and release norepinephrine. In the rat each nucleus locus coeruleus contains approximately 1400 neurons (4) giving rise to axons which are the principal source of all norepinephrine in the forebrain and cerebellum (2,5). The second major group of central catecholamine neurons are those which contain dopamine (2–4). The major dopaminergic systems consist of (1) the nigrostriatal system, whose cell bodies reside in the substantia nigra (A9 group) and whose axons primarily innervate the corpus striatum; (2) the so-called mesolimbic and mesocortical systems, whose cell bodies reside in the A10 group in the ventral tegmentum in the midbrain, and whose axons innervate limbic forebrain regions; and (3) other dopaminergic cell groups with short axons which reside largely in the hypothalamus and retina.

Immunocytochemistry. By the purification of TH and the development of specific antibodies to it (7), it has been possible to prove by immunocytochemistry that the enzyme is indeed exclusively

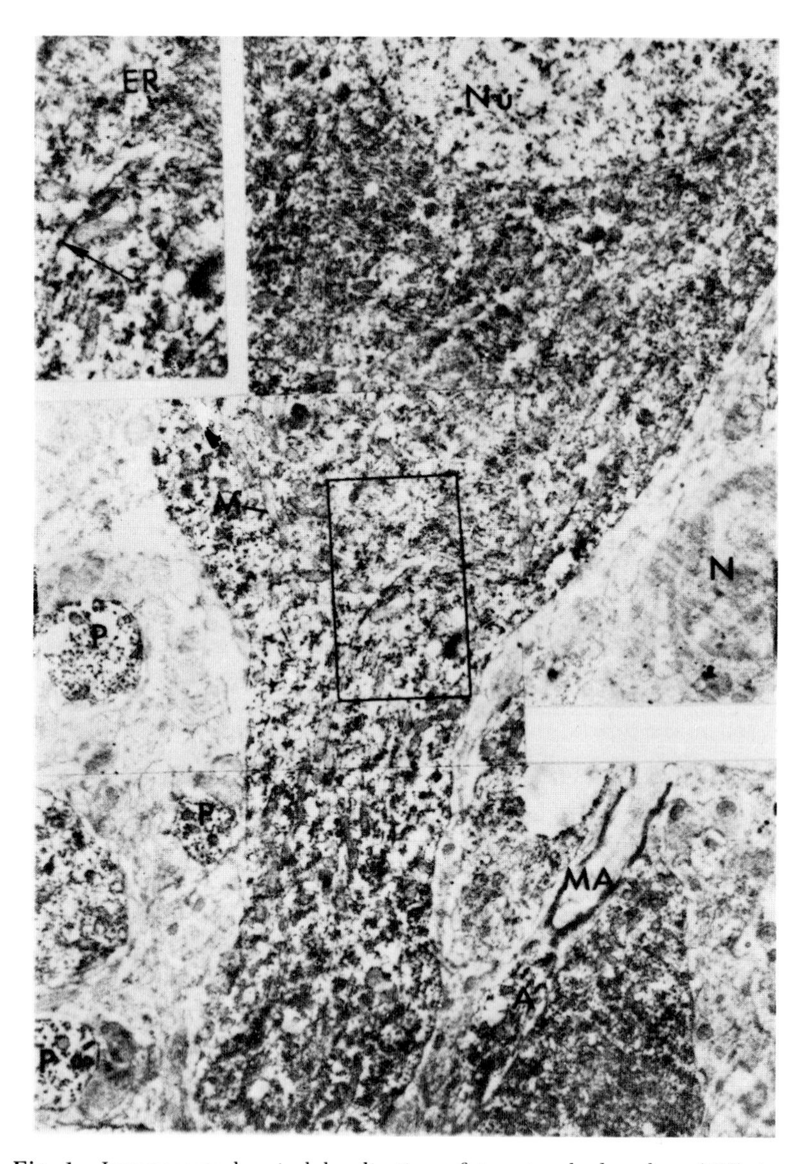

Fig. 1. Immunocytochemical localization of tyrosine hydroxylase (TH) in noradrenergic neurons of the nucleus locus coeruleus using the PAP method. Montage of neuron containing the reaction product for TH. The dense granular cytoplasmic staining can be traced from the lighter nucleus (Nu) into the proximal process which, as indicated by the synapse (S), is a dendrite. The granular peroxidase stain is more intense on the outer surface of the endoplasmic reticulum (ER) and often forms a single strand (arrow) at the junction between the perikaryon and the process, as shown in the

intraneuronal, as suggested by the distribution of the transmitter and by its restriction to central catecholamine neurons (8,9). It is also cytoplasmic and found in all portions of the neuron, including perikarya, dendrites, axons, and terminal processes of the two neuronal systems which synthesize, store, and release dopamine and norepinephrine (Fig. 1).

In the cell body the enzyme is cytoplasmic and is associated with the endoplasmic reticulum and Golgi apparatus, although a substantial amount may be seen free in the cytosol or associated with ribosomes (8,9). In axons and dendrites the enzyme is largely found in association with microtubules, while in the axon terminal the enzyme appears to be in close association with both small and large vesicles. It is not possible, because of the resolution of the staining method, to determine whether or not the enzyme is a constituent of these subcellular organelles, or merely adheres to their surface. The association with microtubules might represent a form of the enzyme in its state of being transported from the cell body to the periphery.

Molecular Weight Forms of TH. Although TH is found in the dopaminergic and noradrenergic neuronal systems of CNS, peripheral sympathetic ganglia, and chromaffin cells of the adrenal medulla, the enzyme is not identical in its molecular weight (MW) forms within these disparate tissues (10). When homogenates of various brain regions, sympathetic ganglia, or adrenal medulla are passed through a Sephadex G-150 column, TH activity can be eluted in different fractions specific to each tissue and differing in molecular weights (MW's) (Fig. 2). TH in noradrenergic neurons, including cell bodies (e.g., the nucleus locus coeruleus) and terminals (e.g., hypothalamus) has an MW of approximately 200,000, is associated with an RNA-containing moiety, and upon immunotitration with an antibody to TH exhibits a biphasic immunotitration curve. After RNase treatment the MW is reduced by approximately 50,000 and the biphasic immunotitration curve becomes monophasic. In contrast, dopaminergic neurons contain enzyme in two MW forms which can be detected both in the cell bodies (e.g., the substantia nigra) and in terminals (e.g., the caudate nucleus). The MW's of these forms are

---

insert in the upper left-hand corner of the figure. Numerous other processes (P) can be distinguished in the surrounding neuropil. Labeled axons (A) are unmyelinated, as compared to unstained myelinated axons (MA). Glial cytoplasm and nucleus (N) were unstained. ×6,000. Insert, ×72,000. (From Pickel *et al.*, 8.)

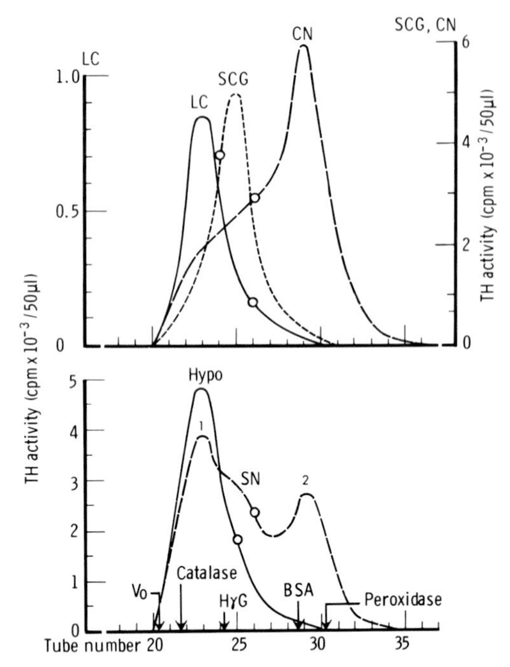

Fig. 2. Sephadex column chromatography of TH from different tissues of rat. One and one-half milliliters of tissue homogenate were passed over a Sephadex G-150 (superfine) grade column (1.5 cm × 27 cm) and collected in fractions of 0.65 ml. Locations of fractions in which standard proteins were eluted are indicated on the abscissa of the lower figure. Open circles on each line represent points at which the ratio of the spectrophotometric readings of 280/260 nm were 1.0. Abbreviations: HγG, human gamma globulin; Hypo, hypothalamus; LC, locus coeruleus; SCG, superior cervical ganglion; SN, substantia nigra; Vo, void volume. (From Joh and Reis, 10.)

200,000 and 65,000, respectively. The 65,000 MW form of the enzyme has a monophasic immunotitration curve, and is unassociated with RNA. TH from sympathetic ganglia has an MW of 130,000.

When TH from rat central noradrenergic or dopaminergic neurons or adrenal medulla is purified to homogeneity and subjected to SDS electrophoresis, the purified TH separates into three separate subunits (Fig. 3) irrespective of its source. The MW's of these subunits are 52,000, 62,000, and 68,000. In contrast, TH purified from human neuroblastoma cell lines (11) can only be isolated as a single protein band with an MW of 62,000.

It is reasonable to assume from these findings that TH in rat catecholamine neurons or chromaffin cells consists of different combinations of three subunits and that the element with an MW of 62,000 rep-

Fig. 3. SDS electrophoretic pattern of TH from caudate nucleus of rat brains (left) and cultured cells of human neuroblastoma (right). Left: Three protein subunits of TH having MW's of 52,000, 62,000, and 68,000. Right: A single protein band of TH from a neuroblastoma. MW is 62,000.

resents the major enzyme protein. On this basis it is probable that TH with sympathetic ganglia having an MW of 130,000 represents a combined form (dimer) of the enzyme containing two subunits of approximately 62,000 MW and that the TH in dopaminergic neurons with an MW of approximately 65,000 is an isolated form of the basic unit. Conceivably, polymerization, aggregation, or combinations of these subunits, alone or in association with an RNase-sensitive moiety may alter the structure and specific activity of the enzyme confirming the tissues-specific characteristics to it. It may also represent a mode of enzyme regulation.

The biochemistry of TH has been extensively reviewed elsewhere (12,13). It should be noted that the formal analyses of the catalytic properties of enzyme have usually been restricted to studies of partially purified material prepared for the most part from bovine adrenal medulla. In light of the recognition of the multiplicity of MW forms of the enzyme, such studies need to be repeated for each specific form.

PROLONGED ELEVATION OF TH ACTIVITY IN BRAIN: INDUCTION, DELAYED ACTIVATION, AND COLLATERAL SPROUTING

Induction. In 1969 Mueller, Theonen, and Axelrod (14) demonstrated that conditions which presumably increased the discharge of sympathetic neurons including the drug reserpine, would increase the activity of the catecholamine biosynthetic enzymes, TH and DBH, in sympathetic ganglia and in chromaffin cells of the adrenal gland. The response (15,16) appeared after a latency of 12–48 hr; was enzyme selective, affecting TH and DBH but not the relatively nonspecific AADC; was prolonged, lasting weeks; was abolished by transection of the cholinergic input (i.e., by transection of the preganglionic cholinergic fibers), or by administration of cholinergic antagonists; and could be reproduced by the administration of cholinergic agonists even after denervation. By use of antibodies to TH, Joh *et al.* (7) demonstrated that the augmentation of TH activity in sympathetic ganglia was entirely attributable to increased accumulation of enzyme protein, most likely as a consequence of increased biosynthesis.

Several years later we (16,17) and, independently, Zigmond *et al.* (18), discovered that reserpine will also increase, in a dose-dependent manner, the activity of TH within the noradrenergic neurons of the nucleus locus coeruleus of the rat brain (Fig. 4). The increase occurs after a latency of 24–48 hr, can reach maximal levels of up to 300% of

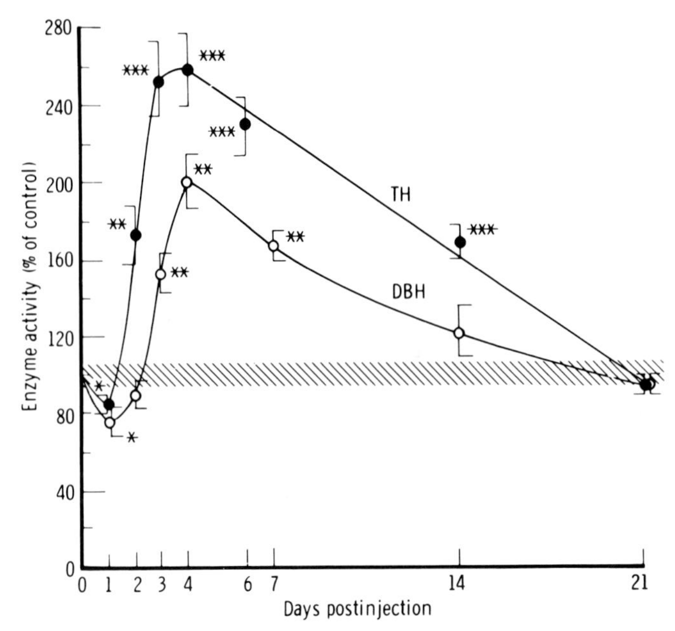

Fig. 4. Time course of changes in TH and DBH activity in the locus coeruleus of the rat following a single injection of reserpine (10 mg/kg ip). Enzyme activity is expressed as percent of mean activity in locus coeruleus in six to eight saline-injected controls. *, $p < 0.02$; **, $p < 0.01$; ***, $p < 0.001$. (From Reis *et al.*, 16.)

control, and may remain elevated for up to 21 days. The rise of TH activity in the locus coeruleus is paralleled by an increase in the activity of DBH but not of AADC. The increase of TH in noradrenergic neurons of the brain is not found in the dopaminergic system and, hence, exhibits anatomical selectivity. The elevation of TH and also of DBH in the locus coeruleus can be demonstrated, by immunotitration, to be due to the accumulation of enzyme protein (Fig. 5). Thus, the response of TH within the locus coeruleus is comparable to that elicited by the drug in sympathetic ganglia and adrenal medulla.

It is not known whether the increased accumulation of TH in the locus coeruleus initiated by reserpine is a consequence of increased synthesis, reduced degradation, or a combination of both processes. Although no information is yet available with respect to TH, we have recently measured the changes in the rate of incorporation of radioactive amino acids into DBH in the locus coeruleus following administration of reserpine (19). DBH protein was isolated by precipi-

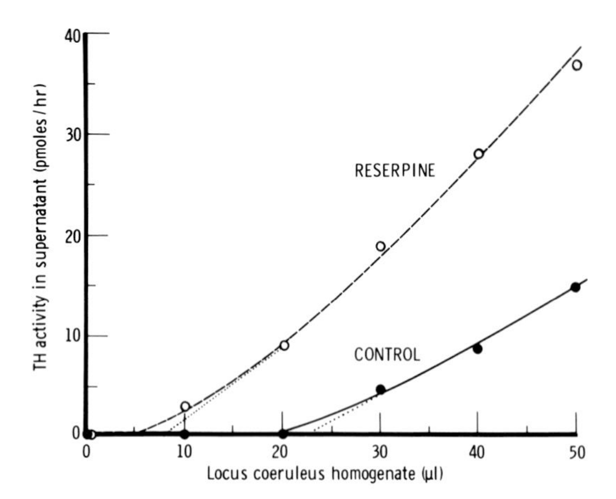

Fig. 5. Immunoprecipitation of TH in the locus coeruleus from reserpine-treated (○--○) and control (●--●) rats. Six rats were treated with a single dose (10 mg/kg ip) of reserpine and killed 4 days later. Enzyme activity was increased 2.8-fold. Ten μl of antibody was added to 10–50 μl of homogenate of treated or control animals and the final volume adjusted to 60 μl with buffer. After the mixture was centrifuged, TH activity was assayed in the supernatant. Note that the equivalence point is shifted to the left in locus coeruleus from reserpine-treated animals, indicating accumulation of more specific enzyme protein. (From Reis *et al.*, 16.)

tating it with an antibody to the enzyme from homogenates of the locus coeruleus and was subsequently separated from contaminating proteins by SDS electrophoresis. After reserpine the rate of incorporation of ^{3}H-leucine or lysine into DBH protein increased to approximately 80% of control (Fig. 6), suggesting that the twofold increase of DBH activity elicited by the drug was entirely attributable to an increase in the rate of synthesis of the enzyme. Preliminary studies of changes in TH suggest that it too is increased by a change in the rate of synthesis (20).

These studies demonstrate that the *activity* of TH can be increased in the central noradrenergic neuron by increasing the number of enzyme molecules via mechanisms which increase the relative rate of its biosynthesis. Whether such inductive processes occur with physiological stimuli is not certain. It has been observed that many days following the increase of TH activity in the locus coeruleus there is a gradual increase of the enzyme activity in the territory innervated by fibers of the nucleus, for example, in the anterior hypothalamus, cerebellum, and frontal cortex (21,22). The accumulation of activity appears to proceed in a proximal–distal manner from the cell body. That it depends upon the integrity of the axon has been demonstrated

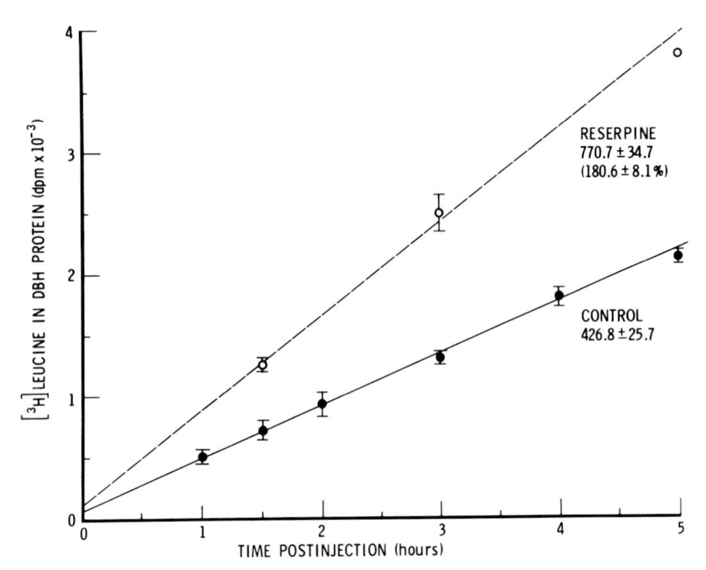

Fig. 6. The rate of incorporation of ^{3}H-leucine into dopamine-β-hydroxylase (DBH) in the locus coeruleus of reserpine-treated (○) and control (●) rats. ^{3}H-leucine (New England Nuclear) in artificial CSF was perfused into the IVth ventricle 48 hr after a single dose (10 mg/kg ip) of reserpine, and rats were killed at various times indicated. Tissues were homogenized in 5 m*M* potassium phosphate buffer and centrifuged at 9000 *g*. Antibody to DBH and an equivalent amount of purified DBH were added to the supernatant. The mixture was incubated at room temperature for 1 hr and allowed to stand overnight in a cold room. Antigen–antibody precipitate was collected by centrifugation and washed with ice-cold saline, followed by SDS electrophoresis. The DBH band on a gel was cut and digested with NCS-tissue solubilizer, and the radioactivity was counted. Note that ^{3}H-leucine incorporation into DBH by reserpine increased approximately 80%.

by interrupting its progression by axonal transection (22). The calculated rate of transfer of the increase of TH activity is at a rate of about 1 mm/day, a rate substantially slower than that required for the usual axonal transport of the enzyme or the transmitter in periphery (23).

The mechanisms accounting for this delayed and remote augmentation (22) of enzyme activity remain unknown. The slow accumulation of TH in distal processes could be due to (1) a slower transport of the enzyme in the CNS than in the periphery; (2) some alteration in the transport mechanism as a consequence of the action of reserpine; or (3) conceivably, some other substance, possibly an activator, which is transported at a low rate. It is not possible without immunotitration to determine whether or not there is more enzyme protein or merely activated enzyme.

Delayed Activation. Since in the periphery the induction of TH in sympathetic ganglia and chromaffin cells of the adrenal medulla is mediated by a cholinergic preganglionic neuron (14,15), we sought to establish if a cholinergic mechanism also initiated induction of this enzyme in the central noradrenergic neurons of the locus coeruleus. Although the locus coeruleus appears to receive a cholinergic innervation (24,25), it is not possible within the CNS, as in the periphery, to selectively denervate the input. To circumvent this limitation we decided to examine the effects of administration of a centrally active cholinergic agonist, oxotremorine, reasoning that if cholinergic mechanisms were involved in the inductive process in the brain they would be triggered by such treatment.

Administration of the centrally acting cholinergic (muscarinic) agonist oxotremorine elicited a 1.5-twofold increase in the activity of TH in the locus coeruleus (Fig. 7) (26). The response, which could be blocked by atropine, occurred after a latency of 24 hr. It reached a peak by 72 hr and the enzyme remained elevated for 14 days. The effect could be initiated by other centrally acting muscarinic agonists. With closer examination it was evident that while sharing a comparable time course to induction, as well as being restricted only to noradrenergic neurons, the oxotremorine-elicited increase of TH differed from that produced by induction. The magnitude of the

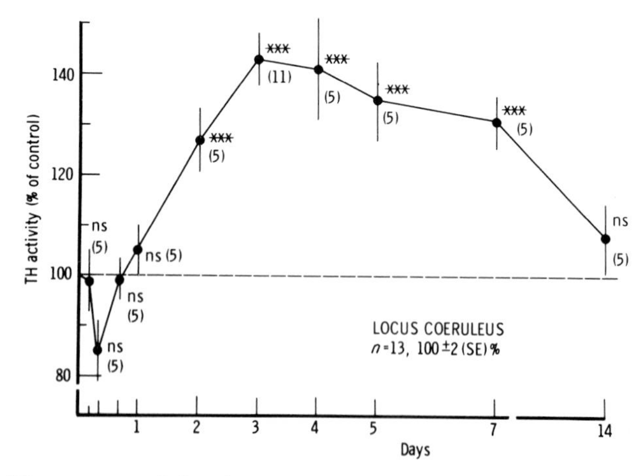

Fig. 7. Time course of the changes in tyrosine hydroxylase (TH) activity in the locus coeruleus of the rat after injection of oxotremorine (1.5 mg/kg subcutaneously). Values (mean ± SEM) are expressed as percentages of controls. Control values were (mean ± SEM; n = 13) 1627 ± 49 pmoles of dopa per pair of locus coeruleus. Figures in brackets represent number of observations. ***, p <0.001 compared with controls; ns, not significant.

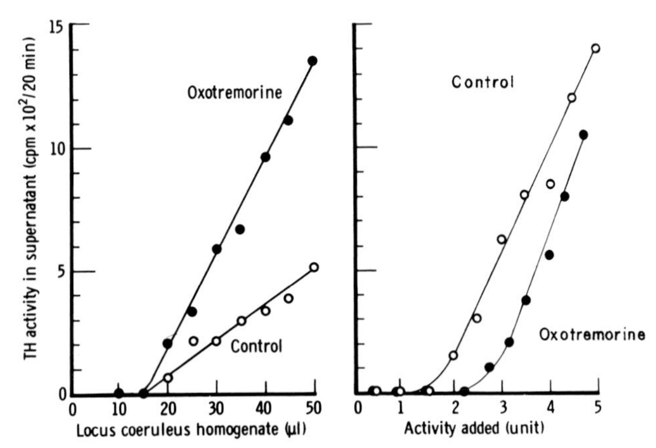

Fig. 8. Immunotitration of TH in LC at 3 days after oxotremorine. Left panel: Immunotitration with equal volumes of homogenate. Note overlapping equivalence points and different slopes. Right panel: Immunotitration with homogenate adjusted to have equal activity. Note curves are separate. These findings indicate activation and not accumulation of enzyme. (From Pickel *et al.*, 9.)

response was smaller and it was unassociated with changes in DBH. The most dramatic difference between the change initiated by oxotremorine and activation was revealed by immunotitration (Fig. 8). Unlike induction the increase of TH activity produced by oxotremorine was due to enhanced catalytic activity of enzyme molecules and not to changes in their number. We therefore termed the response "*delayed activation*" (26) to account for its latency and prolonged duration.

Kinetic analysis (Fig. 9) indicates that the increase of the activity in the locus coeruleus produced by oxotremorine is, like that with reserpine, associated with an elevation of V_{max} without a change of K_m for substrate or cofactor. This finding would suggest that the delayed activation of TH is a consequence of the removal of a noncompetitive inhibitor, the production of a specific activator, or conformational changes of enzyme. Additional experiments, however, indicate that it is unlikely to be due to endogenous activators or inhibitors, and, at present, we favor the view that it is due to activation processes.

The next question is where in the central nervous system oxotremorine exerts its action on TH. One attractive possibility is that oxotremorine activates muscarinic receptors located directly on the noradrenergic cell bodies of the locus coeruleus, or on immediately adjacent ones, which are synaptically linked to the noradrenergic neurons. Histochemical evidence supports this as a possible mecha-

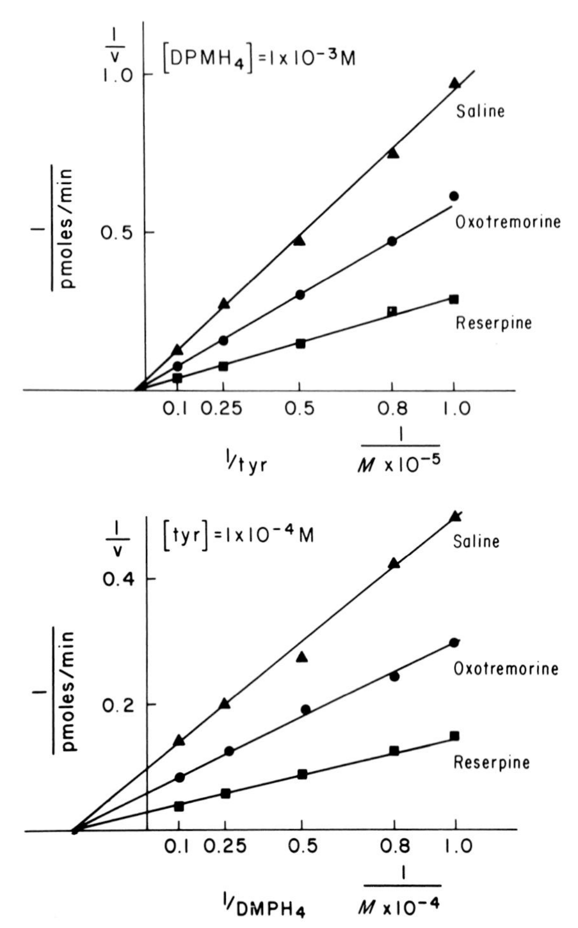

Fig. 9. Kinetic analysis of TH in the LC from reserpine-induced, oxotremorine-activated, and control rat homogenates. Note that both the induced and activated forms did not change K_m for substrates while changing V_{max}. (From Reis *et al.*, 22.)

nism. The locus coeruleus contains many cholinesterase-positive nerve terminals (24) along with substantial quantities of choline acetyltransferase (25).

The functional significance of delayed activation of tyrosine hydroxylase remains to be fully established. The fact that there appears to be a selective increase of the possible rate-limiting enzyme in the biosynthesis of catecholamines would imply that it is a mechanism promoting the availability of neurotransmitter. Moreover, the fact that the enzyme can be activated by physostigmine (26), a drug which facilitates the action of native acetylcholine, implies that it may be a process which occurs in response to endogenously released transmitters. The prolonged time course of the response to a single dose of oxotremorine is surprising, since this drug is not believed, like reserpine, to substantially affect that storage mechanism for noradrenaline. The prolonged time course is provocative because it suggests the existence of a mechanism in the neuron, possibly suited for the long-range adaptation of catalytic activity of tyrosine hydroxylase to transmitter demand.

Collateral Sprouting. A third mode whereby TH activity can be increased in brain is by an increase in the number of TH-containing processes. While this mechanism accounts for most, if not all, of the increase of TH in terminal fields during growth and development of brain (27) it can also occur in adult animals during collateral sprouting (28).

It is now established that catecholamine neurons of the CNS, both noradrenergic and dopaminergic, have the capacity to undergo collateral sprouting (29–31). The most potent stimulus appears to be the removal, by a lesion, of a noncatecholaminergic input in an area innervated by the terminals of catecholamine neurons. In an apparent response to the opening of unoccupied synaptic sites, the intact catecholamine axons sprout and occupy the abandoned synapses.

We have recently observed that there is an increase in TH activity in areas where collateral sprouting of central catecholamine neurons

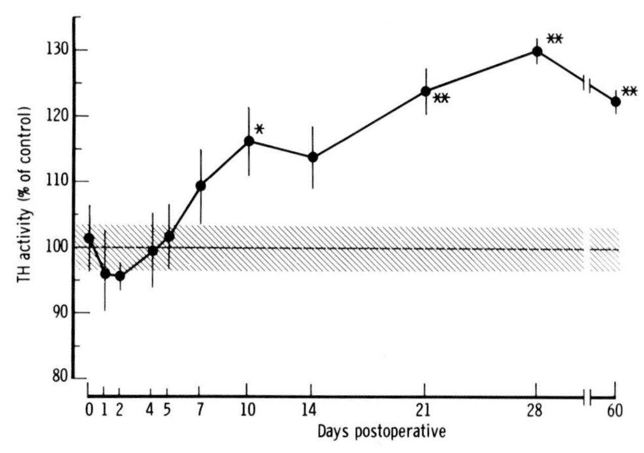

Fig. 10. Changes in TH activity in the olfactory tubercle at various days following ablation of ipsilateral olfactory bulb. The increase in enzyme activity reflects growth of collateral sprouts from dopaminergic terminals. (From Gilad and Reis, 28.) * $p < 0.05$; ** $p < 0.005$.

occurs. Utilizing as a model system the olfactory tubercle in which collateral sprouting of the dopaminergic innervation is promoted by removal of the ipsilateral olfactory bulb, we observed that by 7–10 days following the lesion TH began to gradually increase, rising to about 125% of control by day 28 where it remained permanently elevated (Fig. 10). The increase in TH (as determined by immunocytochemistry) appears to be due to more enzyme protein. Moreover, immunocytochemical examination of the olfactory tubercle demonstrates the presence of more TH-containing fibers, a change in their distribution with increased activity in areas previously not innervated by them, and a concurrent increase in the specific uptake of ^{3}H-dopamine into synaptosomes. Thus, an increase in enzyme activity can be produced in the brain merely by increasing the number of specific axon terminals.

PROLONGED REDUCTION IN BRAIN TYROSINE HYDROXYLASE: NEGATIVE INDUCTION OF ENZYME AND CELL DEATH ASSOCIATED WITH AXONAL LESIONS AND REGENERATION

Negative Induction During the Retrograde Reaction. Reduction in the activity of TH in catecholamine neurons of animals is primarily associated with processes which impair the integrity of the neurons. Lesions of the axons of central catecholamine neurons, both dopaminergic and noradrenergic, will produce profound changes in the activity and the amount of TH distal and proximal to the site of injury (see Reis *et al.*, 32, for review; also 5,6,33–35). Distally, in degenerating terminals during the anterograde reaction, enzyme activity declines to reach minimal values, usually 10–20% of control, persisting to the remainder of the animal's life. While the rate at which the enzyme declines in degenerating terminals differs between central noradrenergic and dopaminergic systems (5,6,33–35), in both instances the fall is totally attributable to a loss of enzyme protein (Fig. 11).

Axonal lesions also produce profound changes in the activity and amount of TH in the parent cell body. Following axonal lesions of central noradrenergic neurons and distal lesions of central dopaminergic neurons, a characteristic pattern of changes in TH activity occurs within the perikarya (Fig. 12). Initially, there is usually a substantial increase of enzyme activity followed, within the first 24–48 hr, by a gradual decline reaching 50–60% of control by days 4–5. Enzyme activity remains depressed for 2–3 weeks and then gradually returns to normal. In noradrenergic neurons the reversible

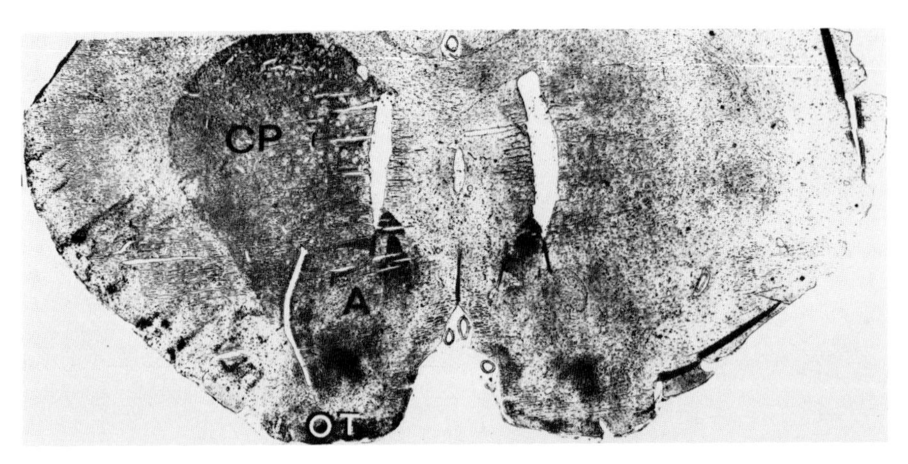

Fig. 11. Cross-section of rat brain at the level of the striatum immunocytochemically stained for TH. A lesion was placed unilaterally 7 days before the animal was killed. The left side of the section is normal (contralateral) and shows dark staining of PAP reaction product primarily within the corpus striatum (CP), olfactory tubercle (OT), and the nucleus accumbens (A). Note the virtual disappearance of stain in the left side, ipsilateral to the lesion. (×7). (From Reis *et al.*, 34.)

changes of TH activity are closely paralleled by changes of DBH (Fig. 12). However, in both dopaminergic and noradrenergic neurons there are no parallel changes in the activity of AADC. The reduction of enzyme activity during the retrograde reaction is due to reduced accumulation of enzyme molecules (5,34,35). Although direct evidence is not available for the mechanisms accounting for the decline of TH, studies of the changes of the rate of synthesis of DBH during the retrograde response (36) indicate that its decline is entirely attributable to a reduction of the rate of synthesis, suggesting that a similar mechanism may account for changes of TH.

The reversible reduced accumulation of neurotransmitter-synthesizing enzymes during the retrograde reaction in central catecholamine neurons appeared to parallel the rate at which regenerative sprouting occurs from the severed axon (32). It has been suggested that the reduction of the enzyme represents a reordering of the priorities of protein biosynthesis, favoring an increased accumulation of proteins involved in the regeneration of cell surface at the expense of those required for neurotransmission (32,37,38).

Another feature of the retrograde response that is of general interest is that the reduced accumulation of enzyme molecules in the cell body is paralleled by a reduction in remote collateral fibers which are uninjured (33). This suggests that the reduced synthesis of enzyme

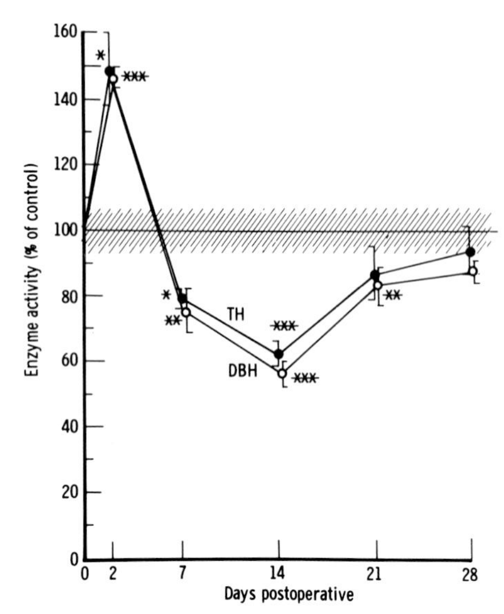

Fig. 12. Time course of changes in TH and DBH activity in ipsilateral locus coeruleus of rat following a unilateral posterolateral hypothalamic lesion. Enzyme activity is expressed as percent of mean activity in locus coeruleus of six to eight unoperated controls. Each point represents mean ± SEM of 6–12 animals. *, $p < 0.01$; **, $p < 0.05$; ***, $p < 0.001$. (From Ross *et al.*, 5.)

initiated in the cell body by a lesion of one of its branches influences the availability of the enzyme to all branches of that nerve cell, possibly including the dendrites.

Cell Death. Axonal lesions of dopaminergic neurons, if sufficiently close to the cell bodies, result in an initial increase of enzyme activity comparable to that produced by distal lesions followed by a prolonged fall of the enzyme to 40–50% of control. However, in contrast to the distal lesions of the dopamine neuron, or lesions anywhere in the noradrenergic system, enzyme activity does not recover (34,35). The permanent reduction of TH activity in the parent cell bodies following such lesions can be entirely attributed to retrograde cell death. This finding indicates again that in any region of the brain the amount of TH is closely related to the number of available nerve cells and/or terminals in which the enzyme is contained.

GENETIC VARIATIONS OF BRAIN TH ACTIVITY

In 1972 Ciaranello *et al.* (39) discovered that the activity of TH varied over a twofold range in the brains of different strains of inbred mice. This finding suggested a probable genetic control over the activity of the enzyme. As discussed above, the variations of TH activity in any brain area of adult animals could be accounted for by certain defined mechanisms, including (1) variations in the type and/or number of catecholamine terminals and/or cell bodies; (2) variations in the amount of enzyme molecules/cell; or (3) variations in the catalytic activity of the enzyme/molecule. We undertook an analysis utilizing immunochemical and immunocytochemical methods to determine which mechanism accounted for the strain-dependent differences of the enzyme (40).

Using one strain of high activity (the BALB/cJ) and another of low TH activity (CBA/J), we were first able to determine that the differences in TH activity between these strains were confined to the dopaminergic neuronal systems. Thus, in the dopaminergic neurons of the substantia nigra–A10 region (Table I) TH activity was 1.8 times greater in the BALB/cJ than in the CBA/J strain; in terminal areas increases of 1.3–1.4 were obtained. In contrast, no differences of enzyme activity were found in the locus coeruleus for TH (Table II), nor for DBH (as a mark of noradrenergic terminals) in the hypothalamus (40). Secondly, by use of immunochemical titration it was possible to determine that the differences of enzyme activity in the two strains were entirely attributable to differences of enzyme protein (Tables I and II). Finally, by immunocytochemical staining for TH and the counting of cells, we observed that the number of TH-containing neurons in the substantia nigra region of the BALB/cJ strain was

TABLE I
Differences in the Activity, Amount, and Number of Cells Containing Tyrosine Hydroxylase in Substantia Nigra–A10 Region of Two Inbred Mouse Strains[a]

	Strain		
	BALB/cJ	CBA/J	BALB/CBA
TH activity (nmoles dopa/nigra/hr)	2.26 ± 0.07 (27)	1.25 ± 0.14 (14)	1.81[b]
Equivalence point (μl of TH antibody)	13.4	7.0	1.91[b]
Number of TH neurons	3384 ± 71 (8)	1664 ± 172 (6)	2.03[b]
TH activity cell	0.667 ± 0.02	0.751 ± .084	0.89[c]

[a] From Ross *et al.* (40).
[b] $p < 0.0001$.
[c] Not significant.

TABLE II
Differences in Activity, Amount, and Number of Cells Containing Tyrosine Hydroxylase in Locus Coeruleus Region of Inbred Mouse Strains

	Strain		
	BALB/cJ	CBA/J	BALB/CBA
TH activity (pmoles dopa/locus/hr)	13.5 ± 1.3 (13)	13.9 ± 1.0 (18)	0.97[b]
Equivalence point (μl of TH antibody)	9.8	9.8	1.00[b]
Number of TH neurons	629 ± 41 (6)	624 ± 53 (4)	1.01[b]
TH activity/cell	0.022 ± .002	0.022 ± .002	1.00[b]

[a] From Ross *et al.* (40).
[b] Not significant.

almost twice that of the CBA/J strain. If one calculated the enzyme activity per neuron between the two strains, no differences were seen. In contrast to the dopaminergic system, there were no differences in the number of neurons in the locus coeruleus.

These results, therefore, demonstrated that the strain-dependent variations of TH activity in the brains of these inbred strains of mice were entirely accounted for by differences in the number of dopaminergic neurons. This finding suggests that there may be a genetic control over the number of chemically specific nerve cells in the brains of different individuals of the same species. The clinical implications of these findings are important since they give credence to an older view, which attributed the vulnerability of degenerative diseases of brain, in part, to variations in the number of such neurons.

SUMMARY

It is evident from the preceding analysis that one macromolecule of importance in the regulation of the transynaptic transfer of information from central catecholamine neurons—the enzyme tyrosine hydroxylase, which catalyzes the first step in catecholamine biosynthesis—is capable of variations in its amount and activity in adult life. Prolonged changes in the activity of the enzyme regionally in the brain can occur in three principal ways. The first is by varying the number of enzyme molecules per neuron, probably by varying the relative rate of its synthesis. This mechanism of induction, usually reversible, can account for the increase of enzyme activity within central noradrenergic neurons elicited by drugs like reserpine, and possibly by stress, and in the reduced accumulation of enzyme in response to axonal lesions. The second mechanism is via an alteration in the catalytic activity of each enzyme molecule, probably as a result of changes in its molecular form. A single example of this is the prolonged increase of TH activity in central noradrenergic neurons elicited by cholinergic stimulation of muscarinic receptors, a phenomenon we have termed "delayed activation." The third mechanism is through regional variations of the number of catecholamine neurons and/or their processes. The number of catecholamine neurons or processes, which in part appear to be under genetic control, can be persistently varied in adults either through processes of collateral sprouting or by retrograde cell death as a consequence of brain injury.

ACKNOWLEDGMENTS

This research was supported by grants from NINCDS, NIMH, and the U.S. Army. Tong Hyub Joh is a Sloan Foundation Fellow in Neurosciences and the recipient of a Research Career Development Award from the NIH.

REFERENCES

1. McGeer, P., and McGeer, E. G. (1973) *Prog. Neurobiol.* **2,** 69–117.
2. Ungerstedt, U. (1971) *Acta Physiol. Scand.* **82,** Suppl. 367, 1–48.
3. Lindvall, O., and Björklund, A. (1974) *Acta Physiol. Scand., Suppl.* **412,** 1–47.
4. Moore, R. Y. (1974) *Neurosci. Res. Program, Bull.* **15,** 160–169.
5. Ross, R. A., Joh, T. H., and Reis, D. J. (1975) *Brain Res.* **92,** 57–72.
6. Ross, R. A., and Reis, D. J. (1974) *Brain Res.* **73,** 161–166.
7. Joh, T. H., Geghman, C., and Reis, D. J. (1973) *Proc. Natl. Acad. Sci. U.S.A.* **70,** 2767–2771.
8. Pickel, V. M., Joh, T. H., and Reis, D. J. (1975) *Proc. Natl. Acad. Sci. U.S.A.* **72,** 659–663.
9. Pickel, V. M., Joh, T. H., and Reis, D. J. (1976) *J. Histochem. Cytochem.* **24,** 792–806.
10. Joh, T. H., and Reis, D. J. (1975) *Brain Res.* **85,** 146–151.
11. Joh, T. H., Ross, R. A., Reis, D. J., and Biedler, J. L. (1978) In preparation.
12. Molinoff, P. B., and Axelrod, J. (1971) *Annu. Rev. Biochem.* **40,** 465–500.
13. Lovenberg, W., and Victor, S. J. (1974) *Life Sci.* **14,** 2337–2353.
14. Theonen, H. (1974) *Life Sci.* **14,** 223–235.
15. Theonen, H. (1975) *Handb. Psychopharmacol.* **3,** 53–86.
16. Reis, D. J., Joh, T. H., Ross, R. A., and Pickel, V. M. (1974) *Brain Res.* **81,** 380–386.
17. Reis, D. J., Joh, T. H., and Ross, R. A. (1975) *J. Pharmacol. Exp. Ther.* **193,** 775–784.

18. Zigmond, R. E., Schon, F., and Iversen, L. K. (1974) *Brain Res.* **70**, 547–552.
19. Ross, T. A., Joh, T. H., and Reis, D. J. (1976) *Am. Soc. Neurochem., Abstr.* p. 79.
20. Joh, T. H., Teitelman, G., and Reis, D. J. (1978) In preparation.
21. Black, I. (1975) *Brain Res.* **95**, 170–176.
22. Reis, D. J., Ross, R. A., Pickel, V. M., Lewander, T., and Joh, T. H. (1975) *In* "Chemical Tools in Catecholamine Research" (C. Jonsson *et al.*, eds.), Vol. 2, pp. 53–60. North-Holland Publ., Amsterdam.
23. Wooten, G. F., and Coyle, J. T. (1973) *J. Neurochem.* **20**, 1361–1371.
24. Ischii, Y. (1957) *Arch. Histol. Jpn.* **12**, 587–612.
25. Palkovits, M., and Jacobowitz, D. M. (1974) *J. Comp. Neurol.* **157**, 29–42.
26. Lewander, T., Joh, T. H., and Reis, D. J. (1977) *J. Pharmacol. Exp. Ther.* **200**, 523–534.
27. Coyle, J. T., and Axelrod, J. (1972) *J. Neurochem.* **19**, 1117–1123.
28. Gilad, G., and Reis, D. J. (1978) *Brain Res.* (in press).
29. Moore, R. Y., Björklund, A., and Stenevi, U. (1971) *Brain Res.* **33**, 13–35.
30. Katzman, R., Björklund, A., Owman, C., Stenevi, U., and West, K. A. (1971) *Brain Res.* **25**, 579–596.
31. Pickel, V. M., Segal, M., and Bloom, F. E. (1974) *J. Comp. Neurol.* **155**, 43–60.
32. Reis, D. J., Ross, R. A., and Joh, T. H. (1978) *In* "Neuronal Plasticity" (C. W. Cotman, ed.). Raven, New York (in press).
33. Reis, D. J., and Ross, R. A. (1973) *Brain Res.* **57**, 307–326.
34. Reis, D. J., Gilad, G., Pickel, V. M., and Joh, T. H. (1978) *Brain Res.* (in press).
35. Gilad, G., and Reis, D. J. (1978) *Brain Res.* (in press).
36. Ross, R. A., Joh, T. H., and Reis, D. J. (1977) *Soc. Neurosci., Abstr.* **3**, 431.
37. Grafstein, B. (1975) *Exp. Neurol.* **48**, 32–51.
38. Lieberman, A. R. (1971) *Int. Rev. Neurobiol.* **14**, 49–124.
39. Ciaranello, R. D., Barchas, R., Kessler, S., and Barchas, J. P. (1972) *Life Sci.* **11**, 565–572.
40. Ross, R. A., Judd, A. B., Pickel, V. M., Joh, T. H., and Reis, D. J. (1976) *Nature* 656.

Regulations of Activity of the Nigrostriatal Dopaminergic Systems

J. GLOWINSKI, A. NIEOULLON,
AND A. CHERAMY
Groupe NB-INSERUM U. 114
Collège de France
Paris, France

INTRODUCTION

During the last few years, a major effort has been made by several groups to understand some of the interneuronal regulatory processes involved in the control of activity of the nigrostriatal dopaminergic neurons. Electrophysiological (1–7) and biochemical (8–11) techniques may be used to record this activity. Our own approach to this problem was to estimate the *in vivo* release of the transmitter from nerve terminals (12,13). The net release of dopamine (DA) reflects any modifications in the dopaminergic neurons activity as well as changes in release resulting from neuronal presynaptic influences on dopaminergic terminals. An original method was developed to study the release of DA. It consists of continuously delivering L-[^{3}H]tyrosine to a push–pull cannula introduced into the caudate nucleus of the cat and measuring ^{3}H-DA released from nerve terminals in superfusates (13). This approach has some advantages when compared to the estimation of the release of unlabeled DA (14,15). Due to its high sensitivity, the time interval of the collected superfusates fractions can be reduced to 10 or 15 min. Furthermore, the separation of ^{3}H-DA from L-[^{3}H]tyrosine and their radioactive

ISBN 0-12-398450-5

metabolites is a much more rapid procedure than the radioenzymatic assay of DA.

Various lines of research were followed: (1) first, we verified that the spontaneous release of newly synthesized ^{3}H-DA was dependent on nerve impulse flow (13); (2) then we examined the effects of the nigral application of substance P (16) and GABA (17) and of some GABA agonists or antagonists (18) on the release of ^{3}H-DA in the ipsilateral caudate nucleus. For this purpose, a second push–pull cannula was introduced into the substantia nigra; (3) experiments were then designed to look for the relationship between the two nigrostriatal dopaminergic pathways and ^{3}H-DA release was simultaneously estimated in each caudate nucleus during the manipulation of one nigrostriatal dopaminergic pathway (19); (4) we then demonstrated the *in vivo* release of ^{3}H-DA from dendrites by delivering L-[^{3}H]tyrosine to a push–pull cannula inserted in the substantia nigra (20); (5) finally, to evaluate the role of the dendritic release of DA in the control of the activity of the dopaminergic neurons, ^{3}H-DA release was determined in each caudate nucleus and each substantia nigra (four push–pull cannula experiments) under several conditions (21, 22). Since most of these studies have been published some of the findings which are of main interest for the understanding of the interneuronal regulatory processes of the nigrostriatal dopaminergic pathways will be briefly summarized.

INFLUENCES OF SUBSTANCE P AND GABAERGIC NEURONS ON THE ACTIVITY OF THE NIGROSTRIATAL DOPAMINERGIC PATHWAY

Several experiments indicate that the release of ^{3}H-DA in the caudate nucleus is dependent on nerve impulse flow. The interruption of firing by local application of tetrodotoxin or by transection of the nigrostriatal dopaminergic pathway blocked the release of ^{3}H-DA (13). On the other hand, the depolarization of the neurons by local application of potassium or electrical stimulation of the substantia nigra stimulated the ^{3}H-transmitter release from nerve terminals (13). Thus, we attempted to detect changes in activity of the dopaminergic neurons by interrupting or simulating messages delivered to the nigral dopaminergic cells or their dendrites.

A striatonigral substance P pathway has been recently discovered (23–25). Moreover, a release of substance P can be evoked by potassium in slices of the rat substantia nigra (26). These substance P neurons may control the activity of the dopaminergic neurons (27). Introduced into the substantia nigra, substance P (10^{-8} M) stimulated the release of ^{3}H-DA in the ipsilateral caudate nucleus in our cat preparation (16). This result supports the hypothesis of an excitatory influence of the substance P pathway on dopaminergic neurons.

From electrophysiological (2,6,7,28) and anatomical (29–32) studies, it is widely accepted that some of the striatonigral descending GABAergic neurons exert a direct inhibitory influence on dopaminergic neurons. Effects induced by pharmacological blockage of the GABAergic transmission supported this hypothesis. Picrotoxin (10^{-5} M) stimulated the release of ^{3}H-DA in the caudate nucleus when introduced into the ipsilateral substantia nigra through a second push–pull cannula (18). A similar effect was observed after the peripheral administration of the GABAergic antagonist (2.5 mg/kg) (18). This activation of the dopaminergic neurons was prevented or abolished when diazepam (10 mg/kg) was injected before or after picrotoxin (33). These data agree with the hypothesis of a direct inhibitory GABAergic input on dopaminergic cells since it is generally thought that the benzodiazepine acts presynaptically by favoring GABA release. However, the complex changes in ^{3}H-DA release observed under the nigral application of GABA suggest that other GABAergic neurons indirectly influence the dopaminergic neurons.

A transient inhibition preceded by a potent stimulation of ^{3}H-DA release was always seen in the caudate nucleus when GABA (10^{-5} M) was introduced for 1 hr in the substantia nigra (17). Furthermore, several GABA-related compounds such as muscimol (10^{-6} M), γ-hydroxybutyrate (10^{-5} M) (34) and baclofen (10^{-6} M) only stimulated the release of ^{3}H-DA (17). This facilitatory effect, similar to that observed with the GABAergic antagonist picrotoxin, suggests an indirect action of GABA and other related compounds on dopaminergic neurons. An inhibition of inhibitory interneurons controlling the dopaminergic neurons could be involved. These interneurons could be glycinergic since glycine is found in large amounts in the substantia nigra (25) and inhibits the activity of nigral cells (36). The effects of glycine and strychnine (an antagonist of GABAergic receptors) on ^{3}H-DA release in the ipsilateral caudate nucleus supported this hypothesis. The nigral application of glycine (10^{-5} M) induced a weak but long-lasting inhibition of ^{3}H-DA release, and this effect was prevented by the simultaneous addition of strychnine (10^{-5} M) (37).

An alternate hypothesis is that GABA (or the other compounds tested) facilitates the release of ^{3}H-DA by extranigral polysynaptic pathways. For instance, this effect could be originally triggered by inhibition of the nigrothalamic neurons (38). According to this hypothesis a nigro-thalamo-cortico-striatal neuronal loop should be involved. This may be the case since the stimulation of the motor or the visual cortex enhanced the release of ^{3}H-DA in the caudate nucleus (39), very likely through an activation of the corticostriatal glutamatergic pathway (40). Indeed, we observed that L-glutamic acid evokes the release of newly synthesized ^{3}H-DA from striatal slices (41). Therefore, the facilitating effect of the nigral application of GABA may indirectly result from a presynaptic influence of the corticostriatal glutamatergic neurons on dopaminergic terminals. Further experiments are required to verify this hypothesis. If such a mechanism was implicated, this will indicate that the dopaminergic transmission can be increased *in vivo* despite the GABA-induced inhibition of the activity of the dopaminergic neurons.

IMBALANCE BETWEEN THE ACTIVITY OF THE TWO NIGROSTRIATAL DOPAMINERGIC PATHWAYS

A relationship between the activity of the two dopaminergic pathways was first suspected by comparing the variations in the spontaneous release of ^{3}H-DA in the right and left caudate nuclei in successive collected fractions. To an increase in release of ^{3}H-DA in one side corresponded a decrease in release of the ^{3}H-transmitter in the other side, and vice versa (19). This was observed both in "encéphale isolé" and halothane-anesthetized cats. This phenomenon occurred in about 70% of 120 paired estimations made in several animals.

This imbalance between the activity of the two dopaminergic pathways was confirmed by measuring the effects of the interruption of nerve firing in one pathway on the release of ^{3}H-DA in both caudate nuclei. Unilateral reduction of firing was obtained by electrocoagulation of one substantia nigra or by the nigral application of DA (10^{-6} *M*) or amphetamine (10^{-6} *M*) (19). Indeed, these two compounds were shown to reduce the activity of dopaminergic cells, most likely by increasing DA levels at dopaminergic autoreceptors sites (2,5). As expected, in all cases, the release of ^{3}H-DA was reduced in the ipsilateral caudate nucleus (19). The interesting finding was that a concomittant increase in ^{3}H-DA release occurred in the contralateral side, suggesting an activation of firing in the corresponding dopaminergic neurons (19).

These data may help us to understand other asymmetric responses observed in caudate nuclei of animals in which one substantia nigra had been lesioned. Indeed, it has been reported that unilateral nigral electrolytical lesions in cats or monkeys induce a slight activation of some cells in the ipsilateral caudate nucleus and reduce the activity of neurons in the contralateral structure (42). Moreover, in recent experiments performed on rats, we observed a decreased number of ^{3}H-atropine binding sites in the right striatum and a concomittant increase of the muscarinic receptor sites in the contralateral side a few days after 6-OH-DA lesions of the right dopaminergic pathway. These effects were no longer seen 21 days after the chemical lesion, revealing the development of compensatory mechanisms (43). The bilateral opposite changes in cell firing rate and in the number of muscarinic receptor sites could be related to asymmetric fluctuations in the activity of the striatal cholinergic neurons triggered by the imbalance of dopaminergic transmission between the two sides. Indeed, according to biochemical and pharmacological data, the nigrostriatal dopaminergic neurons exert a tonic inhibitory influence on the activity of the striatal cholinergic neurons (14,44–47).

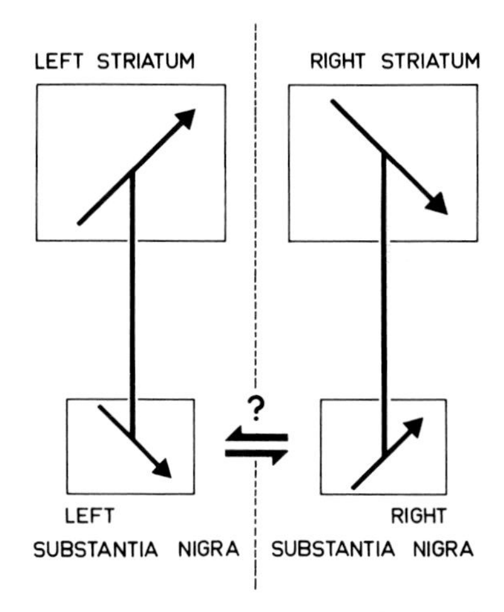

Fig. 1. Schematic representation of the reciprocal control of the activity of the two nigrostriatal dopaminergic pathways. This model illustrates the opposite changes observed in the release of DA in the caudate nuclei and the substantia nigrae during stimulation of the right dentate cerebellar nuclei (22) or during unilateral sensory stimuli (electrical stimulation of the paw of the left forelimb) (21).

THE RELEASE OF DOPAMINE FROM DOPAMINERGIC DENDRITES

A DA sensitive adenylate cyclase has been identified in the substantia nigra (48,49). This enzyme activity, which was found to be higher in the pars reticulata rich in dopaminergic dendrites, was still present after destruction of the dopaminergic neurons (48). This indicated that the dopaminergic receptors coupled to the cyclase were not located on the dopaminergic neurons. The nigral DA-sensitive adenylate cyclase disappeared after lesion of the striatonigral pathways, suggesting that the dopaminergic receptors were distributed on GABAergic or substance P nerve terminals (49). Since DA stimulated the release of ^{3}H-GABA but not of substance P in slices of the rat substantia nigra (50), the presynaptic dopaminergic receptors which appear to be located only on GABAergic terminals could be influenced by DA released from dopaminergic dendrites.

The first data suggesting a dendritic release of DA were obtained *in vitro*. Depolarization with potassium evoked the release of ^{3}H-DA previously taken up in slices of the rat substantia nigra and this effect was shown to be calcium dependent (51). The *in vivo* release of DA from the cat substantia nigra was demonstrated in our laboratory by measuring ^{3}H-DA in superfusates of a push–pull cannula during the continuous delivery of L-[^{3}H]tyrosine (20). As observed in the caudate nucleus, the spontaneous release of newly synthesized ^{3}H-DA in the substantia nigra was enhanced by amphetamine (10^{-6} *M*) or benztropine (10^{-6} *M*), revealing the efficiency of the reuptake process (20). The nigral release of ^{3}H-DA could be influenced by activation of neuronal pathways projecting into the substantia nigra. Thus it was increased under electrical stimulation of the motor cortex (39) and reduced under stimulation of the contralateral dendate nuclei of the cerebellum (22).

To our knowledge, the substantia nigra is not innervated by recurrent collaterals of the dopaminergic neurons. Two facts indicate that ^{3}H-DA released in the substantia nigra originates from dendrites. (1) Tetrodotoxin (5×10^{-7} *M*) failed to reduce the release of ^{3}H-DA in contrast to that observed in the caudate nucleus (20). This suggests that the nigral spontaneous release of ^{3}H-DA exhibits characteristics which are distinct from those observed in nerve terminals. It may not be dependent on the appearance of spikes in dendrites, since it does not appear to be influenced by the blockade of sodium channels. In fact, the dendritic release of ^{3}H-DA was enhanced in the presence of the neurotoxin, suggesting an interruption of inhibitory inputs involved in its control (20). (2) If ^{3}H-DA were released from nerve terminals in the substantia nigra, the activation of the dopaminergic neurons should lead to a stimulation of ^{3}H-DA release in the caudate nucleus as well as in the substantia nigra. In most cases, as will be discussed later, opposite changes in the ^{3}H-DA release were observed in the two structures under activation of the dopaminergic neurons. This provides further indirect evidence for a dendritic origin of ^{3}H-DA released in the substantia nigra.

ROLE OF THE DENDRITIC RELEASE OF DOPAMINE IN THE CONTROL OF THE ACTIVITY OF THE NIGROSTRIATAL DOPAMINERGIC NEURONS

According to anatomical reports, there are reciprocal connections between the cerebellum and the substantia nigra (52,53). A pathway originating from the dentate nuclei projects into the contralateral substantia nigra (52). Several interesting observations were made during the unilateral electrical stimulation of the dentate nuclei in cats implanted with four push–pull cannulae to simultaneously record the release of ^{3}H-DA in each caudate nucleus and each substantia nigra (22). (*1*) The presence of an imbalance between the activity of the two dopaminergic pathways was confirmed. The opposite changes in ^{3}H-DA release observed in the caudate nuclei revealed an activation of the contralateral dopaminergic pathway associated with an inhibition of the ipsilateral system. (2) Opposite changes in ^{3}H-DA release were also seen in the substantia nigrae. But in this case, the dendritic release of ^{3}H-DA was inhibited in the contralateral substantia nigra and activated in the ipsilateral side (Fig. 1). (3) The temporal changes in ^{3}H-DA release from dendrites and terminals were identical. These changes persisted for at least one hour after the end of the stimulus. This suggested a close relationship between the events occurring in the substantia nigrae and those observed in the caudate nuclei.

This inverse relationship between the level of the dendritic release of DA and the level of the transmitter release from nerve terminals also occurred in experiments designed to determine the effects of unilateral sensory stimuli on the activity of the two dopaminergic pathways (21). The electrical stimulation of the paw in the right forelimb or the delivery of light flashes to the right eye activated the ipsilateral dopaminergic pathway and inhibited the contralateral system. These effects were also associated with changes in the dendritic release of ^{3}H-DA in directions opposite to those seen in the respective caudate nuclei. From these data it is tempting to assume that the activity of the dopaminergic neurons is controlled by the dendritic release of DA in physiological states. Such a hypothesis agrees with the inhibitory effect of the nigral application of DA on the activity of the dopaminergic neurons shown in electrophysiological studies (1,2) and in our biochemical experiments (16). DA released from dendrites could act directly on dopaminergic neurons through dopaminergic autoreceptors or indirectly through the dopaminergic receptors located on nigral afferent fibers.

CONCLUDING REMARKS

Several mechanisms are involved in the control of the DA release from nerve terminals. The release of the transmitter is dependent on nerve impulse flow. It can be modulated by presynaptic dopaminergic receptors. Other neurons may contribute to the local regulation of the transmitter release from nerve terminals. *In vitro* experiments have provided strong arguments in favor of the presence of presynaptic cholinergic and glutamatergic receptors on dopaminergic terminals. Both acetylcholine (54) and L-glutamic acid (41) stimulate the release of DA from striatal slices even in the presence of tetrodotoxin added to interrupt nerve firing in neurons contacting the dopaminergic terminals. A reduction of enkephalin binding sites has been observed in the striatum after degeneration of the nigrostriatal dopaminergic neurons, suggesting the presence of enkephalin presynaptic receptors on the dopaminergic terminals (55). Therefore, cholinergic, glutamatergic and enkephalin-containing neurons could contact the dopaminergic terminals and influence the release of DA. Much has to be done to understand how all these various messages are integrated and to demonstrate their physiological significance under different states of activity of the dopaminergic cells.

Undoubtedly, the discovery of a dendritic release of DA has changed our way of thinking about the nigral interneuronal regulatory processes. We already know that the dendritic release of DA can be modulated in physiological or in pharmacological states by messages delivered to the substantia nigra through different neuronal pathways originating from various brain areas. The dendritic release of DA may not only be responsible for the self-regulation of the activity of the dopaminergic neurons, but also for the communication between dopaminergic cells projecting in different striatal or cortical areas.

Indeed, the substantia nigra contains not only the cell bodies of the nigrostriatal dopaminergic neurons but also some of the cell bodies of the mesocortical dopaminergic systems (56). DA released from dendrites may also influence the release of other transmitters in the substantia nigra since dopaminergic receptors are located on some nigral afferent fibers. Finally, it cannot be excluded that DA directly or indirectly affects other nigral cell bodies and thus the activity of efferent pathways. Therefore, the nigrostriatal dopaminergic neurons may control various neuronal pathways not only in the caudate nucleus but also in the substantia nigra.

Another degree of complexity is reached with the regulatory processes involved in the simultaneous control of the activity of the two dopaminergic pathways. In several conditions the two nigrostriatal dopaminergic systems may react similarly. This is the case under peripheral pharmacological treatments. This was also observed under unilateral stimulation of the motor cortex. In this situation the release of ^{3}H-DA was enhanced in both caudate nuclei. This is not surprising since the cortico-striatal projection involved is bilateral (57). In contrast, the unilateral stimulation of the cerebellar dentate nucleus or the delivery of unilateral sensory stimuli induced an asymmetric reactivity of the two dopaminergic pathways. These effects may be mediated by a selective activation or inhibition of one pathway since the interruption of the activity of one dopaminergic system induces an activation of the contralateral pathway. The mechanisms involved in such bilateral regulations remain to be elucidated. They may be of great importance for the understanding of the role of the nigrostriatal dopaminergic systems in the coordination of sensory motor processes.

ACKNOWLEDGMENTS

This research was supported by grants from INSERM (contrat libre 75.5. 153.6), DGRST (75.7.00.41), DRME (76.329), and la Société des Usines Chimiques Rhône-Poulenc.

REFERENCES

1. Aghajanian, G. K., and Bunney B. S. (1973) *In* "Frontiers in Catecholamine Research" (S. H. Snyder and E. Usdin, eds.), pp. 643–648. Pergamon, Oxford.
2. Aghajanian, G. K., and Bunney B. S. (1975) *In* "Neuropsychopharmacology" (J. R. Boissier, H. Hippius, and P. Pichot, eds.), pp. 444–452. Excerpta Med. Found., Amsterdam.

3. Connor, J. D. (1970) *J. Physiol. (London)* **208,** 691–704.
4. Geltz, P., de Champlain J., and Dessama, J. M. (1975) *In* "Neuropsychopharmacology" (J. R. Boissier, H. Hippius, and P. Pichot, eds.), pp. 453–458. Excerpta Med. Found., Amsterdam.
5. Groves, P. M., Wilson, C. J., Yound, S. J., and Rebec, G. V. (1975) *Science* **190,** 522–528.
6. Precht, W., and Yoshida, M. (1971) *Brain Res.* **32,** 229–233.
7. Schaffner, R., and Haefely, W. (1975) *Experientia* **31,** 732.
8. Agid, Y., Javoy, F., and Glowinski, J. (1974) *Brain Res.* **74,** 41–49.
9. Gale, K. N., and Guidotti, A. (1976) *Nature (London)* **263,** 691–693.
10. Korf, J., Zieleman, M., and Westering, B. H. C. (1976) *Nature (London)* **260,** 257–258.
11. Roth, R. H., Murrin, L. C., and Walters, J. R. (1976) *Eur. J. Pharmacol.* **36,** 163–171.
12. Besson, M. J., Chéramy, A., Feltz, P., and Glowinski, J. (1977) *Brain Res.* **32,** 407–424.
13. Nieoullon, A., Chéramy, A., and Glowinski, J. (1977) *J. Neurochem.* **28,** 819–828.
14. Bartholini, G., Stadler, H., Gadea-Ciria, M., and Lloyd, K. G. (1976) *Neuropharmacology* **15,** 515–519.
15. Chéramy, A., Bioulac, B., Besson, M. J., Vincent, J. D., Glowinski, J., and Gauchy, C. (1975) *In* "Neuropsychopharmacology" (J. R. Boissier, H. Hippius, and P. Pichot, eds.), pp. 493–498. Excerpta Med. Found., Amsterdam.
16. Chéramy, A., Nieoullon, A., Michelot, R., and Glowinski, J. (1977) *Neurosci. Lett.* **4,** 105–109.
17. Chéramy, A., Nieoullon, A., and Glowinski, J. (1978) *In* "Interactions among Putative Neurotransmitters in the Brain" (S. Garattini, J. F. Pujol, and R. Samanin, eds.). Raven Press, New York 175–190.
18. Chéramy, A., Nieoullon, A., and Glowinski, J. (1977) *Naunyn-Schmiedeberg's Arch. Pharmacol.* **297,** 31–37.
19. Nieoullon, A., Chéramy, A., and Glowinski, J. (1977) *Science* **198,** 416–418.
20. Nieoullon, A., Chéramy, A., and Glowinski, J. (1977) *Nature (London)* **266,** 375–377.
21. Nieoullon, A., Chéramy, A., and Glowinski, J. (1977) *Nature (London)* **269,** 340–342.
22. Nieoullon, A., Chéramy, A., and Glowinski, J. (1978) *Brain Res.* (in press).
23. Hökfelt, T., Kellerth, J. O., Nilsson, G., and Pernon, B. (1975) *Science* **190,** 889–890.
24. Hong, J. S., Yang, H. Y. T., Racagni, G., and Costa, E. (1977) *Brain Res.* **122,** 541–544.
25. Kanazawa, I., Emson, P. C., and Cuello, A. C. (1977) *Brain Res.* **119,** 447–453.
26. Jessel, T. M., Iversen, L. L., and Kanazawa, I. (1976) *Nature (London)* **264,** 81–83.
27. Davies, J., and Dray, A. (1976) *Brain Res.* **107,** 623–627.
28. Dray, A., Gonye, T. J., and Oakley, N. R. (1976) *J. Physiol. (London)* **259,** 825–849.
29. Bak, I. J., Choi, W. B., Hassler, R., Usunoff, K. G., and Wagner, A. (1975) *Adv. Neurol.* **9,** 25–41.
30. Hassler, R., Bak, I. J., Usunoff, K. J., and Choi, W. B. (1975) *In* "Neuropsychopharmacology" (J. R. Boissier, H. Hippius, and P. Pichot, eds.), pp. 397–411. Excerpta Med. Found., Amsterdam.
31. Hattori, T., McGeer, P. L., Fibiger, H. C., and McGeer, E. G. (1973) *Brain Res.* **54,** 103–114.
32. Ribak, C. E., Vauchn, I. E., Saito, K., Barber, R., and Roberts, E. (1976) *Brain Res.* **116,** 287–298.
33. Chéramy, A., Nieoullon, A., and Glowinski, J. (1977) *Life Sci.* **20,** 811–816.

34. Chéramy, A., Nieoullon A., and Glowinski, J. (1977) *J. Pharmacol. Exp. Ther.* **203,** 282–293.
35. Perry, T. L., Berry, K., Hansen, S., Diamond, S., and Mok, C. (1971) *J. Neurochem.* **18,** 513–519.
36. Dray, A., and Straughan, D. W. (1976) *J. Pharm. Pharmacol.* **28,** 400–405.
37. Chéramy, A., Nieoullon, A., and Glowinski, J. (1978) *Eur. J. Pharmacol.* **47,** 141–147.
38. Deniau, J. M., Feger, J., and Le Guyader, C. (1976) *Brain Res.* **104,** 152–156.
39. Nieoullon, A., Chéramy, A., and Glowinski, J. (1978) *Brain Res.* (in press).
40. Divac, I., Fonnum, F., and Storm-Mathisen, J. (1977) *Nature (London)* **266,** 377–378.
41. Giorguieff, M. F., Kemel, M. L., and Glowinski, J. (1977) *Neurosci. Lett.* (in press).
42. Hull, C. D., Levine, M. E., Buchwald, N. A., Heller, A., and Browing, R. A. (1974) *Brain Res.* **73,** 241–262.
43. Kato, G., Carson, S., Kemel, M. L., Glowinski, J., and Giorguieff, M. F. (1977) *Life Sci.* (in press).
44. Agid, Y., Guyenet, P., Glowinski, J., Beaujouan, J. C., and Javoy, F. (1975) *Brain Res.* **86,** 480–482.
45. Guyenet, P., Euvrard, C., Javoy, F., Herbet, A., and Glowinski, J. (1977) *Brain Res.* **131** (in press).
46. Ladinski, H., Consolo, S., Bianchi, S., Samanin, R., and Ghezzi, D. (1975) *Brain Res.* **84,** 221–226.
47. Racagni, G., Cheney, D. L., Zsilla, G., and Costa, E. (1976) *Neuropharmacology* **15,** 732–736.
48. Premont, J., Thierry, A. M., Tassin, J. P., Glowinski, J., Blanc, G., and Bockaert, J. (1976) *FEBS Lett.* **68,** 99–104.
49. Gale, K., Guidotti, A., and Costa, E. (1977) *Science* **195,** 503–505.
50. Reubi, J. C., Iversen, L. L., and Jessel, T. M. (1977) *Nature (London)* **268,** 652–654.
51. Geffen, L. B., Jessel, T. M., Cuello, A. C., and Iversen, L. L. (1976) *Nature (London)* **260,** 258–260.
52. Snider, R. S., Maiti, A., and Snider, S. R. (1976) *Exp. Neurol.* **53,** 714–728.
53. Chan-Palay, V. (1977) "Cerebellar Dentate Nucleus. Organization, Cytology, and Transmitters," p. 202. Springer-Verlag, Berlin and New York.
54. Giorguieff, M. F., Le Floc'h, M. L., Glowinski, J., and Besson, M. J. (1977) *J. Pharmacol. Exp. Ther.* **200,** 535–540.
55. Pollard, H., Llorens-Cortes, C., and Schwartz, J. C. (1977) *Nature (London)* **268,** 745–746.
56. Lindvall, O., Björklund, A. K., and Divac, I. (1977) *Adv. Biochem. Psychopharmacol.* **16,** 39–46.
57. Webster, K. E. (1956) *J. Anat.* **99,** 329–337.

Regulation of Sensitivity to β-Adrenergic Stimulation in the Rat Pineal

MARTIN ZATZ AND JULIUS AXELROD
Laboratory of Clinical Science
National Institute of Mental Health
Bethesda, Maryland

INTRODUCTION

The pineal gland is a useful model system in which to study the regulation of adrenergic function (1). It provides a relatively simple system, compared to brain, in which the biochemical consequences of adrenergic stimulation and their relation to physiologic function are fairly well understood. In addition, there are physiologic variations in the gland's response to stimulation which illustrate the ways in which cells regulate their own sensitivity to neurotransmitters.

Although surrounded by brain tissue, the pineal gland is actually a peripheral organ which is innervated exclusively by sympathetic nerves coming from the superior cervical ganglia (2). These nerves release norepinephrine, thereby stimulating the pineal's synthesis of melatonin (3), an indoleamine derived from serotonin (Fig. 1) which affects reproductive function. *In vivo,* the pineal gland is driven by a circadian cycle in norepinephrine release. More neurotransmitter is released at night, in the dark, than during the day (4). The nocturnal release of norepinephrine causes an approximately fifty-fold increase in the activity of serotonin *N*-acetyltransferase (5). This increase in enzyme activity appears to be the pivotal step in the nocturnal synthesis of melatonin (6). It causes the levels of serotonin, the enzyme's substrate, to fall (7) after β-adrenergic stimulation and the levels of

ISBN 0-12-398450-5

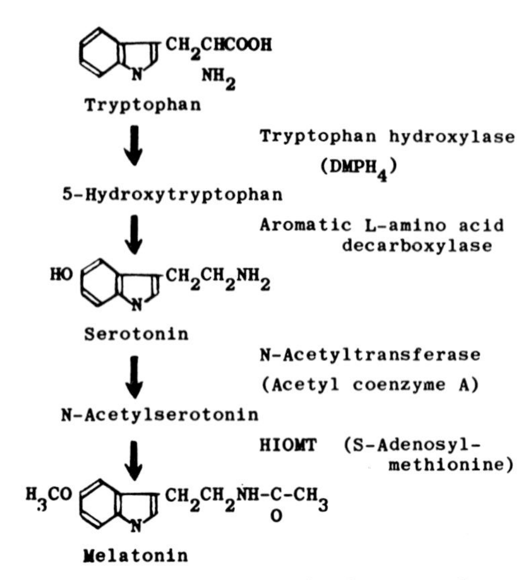

Fig. 1. The pathway for the biosynthesis of melatonin in the rat pineal gland. This metabolic sequence is stimulated by the nocturnal release of norepinephrine. Abbreviations: $DMPH_4$, dimethyltetrahydropteridine; HIOMT, hydroxyindole *O*-methyltransferase.

N-acetylserotonin, the enzyme's product, to rise (8). Methylation of *N*-acetylserotonin by hydroxyindole *O*-methyltransferase (9) then completes the synthesis of melatonin (Fig. 1)

During the day, or experimentally, environmental lighting reduces the release of norepinephrine to such a degree that the induction of *N*-acetyltransferase is prevented (4,5,10,11). Thus, the pineal is a "monodirectional system"; it is activated by stimulation and returns to its "resting state" when stimulation is removed. Pineal *N*-acetyltransferase activity can be increased experimentally in animals exposed to light by the injection of isoproterenol (12), which acts directly on the β-adrenergic receptor. Similarly, enzyme activity can be increased by catecholamines in explant culture (6).

N-Acetyltransferase appears to be an inducible enzyme. The increase in its activity shows a variable lag after stimulation (13), requires protein synthesis (11,14), and, under ordinary conditions, requires RNA synthesis (15,16). There is compelling evidence that the induction of *N*-acetyltransferase is mediated by cyclic AMP. Cyclic AMP levels in the gland are increased by β-adrenergic stimulation *in vivo* (17) and *in vitro* (18). The increase in cyclic AMP precedes the increase in enzyme activity. Adenylate cyclase in pineal homogenates is activated by β-adrenergic agonists but not by other hormones (19). Dibutyryl cyclic AMP (20) and cholera toxin (21) induce *N*-acetyltransferase activity in cultured glands, Phosphodiesterases are present in the gland (22,23) and inductions are potentiated by theophylline (18). Thus, the criteria for cyclic AMP as a second messenger (24) have been essentially satisfied.

VARIATION IN SENSITIVITY OF INDUCTION

The pineal gland responds to β-adrenergic stimulation with an increase in the activity of *N*-acetyltransferase. However, its responsiveness, its sensitivity to stimulation, is a regulated function. A period of increased stimulation leads to a diminished response to subsequent stimulation. This is termed "subsensitivity." Conversely, a period of reduced stimulation leads to an increased response to subsequent stimulation. This is termed "supersensitivity." Thus, glands taken from animals after 12 or 24 hr exposure to light are supersensitive relative to glands taken from animals at the end of their daily exposure to 12 hr darkness (25) (Fig. 2). Isoproterenol is more potent in inducing *N*-acetyltransferase activity in the supersensitive glands and they are capable of a greater maximal response. The glands taken from animals after 12 hr darkness have been physiologically stimulated during the night. Consequently, their sensitivity to subsequent stimulation, by exogenous agonist in culture, is reduced by morning. The effects of nocturnal stimulation can be mimicked by treatment with isoproterenol; exposure of the pineal to isoproterenol also causes a subsensitivity to subsequent stimulation (13).

Glands taken from light-exposed animals are relatively supersensitive consequent to the period of reduced β-adrenergic stimulation. Other manipulations which reduce the level of stimulation also produce supersensitivity. These include denervation or decentralization of the gland and treatment with reserpine or 6-hydroxydopamine (26,27)

Recently, data have been obtained indicating that there are multiple sites involved in the regulation of sensitivity to β-adrenergic stimulation. Indeed, alterations in each of the elements involved in cyclic AMP metabolism—the β-adrenergic binding sites, adenylate

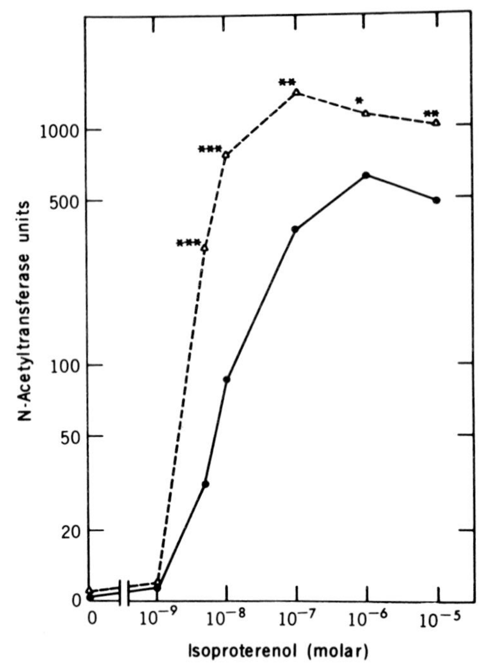

Fig. 2. Diurnal change in sensitivity of rat pineal *N*-acetyltransferase to induction by *l*-isoproterenol in organ culture. Pineals obtained from animals killed after exposure to 12-hr darkness (●) or to 12-hr light (△) were incubated in the presence of various concentrations of *l*-isoproterenol for 10 hr. Glands were homogenized and assayed for *N*-acetyltransferase activity; units are pmoles $gland^{-1}$ 10 min^{-1}. Data from Romero and Axelrod (25).

cyclase, phosphodiesterase, and cyclic AMP-dependent protein kinase—seem to contribute to the overall regulation of sensitivity.

RECEPTORS AND ADENYLATE CYCLASE

The first step in the sequence of events involved in the induction of *N*-acetyltransferase activity is the binding of agonist to the β-adrenergic receptors. These receptors are closely coupled to adenylate cyclase, and their interaction with appropriate agonists results in the activation of the adenylate cyclase and the generation of cyclic AMP.

In order to assess the role of the β-adrenergic receptors in the regulation of sensitivity, we examined the specific binding of ^3H-

dihydroalprenolol (28). The use of this potent β-adrenergic antagonist, radiolabeled to high specific activity, to study β-adrenergic binding sites was introduced by Lefkowitz and associates (29). The characteristics of binding were consistent with the known properties of the β-adrenergic receptor. Binding of the radioactive antagonist was rapid, reversible, saturable, and stereospecific. The order of potency of agonists or antagonists in competing for the binding sites was the same as their order of potency in stimulating or inhibiting adenylate cyclase activity. Indeed the affinity constants calculated from binding data and from adenylate cyclase data were quite similar (28).

We measured ^{3}H-dihydroalprenolol binding in supersensitive and subsensitive glands (30). There were more specific binding sites in homogenates of glands taken from animals which had been exposed to light for 24 hr than in homogenates of glands taken from animals which had been exposed to darkness for 12 hr (Table I). There was no apparent change in the affinity of the available binding sites for agonists or antagonists. The effect of darkness in reducing the number of available binding sites could be mimicked by the injection of isoproterenol *in vivo* (Table I).

These changes in the binding sites correlated very well with the changes in adenylate cyclase activity under similar conditions (30). There was more basal and catecholamine-sensitive adenylate cyclase activity in homogenates of glands taken from light-exposed animals

TABLE I
Specific Binding of ^{3}H-Dihydroalprenolol in Supersensitive and Subsensitive Pineal Glands[a]

Condition	Maximum binding (cpm/mg protein)	K_i of *l*-isoproterenol (μM)
12 hr in dark	7,250	0.4
24 hr in light	11,760	0.6
24 hr in light plus *l*-isoproterenol pretreatment	6,150	0.7

[a] Specific binding of ^{3}H-dihydroalprenolol was determined in homogenates of pineals taken from rats exposed to darkness for 12 hr, light for 24 hr, or isoproterenol bitartrate pretreatment (5 mg/kg, subcutaneously, 2 hr prior to killing) after exposure to light for 24 hr. Maximum binding was determined from the specific binding observed at five concentrations of ^{3}H-dihydroalprenolol. The affinity of *l*-isoproterenol for the binding sites was calculated from the specific binding of ^{3}H-dihydroalprenolol observed in the presence of six concentrations of *l*-isoproterenol. Data from Kebabian *et al.* (30).

TABLE II
Catecholamine-Sensitive Adenylate Cyclase Activity in Supersensitive and Subsensitive Pineal Glands[a]

Condition	Adenylate cyclase activity (pmoles/mg protein per min) No addition	*l*-Isoproterenol (100 μM)	K_a of *l*-isoproterenol (μM)
12 hr in dark	23 ± 3	102 ± 2	0.2
24 hr in light	87 ± 10	225 ± 14	0.2
24 hr in light plus isoproterenol pretreatment	23 ± 1	52 ± 3	0.4

[a] The activity of adenylate cyclase was determined in homogenates of pineals taken from rats exposed to darkness for 12 hr, light for 24 hr, or isoproterenol bitartrate pretreatment (5 mg/kg, subcutaneously, 2 hr prior to killing) after exposure to light for 24 hr. Basal activity (no addition) and catecholamine-sensitive activity (100 μM *l*-isoproterenol) were assayed. The affinity of *l*-isoproterenol was determined from the stimulation of adenylate cyclase activity observed in the presence of five concentrations of *l*-isoproterenol. Data from Kebabian *et al.* (30).

then in homogenates of glands taken from dark-exposed animals (Table II). Similarly, an injection of isoproterenol mimicked the effect of darkness in reducing adenylate cyclase activity several hours later. There was no difference in the potency of isoproterenol to stimulate adenylate cyclase between homogenates of supersensitive and subsensitive glands (Table II).

These data suggest a role for changes in the β-adrenergic receptor in the regulation of sensitivity. Interaction of the binding sites with β-adrenergic agonist results in a reduction in the number of binding sites available for subsequent interaction. Such "desensitization" of receptor sites has been observed in several systems, and is discussed in the chapter by Dr. Lefkowitz. The diminished number of available receptor sites in the subsensitive gland may contribute to the reduced response of adenylate cyclase and, ultimately, to the diminished induction of *N*-acetyltransferase.

Despite the close correlations between changes in binding sites, adenylate cyclase activity, and sensitivity, the changes in the number of available receptors alone cannot fully account for the changes in adenylate cyclase activity or sensitivity. There must be additional changes beyond the binding sites. Adenylate cyclase can be stimulated and *N*-acetyltransferase can be induced by agents whose action does not require binding to the β-adrenergic receptors. Nevertheless, super- and subsensitivity can be demonstrated in the response to these agents.

Weiss and Costa (31) demonstrated that the amount of fluoride-stimulated adenylate cyclase activity is greater in homogenates of denervated glands than in controls. There is also a greater amount of fluoride-sensitive activity in homogenates of glands taken from light-exposed animals than in homogenates of glands taken from dark-exposed animals (Fig. 3). Since the action of fluoride does not require the β-adrenergic receptor, these changes cannot be due simply to an altered number of adrenergic binding sites. Similarly, choleragen activates adenylate cyclase and causes the induction of pineal *N*-acetyltransferase (21) by a mechanism which bypasses the β-adrenergic binding sites (32). When glands were homogenized after exposure to choleragen, there was more adenylate cyclase activity in the supersensitive glands (33) (Fig. 3). Exposure to choleragen fully activated the adenylate cyclase in the intact glands. The addition of isoproterenol or fluoride after the glands were homogenized did not further increase the adenylate cyclase activity. These data suggest that there is a change in the adenylate cyclase as well as in the adrenergic binding sites. The correlations between the changes in the number of

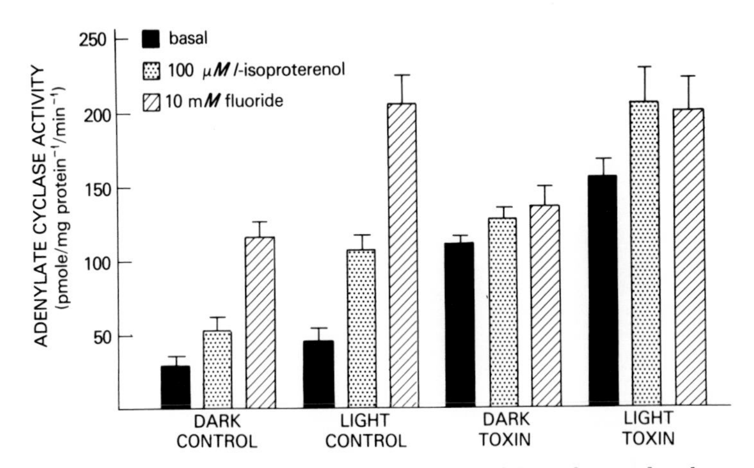

Fig. 3. Effects of cholera toxin, *l*-isoproterenol, and fluoride on adenylate cyclase activity in supersensitive and subsensitive glands. Pineals were removed from rats which had been exposed to darkness for 12 hr, or to light for 24 hr. Intact glands were preincubated in the presence of choleragen (toxin) or in its absence (control) for 15 min. All glands were transferred to enriched medium and incubated for 2 hr. The glands were then homogenized and assayed for adenylate cyclase activity. Aliquots of each homogenate were assayed in the presence of added water (basal), 100 μ*M* *l*-isoproterenol, or 10 m*M* KF. Data from Zatz (33).

available binding sites and adenylate cyclase activity suggest that these changes may share a common cause.

CYCLIC AMP AND PHOSPHODIESTERASE

The changes in adenylate cyclase activity alter the accumulation of cyclic AMP. Glands taken from light exposed animals show a greater accumulation of cyclic AMP in response to isoproterenol than do glands taken from dark-exposed animals (34) (Fig. 4). Similarly, choleragen produces a greater accumulation of cyclic AMP in supersensitive glands (33). These differences in cyclic AMP accumulation are reflected in the induction of *N*-acetyltransferase activity.

The other enzyme involved in the regulation of cyclic AMP levels is phosphodiesterase. There is an increase in phosphodiesterase activity several hours after exposure to isoproterenol (23) or choleragen (21). Increased phosphodiesterase activity would tend to reduce the accumulation of cyclic AMP upon restimulation. These changes in phosphodiesterase activity may contribute to the desensitization following adrenergic stimulation (35). There is also a diurnal cycle in phosphodiesterase activity (36). However, the diurnal cycle in phos-

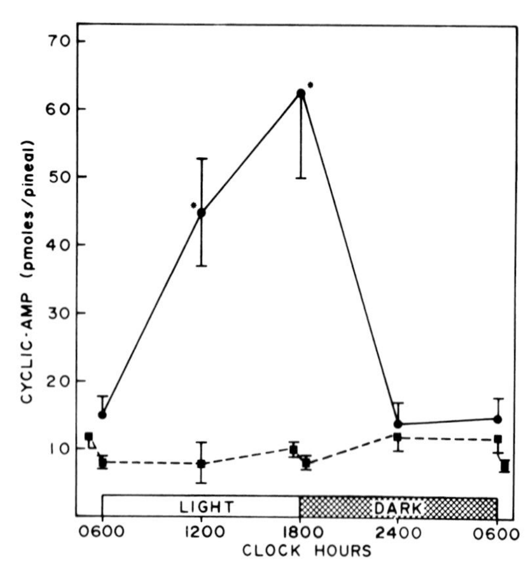

Fig. 4. Diurnal variation in the accumulation of cyclic AMP in the rat pineal gland after *l*-isoproterenol administration. At the times indicated, rats were injected with saline (■) or *l*-isoproterenol bitartrate (5 mg/kg. sc) (●) and pineal cyclic AMP levels were measured 10 min later. Data from Romero *et al.* (34).

phodiesterase activity does not correspond to the diurnal cycle in sensitivity of *N*-acetyltransferase induction (36). Also, there is no reduction in phosphodiesterase activity in denervated glands (36), which are markedly supersensitive (26). Thus, alterations in this enzyme do not appear to contribute to all forms of sensitivity change.

Alterations in the accumulation of cyclic AMP parallel changes in the sensitivity of induction (26,34,37). These appear to be mediated by changes in receptors, adenylate cyclase, and phosphodiesterase, in varying combinations. Nonetheless, the mechanisms regulating the accumulation of cyclic AMP also do not fully account for the changes in sensitivity to induction. Romero and Axelrod (13) showed that dibutyryl cyclic AMP, which bypasses the receptor–adenylate cyclase complex and is resistant to destruction by phosphodiesterase, is more effective in inducing *N*-acetyltransferase activity at the end of the day than at the end of the night. These data suggest a regulatory mechanism beyond cyclic AMP.

PROTEIN KINASE

Cyclic AMP presumably increases *N*-acetyltransferase activity by activating cyclic AMP-dependent protein kinase (38,39). We measured protein kinase activity in supernatants of pineal glands, using histone as substrate (40). Treatment of intact glands with isoproterenol (40) (Table III) or choleragen (33) increased the basal activity of protein kinase. This was probably due to the increased levels of cyclic AMP in the glands which these agents produced. The increment in protein kinase activity after stimulation was greater in supersensitive glands than in subsensitive glands, as would be expected from the greater accumulation of cyclic AMP in the supersensitive glands.

There was, however, also a greater amount of protein kinase activity in the supersensitive glands in the presence of maximally stimulating concentrations of cyclic AMP (40) (Table III). Thus, a given concentration of cyclic AMP provides more protein kinase activity in the supersensitive glands than in the subsensitive glands. The increased effectiveness of dibutyryl cyclic AMP in supersensitive glands may be due to the increased amount of cyclic AMP-dependent protein kinase activity in these glands. The difference in cyclic AMP accumulation between supersensitive and subsensitive glands after β-adrenergic stimulation is amplified by the difference in the effectiveness of cyclic AMP in activating protein kinase. Supersensitive

TABLE III
Protein Kinase Activity in Supersensitive and Subsensitive Pineal Glands[a]

Group	Protein kinase activity (nmoles ^{32}P incorporated mg protein^{-1} 10 min^{-1})	
	−cAMP	+cAMP
12 hr dark		
Control	2.1 ± 0.1	6.4 + 0.4
Isoproterenol	2.6 ± 0.3	5.7 ± 0.3
24 hr light		
Control	3.4 ± 0.1	10.9 ± 0.7
Isoproterenol	4.3 ± 0.3	9.4 ± 0.7

[a] Pineal glands from rats exposed to light for 24 hr or to darkness for 12 hr were placed in organ culture containing 0.1 μM *l*-isoproterenol or in control medium. After a 20 min incubation, glands were homogenized in medium containing 500 m*M* NaCl and protein kinase activity was assayed in the presence and absence of 1 μM cyclic AMP. Data from Zatz and O'Dea (40).

glands have a greater amount of cyclic AMP acting upon a greater amount of cyclic-AMP dependent protein kinase.

The change in protein kinase activity, like that of adenylate cyclase, looks like an increased amount of enzyme. There was no significant change in the apparent affinity for ATP, histone, or cyclic AMP (40). Rather, the V_{max} for each substrate was 50–100% greater in the supersensitive glands. Increases in the cyclic AMP-dependent protein kinase activity were also seen in denervated glands and in glands taken from reserpinized animals (40). These increases were similar in magnitude to the change caused by light. Thus, alterations in protein kinase activity may contribute to the increased sensitivity of the pineal gland caused by light, denervation, or reserpine.

In conclusion, there seem to be multiple sites involved in the regulation of the pineal's sensitivity to β-adrenergic stimulation. These include the β-adrenergic binding sites, the catecholamine-sensitive adenylate cyclase, the high affinity phosphodiesterase, and the cyclic AMP-dependent protein kinase. These sites are likely to also be involved in the modulation of responses to norepinephrine in the central nervous system.

REFERENCES

1. Axelrod, J. (1974) *Science* **184,** 1341–1348.
2. Kappers, J. A. (1960) *Z. Zellforsch. Mikrosk. Anat.* **52,** 153–215.

3. Wurtman, R. J., Axelrod, J., and Kelly, D. E. (1968) "The Pineal." Academic Press, New York.
4. Brownstein, M. J., and Axelrod, J. (1974) *Science* **184,** 163–165.
5. Klein, D. C., and Weller, J. L. (1970) *Science* **169,** 1093–1095.
6. Klein, D. C., and Weller, J. L. (1973) *J. Pharmacol. Exp. Ther.* **186,** 516–527.
7. Brownstein, M., Holz, R., and Axelrod, J. (1973) *J. Pharmacol. Exp. Ther.* **186,** 109–113.
8. Brownstein, M. J., Saavedra, J. M., and Axelrod, J. (1973) *Mol. Pharmacol.* **9,** 605–611.
9. Axelrod, J., and Weissbach, H. (1961) *J. Biol. Chem.* **236,** 211–213.
10. Klein, D. C., and Weller, J. L. (1972) *Science* **177,** 532–533.
11. Deguchi, T., and Axelrod, J. (1972) *Proc. Natl. Acad. Sci. U.S.A.* **69,** 2547–2550.
12. Deguchi, T., and Axelrod, J. (1972) *Proc. Natl. Acad. Sci. U.S.A.* **69,** 2208–2211.
13. Romero, J. A., and Axelrod, J. (1975) *Proc. Natl. Acad. Sci. U.S.A.* **72,** 1661–1665.
14. Klein, D. C., and Berg, G. R. (1970) *Adv. Biochem. Psychopharmacol.* **3,** 241–263.
15. Romero, J. A., Zatz, M., and Axelrod, J. (1975) *Proc. Natl. Acad. Sci. U.S.A.* **72,** 2107–2111.
16. Zatz, M., Romero, J. A., and Axelrod, J. (1976) *Biochem. Pharmacol.* **25,** 903–906.
17. Deguchi, T. (1973) *Mol. Pharmacol.* **9,** 184–190.
18. Strada, S. J., Klein, D. C., Weller, J. L., and Weiss, B. (1972) *Endocrinology* **90,** 1470–1475.
19. Weiss, B., and Costa, E. (1968) *J. Pharmacol. Exp. Ther.* **161,** 310–319.
20. Klein, D. C., Berg, G. R., and Weller, J. L. (1970) *Science* **168,** 979–980.
21. Minneman, K. P., and Iversen, L. L. (1976) *Science* **192,** 803–805.
22. Weiss, B., and Costa, E. (1968) *Biochem. Pharmacol.* **17,** 2107–2116.
23. Oleshansky, M. A., and Neff, N. H. (1975) *Mol. Pharmacol.* **11,** 552–557.
24. Robison, G. A., Butcher, R. W., and Sutherland, E. W. (1971) "Cyclic AMP." Academic Press, New York.
25. Romero, J. A., and Axelrod, J. (1974) *Science* **184,** 1091–1092.
26. Deguchi, T., and Axelrod, J. (1973) *Proc. Natl. Acad. Sci. U.S.A.* **70,** 2411–2414.
27. Deguchi, T., and Axelrod, J. (1973) *Mol. Pharmacol.* **9,** 612–618.
28. Zatz, M., Kebabian, J. W., Romero, J. A., Lefkowitz, R. J., and Axelrod, J. (1976) *J. Pharmacol. Exp. Ther.* **196,** 714–722.
29. Lefkowitz, R. J., Mukherjee, C., Coverstone, M., and Caron, M. G. (1974) *Biochem. Biophys. Res. Commun.* **69,** 703–710.
30. Kebabian, J. W., Zatz, M., Romero, J. A., and Axelrod, J. (1975) *Proc. Natl. Acad. Sci. U.S.A.* **72,** 3735–3739.
31. Weiss, B., and Costa, E. (1967) *Science* **156,** 1750–1752.
32. Finkelstein, R. A. (1973) *Crit. Rev. Microbiol.* **2,** 533–623.
33. Zatz, M. (1977) *Life Sci.* **21,** 1267–1276.
34. Romero, J. A., Zatz, M., Kebabian, J. W., and Axelrod, J. (1975) *Nature (London)* **258,** 435–436.
35. Oleshansky, M. A., and Neff, N. H. (1975) *Life Sci.* **17,** 1429–1432.
36. Minneman, K. P., and Iversen, L. L. (1976) *Nature (London)* **260,** 59–61.
37. Strada, S. J., and Weiss, B. (1974) *Arch. Biochem. Biophys.* **160,** 197–204.
38. Fontana, J. A., and Lovenberg, W. (1971) *Proc. Natl. Acad. Sci. U.S.A.* **68,** 2787–2790.
39. Winters, K. E., Morrissey, J. J., Loos, P. J., and Lovenberg, W. (1977) *Proc. Natl. Acad. Sci. U.S.A.* **74,** 1928–1931.
40. Zatz, M., and O'Dea, R. F. (1976) *J. Cyclic Nucleotide Res.* **2,** 427–439.

Molecular Properties and Regulation of Alpha- and Beta-Adrenergic Receptors

ROBERT J. LEFKOWITZ
Departments of Medicine and Biochemistry
Duke University Medical Center
Durham, North Carolina

INTRODUCTION

Among the naturally occurring hormones and neurotransmitters few have more important and widespread effects than the catecholamines epinephrine and norepinephrine. They have important actions not just in the central nervous system but in a wide variety of peripheral organs including the heart and blood vessels, and the genitourinary, gastrointestinal, and pulmonary systems. Thus, an understanding of the properties and regulatory mechanisms of the receptors for the catecholamines is particularly relevant to an understanding of neuronal information transfer in the central and peripheral nervous systems.

The diverse effects of the catecholamines have been envisioned as being mediated through several distinct types of adrenergic receptor sites. This concept was first introduced by Ahlquist (1) almost 30 years ago. He studied the effects of six catecholamine agonists on a series of physiological systems. Rank orders of potencies of these various compounds for each physiological effect were then determined. His observation was that only two potency series were found. For one type of effect such as stimulation of the heart or relaxation of the blood vessels, isoproterenol, a synthetic amine, was the most potent compound, followed by epinephrine and then norepinephrine. For another series of responses, typified by smooth muscle contraction in

ISBN 0-12-398450-5

a variety of organs, epinephrine was the most potent amine, followed by norepinephrine with isoproterenol the weakest. The latter type of response was termed α-adrenergic and the former β-adrenergic. The two classes of responses were then hypothesized to be due to interaction of the catecholamines respectively with either α- or β-adrenergic receptors which had distinct specificities. A great deal of work over the past three decades has served to validate and extend the concepts originally developed by Ahlquist. Although not available at the time of his studies, specific α and β-adrenergic antagonists have now been developed which interact only with one or the other of the two types of receptors. In addition, subtypes of the β-adrenergic receptors have been defined (2). This subclassification is based on slight differences in the order of potencies of agonists in interacting with β-receptors. Thus, at the β_1-adrenergic receptors epinephrine and norepinephrine are about equally potent, whereas at β_2-adrenergic receptors epinephrine is considerably more potent than norepinephrine (2). β_1-Adrenergic receptors are found, for example, in the heart and in adipose tissue whereas β_2-adrenergic receptors are found in smooth muscle. Figure 1 summarizes in a schematic way some of the pharmacological properties of α- and β-adrenergic receptors as represented in a smooth muscle cell.

A second major conceptual advance in this area was the demonstration, initially by Sutherland and his co-workers, that the β-adrenergic effects of catecholamines are often mediated by stimulation of the membrane bound enzyme adenylate cyclase with elevation of the intracellular concentrations of cyclic AMP (3). This was an example of Sutherland's "second messenger hypothesis" in which hormones and drugs circulating in the blood ("first messengers")

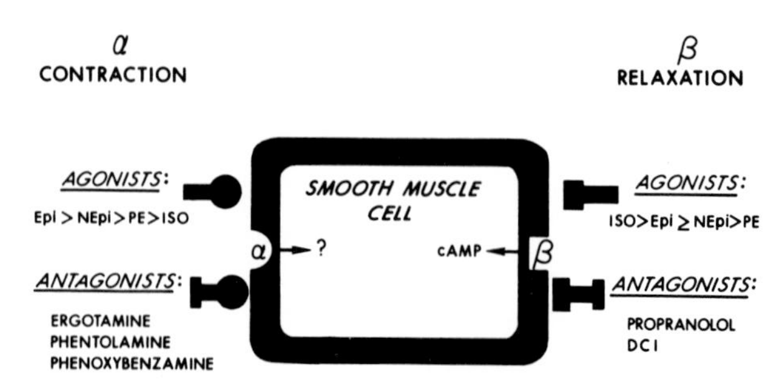

Fig. 1. α- and β-Adrenergic receptors in a smooth muscle cell. The abbreviations used are Epi, epinephrine, NEpi, norepinephrine; PE, phenylephrine; ISO, isoproterenol.

elevated intracellular concentrations of a "second messenger," cyclic AMP, which was then responsible for initiating the characteristic cascade of biochemical events responsible for typical physiological effects. The experimental evidence linking β-adrenergic receptors and adenylate cyclase in many tissues is extensive. Thus the β-adrenergic receptors appear to be linked or coupled in some way to the enzyme adenylate cyclase in membranes from a wide variety of tissues (4). By contrast, the biochemical mechanism of action for α-adrenergic responses remains obscure. Candidates for a "second messenger" role for α-adrenergic responses include cyclic GMP and calcium. However, at this time no clearcut answer is available.

The experimental approach used by Ahlquist to delineate the α- and β-adrenergic receptors typifies the classical pharmacological approach to the classification of drug receptors (1). Thus, the receptors are defined on the basis of their specificity, i.e., by the rank potency orders of agonists or antagonists for interaction with or blockade of a specific physiological effect. Thus the β-adrenergic receptor was originally defined as a potency series: isoproterenol $>$ epinephrine $\geq$ norepinephrine, etc. Although this approach has served pharmacologists well over the years it obviously has shortcomings when it comes to elucidation of the molecular or biochemical properties of the receptors themselves. Most notably, receptors are the most proximal link in the chain of drug effects, yet they are being characterized by observation and quantitation of the ultimate physiological response, which is in a sense the most distal point in the chain of response. Over the past decade a more direct approach has evolved and has permitted great progress in the study of a wide variety of drug receptors including the adrenergic receptors for catecholamines. This is the direct binding approach (5). A radioactively labeled agonist or antagonist, termed a "radioligand," is bound directly to the receptors in appropriate membrane fractions from responsive tissues. This permits the direct observation and study of the drug or hormone receptor interaction. Although this has proven to be an exceedingly powerful tool for learning about the molecular properties of adrenergic and other types of receptors over the past few years, it is a technique that is not without pitfalls. Thus it is important to use rigorous criteria in determining whether any particular binding site is in fact equivalent to the physiological receptor which one would like to study. A variety of other potential binding sites which may bind radioligands are also found in membranes and may confuse the picture.

IDENTIFICATION OF α- AND β-ADRENERGIC RECEPTORS BY RADIOLIGAND BINDING

Several criteria which have been widely used in the field of adrenergic receptor research are summarized in Table I. In general they simply represent the fact that the receptor binding sites should display characteristics which are appropriate and which can be deduced from classic physiological and pharmacological experiments.

Of the criteria listed in the table perhaps the most important issue is that of the specificity of the binding sites. This is because the major identifying feature by which receptors are characterized is their unique specificity for drug action. The expectation is that any receptor binding site will display precisely the same specificity and or stereospecificity in binding studies which can be deduced from the physiological action of drugs on this receptor. Our laboratory has recently developed ligands which display appropriate binding specificity toward the β- and α-adrenergic receptors, respectively. The availability of these ligands makes possible a direct experimental approach to studying both the α- and β-adrenergic receptors.

A ligand we have developed for studies of β-adrenergic receptors is [^{3}H]dihydroalprenolol, that for α-adrenergic receptors is [^{3}H]dihydroergocryptine. Both of these agents are very potent receptor antagonists for the β- and α-adrenergic receptors, respectively. [^{3}H]Dihydroalprenolol was initially characterized in a simple model system the frog erythrocyte plasma membrane which contains β-adrenergic receptors and adenylate cyclase (6–8). However, it has been used subsequently to study β-adrenergic receptors in a wide variety of mammalian and nonmammalian tissues (4). In the case of the β-adrenergic receptor the ability of various agonists and antagonists to either stimulate or block stimulation of the enzyme adenylate cyclase provides a convenient biochemical response with which receptor binding data can be correlated. It was found that the potency

TABLE I
Criteria for Identification of Adrenergic Receptors by Radioligand Binding

1. Binding should display appropriate kinetics and reversibility
2. Binding should be saturable
3. Binding should display appropriate specificiy and affinity
4. Binding should display appropriate stereospecificity

of a wide variety of drugs including both agonists and antagonists to inhibit [^{3}H]dihydroalprenolol binding to frog erythrocyte membranes correlated quite well with their potency for either activating or inhibiting activation of the enzyme adenylate cyclase in the same membrane (6–8). From the binding studies equilibrium dissociation constants for each drug could be determined. Dissociation constants for the same drugs for interaction with the membrane-bound adenylate cyclase could also be determined. Figure 2 indicates the excellent correlation (for both agonists and antagonists) which was observed between the two sets of experimental data. Thus the affinity constants of these drugs determined by direct binding or by the biochemical experiments were essentially the same. It should be noted that the

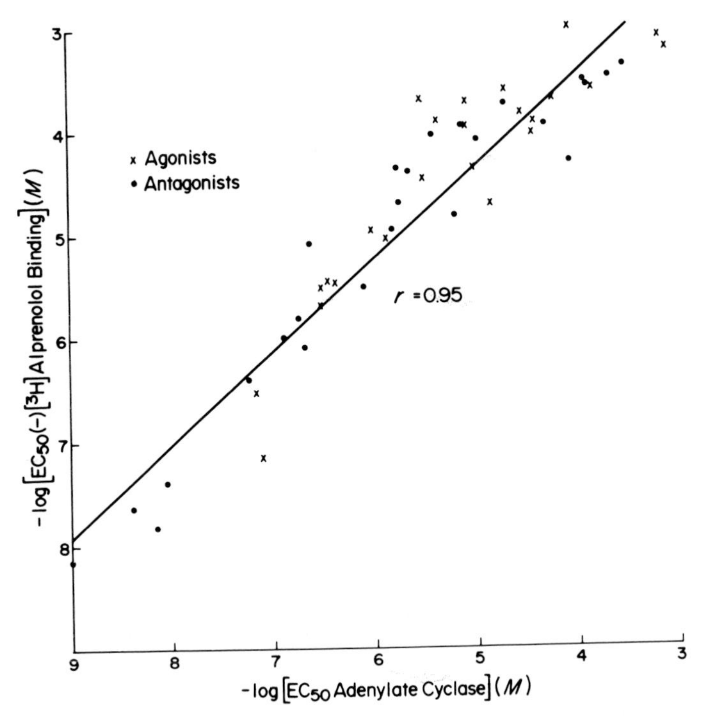

Fig. 2. Correlation of EC_{50}'s of β-adrenergic agents for frog erythrocyte β-adrenergic receptors determined by direct binding and adenylate cyclase studies. The EC_{50} for [^{3}H](−)-alprenolol binding represents the concentration of each agent which inhibits the specific binding of the radioligand to frog erythrocyte membranes by 50%. The EC_{50} for adenylate cyclase represents the concentrations of agonist which one-half maximally stimulate the enzyme or the concentrations of antagonists which cause a twofold rightward shift in the isoproterenol stimulation curve.

drugs used had affinity constants varying over a 10^6-fold range of potencies. Data such as these are essential for supporting the contention that a radioligand binding site is in fact equivalent to a physiologically significant receptor.

Binding of [^{3}H]dihydroergocryptine was initially studied in membranes derived from the rabbit uterus (9,10). In analogy with the findings quoted above for the β-adrenergic receptor the binding of [^{3}H]dihydroergocryptine to sites in these membranes has all the characteristics which one would expect for binding to the α-adrenergic receptors. Thus, for a wide range of α-adrenergic agonists and antagonists ability to compete for the membrane binding sites was directly parallel to the previously determined affinity or potency series of these agents for either stimulating uterine contraction (an α-adrenergic response) or for inhibiting stimulation by epinephrine. Figure 3A and B shows correlation plots for agonists and antagonists of binding data and physiological response data. The excellent correlation is apparent and again supports the contention that the binding is occurring to the relevant α-adrenergic receptor binding sites.

The ability to directly study the α- and β-adrenergic receptors by radioligand binding techniques has opened up a new era of investigation in the area of receptor pharmacology. These investigations have two major goals. The first is to examine the molecular properties of the receptors. The second is to learn how receptor function is regulated under both physiological and pathophysiological conditions. It is this latter area of receptor regulation which has great potential relevance to the subject of information transfer in biological systems. Several examples of such newly understood regulatory phenomena are discussed below.

DESENSITIZATION OF ADRENERGIC RECEPTORS

It has been known for some time that, for a wide variety of biological responses, the response becomes attenuated with time despite the continued presence of a hormone or agonist drug. This phenomenon has received several names in the pharmacological literature including tolerance, tachyphylaxis, refractoriness, and desensitization. None of these terms has an exact meaning and they are often used interchangeably. However they also cover a fairly wide variety of different biological regulatory phenomena. One particularly interesting type of hormone refractoriness is that which appears to be re-

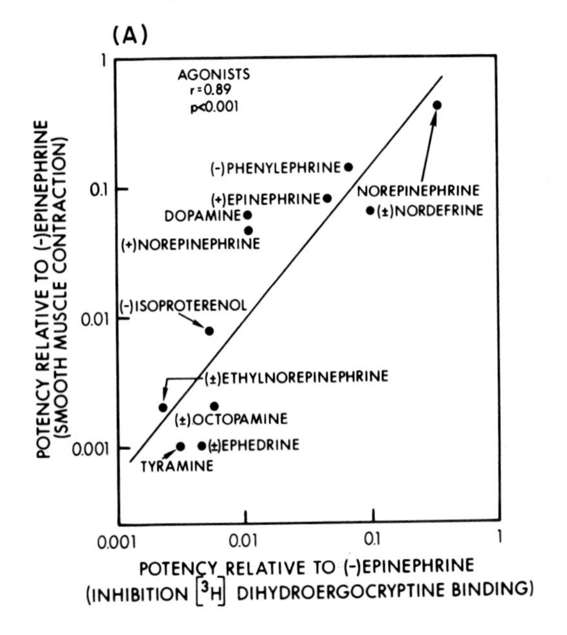

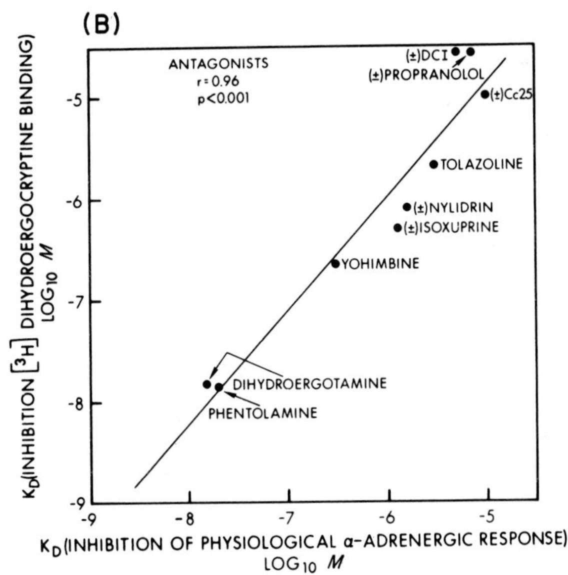

Fig. 3. Correlation of [^{3}H]dihydroergocryptine binding and physiological response in smooth muscle preparations for (A) adrenergic agonists and (B) adrenergic antagonists. The binding values are the calculated dissociation constants of the indicated agents determined by competition binding with [^{3}H]dihydroergocryptine in rabbit uterine smooth muscle membrane preparations and are taken from reference 10. Physiological data are taken from a variety of literature sources as described in William *et al*, (10).

ceptor specific. Here we are discussing a phenomenon characterized by the development of selective refractoriness to stimulation by a hormone when a tissue is chronically exposed to that hormone. The response mechanism remains intact and is normally responsive to other hormonal or drug effectors. Only the biological responsiveness to the particular hormone or drug which is chronically present becomes attenuated. Teleologically the protective value of such a mechanism is obvious.

We have studied desensitization of the β-adrenergic receptor response in a very useful model system the frog erythrocyte. These cells contain an adenylate cyclase enzyme which responds to two different classes of hormonal effects, catecholamines through a β-adrenergic receptor and prostaglandins of the E series through a

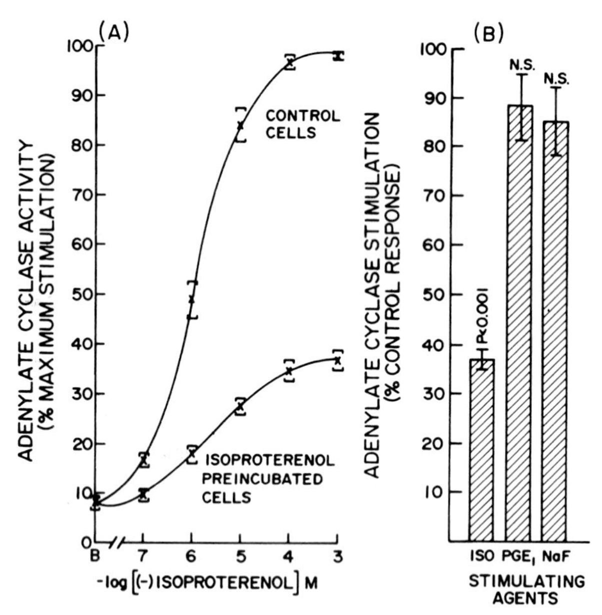

Fig. 4 (A) Dose response curves for stimulation of frog erythrocyte membrane adenylate cyclase by isoproterenol in membranes from control and desensitized cells. Isoproterenol preincubated cells were incubated with 10^{-5} *M* isoproterenol for 3 hr at room temperature. Cells were then washed three times. Membrane fractions were prepared and were washed an additional three times. (B) Stimulation of frog erythrocyte adenylate cyclase by isoproterenol PGE_1 and sodium fluoride in membranes derived from isoproterenol-preincubated cells. Isoproterenol preincubations were performed as described previously. The concentrations of the various stimulators in the enzyme assays were isoproterenol, $10^{-4}M$; PGE_1, $10^{-5}M$; and sodium fluoride, $10^{-2}M$. This figure is taken from Mickey *et al.* (13).

prostaglandin receptor. When these cells are exposed for several hours to a β-adrenergic agonist such as isoproterenol, selective desensitization to further isoproterenol stimulation occurs (11–14). This is demonstrated in Fig. 4A and B. It can be seen that the maximum enzyme response to isoproterenol stimulation is markedly reduced in membranes derived from the cells. It can be seen that the concentration of isoproterenol causing half-maximal stimulation is unaltered, suggesting that the affinity of the β-adrenergic receptors has not changed. It can also be seen in Fig. 4B that the enzyme response to fluoride, and to prostaglandin E_1, is normal in membranes derived from the cells preexposed to isoproterenol. This data exemplifies the receptor-specific nature of the desensitization induced by isoproterenol in this system. Conversely, if the cells are preexposed to PGE_1, the enzyme becomes desensitized to further PGE_1 stimulation whereas it remains normally responsive to isoproterenol (15).

We investigated whether the β-adrenergic receptors themselves were altered in the desensitized cell membranes. Figure 5A and B demonstrate the results of these studies. Saturation experiments were performed by adding increasing amounts of dihydroalprenolol to membrane protein derived from control and desensitized cells. It can be seen that at saturation there was a considerable decrease in the

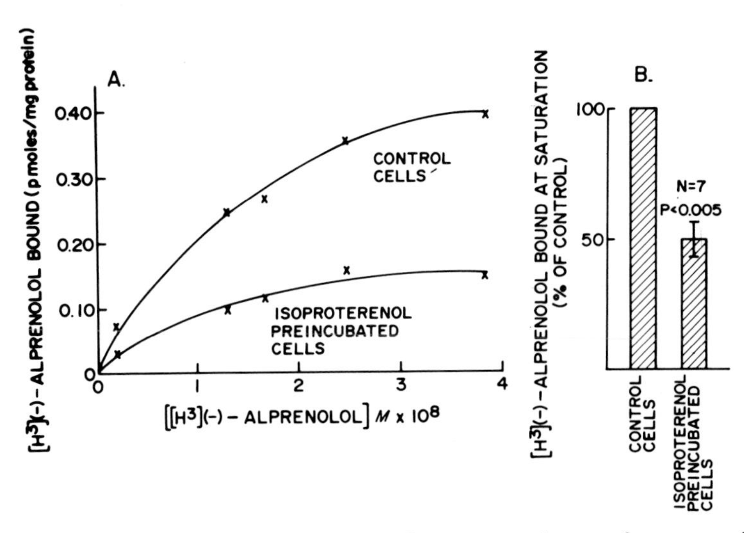

Fig. 5A and B. [^{3}H](−)-Alprenolol binding to membranes from control and isoproterenol-preincubated cells. Isoproterenol preincubation was performed as described in legend to Fig. 4A. This figure is taken from Mickey *et al.* (13).

amount of [^{3}H]dihydroalprenolol bound to membranes from the densensitized cells. The affinity of binding, however, appeared unaltered as indicated by the comparable concentrations of ligand causing half-maximal saturation of the binding sites in both cases. The decrease in binding, which generally amounted to about 50%, was quite consistent and highly statistically significant. These results indicate that exposure of cells to β-adrenergic agonist can lead to desensitization of the biological response to the β-adrenergic agent which is associated with a decrease in the number of functional β-adrenergic receptors. Over the past several years extensive investigations in our laboratory have indicated that the ability of the β-adrenergic agonists to selectively inactivate the β-adrenergic receptors appears to be an important and fundamental mechanism for control of sensitivity of tissues to adrenergic stimulation. The detailed molecular mechanisms of this important regulatory phenomenon have not yet been fully elucidated. However, it is our belief that conformational alterations in the β-adrenergic receptors induced only by agonists (not by antagonists) may be involved. When the agonist is removed from the tissue, receptor number gradually returns to normal in association with a concordant increase in biological responsiveness to normal levels. This process takes a number of hours (12,14).

Very comparable data has been obtained recently for an α-adrenergic receptor system (16,17). α-Adrenergic agonists stimulate the release of potassium from dispersed parotid acinar cells (18). This biological effect has all the specificity characteristics of a typical α-adrenergic response. The effects of α-agonists are antagonized by phentolamine but not by the β-blocker propranolol. The α-adrenergic receptor binding sites can be studied directly in intact parotid cells and in parotid membrane fractions with [^{3}H]dihydroergocryptine. When these cells are exposed to the α-agonist epinephrine for a period greater than 15 min, it can be demonstrated that they specifically lose their responsiveness to epinephrine in terms of potassium release. Desensitization is again receptor specific since muscarinic cholinergic agonists retain their ability to stimulate potassium release normally. The desensitization to α-adrenergic agonists is accompanied by a highly significant decline in [^{3}H]dihydroergocryptine binding to the intact cells. Both the desensitization and the fall in dihydroergocryptine binding are blocked by the α-adrenergic antagonist phentolamine. Thus, in this model system α-adrenergic desensitization has many of the same properties as β-adrenergic receptor desensitization in the frog erythrocyte system. The mechanisms by which α-agonists are able to desensitize their receptors also remain to be determined. The potential generality of these mechanisms for desensitization of neurotransmitter receptors by agonists has yet to be fully evaluated.

RECEPTOR SUPERSENSITIVITY

Since chronic exposure of receptors to high concentrations of agonist is capable of leading to receptor desensitization, it might reasonably be inquired whether removal of endogenous agonist from tissues is associated with increased receptor number and receptor supersensitivity. Preliminary data appear to indicate that this may be the case. We have depleted tissue stores of norepinephrine from the heart by either 6-hydroxydopamine or chronic guanethidine treatment. After such treatment tissue norepinephrine levels declined dramatically. In cardiac membranes from the hearts of rats treated with either of these protocols we observed a highly statistically significant 50–100% increase in the number of β-adrenergic receptor binding sites with no change in the binding affinity. These data may indicate that removal of normal endogenous β-agonist (norepinephrine) from tissues is associated with an increase in functional β-adrenergic receptor number, perhaps due to removal of chronic desensitization. Other mechanisms, however, are also possible and might include such factors as increase in *de novo* receptor synthesis, decreased receptor degradation, etc.

Similar findings have recently been reported by Molinoff *et al.* in the rat brain. When 6-hydroxydopamine was injected intraventricularly, a highly statistically significant 20% increase in β-adrenergic receptor number was noted in cerebral membranes. Again, no change in β-adrenergic receptor binding affinity was noted. In this system the increase in receptor number was associated with supersensitivity of the brain adenylate cyclase to catecholamine stimulation (19). These data appear to indicate that, just as high concentrations of agonist are associated with decreased receptor number and subsensitivity, so too are decreased agonist concentrations in tissues associated with increased receptor number and supersensitivity to catecholamine stimulation.

SUMMARY AND CONCLUSIONS

The recent development of direct radioligand binding methods for studying the α- and β-adrenergic receptors has greatly accelerated the pace of research aimed at understanding the way in which adrenergic receptor function is regulated. It has been learned that the concentrations of agonists either in the circulation or in tissues play an important if not crucial role in determining the size of the functional adrenergic receptor pool. Increased concentrations of agonist are associated with decreased receptor number and subsensitivity and decreased agonist concentrations are associated with increased receptor number and supersensitivity. At present, little is known about the factors which modulate these desensitizing and resensitizing processes. However, as more information is gathered about the nature of such factors, the processes by which neurotransmitters control their own receptors and hence modulate the sensitivity of tissues to their own effects will become understood with greater clarity.

ACKNOWLEDGMENTS

This study was supported by Grant HL 16037 and HL20339 from the National Institutes of Health and by a grant-in-aid from the American Heart Association, with funds contributed in part by the North Carolina Heart Association. Dr. Robert Lefkowitz is an Investigator of the Howard Hughes Medical Institute.

REFERENCES

1. Ahlquist, R. P. (1948) *Am. J. Physiol.* **153,** 586–595.
2. Lands, A. N., Arnold, A., McAuliff, J. P., Luduena, F. L., and Brown, T. G. (1967) *Nature (London)* **214,** 597–600.
3. Sutherland, E. W., and Rall, T. W. (1960) *Pharmacol. Rev.* **12,** 265–290.
4. Lefkowitz, R. J., Limbird, L. E., Mukherjee, C., and Caron, M. G. (1976) *Biomembr. Rev.* **457,** 1–39.
5. Lefkowitz, R. J., Caron, M. G., Limbird, L. E., Mukherjee, C., and Williams, L. T. (1976) *In* "The Enzymes of Biological Membranes" (A. Martonosi, ed.), 1st ed., Vol. 4, pp. 283–310. Plenum, New York.
6. Lefkowitz, R. J., Mukherjee, C., Coverstone, M., and Caron, M. G. (1974) *Biochem. Biophys. Res. Commun.* **60,** 703–709.
7. Mukherjee, C., Caron, M. G., Coverstone, M., and Lefkowitz, R. J. (1975) *J. Biol. Chem.* **250,** 4869–4875.
8. Mukherjee, C., Caron, M. G., Mullikin, D., and Lefkowitz, R. J. (1976) *Mol. Pharmacol.* **12,** 16–31.
9. Williams, L. T., and Lefkowitz, R. J. (1976) *Science* **192,** 791–793.
10. Williams, L. T., Mullikin, , D., and Lefkowitz, R. J. (1976) *J. Biol. Chem.* **251,** 6915–6923.
11. Mukherjee, C., Caron, M. G., and Lefkowitz, R. J. (1975) *Proc. Natl. Acad. Sci. U.S.A.* **72,** 1945–1949.

12. Mukherjee, C., Caron, M. G., and Lefkowitz, R. J. (1976) *Endocrinology* **99,** 343–353.
13. Mickey, J. V., Tate, R., and Lefkowitz, R. J. (1975) *J. Biol. Chem.* **250,** 5727–5730.
14. Mickey, J. V., Tate, R., Mullikin, D., and Lefkowitz, R. J. (1976) *Mol. Pharmacol.* **12,** 409–419.
15. Lefkowitz, R. J., Mullikin, D., Wood, C., Gore, T., and Mukherjee, C. (1977) *J. Biol. Chem.* (in press).
16. Strittmatter, W. J., Davis, J. N., and Lefkowitz, R. J. (1977) *J. Biol. Chem.* (in press).
17. Strittmatter, W. J., Davis, J. N., and Lefkowitz, R. J. (1977) *J. Biol. Chem.* (in press).
18. Batzri, S., Sellinger, Z., Schramm, M., and Rabinovitch, M. R. (1973) *J. Biol. Chem.* **248,** 361–368.
19. Sporn, J. R., Harden, T. K., Wolfe, B. B., and Molinoff, P. B. (1976) *Science* **194,** 624–626.

Biochemical Characterization of Neurotransmitter Receptors in the Brain

IAN CREESE AND SOLOMON H. SNYDER
Departments of Pharmacology and Experimental Therapeutics
and Psychiatry and Behavioral Sciences
The Johns Hopkins University School of Medicine
Baltimore, Maryland

INTRODUCTION

Neurotransmitters are hypothesized to exert their effects by interacting with specific receptors on cell membranes. Until very recently, studies of neurotransmitter receptors in the brain have relied almost exclusively on neurophysiological techniques. Indeed, the major criterion for the identification of a compound as a neurotransmitter, that it mimic the actions of the natural transmitter, implies neurophysiological approaches. However, the detailed characterization of receptor sites by neurophysiological studies suffers from some inherent limitations. The examination of large numbers of drugs sufficient to describe, in detail, the structure-activity characteristics of a neurotransmitter receptor is much more readily accomplished by means of *in vitro* techniques. It has been hypothesized that many of the psychoactive drugs in use today must also interact with these same neurotransmitter receptor sites. Such drugs can be either neurotransmitter agonists or antagonists; they exhibit precise structural requirements and their interactions with neurotransmitters are often of a competitive nature. The study of neurotransmitter receptors should thus not only assist in our understanding of the molecular mechanisms regulating synaptic transmission but also the interaction of exogenous drugs with such systems. The possibility also exists that changes in the functioning of these receptor sites may occur in many psychiatric and neurological diseases and be central in their etiology and symptomatology.

One *in vitro* method of studying central nervous system neurotransmitter receptors which we have pioneered is to biochemically label receptors by binding radioactive ligands to them. By definition, such binding studies label the recognition site of the receptor. Of course, following the recognition and binding of the neurotransmitter to its receptor, transduction of this information into a biochemical effect occurs, altering the functioning of the postsynaptic cell. Whether the same or separate molecules mediate both recognition and transduction functions (such as a change in ion conductance or enzyme activity) is not clear, although they are probably closely linked.

METHODOLOGICAL PRINCIPLES

In the peripheral nervous system the nicotinic acetylcholine receptor in, for example, the electric organ of the electric eel, has been successfully characterized by labeling the receptor with virtually irreversible, radiolabeled, polypeptide toxins. Unfortunately, no irreversible toxins have yet been discovered with specific affinity for brain neurotransmitter receptors, although recently some of the toxins previously used in the periphery have been utilized to study central cholinergic receptors. In order to characterize central neurotransmitter receptors it has been necessary to resort to binding studies with the radiolabeled neurotransmitter itself or agonists and antagonists which bind reversibly. The success in labeling the many neurotransmitter and putative neurotransmitter receptors which we have studied in our laboratory (Table I) has depended on solving certain technical problems to allow the use of such reversible ligands.

Most radioactive ligands bind to biological membranes in a relatively nonspecific manner by hydrophobic interactions, van der Waals forces, and ionic attractions. As neurotransmitter receptor density in the brain is low, 1–100 pmoles/g, and the number of nonspecific binding sites is effectively infinite, it is difficult to distinguish specific binding from nonspecific binding. In order to maximize the ratio of specific to nonspecific binding it is necessary to use low concentrations of high-specific-activity, radiolabeled ligands which have a high receptor affinity. Even under these conditions it is gener-

TABLE I
Central Nervous System Neurotransmitter Receptors Labeled in Our Laboratory

Receptor	Ligand	
	Agonist	Antagonist
Opiate–Enkephalin	Dihydromorphine	Naloxone
	Etorphine	Diprenorphine
	Enkephalins	—
Dopamine	Dopamine	Haloperidol
	Apomorphine	Spiroperidol
Serotonin	Serotonin	LSD
Muscarinic cholinergic	—	QNB
α-Adrenergic	Clonidine	WB-4101
	Norepinephrine	—
	Epinephrine	—
	Dihydroergocryptine	—
β-Adrenergic	Epinephrine	Dihydroalprenolol
Glycine	—	Strychnine
GABA	GABA	Bicuculline
Glutamate	Kainic acid	—
Potential neurotransmitters		
TRH	TRH	—
Neurotensin	Neurotensin	—
Angiotensin	Angiotensin	—

ally necessary to rinse tissue preparations following binding by rapid filtration on glass fiber filters under vacuum to remove the lower affinity, nonspecifically bound ligand. However, if the dissociation rate of the ligand from its receptor is rapid, vigorous washing of the membranes is not possible: strychnine binding to the glycine receptor ($t_{1/2}$ = 30 sec at 0°C) is routinely measured under conditions in which the membranes are separated from the incubation mix by centrifugation. In studies of the α-adrenergic receptor, utilizing ^{3}H-catecholamines as ligands, nonspecific binding is reduced by another method. Incubations contain a high concentration of pyrocatechol which blocks a great proportion of the nonspecific binding sites without affecting specific binding.

In binding studies of any neurotransmitter receptor it cannot be reiterated too often that there are certain criteria that must be satisfied before one can conclude that the binding site is the pharmacologically and behaviorally relevant receptor. These are: (1) saturability—

radiolabeled ligand binding must saturate with increasing concentrations of radiolabeled ligand, indicating that the binding sites are finite in number; (2) regional localization—binding sites should be found only in areas where the neurotransmitter itself is present; however, this does not necessarily imply a perfect correlation between the level of neurotransmitter and the concentration of its receptor sites in various brain areas; and (3) pharmacological specificity—agonists and antagonists which differ in potency in *in vivo* behavioral and pharmacological tests should exhibit parallel differences in potency in competing for the radiolabeled ligand's binding sites. This criterion takes on added importance if optical isomers of a drug have markedly different behavioral and clinical potencies. Their ability to interact with the relevant neurotransmitter receptor must also exhibit isomeric specificity and thus be able to be used to define stereospecific receptor binding.

We shall now discuss our recent studies characterizing the dopamine, muscarinic cholinergic, and α-adrenergic receptors and the light they shed on the mechanism of action of neuroleptic drugs.

THE DOPAMINE RECEPTOR

An abundance of receptor research suggests that the antischizophrenic phenothiazine, butyrophenone, and similar drugs may exert their therapeutic actions and induce Parkinson's disease-like, extrapyramidal side effects by blocking dopamine receptors in the brain (1). While molecular modeling indicates how phenothiazines can assume the preferred conformation of dopamine, the conformation of butyrophenones such as haloperidol at their receptor sites is unclear (2). Nevertheless, in behavioral tests both phenothiazines and butyrophenones block dopamine-mediated behaviors in animals induced by amphetamine and apomorphine in proportion to their clinical potencies (3).

A dopamine-sensitive adenylate cyclase, localized to areas of the brain rich in dopamine terminals, appears to be associated with the postsynaptic dopamine receptor and might therefore predict potencies of dopamine antagonists (4). While there are some correlations between the pharmacological potencies of phenothiazines and their inhibition of the dopamine-sensitive adenylate cyclase, major discrepancies exist for the butyrophenones. Although butyrophenone and related neuroleptics such as spiroperidol and pimozide are weaker than chlorpromazine in inhibiting the dopamine-sensitive adenylate cyclase, *in vivo* behavioral and clinical data show them to be considerably more potent than chlorpromazine (5). These discrepancies can be construed as challenges to the hypothesis that antischizophrenic drugs produce their therapeutic effects by blocking postsynaptic dopamine receptors.

The biochemical labeling of the dopamine receptor with radioactive ligands should thus have theoretical and practical benefits. Understanding the basic mechanisms involved in dopamine receptor binding may indicate how recognition of the neurotransmitter is translated into physiological activity. Such receptor binding studies should also facilitate the determination of structure–activity relationships for both dopaminergic agonist and antagonist drugs. This should not only result in rapid quantitative screening of potentially useful drugs but also give insight into the formulation of new therapeutic compounds with more potent and specific interactions.

Recently in our and in Seeman's laboratory the dopamine receptor has been labeled with both agonists, ^{3}H-dopamine and ^{3}H-apomorphine, and antagonists, ^{3}H-haloperidol and ^{3}H-spiroperidol (6–9). Binding of ^{3}H-dopamine to membranes of calf brain caudate nucleus (which has one of the largest dopamine innervations) is saturable with a dissociation constant between 10–20 n*M*. ^{3}H-Haloperidol binding is also saturable with a dissociation constant of between 1–3 n*M* determined in equilibrium and kinetic studies. Displacement of ^{3}H-haloperidol with nonradioactive haloperidol indicates multiple components of binding to both the specific dopamine receptor and to nonspecific sites. Specific binding to the dopamine receptor can be distinguished from nonspecific binding by including nonradioactive drugs in the incubation, which interact with the dopamine receptors (Fig. 1). One such drug is butaclamol, a new antischizophrenic agent which exists as optical isomers, with virtually all the dopamine blocking activity residing in the (+)-isomer. The maximum stereospecific difference between the binding of the ^{3}H-ligand in the presence of (+)-butaclamol and that in the presence of an equal concentration of (−)-butaclamol is thus a measure of the stereospecific binding of the ^{3}H-ligand to the dopamine receptor. For both ^{3}H-dopamine and ^{3}H-haloperidol binding sites (+)-butaclamol is between 100 and 1000 times more potent than its (−)-isomer. Other known dopamine agonists and antagonists reduce the ^{3}H-ligand binding competitively to the same extent as the high affinity component of the displacement by (+)-butaclamol and the maximum high affinity components are not additive, indicating that these drugs are all competing for the same class of ^{3}H-ligand binding sites.

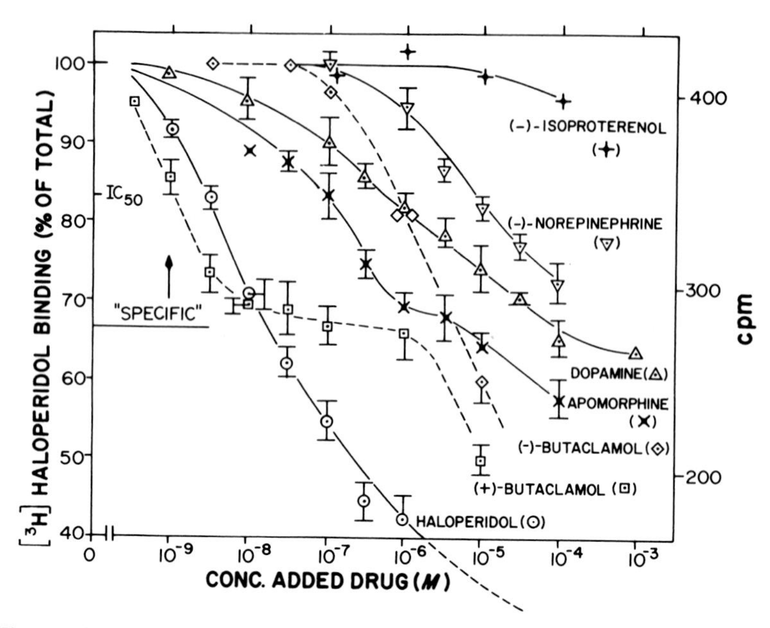

Fig. 1. Competition of drugs for binding of ^{3}H-haloperidol. Increasing concentrations of nonradioactive drugs were added to tubes containing 2 n*M* ^{3}H-haloperidol and calf striatal membranes (from Burt *et al.*, 8).

The relative potencies of other dopaminergic agonists and antagonists in competing for both ^{3}H-dopamine and ^{3}H-haloperidol binding are similar, which supports the hypothesis that both ligands bind to the same receptor (8). For both ligands, apomorphine is the agonist with the highest affinity, somewhat greater than that of dopamine itself. Dopamine is more than ten times as potent as norepinephrine, while isoproterenol, the most active catecholamine at β-receptors, is essentially inactive. This series closely parallels the ability of these agents to stimulate the dopamine-sensitive adenylate cyclase. Among the neuroleptic, dopamine antagonists there is a general correlation with pharmacological potency for the phenothiazines at both dopamine and haloperidol sites. Fluphenazine is more active than chlorpromazine, which is more active than promazine and promethazine.

One of the major items of evidence that ^{3}H-dopamine and ^{3}H-haloperidol bind to the same dopamine receptors derives from regional studies. The ^{3}H-ligands display very similar regional variations in binding. Highest binding for both ligands occurs in the caudate nucleus of the calf brain, with lesser amounts in the globus pallidus, putamen, olfactory tubercle, and nucleus accumbens. Receptor binding has not been detected in areas such as cerebral cortex, thalamus, hippocampus, hypothalamus, and cerebellum (8). We have recently detected binding in the pituitary, where the receptor sites may be involved in the control of prolactin release.

DOPAMINE RECEPTOR BINDING PREDICTS CLINICAL AND PHARMACOLOGICAL POTENCIES OF ANTISCHIZOPHRENIC DRUGS

In examining a larger number of phenothiazines, butyrophenones, and other neuroleptic agents both we and Seeman have demonstrated that there is an excellent correlation between the molar pharmacological potencies of these agents in animals and man and their affinities for ^{3}H-haloperidol binding sites (10–12). Apomorphine-induced stereotyped behavior in rats is accepted by most pharmacologists as involving a stimulation of dopamine receptors and inhibition of these apomorphine effects is presumed to result from blockade of dopamine receptors (10). The affinities of the drugs we have examined for ^{3}H-haloperidol binding sites correlate highly with their molar potency in antagonism of apomorphine-induced stereotypy, $r = 0.94$, $p < 0.001$. Amphetamine-induced stereotyped behavior is thought to follow from a release of dopamine onto its receptor sites and represents an animal model of amphetamine psychosis (10). Neuroleptic antagonism of this syndrome correlates with competition for ^{3}H-haloperidol binding impressively, $r = 0.93$, $p < 0.001$ (Fig. 2). Similarly blockage of apomorphine-induced emesis in dogs, which is one of the most sensitive *in vivo* neuroleptic assays and is presumed to involve stimulation of dopamine receptors in the vicinity of the chemoreceptor trigger zone in the brainstem (10), correlates closely with ^{3}H-haloperidol binding site affinity, $r = 0.93$, $p < 0.001$. These animal data are taken from Janssen (reviewed in 3). It is dramatic that clinical potency in man as antipsychotic agents simply determined by the average oral effective dose, correlates very highly with competition for ^{3}H-haloperidol binding, $r = 0.87$, $p < 0.001$ (Fig. 3) (10,12). Similar correlations between *in vivo* data and inhibition of dopamine-sensitive adenylate cyclase activity are insignificant.

These impressive correlations indicate that the affinity of a drug for the ^{3}H-haloperidol binding site of dopamine receptors is a powerful predictor of clinical activity. Seeman (11) has calculated that these inhibition constants determined *in vitro* are very similar to the plasma

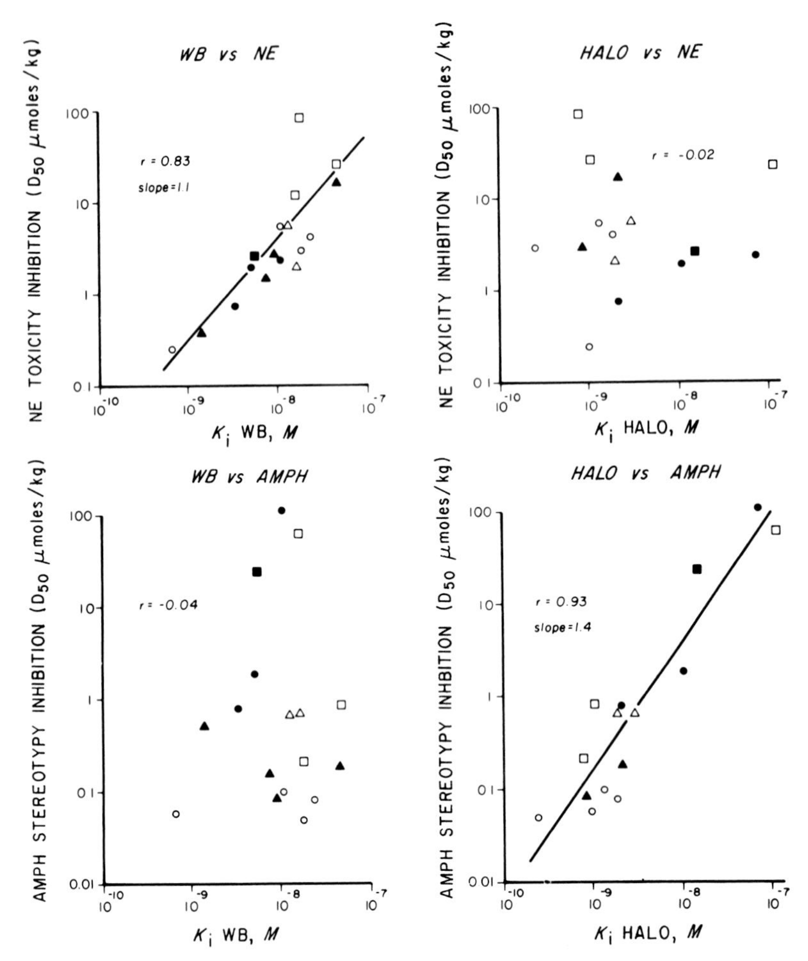

Fig. 2. Correlations between affinity for α-receptors (^{3}H-WB-4101 binding) and dopamine receptors (^{3}H-haloperidol binding) and potency in antinorepinephrine (NE) and antiamphetamine (AMPH) tests. Neuroleptic drug classes phenothiazines ●, alkylamino; ■, piperidine; ▲, piperazine; ○, butyrophenones; △, thioxanthenes; □, others. Derived from Peroutka *et al.* (22).

concentrations of the antipsychotic drugs at therapeutic dose levels, further reinforcing the concept that the blocking of dopamine receptors is responsible for their antipsychotic activity. Can neurotransmitter receptor binding sites also predict the propensity of a drug to produce the various side effects associated with neuroleptic therapy?

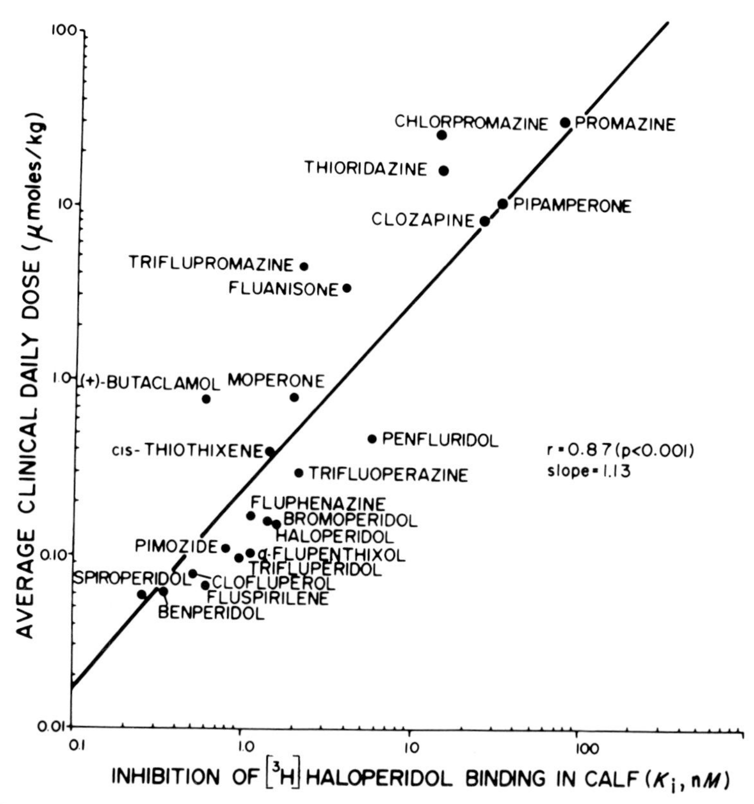

Fig. 3. Antischizophrenic drugs: correlation between affinities for ^{3}H-haloperidol binding and clinical potencies. Clinical data were derived from published results (reviewed in Creese *et al.*, 10). The correlation coefficient $r = 0.87$ is significant at the $p < 0.001$ level.

EXTRAPYRAMIDAL SIDE EFFECTS AND MUSCARINIC BINDING

One of the major side effects of neuroleptic therapy is rigidity and akinesia. It has been hypothesized that dopamine receptor blockade in the corpus striatum is responsible for these extrapyramidal side effects, while dopamine receptor blockade in the limbic forebrain, regions classically associated with emotional behaviors, is responsible for the antischizophrenic efficacy of neuroleptic agents (1). However, regional studies of ^{3}H-haloperidol binding have not indicated any fundamental differences in dopamine receptor binding between the corpus striatum, olfactory tubercle, or nucleus accumbens, even for neuroleptics such as thioridazine and clozapine which elicit a much lower incidence of extrapyramidal side effects (8,10).

Recent studies of the muscarinic acetylcholine receptor in the brain may provide a resolution of this dilemma (13,14). It is well known that concurrent administration of anticholinergic drugs is especially effective in antagonizing the extrapyramidal side effects of neuroleptics without apparently reducing their antipsychotic potency (1). The therapeutic efficacy of the anticholinergics apparently reflects a balance in the corpus striatum between dopamine and acetylcholine involved in motor control such that antagonizing acetylcholine effects is equivalent to enhancing those of dopamine and vice versa. Thus, if neuroleptics vary in their anticholinergic properties, they may well vary in their propensities to induce extrapyramidal side effects. In studies of the binding of 3-quinuclidinyl benzilate (QNB), a potent antagonist of muscarinic cholinergic receptors, to striatal membrane preparations, this hypothesis was confirmed. Clozapine, which is almost devoid of extrapyramidal side effects, has the greatest affinity for muscarinic receptors, similar to that of classical anticholinergic agents. Thioridazine, which, next to the clozapine, elicits the fewest extrapyramidal symptoms is second most potent. In contrast, piperazine phenothiazines and the butyrophenones, whose frequency of extrapyramidal effects is greatest, have the least affinity for the muscarinic receptor (13). According to this hypothesis, when given at therapeutic antischizophrenic doses, all neuroleptics produce comparable dopamine receptor blockade and thus all do have about the same tendency to elicit extrapyramidal side effects. The simultaneous blockade of acetylcholine receptors by drugs such as clozapine and thioridazine antagonizes these extrapyramidal side effects while, because of their negligible anticholinergic activity at normal doses, drugs such as haloperidol elicit many more extrapyramidal side effects. Screening of potentially useful antipsychotic drugs for muscarinic receptor affinity may thus provide a simple *in vitro* predictor of their propensity to induce extrapyramidal side effects.

TARDIVE DYSKINESIA AND DOPAMINE RECEPTOR SUPERSENSITIVITY

Tardive dyskinesia is another major complication of long-term treatment with neuroleptic drugs (15). It is characterized by abnormal movement of facial muscles and extremities which frequently worsen when the neuroleptic dose is lowered or terminated. Increasing the dose, however, may temporarily alleviate the symptoms. The chronic treatment of rats and mice with neuroleptics leads to an increased motor activity and enhanced sensitivity to the motor stimulant effects of apomorphine, a direct dopamine receptor agonist (16). A similar motor supersensitivity to dopamine receptor stimulants is apparent when dopamine synaptic activity is reduced by inhibiting synthesis of dopamine with α-methyltyrosine or by depleting dopamine storage sites with reserpine. Since lesioning the nigrostriatal dopamine pathway also produces an enhanced sensitivity to dopamine receptor agonists, which is hypothesized to result from a dopamine receptor supersensitivity (17), speculations have linked the development of tardive dyskinesia with the supersensitivity of dopamine receptors after prolonged blockade by chronic drug administration (16,18).

In order to investigate this hypothesis directly, rats were treated for 3 weeks with the potent butyrophenone neuroleptic haloperidol (0.5 mg kg^{-1} day^{-1}). Five days after terminating the chronic treatment there was a highly significant ($p < 0.001$) 20% increase in specific haloperidol binding (19).

Fluphenazine, one of the most potent phenothiazine neuroleptics, produced a similar increase in binding after administration at the same dose level for 3 weeks. By contrast, treatment for 3 weeks with a five-fold higher dose of the phenothiazine promethazine, which lacks antischizophrenic activity, failed to significantly enhance ^{3}H-haloperidol binding. Depletion of brain dopamine by chronic administration of reserpine (0.25 mg kg^{-1} day^{-1}) also produced a similar 20% augmentation of ^{3}H-haloperidol binding. Scatchard analysis of saturation data indicated that this increased binding was the result of an increased number of binding sites with no change in their affinity.

These data indicate that the motor changes seen after chronic neuroleptic treatment are associated with an increase in the number of dopamine receptor sites. This increase in the number of ^{3}H-haloperidol binding sites is consistent with the behavioral supersensitivity to apomorphine in rats treated with a similar dose schedule of neuroleptics. However, the greater relative enhancement of apomorphine stimulant effects in such rats compared to the increased dopamine receptor binding described here indicates that other components in the overall system determining the behavioral response may also be changed during chronic neuroleptic treatment, producing additive effects.

Behavioral supersensitivity to apomorphine is more pronounced after lesions of the nigrostriatal dopamine pathway than after chronic treatment with neuroleptic drugs. Consonant with this, we have found that following a unilateral 6-hydroxydopamine-induced lesion of the dopamine cell bodies in the substantia nigra there is a 20–120% increase in striatal ^{3}H-haloperidol binding 2–7 months following the lesion (20). This increased ^{3}H-haloperidol binding is also the result of an increased number of binding sites. Rats which are more behaviorally supersensitive also tend to show a greater increase in dopamine receptor binding.

It is possible that enhanced dopamine receptor binding following chronic drug treatment may be a useful *in vitro* predictor of *in vivo* propensity to produce tardive dyskinesia.

NEUROLEPTIC INTERACTIONS WITH THE NORADRENERGIC α-RECEPTOR

Autonomic sympatholytic effects such as orthostatic hypotension and sedation are among the most prominent untoward actions of neuroleptic drugs. These side effects have been attributed to the blockade of central and peripheral adrenergic α-receptors, but direct quantitative evaluation of α-receptor blockade in the CNS by these agents has not been heretofore feasible. In the past year it has become possible to label the α-receptor for norepinephrine with a specific antagonist, ^{3}H-WB-4101 (21).

Some neuroleptics are highly potent in competing for ^{3}H-WB-4101 binding to α-receptor sites in the rat brain (22). All the commonly used neuroleptics display K_i values between 1–50 nM, putting them in the same range of potency as the classical α-adrenergic antagonists. Thus the neuroleptics, as a general class, are approximately equipotent in displacing labeled α-receptor and dopaminergic receptor antagonists. This similarity is further underlined by the finding that neuroleptics also manifest stereoselectivity in competing for ^{3}H-WB-4101 binding, although to a lesser extent than for ^{3}H-haloperidol binding. Although the neuroleptics are potent inhibitors of α-receptor binding, their relative activity differs markedly from their relative influences in inhibiting ^{3}H-haloperidol binding. For instance, spiroperidol is the most potent neuroleptic in competing for dopamine receptor binding but is one of the weaker agents in inhibiting α-receptor binding. Droperidol is one-fourth as potent as spiroperidol at the dopamine receptor but 26 times more potent than spiroperidol at the α-receptor (22).

As an index of α-receptor antagonism neuroleptics are often screened for their ability to antagonize the lethal effects of norepinephrine and epinephrine administered intravenously (3). The fatal α-adrenergic vasopressor activity of norepinephrine and epinephrine is blocked by α-antagonists such as the ergot alkaloids, phentolamine, and phenoxybenzamine but not by β-antagonists or other drugs. The pharmacological relevance of WB-4101 binding sites is attested to by the high correlation between the potencies of drugs in competing for ^{3}H-WB-4101 binding and their potencies in blocking norepinephrine and epinephrine toxicity (see Fig. 2) [$r = 0.94$, $p < 0.001$; and $r = 0.88$, $p < 0.001$, respectively, animal data from Janssen (3)]. This correlation across all neuroleptics is highly selective since there is no significant correlation between affinity for α-receptor binding sites and neuroleptic potency as measured in any dopamine receptor blocking tests such as catalepsy, amphetamine, or apomorphine antagonism (22). Similarly, there is a poor correlation between neuroleptic affinity for ^{3}H-haloperidol binding sites and antagonism of norepinephrine and epinephrine toxicity.

As therapeutic brain levels of neuroleptics may be expected to correspond to concentrations of the drugs which are required to obtain an optimal blockade of dopamine receptors, the clinical propensity of neuroleptics to block α-receptors would then not be related to their absolute potencies as α-blockers, but to the ratio of their potencies as α-antagonists to their potencies as dopamine antagonists. Drugs with low ratios would be anticipated to elicit a substantial amount of α-adrenergic blockade at blood and brain levels of the drug required for adequate dopamine receptor blockade. By contrast, drugs with high ratios would be employed clinically at the very low dose levels required to secure dopamine receptor blockade and so, in general, would be less likely to elicit the side effects associated with α-adrenergic blockade. Butyrophenones, such as haloperidol and spiroperidol, and piperazine phenothiazines, such as fluphenazine and trifluoperazine, have a relatively low propensity to elicit hypotension and sedation and display ratios (K_i WB/K_i haloperidol) greater than 10. By contrast, promazine and clozapine, the neuroleptics with the greatest tendency to cause orthostatic hypotension and sedation, have ratios of less than 0.2. In general, the finding that alkylamino and piperidine phenothiazines are more sedating and hypotensive than the piperazine agents is manifested in the lower ratios (K_i WB/K_i haloperidol of the former drugs). In general, the butyrophenones tend to be relatively nonsedating and to have a low incidence of orthosatatic hypotension and substantially higher ratios (22).

These results emphasize that one must critically examine how reliably stereospecificity and correlations between clinical and biochemical effects can reveal the biochemical basis of neuroleptic drug action. We investigated the stereospecific influences on neuroleptics on receptor binding for ^{3}H-GABA, for the opiates ^{3}H-naloxone and ^{3}H-dihydromorphine, for binding of ^{3}H-strychnine to the glycine receptor, for the binding of ^{3}H-QNB to the muscarinic cholinergic receptor, for ^{3}H-dihydroalprenolol binding to the noradrenergic β-receptor, and for ^{3}H-serotonin and ^{3}H-lysergic acid diethylamide (LSD) to the serotonin receptor (23). Only the binding of ^{3}H-LSD and ^{3}H-serotonin is also inhibited stereospecifically and with reasonable potency (between 50 to 1000 n*M*) by various neuroleptics. However, since the neuroleptics are at least 50 times weaker at inhibiting ^{3}H-LSD binding as they are in inhibiting ^{3}H-haloperidol binding, in spite of these stereospecific effects, blockade of 5-HT receptors is probably not a major source of neuroleptic clinical efficacy. Furthermore, the relative influences of an extensive series of neuroleptics on ^{3}H-LSD binding does not correlate with clinical potency. Similarly, although the butyrophenones and related neuroleptics are reasonably active ($IC_{50} \sim 10\ \mu M$) at inhibiting GABA uptake or ^{3}H-naloxone binding to the opiate receptor, it is unlikely that either of these properties is the main determinant of their antischizophrenic activity. Their affinity is about 1000-fold lower in these systems than at the dopamine receptor, ^{3}H-haloperidol binding site, and when phenothiazine affinity for GABA uptake sites or opiate receptors is considered as well there is a poor correlation with clinical efficacy (23).

EVIDENCE FOR A TWO-STATE MODEL OF NEUROTRANSMITTER RECEPTORS

To date we have been able to label a number of neurotransmitter receptors with both labeled agonists and antagonists. A common feature of such studies has been that labeled agonists and antagonists appear to bind to distinct sites on their respective receptors. In some cases, for example, the opiate/enkephalin receptor, these agonist and antagonist binding sites appear to interconvert under the allosteric influence of ions (24). For example, sodium can increase the number of antagonist binding sites while concurrently decreasing the number of agonist sites. Manganese ions work in the opposite direction. Recent eletrophysiological evidence implicates changes in sodium conductance as a major synaptic mechanism of opiate action, bolstering this hypothesis (25). In this case agonist and antagonist states of the receptor are hypothesized to exist in equilibrium so that pharmacological effects of antagonists occur, not by directly blocking agonist access to receptor sites, but indirectly, by binding to the antagonist states of the receptor and decreasing the number of agonist states available (Fig. 4). This model also explains how neurotransmitter rec-

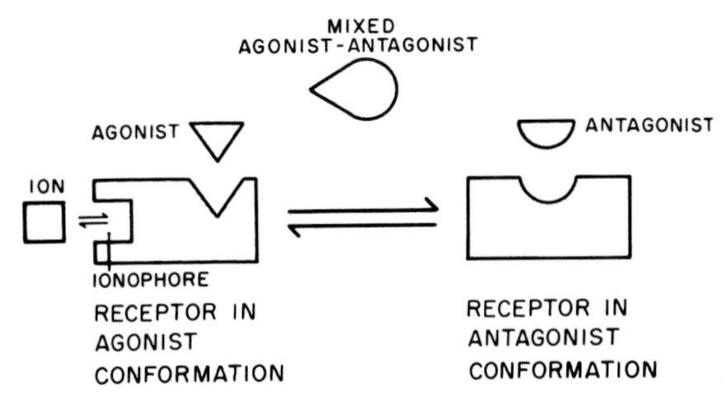

Fig. 4. Generalized two-state model of receptor action (from Snyder, 26).

ognition is translated into an alteration in ion conductance. The appropriate ion, in this case sodium, is postulated to have selective affinity for the antagonist state of the receptor. In its resting condition the receptor is largely in the antagonist binding state. When the neurotransmitter binds to the receptor and transforms a portion of the receptors into the agonist state, the binding of the crucial ion also changes, eliciting the appropriate change in conductance (26). In the case of the glycine receptor, synaptic action is mediated by changes in chloride conductance and chloride ions have been directly shown to influence interconvertible binding states of the receptor (27).

Although we have yet to demonstrate allosteric ionic influences on the serotonin, dopamine, muscarinic cholinergic, and α-adrenergic receptors it is apparent that agonist and antagonist binding sites may also exist for these receptors. In the case of the dopamine receptor, although ^{3}H-dopamine and ^{3}H-haloperidol appear to be labeling the same or related receptors, there are pronounced quantitative differences in the potencies of agonists and antagonists to displace the two ligands. If the dopamine receptor were performing as a simple "classical" binding site where antagonists block agonist activity by binding to the same site but lack intrinsic activity, then irrespective of which ^{3}H-ligand is used to label the receptor, competing unlabeled drugs should demonstrate the same K_i values. This is clearly not the case (8). Whereas the K_i for haloperidol to displace ^{3}H-haloperidol is 1.4 nM, its K_i in displacing ^{3}H-dopamine is 920 nM. In contrast, the K_i for dopamine to displace ^{3}H-dopamine is 17.5 nM while its K_i in displacing ^{3}H-haloperidol is 670 nM. In general, agonists are more potent in displacing the agonist ligand, ^{3}H-dopamine, and relatively weak in displacing the antagonist ligand, ^{3}H-haloperidol, while the reverse holds for antagonists which are potent in displacing ^{3}H-haloperidol binding and weak in displacing ^{3}H-dopamine (Table II). Moreover, Hill slopes of these displacement curves are 1.0 when

TABLE II
Affinities for ^{3}H-Dopamine and ^{3}H-Haloperidol Binding Sites in Calf Striatum

	K_i (nM)	
	^{3}H-Dopamine	^{3}H-Haloperidol
Agonists		
Dopamine	17.5	670
Apomorphine	8.6	51
Antagonists		
Haloperidol	920	1.4
Fluphenazine	230	0.9
Chlorpromazine	900	10.2

agonists displace ^{3}H-dopamine or when antagonists displace ^{3}H-haloperidol, but less than 1 when agonists displace ^{3}H-haloperidol and vice versa (8). These data clearly indicate that we are not dealing with a "classical" receptor.

Similar results have been found with the α-adrenergic receptor, where differing relative agonist/antagonist potencies are also shown (21). However, in this case Hill slopes for the displacement of either agonist or antagonist ligand by unlabeled agonists or antagonists are always 1.0. This indicates that if the two sites interact they must do so over a longer time period than that used in these experiments or under different ionic conditions.

It is possible that in these binding studies we are labeling distinct receptors with different pharmacological characteristics. Regional studies indicate that the relative proportions of agonist to antagonist binding sites is similar and various lesions which alter receptor binding have not provided evidence to support this hypothesis. Since there is much evidence to link both the dopamine and α-adrenergic receptors with control of adenylate cyclase it has been tempting to speculate that the different binding states of the receptors may be related to whether the receptor is free or linked to the adenylate cyclase (28). Studies of β-adrenergic receptors by Lefkowitz (29) and the nicotinic cholinergic receptor by Changeux (30) have indicated that desensitized receptors have a high agonist affinity and in the case of the β-receptor may be a state in which the receptor remains coupled to, but no longer activating, the cyclase. Thus, for example, ^{3}H-dopamine binding in the calf brain, which has a high affinity, may be a form of the receptor which is desensitized. Labeling the receptor with ^{3}H-haloperidol, which demonstrates a low affinity displacement by unlabeled dopamine in the micromolar range (equivalent to its EC_{50}

on the cyclase), may indicate that ^{3}H-haloperidol labels the active form of the dopamine receptor which can couple with, and activate, the cyclase when neurotransmitter binding occurs. Thus it would not be surprising that an excellent correlation with *in vivo* potency of drugs and behavioral or clinical phenomena is found for the inhibition of ^{3}H-haloperidol binding rather than ^{3}H-dopamine binding (which is looking at desensitized and nonphysiologically active receptor sites). Thus, unlike the opiate receptor, where interconversion is related to the differential binding of the ion whose ionophore is directly linked to the opiate receptor, in the case of the dopamine receptor, interconversion between conformations of the receptor with high and low agonist and antagonist affinity may be dependent on the coupling of the receptor with the adenylate cyclase which mediates synaptic activation.

Some recent data, however, has raised questions on the direct association of the dopamine receptor as labeled by ^{3}H-haloperidol and the dopamine-sensitive adenylate cyclase. Stereotaxic microinjections of kainic acid, a glutamic acid analog, have been shown to specifically lesion cell bodies within the striatum while sparing the innervation from extrastriatal areas (31). Following such lesions, dopamine-sensitive adenylate cyclase activity is lost within 2 days while ^{3}H-haloperidol binding falls by only about 40% over a 6-day period (32). Since the synthetic enzymes for acetylcholine and GABA are also severely depleted, this would suggest that the majority of the dopamine-sensitive adenylate cyclase is located on cholinergic and GABAergic cells within the striatum. Only about 40% of ^{3}H-haloperidol binding sites would be similarly located and possibly linked with the cyclase. Where are the other ^{3}H-haloperidol binding sites? Only three possible locations are apparent—on glial cells, blood vessels, or on the presynaptic terminals of axons synapsing in the striatum. Since the striatum receives a large input from the cortex, we made massive unilateral cortical ablations and compared striatal haloperidol binding on the lesioned and control sides. Cortical lesions led to about a 40% reduction in ^{3}H-haloperidol binding which was additive to that following striatal kainate injection. As of yet we have not measured ^{3}H-dopamine or ^{3}H-apomorphine binding following similar manipulations.

In conclusion, our studies of the dopamine receptor have demonstrated unequivocally that neuroleptic drugs do indeed block dopamine receptors and that their affinities for these sites correlate impressively with their *in vivo* pharmacological and clinical potencies. Such *in vitro* screening of new psychotropic drugs for dopamine receptor affinity may be predictive of antipsychotic activity and ability to produce tardive dyskinesia following chronic treatment. By comparing the ability of the same drug to interact with muscarinic cholinergic and norepinephrine α-receptors in *in vitro* binding studies it may also be possible to predict its propensities for extrapyramidal and sympatholytic side effects. Such *in vitro* receptor binding methods may thus provide inexpensive, quick and effective screens for potent neuroleptic agents with a lower propensity for unwanted side effects. The discovery of differing agonist and antagonist binding sites for many of the neurotransmitters that we have studied may indicate this to be a general principal of neurotransmitter synaptic transmission.

REFERENCES

1. Snyder, S. H., Banerjee, S. P., Yamamura, H. I., and Greenberg, D. A. (1974) *Science* **184,** 1243–1253.
2. Feinberg, A. P., and Snyder, S. H. (1975) *Proc. Natl. Acad. Sci. U.S.A.* **72,** 1899–1902.
3. Janssen, P. A. J., and Van Bever, W. F. (1975) *Curr. Dev. Psychopharmacol.* **2,** 165–184.
4. Iversen, L. L. (1975) *Science* **188,** 1084–1089.
5. Snyder, S. H., Creese, I., and Burt, D. R. (1975) *Psychopharmacol. Commun.* **1,** 663–673.
6. Burt, D. R., Enna, S. J., Creese, I., and Snyder, S. H. (1975) *Proc. Natl. Acad. Sci. U.S.A.* **72,** 4655–4659.
7. Seeman, P., Chau-Wong, M., Tedesco, J., and Wong, K. (1975) *Proc. Natl. Acad. Sci. U.S.A.* **72,** 4376–4380.
8. Burt, D. R., Creese, I., and Snyder, S. H. (1976) *Mol. Pharmacol.* **12,** 800–812.
9. Seeman, P., Lee, T., Chau-Wong, M., Tedesco, J., and Wong, K. (1976) *Proc. Natl. Acad. Sci. U.S.A.* **73,** 4354–4358.
10. Creese, I., Burt, D. R., and Snyder, S. H. (1976) *Science* **192,** 481–483.
11. Seeman, P., Lee, T., Chau-Wong, M., and Wong, K. (1976) *Nature (London)* **261,** 717–719.
12. Creese, I., Burt, D. R., and Snyder, S. H. (1976) *Science* **194,** 546.
13. Snyder, S. H., Chang, K. J., Kuhar, M. J., and Yamamura, H. I. (1975) *Fed. Proc. Fed. Am. Soc. Exp. Biol.* **34,** 1915–1921.
14. Miller, R. J., and Hilley, C. R. (1974) *Nature (London)* **248,** 596–597.
15. Kobayashi, R. K. (1977) *N. Engl. J. Med.* **296,** 257–260.
16. Baldessarini, R. J., and Tarsy, D. (1976) *In* "The Basal Ganglia" (M. D. Yahr, ed.), pp. 25–36. Raven Press, New York.
17. Creese, I., and Iversen, S. D. (1975) *In* "Pre- and Postsynaptic Receptors" (E. Usdin and W. E. Bunney, eds.), pp. 171–190. Dekker, New York.
18. Klawans, H. L. (1973) *Am. J. Psychiatry* **130,** 82–86.
19. Burt, D. R., Creese, I., and Snyder, S. H. (1977) *Science* **196,** 326–328.
20. Creese, I., Burt, D. R., and Snyder, S. H. (1977) *Science* **197,** 596–598.

21. U'Prichard, D. C., Greenberg, D. A., and Snyder, S. H. (1977) *Mol. Pharmacol.* **13**, 454–473.
22. Peroutka, S. J., U'Prichard, D. C., Greenberg, D. A., and Snyder, S. H. (1977) *Neuropharmacology* **16**, 549–556.
23. Enna, S. J., Bennett, J. P., Jr., Burt, D. R., Creese, I., and Snyder, S. H. (1976) *Nature (London)* **263**, 338–341.
24. Snyder, S. H. (1977) *N. Engl. J. Med.* **296**, 266–271.
25. Zieglgansberger, W., and Fry, J. P. (1976) *In* Opiates and Endogenous Opiate Peptides" (H. W. Kosterlitz, ed.), pp. 231–238. North-Holland Publ., Amsterdam.
26. Snyder, S. H. (1975) *Biochem. Pharmacol.* **24**, 1371–1374.
27. Young, A. B., and Snyder, S. H. (1974) *Proc. Natl. Acad. Sci. U.S.A.* **71**, 4002–4005.
28. Creese, I., and Snyder S. H. (1978) *In* "Psychopharmacology: A Generation of Progress" (M. A. Lipton, A. DiMascio, K. Killam, eds.), pp. 377–388. Raven Press, New York.
29. Mukherjee C., Carron, M. G., and Lefkowitz, R. J. (1975) *Proc. Natl. Acad. Sci. U.S.A.* **72**, 1945–1949.
30. Weber, M., David-Pfeuty, T., and Changeux, J. P. (1975) *Proc. Natl. Acad. Sci. U.S.A.* **72**, 3443–3445.
31. Coyle, J. T., and Schwarcz, R. (1976) *Nature (London)* **263**, 244–246.
32. Schwarcz, R., Creese, I., Coyle, J. T., and Snyder, S. H. (1978) *Nature* **271**, 766–768.

PART II

CHOLINERGIC SYSTEM

The Cholinergic Electromotor System of *Torpedo*: Recent Biochemical and Morphological Findings

V. P. WHITTAKER
Abteilung für Neurochemie
Max-Planck-Institut für Biophysikalische Chemie
Göttingen, Federal Republic of Germany

INTRODUCTION

The electromotor neurons and the synapses they form with the electrocytes of the electric organ in *Torpedo* are now widely utilized as a source material for the study of cholinergic transmission (1). The cholinoceptive membranes of the electrocytes provide relatively large amounts of a protein, usually referred to as the nicotinic acetylcholine receptor (2,3), though whether this protein constitutes merely the recognition site of the receptor or the complete acetylcholine-activated ionophore is not yet entirely clear. Injection of this protein into animals induces an experimental condition similar to myasthenia gravis (4). From the presynaptic terminals, very pure preparations of synaptic vesicles can be isolated (5,6), the large electromotor axons may be used for studies of axonal flow (7,8), and the perikarya of the electromotor neurons may be readily isolated from the electric lobe to which they contribute about half the mass (9).

In this chapter a brief summary will be given of recent work on the *Torpedo* electromotor system by members of this Department. For further details the reader is referred to other recent reviews (10,11).

DEVELOPMENTAL STUDIES

ELECTRIC ORGAN

Morphology. Light microscopic studies in the nineteenth century (12,13) indicated that the electrocytes of the electric organ are derived from myoblasts. Are these myoblasts typical or should they be regarded rather as "electroblasts"? Does the differentiation of the electrocyte part company with that of muscle after the formation of myotubes (Fig. 1, sequence I) or at the stage of mesodermal differentiation (Fig. 1, sequence II)? Recent electron-microscopic studies (14) indicate the correctness of earlier conclusions that true myotubes are formed. Figure 2 shows our concept of how development takes place. The vertically oriented myoblasts growing out from the mesodermal lining of outpouchings of the branchial arches join like the stalagtites and stalagmites in a cave to form columns each one of which will eventually become a stack of electrocytes in the fully developed organ. Differentiation involves fusion of myoblasts to form myotubes, transient appearance of myofibrils, flattening of the myotubes to form electrocytes, and disappearance of myofibrils. These myotubes are at this stage indistinguishable in form from similar myotubes in the nearby branchial musculature. At all stages outgrowing axons of the electromotor nuclei are in close proximity to the columns, but actual synapse formation is a late and rather prolonged event occurring between 60 and 80 mm of embryo length after the appearance of typical electrocytes and the differentiation of their ventral surfaces to form postsynaptic membranes.

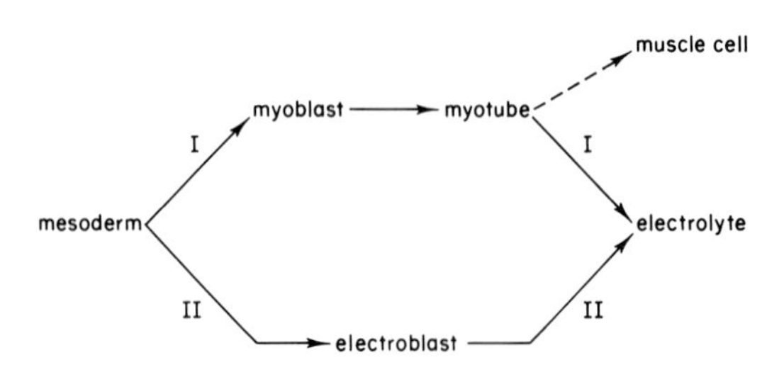

Fig. 1. Alternative schemes for electrocyte differentiation: (I) via a true myoblast; (II) via a myoblastlike "electroblast."

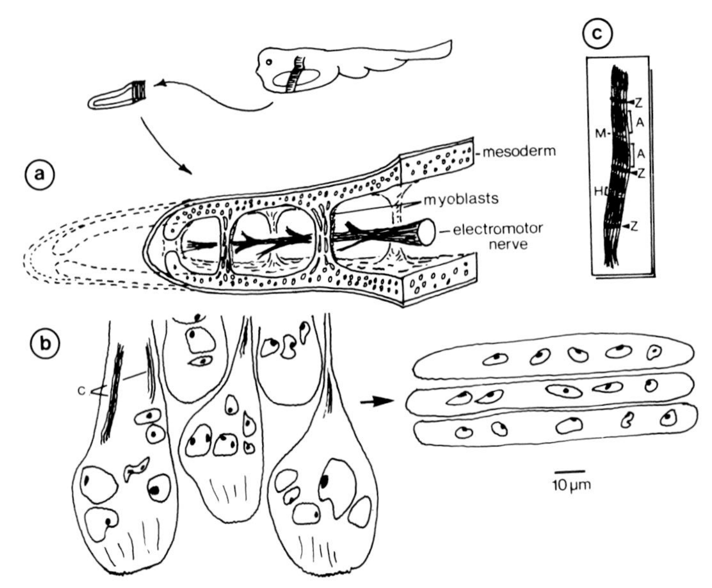

Fig. 2. Differentiation of the electric organ in *Torpedo*. (a) Mesodermal cells lining outpouchings of the branchial arches form myoblasts which arrange themselves into vertical columns. The pouches extend laterally and rostrocaudally and fuse with each other. Eventually there are as many columns as there will be stacks of electrocytes in the electric organ. (b) Fusion of myoblasts takes place. The nuclei of the myotubes collect in a horizontal plane and the cytoplasm below the nuclear layer swells laterally. The pear-shaped myotube flattens to become the primitive electrocyte and the myofibrils (c) disintegrate (14). For clarity interstitial cells have been omitted from (a).

Biochemistry. The results to date are summarized in Fig. 3b. The myoblasts present at 25–40 mm embryo length contain typical muscle myosin and this constitutes about 4% of total tissue protein. When differentiation into electrocytes begins, the myosin content falls by about 70% and there is some evidence that the light chains, involved in Ca^{2+} regulation, change in character.

Differentiation of the postsynaptic membrane begins at about 50 mm and can be followed by the rise of the postsynaptic membrane marker acetylcholinesterase (Fig. 3b). Not until these membranes, with their characteristic infoldings, have begun to differentiate do synapses form. Choline acetyltransferase, the characteristic enzymic constituent of the presynaptic terminals, makes its appearance in the organ at about this time, but even at birth it is only about 50% of its adult value.

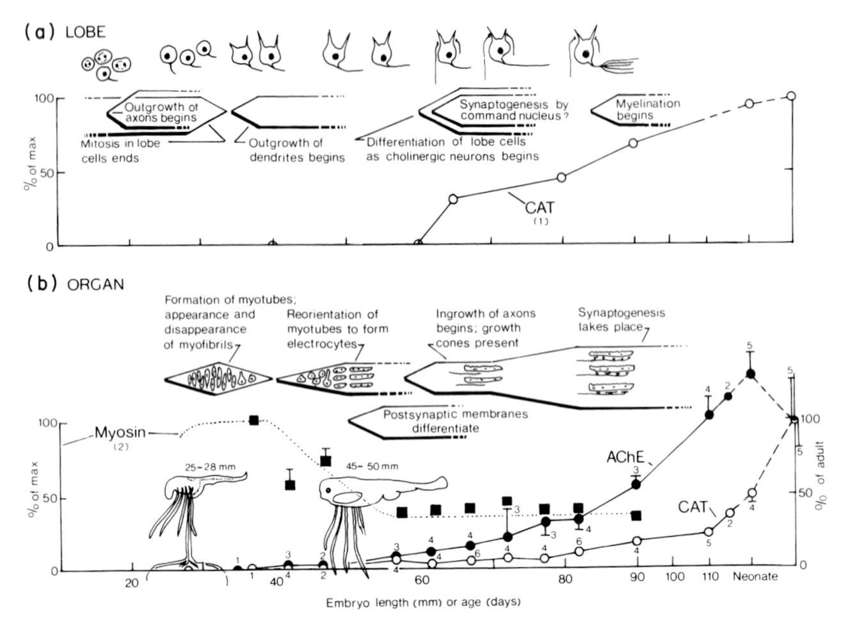

Fig. 3. Summary diagram showing the main stages of morphological and biochemical differentiation in (a) the electric lobe and (b) the electric organ of *Torpedo marmorata.* Points are either single values or means of the number of determinations shown by the adjacent small figures; bars are range (two experiments) or SEM (three or more experiments) where these are larger than the diameter of the points. Abbreviations: AChE, acetylcholinesterase; CAT, choline acetyltransferase. See text for discussion.

ELECTRIC LOBE

The perikarya of the electromotor neurons are formed clustered together in paired, yellowish lobes on top of the brain stem just caudal to the cerebellum. In the adult they are large (125 μm in diameter) with prominent nuclei (20 μm in diameter). Only one type of synaptic connection is present in the lobe, that made by incoming axons from the command nucleus, situated below the electric lobes in the brainstem, on the sparse thin dendrites of the electromotor perikarya (15). Morphological differentiation of these cells is complete by about a 30-mm embryo length. However, choline acetyltransferase, a specific component of cholinergic neurons, does not make its appearance in the lobe until about a 65-mm embryo length. There is thus a considerable period between the end of morphological differentiation and the beginning of biochemical differentiation. The choline acetyltransferase of the cells rises slowly, reaching adult values at birth (Fig. 3a).

Acetylcholinesterase activity (not shown) follows a similar time course.

Synaptogenesis, in the lobe, as in the organ, is a late phenomenon; it takes place at about a 60–70-mm embryo length. Attempts are now being made to find the transmitter at these synapses; it does not appear to be acetylcholine.

In Vitro STUDIES

Attempts are now being made, with limited success, to culture embryos, tissues, and cells and to study the factors involved in differentiation. The embryonic electric organ, particularly, should provide a valuable model system in which to study the mechanisms of myoblast fusion, myofibril formation, and synaptogenesis in a muscle-related cell, and might lead to the identification of trophic factors governing nerve-target cell interactions in a cholinergic system.

The long gap between the morphological differentiation of electric lobe neurons and their acquisition of typical cholinergic enzymes suggests that cultured lobe neurons should provide a useful preparation in which to study the factors involved in the differentiation of a specifically cholinergic neuron, especially as the only neuronal perikarya present in the lobe are those of electromotor neurons.

TISSUE FRACTIONATION

ISOLATION OF ELECTROMOTOR NEURON PERIKARYA

Comminution of electric lobe tissue by homogenization at a low rate of liquid shear in a hand-operated, loosely fitting homogenizer, or by teasing gently through 500-mesh nylon bolting, breaks off the dendrites and axons of the electromotor neuron perikarya and releases them from their investing glial cells and blood vessels. Using 1.5–1.8 *M* sucrose as the suspension medium, a simple density gradient centrifugation procedure delivers the cell bodies free from glial, axonal, and dendritic fragments and nuclei as a loosely packed pellicle which can be readily resuspended in sucrose or saline media (Fig. 4a,c). The perikarya exclude dyes, respire, and show a saturable, carrier-mediated choline uptake system with a K_m similar to that of the high-affinity choline uptake system found in cholinergic nerve terminals (9,16,17).

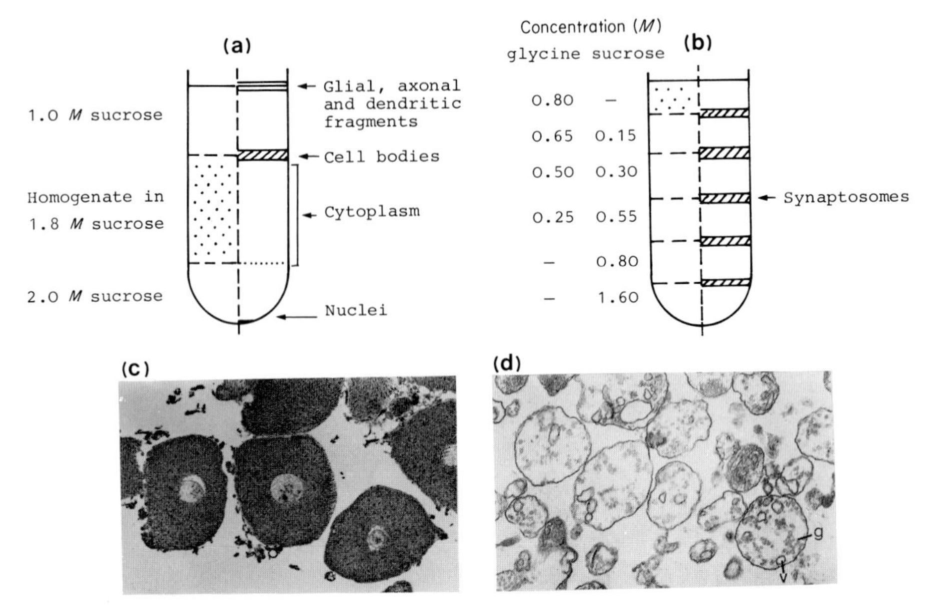

Fig. 4. Isolation of (a) cell bodies and (b) nerve terminals of the electromotor neurons of *Torpedo*. The diagrams show the step gradients before (left) and after (right) centrifuging. Electron micrographs of (c) cell bodies showing well-preserved cytoplasm, external membranes, and nuclei, and (d) isolated nerve terminals showing intact plasma membrane and cytoplasm containing glycogen granules (g) and synaptic vesicles (sv). Results of Fiore and Whittaker (9,16) and Dowdall and Zimmermann (17).

ISOLATION OF ELECTROMOTOR NERVE TERMINALS

Mechanical homogenization of the electric organ followed by differential and density-gradient separation on a sucrose–glycine gradient (Fig. 4b), provide, in low yield, a fraction enriched in detached presynaptic nerve terminals (17). Unlike synaptosomes derived from the mammalian cortex, these structures represent only small fragments of the nerve terminals and are probably depleted in soluble cytoplasmic components (e.g., choline acetyltransferase). Nevertheless, they are sealed structures and take up choline avidly by an exclusively high-affinity choline permease system resembling that found in squid (18) and mammalian (19) synaptosomes. Less vigorous tissue disruption results in larger synaptosomes which may be less depleted in vesicles and soluble cytoplasmic constituents (20).

The availability of such preparations enables a comparison to be made (Table I) of the concentrations of the characteristic components of the cholinergic neuron in the cell bodies and nerve terminals. It will be seen that although the various components—the enzymes

TABLE I
Comparison of the Composition of Isolated Electromotor Perikarya and Terminals

Component	Activity (units/mg of protein)			
	Units	Synaptosomes	Perikarya	Ratio
Lactate dehydrogenase	μmoles/min	0.54	0.17	3.13
Acetylcholine	nmoles	40.8	3.44	11.9
Choline acetyltransferase	nmoles/min	15.0	4.03	3.72
Acetylcholinesterase	μmoles/min	1.08	0.08	13.5
Choline uptake[a]	pmoles/min[b]	139	6.21	22.3

[a] High-affinity uptake system; $K_m = 2\ \mu M$ at 24°C (synaptosomes) or 4 μM at 20°C (cells).
[b] V_{max} at 24°C (synaptosomes) or 20°C (cells).

of synthesis (choline acetyltransferase) and breakdown (acetylcholinesterase), acetylcholine itself, and the high-affinity choline permease—are present both in the cell body and the terminal, all are concentrated (4–14 times) in the terminal. The available evidence suggests that the site of synthesis of such components is in the cell body and that they are conveyed to the terminal by a process known as axonal flow. However, there are some difficulties.

AXONAL TRANSPORT

Axonal transport of components of the cholinergic system may be observed (7,8,21) in the electromotor nerve trunks of *Torpedo*, as in mammalian cholinergic nerves (22,23), using the double-ligature technique *in vivo* or lengths of axon maintained *in vitro* in an oxygenated elasmobranch Ringer solution to which antibiotics have been added. However, some differences between *Torpedo* and mammalian nerves have been noted. The advantage of the double ligature and isolated nerve segment techniques, it should be said, is that observations are confined to the known and fixed amount of component trapped in the nerve segment and estimates can be made of the proportion of the component moving, which much affects the estimate of transport velocity.

Choline acetyltransferase moves (Fig. 5) in an orthograde direction in both types of preparation at about the same rate (21). At 15° to 17°C *in vitro* about 13 ± SEM 3% (seven experiments) of the enzyme is estimated to be transported, at a rate of 50–80 mm/day. This is similar to results with the homologous hypoglossal nerve of the rabbit (23),

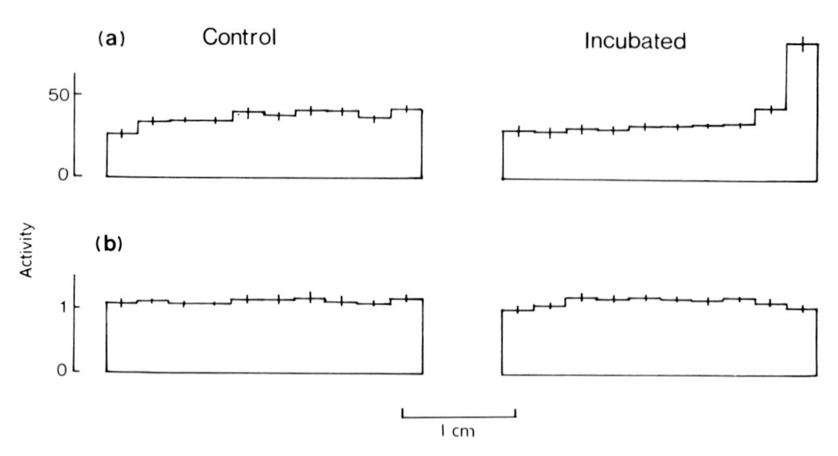

Fig. 5. *In vitro* accumulation of enzyme at the distal end of isolated 3-cm segments of electromotor nerve. Control nerves were frozen immediately, cut into 2.9-mm segments, crushed, extracted, and assayed. Other nerves were incubated at 15°–17°C in *Torpedo* Ringer solution for 24 hr before sectioning and assay. (a) Choline acetyltransferase; (b) lactate dehydrogenase. Activities are (a) nmoles acetylcholine synthesized hr^{-1} mg^{-1} of protein and (b) μmoles $NADH^+$ oxidized min^{-1} mg^{-1} of protein and are means of four nerves. SEM's are shown by the small bars. Note that the transferase accumulates distally in the incubated (but not in the control) segment and that the dehydrogenase does not.

but the transport rate in the *Torpedo* must be regarded as a fast rather than an intermediate rate when the temperature difference of the two species is taken into account. A small amount of accumulation occurs at the proximal end of axonal segments but this retrograde flow is only about 10% of the orthograde. By contrast, neither lactate dehydrogenase nor acetylcholinesterase are transported; the latter finding is surprising in view of the transport of this enzyme in mammalian nerves, but perhaps a much larger proportion of it is extraneuronal.

Further evidence for transport of choline acetyltransferase, and also for acetylcholine, but not for acetylcholinesterase or lactate dehydrogenase, was obtained when nerves were cut and the concentrations of components in the nerve segments proximal and distal to the cut were compared (21). The proximal:distal ratio for 5-mm nerve segments at 28 days for choline acetyltransferase was about 13:1, that for acetylcholine 10:1, but that for acetylcholinesterase 0.7:1 and for lactate dehydrogenase 1:1.

From the amounts of choline acetyltransferase being transported and the size of the perikaryal and terminal pools one can calculate the turnover of the enzyme at the presumed sites of synthesis and accumulation. Choline acetyltransferase in the cell bodies appears to be replaced every 3–5 days compared to 1 day for rabbit hypoglossal motor cells (23), not an unreasonable figure for a poikilotherm. However, in the terminal the turnover must be reckoned in years rather than days, which seems unlikely. Since local synthesis is also unlikely, one wonders if the enzyme is transported mainly in an inactive form and activated when it reaches the terminal.

The ATP content of axonal segments varies very much according to the method of extraction. If ligatured nerves are frozen in liquid nitrogen before comminution and extracted while still frozen, levels of 16.8 ± SEM 0.7(4) nmoles/mg Lowry protein are recorded and no evidence is obtained for axonal transport. If the segments are allowed to thaw for 20 min or more new, relatively stable ATP values are obtained which are about 4–5% of the initial ones. This fraction of ATP shows proximal accumulation at ligatures and presumably represents a relatively stable transportable intraaxonal pool.

The transport of synaptic vesicles may be inferred from (1) the presence of large numbers of appropriately sized vesicles among the cisternae of the profuse Golgi membranes of the perikaryal cytoplasm; (2) their accumulation above a ligature; (3) the accumulation of synaptic vesicle proteins, detected by indirect fluorescence immunohistochemistry, above a ligature (8); and (4) the similar accumulation of acetylcholine and the "stable" fraction of ATP described above in, however, not quite the same ratio (0.8) as that found in synaptic vesicles isolated from the electromotor nerve terminals (5.3). However, the transport of whole vesicles has yet to be confirmed by isolation and further work needs to be done.

ISOLATION OF SYNAPTIC VESICLES

Synaptic vesicles may be bulk-isolated from electric tissue (5,6) by freezing the latter in liquid Freon or liquid nitrogen, crushing the frozen tissue, and extracting the fragments with an extraction medium (0.2 *M* sucrose + 0.3 *M* NaCl or 0.4 *M* NaCl + 10 m*M* Tris buffer, pH 7.4) isoosmotic to elasmobranch plasma. The cytoplasmic extract so obtained is then submitted to density gradient separation in a zonal rotor after removing coarse particles by low-speed centrifuging.

Such vesicles, if carefully prepared on a shallow gradient, have an acetylcholine content per milligram protein that cannot be much increased by further purification either by recentrifuging or by chromatography on columns of porous glass beads (24) and appear to be pure by conventional morphological and biochemical criteria; that is, they are free from larger membrane fragments and from cytoplasmic or microsomal enzymes. However, recent work (25) on the protein composition of such vesicles, using slab gel electrophoresis in SDS, shows that the banding pattern can be further simplified by preparative procedures which include the addition of EGTA to the initial extraction medium and a preliminary concentration of the vesicles on a sucrose–NaCl step gradient in a swinging-bucket rotor. Evidently, some cytoplasmic proteins are tenaciously adsorbed onto the vesicle surface and since the surface-to-volume ratio of synaptic vesicles is large in comparison with other subcellular organelles, such contamination is more obvious and more difficult to remove. Thus, vesicles prepared from unstimulated tissue by means of a single purification step (Fig. 6b) show the presence of both actin and tubulin. Vesicles

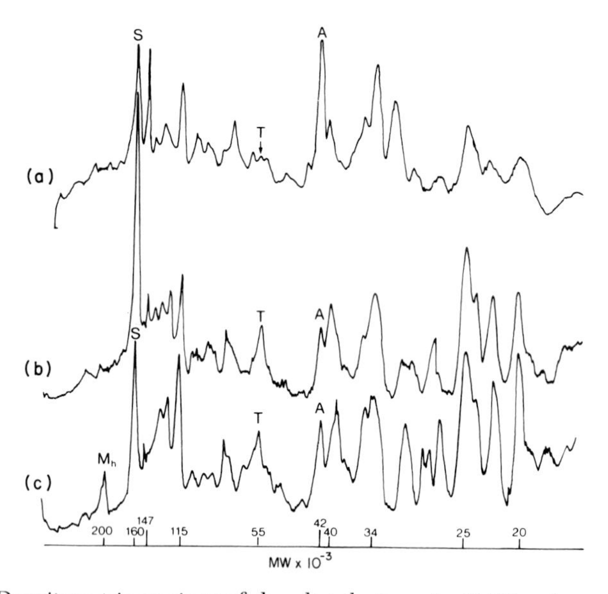

Fig. 6. Densitometric tracings of dye distributions in 12.5% polyacrylamide slab gels after electrophoresis of synaptic vesicle proteins. (a) Highly purified vesicles in which additional purification steps preceeded the zonal run. Vesicles prepared by our standard method from (b) unstimulated tissue and (c) tissue stimulated at 0.1 Hz for 5 hr, a treatment that appears to submit 80% of all vesicles to at least one cycle of exo- and endocytosis (see Fig. 7). Note the presence of a protein identified as actin (A) in all preparations and the elimination of another component, identified as tubulin (T), as well as other minor components, by the extra purification steps. Note also the absence, from all preparations, of clathrin (MW 180,000), the reduction, relative to other components, of component S (MW 160,000) by stimulation (cf., Figs. 2 and 3), and the appearance of a component (M_h) of MW 200,000 identified as the heavy chains of myosin as the result of stimulation. (Results from Stadler and Tashiro, 25).

submitted to two-step purification and exposure to EGTA lose their tubulin and some other minor components, but retain actin (Fig. 6a). Myosin is not a component of these vesicles. By contrast, vesicles isolated from stimulated tissue (Fig. 6c) do contain a component (M_h) identical with the heavy chain of myosin; another component, labeled S, is apparently reduced by stimulation. The recently described coat protein of coated vesicles (MW 180,000) (26) is not present.

These findings, indicating that actin is a tightly bound constituent of vesicles derived from both unstimulated and stimulated tissue and that the myosinlike component is only present after stimulation, differ considerably from those reported for mammalian vesicles and presynaptic membranes (27) in which actin ("neurin") was assigned to the presynaptic membranes and myosin ("stenin") to the vesicles. Further work will be needed to resolve this paradox.

STUDIES OF SYNAPTIC VESICLE DYNAMICS

MORPHOLOGICAL CHANGES IN ELECTROMOTOR SYNAPSES ON STIMULATION

When the electric organ is stimulated by electrodes placed on the electric lobes (28,29) certain changes in vesicle morphology can be detected by reference to a control organ whose nerve supply has been severed at the beginning of the experiment and which therefore remains unstimulated. These are: (1) progressive replacement of the normal population of vesicles characteristic of an unstimulated organ by a population of vesicles with a mean diameter about 25% smaller; (2) at high (5 Hz) frequency, a reduction in vesicle numbers and a corresponding increase (30) in the surface area of the external presynaptic membrane and its invaginations; (3) at low frequency (0.1 Hz) this depletion is absent or small; (4) vesicles tend to line up against the external membrane. It is well known that synaptic morphology varies considerably according to the fixation conditions employed, but these observations are reproducible under the conditions described and are reversible if the fish is allowed to recover.

Essentially the same changes can be seen in perfused blocks of tissue corresponding to the territory of an electromotor nerve and its accompanying blood vessels (31–33). Figure 7 shows the progressive increase in the population of small vesicles at the expense of that of the larger vesicles on stimulation for increasing lengths of time. If

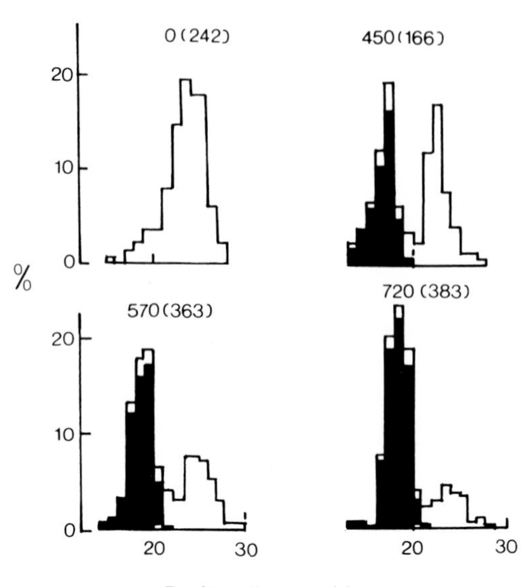

Fig. 7. Effect of stimulation on vesicle size in tissue blocks. Progressive stimulation at 0.1 Hz (figures indicate number of stimuli given and, in parentheses, number of vesicles measured) causes the appearance of a second, small population of vesicles. Dextran labeling (black blocks) is exclusively into this second population. Abscissae: arbitrary units of the Zeiss Particle-size Analyser. (Results from Zimmerman *et al.*, 31,32.)

dextran (MW 10,000) is perfused through the block during stimulation, dextran particles (readily identified under the electron microscope) become incorporated into vesicles. The distribution of profile diameters of the dextran-containing vesicles is identical with the population of "small vesicles" and 80% of these are so labeled (Fig. 7, black blocks). It is concluded that the small vesicle population is generated from the normal population as a result of one or more cycles of stimulus-induced exo- and endocytosis, during which dextran is taken up from the extracellular spaces.

In attempts to isolate the small vesicle population, cytoplasmic extracts of frozen and crushed control and stimulated tissue blocks were submitted to zonal density gradient centrifuging according to standard procedures. As shown in Fig. 8 (open triangles), vesicle-bound acetylcholine from the unstimulated block distributed itself, as in our original studies (5,6), as a single peak (Fig. 8a, VP) whereas the depleted vesicle-bound acetylcholine from the stimulated block appeared as two peaks (Fig. 8b), the first (VP_1) in the same position as the control peak, the second (VP_2) in a denser region of the gradient.

Though VP_2 (unlike VP_1) was not morphologically homogeneous, the acetylcholine in it was not due to entrapped cytoplasm, since the small amount of cytoplasmic markers such as lactate dehydrogenase (open squares) or choline acetyltransferase (not shown) recovered in this region of the gradient formed a distinct peak (asterisked) of even greater density than VP_2. Further studies (not shown) using shallower gradients have permitted the almost complete separation of VP_2 from membrane fragments and cytoplasmic occlusions.

Many of the vesicles in VP_2 contain what appear to be dextran particles; the size distribution of vesicles of this range of diameters is shown in the insert diagram of Fig. 8 (dashed lines) and this, it will be seen, is identical with the size distribution of dextran-containing vesicles (black blocks) which comprise 80% of the total population of this size range. By contrast, vesicles of VP_1 do not contain dextran and have a mean diameter considerably larger than those of VP_2. It would thus appear that the two populations of vesicles have been successfully separated.

When a radioactive precursor of acetylcholine, [^{3}H]acetate (as in the experiment shown in Fig. 8) or tritium- or ^{14}C-labeled choline, is added to the perfusion fluid, radioactive acetylcholine (Fig. 8, filled circles) is incorporated into the vesicles. Incorporation is small in unstimulated blocks (Fig. 8a); on stimulation (Fig. 8b) little incorporation takes place into VP_1 but VP_2 becomes highly labeled. This is taken to mean that uptake of newly synthesized acetylcholine is dependent on prior emptying of vesicles via at least one cycle of exo- and endocytosis.

The physical factors which enable the two types of vesicle to be separated when these are isolated from perfused blocks (but not from whole fish stimulated *in vivo*) have not yet been identified. The incorporation of dextran is not necessary, but the presence of sucrose may be, since stimulated blocks perfused with an elasmobranch Ringer solution in which urea replaced sucrose gave poor separations. However, recent experiments suggest that a rather alkaline pH (above pH 7.7) of the extraction medium may be a critical factor (J. Suszkiw, unpublished).

This demonstration that the vesicle population in stimulated tissue is morphologically and metabolically heterogeneous and that radioactive acetylcholine is incorporated during stimulation into a subpopulation of metabolically active vesicles goes far to remove recent objections to the vesicle hypothesis of transmitter storage and release (34) as applied to cholinergic terminals. Experiments in progress (J. Suszkiw, unpublished) show that the specific radioactivity of acetyl-

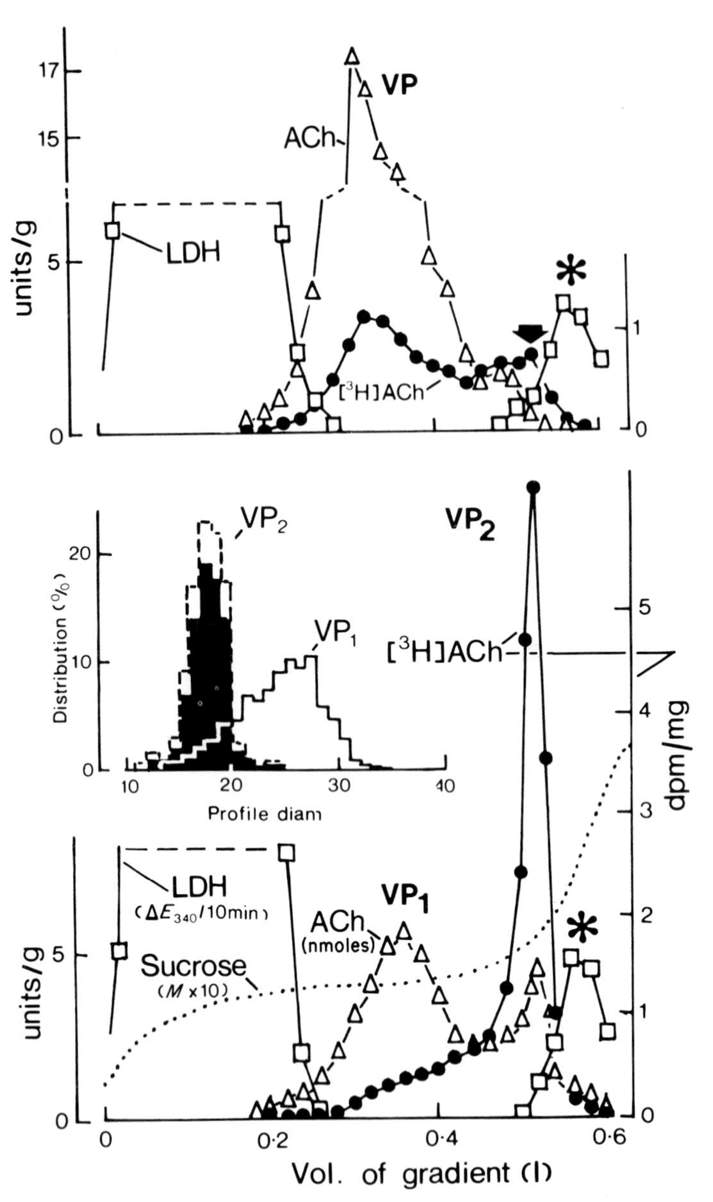

Fig. 8. Separation, on zonal density gradients, of vesicles labeled with endogenous (open triangles) or radioactive (filled circles) acetylcholine (ACh) from cytoplasmic extracts of perfused, innervated blocks of electric tissue frozen and crushed after perfusion for 5 hr with elasmobranch Ringer solution containing sucrose, [^{14}C]acetate, and dextran (MW 10^4) (a) at rest or (b) stimulated at 0.1 Hz. Also shown is the distribution of the cytoplasmic marker lactate dehydrogenase (LDH, open squares), which is mainly recovered in a broad peak of soluble protein in the upper part of the gradient but also appears as a small peak (asterisked) of entrapped enzyme in a dense

choline released from stimulated blocks whose acetylcholine stores have been preloaded with radioactive transmitter by means of a "loading" stimulus can be largely accounted for by VP_2 with a contribution from VP_1 when the release stimulus is at high (5 Hz) frequency. Other experiments, using the false transmitter precursor pyrrolidine choline (10), are also consistent with the vesicle hypothesis. This substance is readily taken up, acetylated, and incorporated into vesicles when perfused through electric tissue blocks, and on stimulation is released in the same ratio relative to labeled acetylcholine as it is in vesicles.

CONCLUSIONS

The electromotor neurons of *Torpedo* sp (we have worked mainly with *T. marmorata* from Arcachon, France) provide an almost ideal model system for the investigation of cholinergic function at the molecular level. Relatively large amounts of material are available. From a single adult fish about 400 mg of electric lobe, half of which consists of the easily isolated perikarya of electromotor neurons uncontaminated by other types of neuron, eight nerve trunks, each over 5 cm long and 2 mm in diameter on which axonal flow studies may be easily carried out, and about 0.5 kg of electric tissue with acetylcholine levels of the order of 800 nmoles/g of tissue from which cholinergic nerve terminals, synaptic vesicles, and fragments of pre- and postsynaptic membrane may be isolated in milligram quantities. Electrophysiological studies may be carried out with lobe cells or blocks of isolated organ. Changes in synaptic vesicle morphology and composition as a result of stimulation may be investigated. The results to date are consistent with the concept that cholinergic transmission involves a specialized and conservative type of microsecretion, in which synaptic vesicles, originating in the cell body of the cholinergic neuron, migrate to the nerve terminal where they accumulate and take up acetylcholine synthesized by the enzyme choline acetyltransferase which also originates in the cell body. Release of this stored acetylcholine as a result of low frequency (0.1–1.0 Hz) stimulation of the electromotor nerve appears to selectively involve a small population of vesicles close to the external membrane. These release their acetylcholine into

---

region of the gradient. Insert: size distribution of vesicles in (continuous lines) VP_1 and (dashed lines) VP_2. The distribution of dextran-containing profiles (black blocks) is also shown (as a percent of the total distribution in VP_2) (Results from Zimmerman *et al.*, 31–33).

the cleft by a process of transient exocytosis and are reutilized. Studies of the protein and enzyme composition of the synaptic vesicle membrane and the presynaptic plasma membrane now in progress will, it is hoped, elucidate the molecular mechanisms involved in transmitter uptake and release and transient exocytosis.

The mechanisms of storage and release of transmitter in the cholinergic and adrenergic systems, while differing in many points of detail, have a clear similarity, and we may thus regard them as "variations on a theme" rather than operating by fundamentally different mechanisms. Useful as it is for investigating the molecular basis of cholinergic transmission, the *Torpedo* electromotor system also promises to be useful in the study of the differentiation of cholinergic neurons. This will require a solution to the difficult problem of the culture of embryonic elasmobranch tissues and cells *in vitro*.

ACKNOWLEDGMENTS

I am grateful to my colleagues of the Abteilung für Neurochemie for permission to include in this review results that are either unpublished or published only in abstract form.

REFERENCES

1. Whittaker, V. P., and Zimmermann, H. (1976) *Biochem. Biophys. Perspect. Mar. Biol.* **3**, 67–116.
2. Raftery, M. A., Vandlen, R. L., Reed, K. L., and Lee, T. (1975) *Cold Spring Harbor Synp. Quant. Biol.* **40**, 193–202.
3. Changeux, J.-P., Benedetti, L., Bourgeois, J.-P., Brisson, A., Cartaud, J., Devaux, P., Grünhagen, H., Moreau, M., Popot, J.-L., Sobel, A., and Weber, M. (1975) *Cold Spring Harbor Symp. Quant. Biol.* **40**, 211–230.
4. Patrick, J., and Lindström, J. (1973) *Science* 180, 871–872.
5. Whittaker, V. P., Essman, W. B., and Dowe, G. H. C. (1972) *Biochem. J.* **128**, 833–846.
6. Dowdall, M. J., Boyne, A. F., and Whittaker, V. P. (1974) *Biochem. J.* **140**, 1–12.
7. Zimmermann, H., and Whittaker, V. P. (1973) *Abstr., Int. Meet. Int. Soc. Neurochem., 4th, 1975* p. 245.
8. Ulmar, G., and Whittaker, V. P. (1974) *Brain Res.* **71**, 155–159.
9. Fiore, L., and Whittaker, V. P. (1975) *Abstr., Int. Meet, Int. Soc. Neurochem., 5th 1975* p. 130.
10. Dowdall, M. J., Fox, G., Wächtler, K., Whittaker, V. P., and Zimmermann, H. (1975) *Cold Spring Harbor Symp. Quant. Biol.* **40**, 65–82.
11. Whittaker, V. P. (1977) *Naturwissenschaften* **64**, 606–611.
12. Fritsch, G. (1890) "Die elektrischen Fische." Von Veit, Leipzig.
13. Ogneff, J. (1897) *Arch. Anat. Physiol., Physiol. Abt.* pp. 270–304.

14. Fox, G. Q., Tashiro, T., Wächtler, K., and Whittaker, V. P. (1977) *Hoppe-Seyler's Z. Physiol. Chem.* **358,** 234.
15. Roberts, B. L., and Ryan, K. P. (1975) *J. Mar. Biol. Assoc. U.K.* **55,** 123–131.
16. Whittaker, V. P. (1975) *In* "Biochemistry of Sensory Functions" (L. Jaenike, ed.), pp. 521–534. Springer-Verlag, Berlin and New York.
17. Dowdall, M. J., and Zimmermann, H. (1975) *Exp. Brain Res.* **24,** 7.
18. Dowdall, M. J., and Simon, E. J. (1973) *J. Neurochem.* **21,** 969–982.
19. Yamamura, H. I., and Snyder, S. H. (1972) *Science* **178,** 626–628.
20. Israël, M., Manaranche, R., Mastour-Franchon, P., and Morel, N. (1976) *Biochem. J.* **160,** 113–115.
21. Davies, L., Whittaker, V. P., and Zimmermann, H. (1977) *Exp. Brain Res.* **30,** 493–510.
22. Saunders, N. R., Dziegielewska, K., Häggendahl, C. J., and Dahlström, A. B. (1973). *J. Neurobiol.* **4,** 95–103.
23. Fonnum, F., Frizell, M., and Sjöstrand, J. (1973) *J. Neurochem.* **21,** 1109–1120.
24. Nagy, A., Baker, R. R., Morris, S. J., and Whittaker, V. P. (1976) *Brain Res.* **109,** 285–309.
25. Stadler, H., and Tashiro, T. (1977) *Hoppe-Seyler's Z. Physiol. Chem.* **358,** 311.
26. Pearse, B. M. F. (1976) *Proc. Natl. Acad. Sci. U.S.A.* **73,** 1255–1259.
27. Berl, S., Puszkin, S., and Nicklas, W. J. (1973) *Science* **179,** 441–446.
28. Zimmermann, H., and Whittaker, V. P. (1974) *J. Neurochem.* **22,** 435–457.
29. Zimmermann, H., and Whittaker, V. P. (1974) *J. Neurochem.* **22,** 1109–1114.
30. Boyne, A. F., Bohan, T., and Williams, T. H. (1975) *J. Cell Biol.* **67,** 814–825.
31. Zimmermann, H., and Dentson, C. R. (1977) *Neuroscience* **2,** 715–730.
32. Zimmermann, H., and Whittaker, V. P. (1977) *Nature, Lond.* **267,** 633–635.
33. Zimmermann, H. (1976) Habilitationsschrift, Göttingen.
34. MacIntosh, F. C., and Collier, B. (1976) *Handb. Exp. Pharmakol.* Ergänzungswerk **42,** Suppl., 99–228.

Studies on the Mechanism of Acetylcholine Release in Mammalian Tissues

B. COLLIER, P. BOKSA, AND D. ILSON
Department of Pharmacology and Therapeutics
McGill University
Montreal, Quebec, Canada

INTRODUCTION

Of all substances that mediate information transfer between cells within the nervous system and between neurons and the cells innervated by them, acetylcholine (ACh) is most often used as the prototypal neurotransmitter. This presumably results from the established function of ACh as a synaptic transmitter in the mammalian peripheral nervous system as well as its likely similar role in the central nervous system. However, our understanding of the mechanism of ACh release is still far from complete.

It is clear that, under physiological conditions, nerve impulses release ACh by a Ca^{2+}-dependent process that results in an increased rate of release of transmitter quanta. This is certainly so for ACh release from motor nerve endings (see 1, 2) and from preganglionic nerve terminals (1), and it is usually assumed to be so at other cholinergic synapses, although direct evidence for quantal release is scarce. The origin of transmitter quanta is still not entirely clear. The simplest and most often accepted concept is that illustrated by Fig. 1a. This, usually called the "vesicle hypothesis," postulates that a quantum of ACh is stored in a synaptic vesicle and that the release of ACh occurs by exocytosis of the content of a synaptic vesicle. Thus, the release of ACh from one vesicle is the release of one quantum of transmitter and results in the generation of one miniature synaptic

ISBN 0-12-398450-5

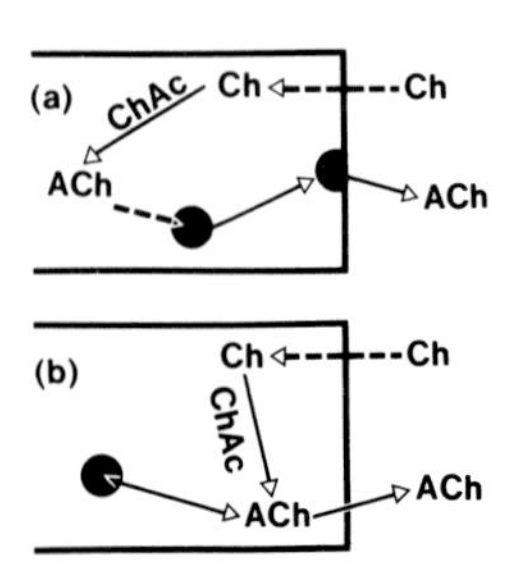

Fig. 1. Schematic representation of two hypothetical mechanisms for the release of acetylcholine (ACh) from a cholinergic nerve terminal. In (a) the vesicle hypothesis is illustrated: the vesicle moves to the presynaptic membrane and releases its contents directly into the synaptic cleft. In (b) the cytosol hypothesis is illustrated: ACh is released from the nerve-terminal cytoplasm to the synaptic cleft through a gate in the presynaptic membrane. Both (a) and (b) illustrate the uptake of choline (Ch) and its conversion to ACh by choline acetyltransferase (ChAc) in the nerve-terminal cytoplasm.

potential; the simultaneous release of ACh from several vesicles results in an evoked synaptic potential. The evidence for the existence of synaptic vesicles in cholinergic nerve terminals is indisputable (see 3), as is the evidence that synaptic vesicles isolated from mammalian cholinergic nerve terminals contain ACh (see reviews 4,5). However, it has never been shown with any conviction that the transmitter that is immediately available for release by nerve impulses originates directly from synaptic vesicles, and, thus, the vesicle hypothesis remains a hypothesis.

The main alternate hypothesis (Fig. 1b) is that synaptic vesicles represent a reservoir of transmitter that is not immediately available for release by nerve impulses, and that a quantum of transmitter represents ACh that is released from the nerve terminal cytosol by the transient opening of a gate or channel in the presynaptic membrane. The evidence that not all nerve terminal ACh is stored in synaptic vesicles is convincing (see 4,5), and the "cytosol hypothesis" is at least plausible until excluded. This hypothesis has its proponents, as well as experimental evidence that can be used in its support (e.g., 6–9); it should be noted that not all opponents of the vesicle hypothesis support the cytosol hypothesis in its simplest form outlined above (see, e.g., 10), and that much of the evidence supporting it is equivocal or open to alternate interpretation.

Until one or the other of the above hypotheses can be excluded, there appears to be mainly predictive value in attempting to explain the mechanism of ACh release in such detailed terms as involving a membrane-bound Na^+- and K^+-activated ATPase (11), an actomyosin-like contractile protein (12), a cation-exchange process (13), or adenylate cyclase (14).

AMOUNT OF ACh IN A VESICLE AND IN A QUANTUM

A common approach to the question of whether a synaptic vesicle contains the ACh that is released as a quantum of transmitter is to compare estimates of the ACh content of these two entities. The ACh content of a synaptic vesicle is calculated from direct measurement of the ACh content of a purified vesicle preparation, an estimate of the proportion of vesicles from cholinergic nerve terminals in the preparation, and a correction for ACh loss during their isolation. The ACh content of a quantum is calculated from measured ACh release per impulse from a tissue whose cholinergic nerve is stimulated [corrected for nonquantal leakage which certainly occurs (15)], an estimate of the number of synapses, and an estimate of the quantal content of an evoked potential under the conditions used. Some of these estimates for mammalian tissue are summarized in Table I (5,16–21). Although there is a wide range in the values calculated for the ACh content of a quantum, there is an embarrasing tendency for these estimates to exceed considerably the calculated ACh content of a synaptic vesicle, for which the two available estimates agree very well. There are several possible explanations for this discrepancy (see 5) which allow the vesicle hypothesis to survive. Most of these postulate overestimation of the ACh content of a quantum or underestimation of that of a vesicle, but one less mundane possibility is that a quantum results

TABLE I
Some Estimates of the Amount of ACh in a Synaptic Vesicle and in a Quantum of Transmitter Released from Mammalian Tissues

	Tissue	ACh content (molecules)	Reference
Synaptic vesicles	Cerebral cortex	1,650–2,500	16,17
	Sympathetic ganglion	1,630	18
Quanta	Neuromuscular junction	15,000	5
	Neuromuscular junction	20,000	19
	Neuromuscular junction	12,000–21,000	20
	Neuromuscular junction	6,250	21
	Sympathetic ganglion	45,000	5

from the release of ACh from more than one vesicle. This proposal receives some support from the observations that subminiature EPP's can be recorded from mammalian neuromuscular junctions (22), and that miniature EPP's might be composed of subunits of the smallest subminiature event (23). In Kriebel *et al.*'s analysis, the smallest subminiature potential was about one-tenth the largest miniature potential, and, thus, if a "quantum" is not a quantum but is some 10 quanta, the discrepancy between the ACh content of synaptic vesicles and "quanta" would be largely resolved. It must, however, be admitted that this is rather speculative, and that the concept that subminiature EPP's truly represent quanta of transmitter is not universally accepted (e.g., 24).

SPECIFICITY OF ACh RELEASE AND STORAGE

Information about the mechanism of transmitter release might be obtained by studying the selectivity of events involved in the storage and release of ACh and of cholinergic false transmitters. The first question to be asked is whether the release process is specific for ACh or whether choline instead can be released. If transmitter release occurs from the nerve terminal cytosol through a gate in the plasma membrane, one might expect either choline or ACh to be able to escape. If transmitter release occurs by exocytosis from synaptic vesicles, the selective release of ACh without choline might be predicted, particularly if there is some link between the acetylation of choline and the entry of ACh into vesicles (see 5,25–28).

The release of choline along with ACh is difficult to test because choline transported into nerve terminals is rapidly acetylated (e.g., 29,30), so that intraterminal free choline likely has a rather transient existence. In an attempt to overcome this problem, we have used analogs of choline which are adequate substrates for the choline transport mechanism at the nerve terminal membrane, but which are poor substrates for choline acetyltransferase. The assumption in this approach is that a plasma membrane gate involved in transmitter release would not fully distinguish the choline analog from choline. Thus the compound would be transported into the nerve terminal, not suffer metabolic transformation, and should be available for release through an ACh gate. In theory, the most suitable analog for this purpose appeared to be γ-homocholine (3-hydroxypropyltrimethylammonium), a compound that can substitute for choline as a substrate for uptake but that is not acetylated in tests using choline acetyltransferase *in vitro* (31–34). In practice, homocholine is less than ideal because some acetylated product is generated *in situ*, although relatively brief exposure to homocholine largely avoids this problem in ganglia (35). Acetylation of homocholine was demonstrated (34) by experiments in which the cat's superior cervical ganglion was perfused with [^{3}H]homocholine; after 60 min exposure to the choline analogue, [^{3}H]acetylhomocholine was detected in tissue extracts. Preganglionic nerve stimulation increased the acetylation of homocholine as well as the accumulation of unchanged homocholine. Because less than 10% of the total radioactivity accumulated by stimulated ganglia was acetylhomocholine, subsequent test of the release of radioactivity should readily determine whether unchanged homocholine or acetylated homocholine is available for release. Such experiments (e.g., Fig. 2) show that nerve stimulation releases radioactivity from ganglia previously exposed to [^{3}H]homocholine and that evoked release is fully accounted for as acetylhomocholine, not as homocholine itself. This result, besides indicating some difference between *in vitro* and *in situ* acetylation, shows the selectivity of the release process for acetylated product. This selectivity has been confirmed with all analogs of choline so far tested; these include monoethyl-

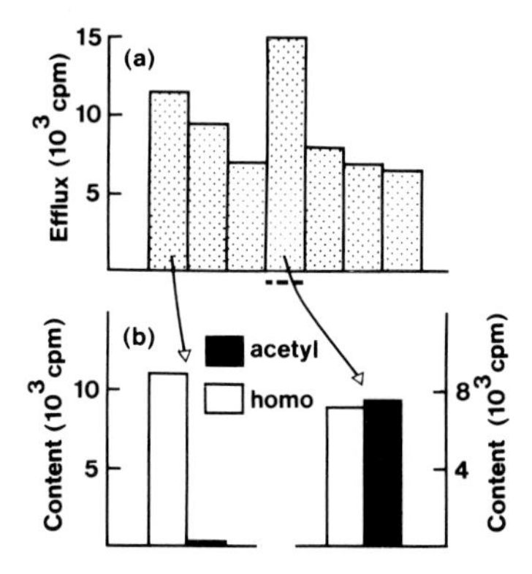

Fig. 2. Release of acetylhomocholine, but not of homocholine, by a cat's superior cervical ganglion. The ganglion had been perfused for 60 min with Krebs solution containing eserine and [^{3}H]homocholine during preganglionic nerve stimulation (20 Hz); it was then washed with eserine–Krebs solution for 15 min (no stimulation). In (a) the efflux of radioactivity from the ganglion is illustrated; each column represents a 2-min collection period and during the fourth of these (identified by the broken line below the column) the preganglionic nerve was stimulated (20 Hz). In (b) the identity of released radioactive material is illustrated; this was determined as acetylhomocholine (acetyl, black columns) or as unchanged homocholine (homo, white columns) by thin-layer chromatography. The arrows between (a) and (b) show which collected sample of ganglion effluent from (a) was used for the identification in (b).

TABLE II
Release of Acetylated Choline Analogs from Ganglia

Precursor	Release	Percent of released compound acetylated
Monoethylcholine	+	100 ± 1
Triethylcholine	+	100 ± 3
Homocholine	+	90 ± 5
Pyrrolidinecholine	+	99 ± 2

choline, triethylcholine, and pyrrolidinecholine (also called pyrrolcholine) (36,37). With all compounds, stimulation releases acetylated product, but not the unchanged precursor to the false transmitter (Table II).

The selectivity of the transmitter release mechanism that requires acetylation of the aminoalcohols, of course, does not disprove the cytosol hypothesis, for an ACh gate might be able to distinguish ACh from choline. If this were so, it might be expected that the gate would display some specificity with respect to the false transmitters, some of which differ considerably from ACh in their chemical structure (Fig. 3). However, there appears to be no such structural specificity in the release of cholinergic false or true transmitter. That this is so is shown in Table III. Because there is some difference in the total amount of the various false transmitters synthesized by ganglia, comparison of releasability is made by estimating the proportion of stored acetyl compound released per impulse. Clearly, all compounds are released about equally well, showing the lack of structural specificity of the re-

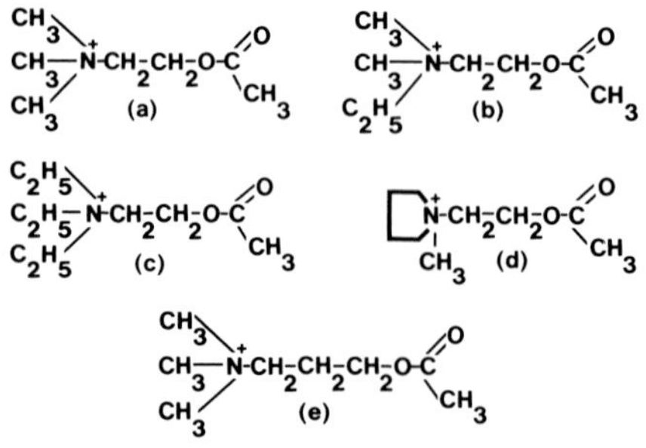

Fig. 3. Chemical structure of cholinergic false transmitters compared to that of acetylcholine. The structures shown are (a) acetylcholine; (b) acetylmonoethylcholine; (c) acetyltriethylcholine; (d) acetylpyrrolidinecholine; (e) acetylhomocholine.

TABLE III
Release of ACh and of Cholinergic False Transmitters from Ganglia

Compound	Release (mean ± SEM) (percent of store release/impulse)
Acetylcholine	$7.9 \pm 0.8 \times 10^{-3}$
Acetylmonoethylcholine	$8.3 \pm 0.8 \times 10^{-3}$
Acetyltriethylcholine	$12.8 \pm 4.1 \times 10^{-3}$
Acetylpyrrolidinecholine	$8.7 \pm 1.0 \times 10^{-3}$
Acetylhomocholine	$8.8 \pm 1.0 \times 10^{-3}$

lease process; the apparent greater release of acetyltriethylcholine is not statistically significant.

These results do not prove either model of transmitter release that was illustrated in Fig. 1, but they appear most consistent with exocytosis from synaptic vesicles. This model might predict that any product that can be stored in a vesicle would be releasable, whereas the cytosol hypothesis requires the postulate that a gate exists which can distinguish acetylated product from nonacetylated product, yet cannot distinguish between acetylated products. It must, however, be admitted that if the vesicle hypothesis is favored, the mechanism of transfer of acetylated product from the cytoplasm [its presumed site of synthesis (see 38)] to the vesicles must not be particularly specific, for there is, as yet, no example of a choline analog that is acetylated but not releasable. This is consistent with the idea mentioned earlier that acetylation of choline, or analog, and vesicular uptake of the product might be linked in some way.

The experiments summarized above show that cholinergic false transmitters can be formed and released by cholinergic nerve terminals in sympathetic ganglia. There is also evidence that triethylcholine can be acetylated and released from cholinergic synapses in rat cerebral cortex (37), that acetylpyrrolidinecholine can be synthesized and released in the myenteric plexus of the guinea pig's gut (39), as well as in nonmammalian preparations such as *Torpedo* electric tissue (40), and that acetylmonoethylcholine can behave as a false transmitter at a mammalian neuromuscular junction (41). Since most of these false transmitters are less active pharmacologically than is the true transmitter, they reduce the safety margin of transmission at cholinergic synapses. At least at the neuromuscular junction, the weaker effect of acetylmonoethylcholine compared to ACh is manifest because the false transmitter activates ionic channels in the postsynaptic membrane with a shorter average lifetime than does ACh (41).

In order for studies on false transmitters to contribute fully to the elucidation of transmitter release mechanisms, knowledge of their subcellular storage is essential. Some information about the distribution of acetylpyrrolidinecholine in subcellular fractions prepared from *Torpedo* has been reported (40). It is stored in synaptic vesicles and this has also been shown for mammalian brain tissue (42). We have studied the subcellular localization of acetyltriethylcholine in experiments using sliced cerebral cortex of rats. In these experiments, sliced tissue was incubated with [^{14}C]triethylcholine, or with [^{3}H]choline, and the amount of [^{14}C]acetyltriethylcholine and [^{3}H]ACh in nerve-ending free and nerve-ending bound stores was measured after homogenizing the tissue and preparing these two fractions from synaptosomes. Both nerve terminal stores were labeled from either precursor and the relative distribution of labeled false or true transmitter in the two compartments was similar (Fig. 4). Thus, these results, although consistent with the concept that triethylcholine forms a cholinergic false transmitter, do not favor either the vesicle or the cytosol hypothesis of transmitter release.

One unexpected finding in experiments upon the formation and release of acetyltriethylcholine in brain tissue was the poor correlation between the total tissue content of acetyltriethylcholine and its releasability upon stimulation with K^+ (37). Unlike sympathetic ganglia, where all performed acetyltriethylcholine was releasable, brain tis-

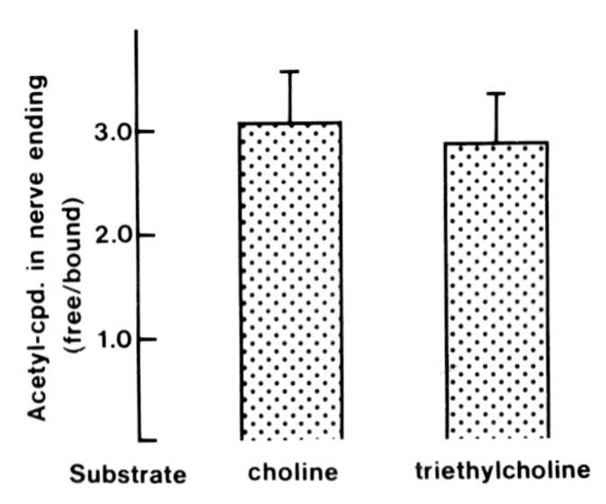

Fig. 4. Relative distribution of [^{3}H]acetylcholine and of [^{14}C]acetyltriethylcholine in two nerve- ending compartments prepared from rat brain. Slices of rat cerebral cortex were incubated for 60 min with either [^{3}H]choline or [^{14}C]triethylcholine; the tissue was then homogenized and synaptosomes were prepared and lysed by hypoosmotic shock. The nerve-ending-free and nerve-ending-bound fractions were prepared from the lysed synaptosomes. Results are expressed as mean ± SEM of six to eight experiments.

sue retained considerable false transmitter at a time when its evoked release was hardly detectable. This result suggested that in brain tissue there was a continued synthesis of acetyltriethylcholine from trapped precursor throughout the experiment, but that this was not available for release. A preliminary experiment testing the subcellular distribution of acetyltriethylcholine before and after stimulation is illustrated by Fig. 5. In this experiment stimulation depleted releasable false transmitter by some 70%, but tissue acetyltriethylcholine was depleted by less than 40%. The loss of releasable false transmitter appears to be better correlated to a loss of nerve ending bound acetyltriethylcholine than to a loss of nerve ending free acetyltriethylcholine. However, it is clear that there is some exchange of false transmitter between the free and the bound stores within the nerve ending,

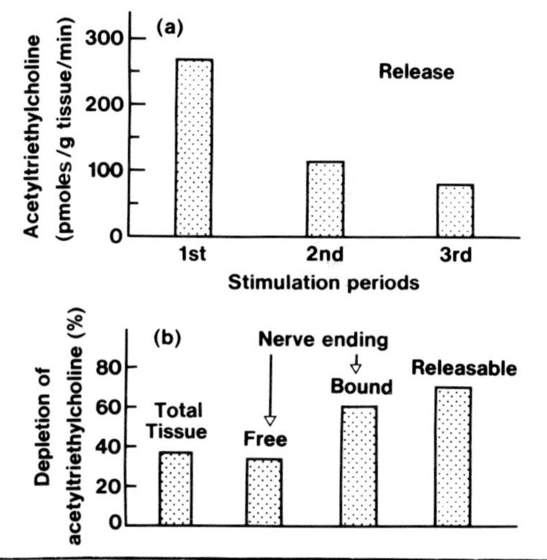

Fig. 5. Relationship between releasable acetyltriethylcholine and its distribution in subcellular fractions prepared from rat brain. Sliced cerebral cortex was first incubated for 60 min with [^{14}C]triethylcholine under conditions described before (37); the tissue was then washed and incubated for 5-min collection periods in Krebs solution containing eserine. At various intervals, the tissue was stimulated to release acetyltriethylcholine by increased K^+ (tenfold) in the presence of atropine. (a) illustrates the release of acetyltriethylcholine by three intermittent periods of stimulation. (b) Illustrates the following: The depletion of releasable acetyltriethylcholine (far right column) calculated from the first and third release periods in (a). The depletion of total tissue acetyltriethylcholine (far left column) calculated from measurements made on tissue collected before the first stimulation period and after the third stimulation period. The depletion of acetyltriethylcholine in nerve ending free and nerve ending bound stores (middle columns) calculated from measurements made on fractions prepared from tissue collected before the first stimulation period and after the third stimulation period.

because some free acetyltriethylcholine was also lost as a consequence of tissue stimulation. The equilibration of the two nerve ending stores of acetyltriethylcholine during stimulation appears less complete than that of acetylcholine under somewhat similar conditions (43), but whether this is a significant difference remains to be properly tested. The easiest interpretation of the result of the experiment showing greater depletion of nerve ending bound than free acetyltriethylcholine is that it is more consistent with the vesicle hypothesis than it is with the cytosol hypothesis in its simplest form.

TURNOVER OF ACh IN NERVE TERMINAL POOLS

The most direct way to identify the subcellular compartment that contains releasable transmitter might appear to be the measurement of ACh turnover in those subcellular compartments. If the ACh in the two nerve-terminal stores were to be labeled from a radioactive precursor to a different specific radioactivity, a situation that can be achieved (e.g., 27,44,45), then comparison of the specific radioactivity of released transmitter to that in the subcellular fractions should, in principle, identify the source of releasable transmitter. This kind of experiment has been attempted using brain tissue, and the results have consistently shown released transmitter to be labeled to a higher specific activity than either cytoplasmic or vesicular ACh (45–48).

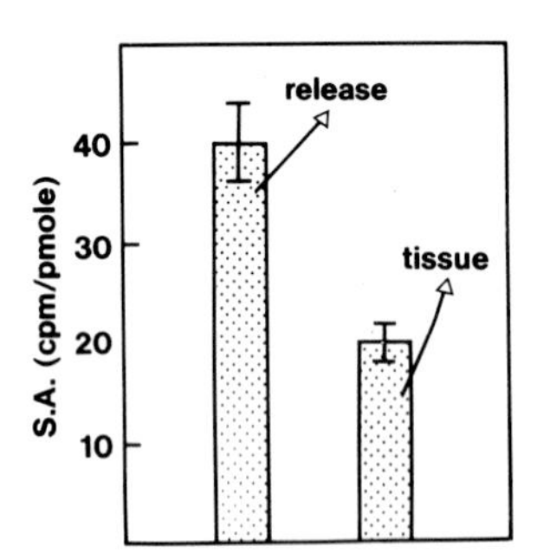

Fig. 6. Preferential release of newly synthesized acetylcholine by cat superior cervical ganglia. The ganglia were perfused for 16 min with Krebs solution containing neostigmine and [^{3}H]choline during continuous preganglionic nerve stimulation (20 Hz). The column labeled "release" represents the specific radioactivity of acetylcholine measured in the effluent collected from the ganglion in the last 2 min of the experiment. The column labeled "tissue" represents the specific radioactivity of acetylcholine measured in an extract of the ganglion which was removed immediately following the collection of the sample labeled "release." Results are expressed as mean ± SEM of four experiments.

One likely problem with this kind of experiment is the existence of a rapidly turning-over pool of ACh that contributes more to transmitter release than does the rest of the nerve terminal ACh. This concept was used to explain the phenomenon that in sympathetic ganglia newly synthesized transmitter appears to be released in preference to preformed transmitter (49,50); a similar phenomenon appears to occur in skeletal muscle (51) and in the brain (52). Although the basis for the original observations on ganglia has been questioned (53), the phenomenon can be confirmed without introducing the possible artifact identified by these authors. That this is so is shown by Fig. 6 which illustrates the results of experiments on ganglia that measured the specific radioactivity of ACh released by nerve stimulation (20 Hz) during tissue perfusion with [^{3}H]choline. During stimulation, the amount of [^{3}H]ACh increased so that after 16 min the specific activity of released transmitter was about twice that of tissue ACh. Clearly, releasable ACh was not derived equally from all tissue stores, and the phenomenon of the preferential release of newly synthesized transmitter appears real.

It is not yet clear whether this pool of newly synthesized ACh that preferentially contributes to releasable transmitter in ganglia is vesicle-bound ACh or not. Although the preparation of subcellular fractions from ganglionic tissue has been only modestly successful (18,54,55), the technique of these authors, who use collagenase to

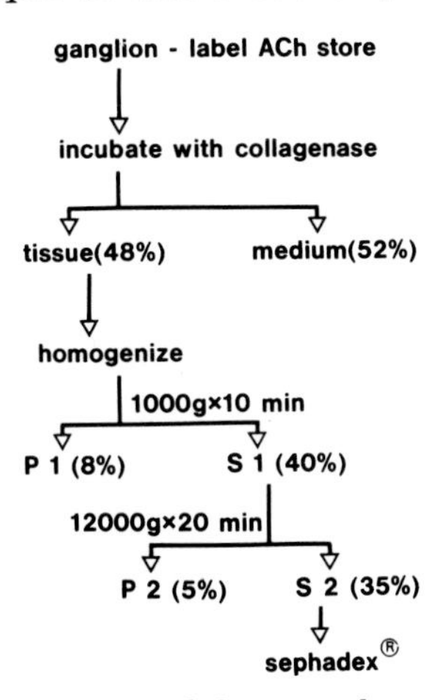

Fig. 7. Schematic representation of the procedure used to prepare subcellular fractions from a cat's superior cervical ganglion. The values in parentheses indicate the relative distribution of radioactivity in the various fractions. The ganglion's ACh store was labeled by perfusing the tissue for 60 min with [^{3}H]choline and stimulating the preganglionic nerve (20 Hz); the ganglion was then washed by perfusion for 40 min.

soften the tissue before homogenization, should provide some information on this point. We have applied this approach to single superior cervical ganglia from cats. The ganglia were first perfused with [^{3}H]choline during preganglionic nerve stimulation, then washed by perfusion with nonradioactive medium to remove [^{3}H]choline, but not [^{3}H]ACh (see 49). Incubating such ganglia with collagenase resulted in considerable loss of radioactivity (about 50%), but that retained in the tissue was mostly freed by gentle homogenization in eserine-sucrose (Fig. 7). Centrifuging the homogenate at 12,000 *g* for 20 min yielded a pellet containing only 10% of the homogenate's radioactivity, indicating the formation of few synaptosomes. However, gel filtration of the homogenate on Sephadex G-25, resolved the radioactivity into two peaks (Fig. 8): one (fraction O) coincided to the elution of blue dextran, and one (fraction F) coincided to the elution of free ACh. Both fraction O and fraction F, but not other eluates from the Sephadex, contained ACh. Thus, this technique appears to separate an occluded fraction of nerve terminal ACh from a nonoccluded pool of ACh. Whether the occluded ACh pool corresponds to vesicle-bound ACh is not yet known.

The experiment illustrated by Fig. 9 was an attempt to test whether the specific activity of released ACh from a ganglion previously exposed to [^{3}H]choline was similar to the specific activity of fraction O or of fraction F prepared from the ganglion. For this, the ganglion's ACh was first labeled by perfusion with [^{3}H]choline for 20 min during

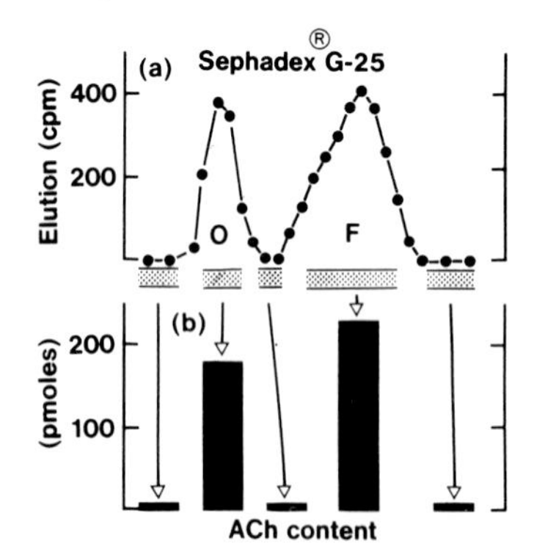

Fig. 8. Separation by gel filtration of two fractions from homogenate of a cat's superior cervical ganglion. The ganglion was perfused with [^{3}H]choline for 60 min during preganglionic nerve stimulation, washed for 30 min, processed as illustrated by Fig. 7, and the S2 fraction was passed through a column of Sephadex G-25. (a) Illustrates the elution of radioactivity from the Sephadex; the eluates indicated by the horizontal spotted bars were collected separately, and each was assayed for acetylcholine. The results of the acetylcholine assay are illustrated in (b).

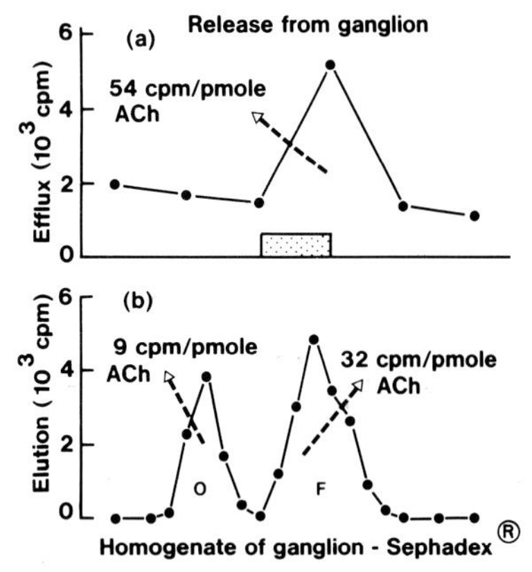

Fig. 9. Comparison of specific radioactivity of acetylcholine released from a cat's superior cervical ganglion to that of acetylcholine in subcellular fractions prepared from the tissue. The ganglion had been perfused for 20 min with [^{3}H]choline during preganglionic nerve stimulation; it was then washed for 20 min with Krebs solution containing eserine and hemicholinium. (a) Shows the efflux of radioactivity from the ganglion, its increase by preganglionic nerve stimulation (20 Hz for 1 min) during the period indicated by the spotted bar, and the measured specific radioactivity of ACh released by stimulation. At the end of the last collection period in (a), the ganglion was removed, treated as described by Fig. 7 (except that hemicholinium was present during incubation with collagenase), and the S2 fraction was passed through Sephadex. (b) Illustrates the elution of radioactivity from the Sephadex column and the measured specific radioactivity of acetylcholine in the two fractions, O and F.

preganglionic nerve stimulation; this procedure labels about half of the tissue's ACh (49). The ganglion was then washed by perfusion with Krebs medium containing eserine (to preserve released ACh) and hemicholinium (to prevent ACh synthesis during this part of the experiment), ACh release was evoked by preganglionic nerve stimulation (1 min), and finally the tissue was removed for collagenase treatment (in the presence of hemicholinium), homogenization, and fractionation. Stimulation released ACh that was more radioactive than either tissue fraction. The subcellular fraction that was of specific activity closest to releasable ACh was the free ACh rather than the one containing occluded ACh. This result has been confirmed by other experiments: released ACh was labeled to a specific radioactivity that was 1.7 ± 0.3 times that of fraction F and 5.0 ± 0.8 times that of fraction O.

Thus, these experiments do not identify the subcellular localization of releasable ACh, but they show that if it is particle bound within the nerve terminal it is not contained in those particles that survive homogenization to be isolated as fraction O in the present experiments. Further characterization of the fractions produced is clearly required before a definite interpretation can be attempted, but, as yet, the results can not easily be used to support the vesicle hypothesis.

TISSUE DIFFERENCES IN ACh STORAGE AND RELEASE OR THEIR CONTROL

It is often assumed that a common mechanism exists for ACh release at all cholinergic nerve terminals, at least in the mammalian nervous system, and that experimental results produced from one tissue can readily be extrapolated to another. In some respects this is a false assumption, and the possibility of tissue-specific control mechanisms must be recognized.

One appreciable difference between cholinergic nerve endings in the cerebral cortex and those in sympathetic ganglia appears to be the presence on the former of presynaptic cholinoceptive sites that regulate release. In the cortex, ACh-like agents of a muscarinic type inhibit ACh release, and antimuscarinic agents like atropine relieve such inhibition to produce an apparent increase in ACh release (56–58). In sympathetic ganglia, however, neither ACh (59) nor atropine (60) affect transmitter release. It is likely that the neuromuscular junction also lacks any negative feedback mechanism on release, for atropine does not facilitate ACh release (61), whereas in the myenteric plexus, cholinergic terminals might resemble those in cerebral cortex, for atropine appears to increase release (62,63). In cat spinal cord, atropine also increases ACh release (64), but it is not clear that the drug's effect involves presynaptic muscarinic receptors (65). These results indicate that pharmacological differences are likely to exist between cholinergic terminals of various tissues. If presynaptic ACh receptors are functional under physiological conditions, different control mechanisms might well operate at different cholinergic nerve endings.

A difference between tissues that is of particular concern to those who favor a uniform model for storage and release of ACh is the apparently dissimilar pattern of transmitter release at the sympathetic ganglion and the neuromuscular junction in the presence of hemicholinium. This drug, by blocking ACh synthesis but not ACh release, depletes ACh stores. The characterization of transmitter release as stores are depleted should provide important information about transmitter release mechanism. Thus, if ACh is stored in preformed quanta, one would expect hemicholinium to reduce quantal content and not quantal size. On the other hand, if quanta are formed upon demand from a resevoir of preformed ACh, one would expect hemicholinium to reduce quantal size but not quantal content. In ganglia (66), quantum size remains constant and the number of quanta released by a nerve impulse falls in the presence of hemicholinium, whereas at the neuromuscular junction, quantal content is maintained when quantum size steadily falls as transmitter stores become depleted (67). The most logical interpretation of this difference appears to be that transmitter storage and release have a different relationship in these two tissues. Biochemical studies of the subcellular distribution of ACh during depletion of transmitter stores in the presence of hemicholinium have not yet been done on ganglia or on skeletal muscle, but if such were possible, they might clarify this issue. In cerebral cortex, where nothing is known about quantum size or quantal content in the presence of hemicholinium, depletion of transmitter stores is associated with a parallel depletion of both cytoplasmic and vesicle-bound ACh (43).

ACKNOWLEDGMENTS

The unpublished work referred to in this article was supported by the Canadian Medical Research Council.

REFERENCES

1. Kuno, M. (1971) *Physiol. Rev.* **51,** 647–678.
2. Ginsborg, B. L., and Jenkinson, D. H. (1976) *In* "Neuromuscular Junction" (E. Zaimis, ed.), pp. 229–364. Springer-Verlag, Berlin and New York.
3. Bowden, R. E. M., and Duchen, L. W. (1976) *In* "Neuromuscular Junction" (E. Zaimis, ed.), pp. 23–97. Springer-Verlag, Berlin and New York.
4. Barker, L. A. (1976) *In* "Biology of Cholinergic Function" (A. M. Goldberg and I. Hanin, ed.), pp. 203–238. Raven Press, New York.
5. MacIntosh, F. C., and Collier, B. (1976) *In* "Neuromuscular Junction" (E. Zaimis, ed.), pp. 99–228. Springer-Verlag, Berlin and New York.
6. Dunant, Y., Gautron, J., Israël, M., Lesbats, B., and Manaranche, R. (1972) *J. Neurochem.* **19,** 1987–2020.
7. Birks, R. I. (1974) *J. Neurocytol.* **3,** 133–160.
8. Tauc, L., Hoffmann, A., Tsuji, S., Hinzen, D. H., and Faille, L. (1974) *Nature (London)* **250,** 496–498.
9. Hutchinson, M., Kosterlitz, H. W., and Gilbert, J. C. (1976) *Eur. J. Pharmacol.* **39,** 221–235.
10. Israël, M., and Dunant, Y. (1975) *In* "Metabolic Compartmentation and Neurotransmission" (S. Berl, D. D. Clarke, ad D. Schneider, eds.), pp. 621–639. Plenum, New York.

11. Vizi, E. S. (1975) *In* "Cholinergic Mechanisms" (P. G. Waser, ed.), pp. 199–211. Raven Press, New York.
12. Berl, S., Puszkin, S., and Nicklas, W. J. (1973) *Science* **179**, 441–446.
13. Üvnäs, B. (1973) *Acta Physiol. Scand.* **87**, 168–175.
14. Standaert, F. C., Dretchen, K. L., Skirboll, L. R., and Morgenroth, V. H. (1976) *J. Pharmacol. Exp. Ther.* **199**, 553–564.
15. Katz, B., and Miledi, R. (1977) *Proc. R. Soc. London, Ser. B* **196**, 59–72.
16. Whittaker, V. P. (1965) *Prog. Biophys. Mol. Biol.* **15**, 39–96.
17. Whittaker, V. P., and Sheridan, M. N. (1965) *J. Neurochem.* **12**, 363–372.
18. Wilson, W. S., Schulz, R. A., and Cooper, J. R. (1973) *J. Neurochem.* **20**, 659–667.
19. Potter, L. T. (1972) *In* "The Structure and Function of the Nervous System" (G. H. Bourne, ed.), Vol. 4, pp. 105–128. Academic Press, New York.
20. Hubbard, J. I., and Wilson, D. F. (1973) *J. Physiol. (London)* **228**, 307–325.
21. Fletcher, P., and Forrester, T. (1975) *J. Physiol. (London)* **251**, 131–144.
22. Cooke, J. D., and Quastel, D. M. J. (1973) *J. Physiol. (London)* **228**, 377–405.
23. Kriebel, M. E., Llados, F., and Matteson, D. R. (1976) *J. Physiol. (London)* **262**, 553–581.
24. Bevan, S. (1976) *J. Physiol. (London)* **258**, 145–155.
25. Collier, B., and Katz, H. S. (1971) *J. Physiol. (London)* **214**, 537–552.
26. Hebb, C. (1972) *Physiol. Rev.* **52**, 918–957.
27. Aquilonius, S. M., Flentge, F., Schuberth, J., Sparf, B., and Sundwall, A. (1973) *J. Neurochem.* **20**, 1509–1521.
28. Feigenson, M. E., and Barrnett, R. J. (1977) *Brain Res.* **119**, 155–179.
29. Yamamura, H. I., and Snyder, S. H. (1973) *J. Neurochem.* **21**, 1355–1374.
30. Barker, L. A., and Mittag, T. W. (1975) *J. Pharmacol. Exp. Ther.* **192**, 86–94.
31. Burgen, A. S. V., Burke, G., and Desbarats-Schonbaum, M.-L. (1956) *Br. J. Pharmacol. Chemother.* **11**, 308–312.
32. Dauterman, W. C., and Mehrotra, K. N. (1963) *J. Neurochem.* **10**, 113–117.
33. Currier, S. F., and Mautner, H. G. (1974) *Proc. Natl. Acad. Sci. U.S.A.* **71**, 3355–3358.
34. Collier, B., Lovat, S., Ilson, D., Barker, L. A., and Mittag, T. W. (1977) *J. Neurochem.* **28**, 331–339.
35. Collier, B., and Ilson, D. (1977) *J. Physiol. (London)* **264**, 489–509.
36. Collier, B., Barker, L. A., and Mittag, T. W. (1976) *Mol. Pharmacol.* **12**, 340–344.
37. Ilson, D., Collier, B., and Boksa, P. (1977) *J. Neurochem.* **28**, 371–381.
38. Fonnum, F. (1975) *In* "Cholinergic Mechanisms" (P. G. Waser, ed.), pp. 145–159. Raven Press, New York.
39. Kilbinger, H. (1977) *Naunyn-Schmiedeberg's Arch. Pharmacol.* **296**, 153–158.
40. Dowdall, M. J., Fox, G., Wächtler, K., Whittaker, V. P., and Zimmermann, H. (1976) *Cold Spring Habor Symp. Quant. Biol.* **40**, 65–81.
41. Colquhoun, D., Large, W. A., and Rang, H. P. (1977) *J. Physiol. (London)* **266**, 361–395.
42. von Schwarzenfeld, I. (1978) *In* "Cholinergic Mechanisms and Psychopharmacology" (D. J. Jenden, ed.), pp. 657–672. Plenum, New York.
43. Salehmoghaddam, S. H., and Collier, B. (1976) *J. Neurochem.* **27**, 71–76.
44. Chakrin, L. W., and Whittaker, V. P. (1969) *Biochem. J.* **113**, 97–107.
45. Richter, J. A., and Marchbanks, R. M. (1971) *J. Neurochem.* **18**, 705–712.
46. Richter, J. A., and Marchbanks, R. M. (1971) *J. Neurochem.* **18**, 691–703.
47. Chakrin, L. W., Marchbanks, R. M., Mitchell, J. F., and Whittaker, V. P. (1972) *J. Neurochem.* **19**, 2727–2736.

48. Molenaar, P. C., Polak, R. L., and Nickolson, V. J. (1973) *J. Neurochem.* **21**, 667–678.
49. Collier, B., and MacIntosh, F. C. (1969) *Can. J. Physiol. Pharmacol.* **47**, 127–135.
50. Collier, B. (1969) *J. Physiol. (London)* **205**, 341–352.
51. Potter, L. T. (1970) *J. Physiol. (London)* **206**, 145–166.
52. Molenaar, P. C., Nickolson, V. J., and Polak, R. L. (1973) *Br. J. Pharmacol.* **47**, 97–108.
53. Birks, R. I., and Fitch, S. J. G. (1974) *J. Physiol. (London)* **240**, 125–134.
54. Wilson, W. S., and Cooper, J. R. (1972) *J. Neurochem.* **19**, 2779–2790.
55. Burt, D. R., and Larrabee, M. G. (1973) *J. Neurochem.* **21**, 255–272.
56. Polak, R. L. (1971) *Br. J. Pharmacol.* **41**, 600–606.
57. Szerb, J. C., and Somogyi, G. T. (1973) *Nature (London), New Biol.* **241**, 121—122.
58. Hadházy, P., and Szerb, J. C. (1977) *Brain Res.* **123**, 311–322.
59. Collier, B., and Katz, H. S. (1970) *Br. J. Pharmacol.* **39**, 428–438.
60. Kato, A. C., Collier, B., Ilson, D., and Wright, J. M. (1975) *Can. J. Physiol. Pharmacol.* **53**, 1050–1057.
61. Beránek, R., and Vyskočil, F. (1967) *J. Physiol. (London)* **188**, 53–66.
62. Kilbinger, H. (1978) *In* "Cholinergic Mechanisms and Psychopharmacology" (D. J. Jenden, ed.), pp. 401–410. Plenum, New York.
63. Sawynok, J., and Jhamandas, K. (1977) *Can. J. Physiol. Pharmacol.* **55**, 909–916.
64. Jordan, C. C., and Webster, R. A. (1971) *Br. J. Pharmacol.* **43**, 441P.
65. Nistri, A. (1976) *Naunyn-Schmiedeberg's Arch. Pharmacol.* **295**, 89–94.
66. Sacchi, O., and Perri, V. (1973) *J. Gen. Physiol.* **61**, 342–360.
67. Elmqvist, D., and Quastel, D. M. J. (1965) *J. Physiol. (London)* **177**, 463–482.

Nerve Excitability: From Descriptive Phenomenology to Molecular Interpretation

DAVID NACHMANSOHN
Departments of Neurology and Biochemistry
College of Physicians and Surgeons
Columbia University
New York, New York

INTRODUCTION: EARLY THEORIES OF AXONAL CONDUCTION AND SYNAPTIC TRANSMISSION

For over a century it was generally accepted that conduction along nerve and muscle fibers is effected by electric currents. At the turn of this century it was recognized in addition that Na^+ and K^- ions are the carriers of these currents. Using the voltage clamp technique, Hodgkin and Huxley (19) achieved a quantitative analysis of the various parameters of these ion movements during electrical activity. A mathematical formalism was proposed based on classical equilibrium thermodynamics and on the assumption of a simple electrodiffusion process. In 1957 it was shown by A. V. Hill and his associates (Abbott *et al.*, 1) that a strong heat production and absorption coincides with the action potential. At a symposium in 1958, A. V. Hill made the statement that he does not see any alternative to the assumption that the heat changes during electrical activity are due to chemical reactions associated with the permeability cycle responsible for the ion fluxes across the excitable membrane. At the same meeting, Peter Debye stressed emphatically that it is inconceivable that electricity in a fluid system such as a living cell, i.e., ion fluxes across membranes, take place without any chemical reaction. The Cambridge group nevertheless specifically excluded any chemical reactions controlling the ion movements (see, e.g., Keynes and Aubert, 24).

In the 1930's Dale and his associates accumulated a considerable amount of pharmacological data, on the basis of which they proposed the hypothesis that acetylcholine (ACh)* is released, on stimulation of the axon, from nerve endings and acts as a chemical transmitter across the nonconducting gap, neuromuscular or synaptic junctions. Many eminent neurobiologists, among them Erlanger, Gasser, Fulton, the school of Sherrington, and many others, vigorously objected to this hypothesis (see, e.g., Erlanger, 16). They did not question the data, but their interpretation. The electrical signs of nerve impulse propagation seemed to them difficult to reconcile with two fundamentally different mechanisms: a purely physical one along axons and a chemical one across synaptic junctions. The classical pharmacological methods used were inadequate to explain the basic molecular mechanism.

ALTERNATIVE INTERPRETATION OF THE FUNCTION OF ACH IN EXCITABLE MEMBRANES AS A RESULT OF BIOCHEMICAL AND PHYSICOCHEMICAL ANALYSES

A biochemical approach was initiated by the author in 1936. I had been trained in Otto Meyerhof's laboratory in the Kaiser-Wilhelm-Institutes in Berlin-Dahlem in the 1920's, at that time one of the most brilliant scientific centers in which the foundation of modern biochemistry was laid. Enzymes in particular and proteins in general were at the core of all theories associated with cellular function. Meyerhof's main interest was the transformation of chemical into mechanical energy during muscular contraction. The author worked there for several years on the particular role played by phosphocreatine in this process and became deeply influenced by the basic notions introduced by Meyerhof for the analysis of cellular functions: (1) the paramount importance of bioenergetics in general and the elucidation of the sequence of energy transformations associated with a cellular function; (2) in view of the vital role of enzymes, the importance of isolation, purification, and investigation of their properties; (3) the fundamental role of high-energy phosphate derivatives in intermediary metabolism; (4) the necessity of correlating chemical reactions with cell function; and (5) the cyclic character of cell reactions tentatively suggested by Meyerhof, but later firmly established by Hans A. Krebs with the urea and citric acid cycles. These five key notions formed the basis of the author's approach to the analysis of the transduction of

* The symbol ACh is used here, although the conventional abbreviation for acetyl is Ac, rather than A.

chemical into electrical energy, i.e., the mechanism underlying nerve conduction and bioelectricity.

Frequently attending the meetings of the English Physiological Society and listening to the controversies about the role of ACh, the author was struck by the absence of any chemical investigation. In 1936 and 1937 I tested the distribution and concentration of acetylcholinesterase in a large variety of excitable tissues, nerve and muscle fibers, using a great number of different species. In 1937, I came across the electric organ of *Torpedo marmorata*, a tissue highly specialized in generating bioelectricity and, in addition, formed by only 3% protein and 92% water. One kg of electric tissue hydrolyzes 3–4 kg of ACh per hour. Similar values were found by me in the following year in the electric tissue of *Electrophorus electricus*. These values seemed to be extraordinarily high for a tissue poor in proteins and suggested a close relationship with its primary function, i.e., the generation of bioelectricity. It became immediately apparent that this tissue would offer a uniquely favorable material for the analysis of the proteins (including enzymes) associated with ACh and with bioelectricity in general. Actually the concentration of acetylcholinesterase found in 1937 does not yet present a real picture of its activity. As was found by Changeux and his associates (6), the enzyme is almost exclusively localized in the excitable membrane of the electroplax of *Electrophorus*. Thus a more realistic value is the ability of one gram excitable membrane of *Electrophorus* to hydrolyze more than 30 kg of ACh per hour.

The electric tissue proved in the last four decades instrumental in the isolation and purification of the proteins associated with the function of ACh, and for the elucidation of their properties and function. During the last 15 years two other factors were crucial for the advances achieved in the molecular interpretation of nerve impulse conduction and bioelectricity: (1) the spectacular rise of protein and macromolecular chemistry, and (2) the vast amount of information accumulated on biomembranes by a combination of techniques, particularly biochemical studies in combination with electron microscopy. Cell membranes turned out to be the site of many vital cellular functions, such as energy supply, active transport, and vision, in addition to the long-assumed process of conduction. Proteins make up more than two-thirds of the mass of most biomembranes; more than 30 different proteins have been isolated from some membranes. Proteins account readily for the great diversity, specificity, and efficiency of membrane functions. Figure 1 shows two models proposed as an illustration of the progress achieved within one decade: the upper model

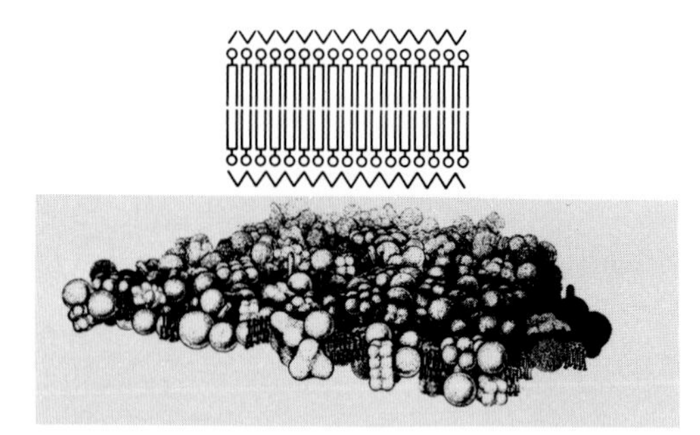

Fig. 1. Membrane models. Upper part: "unit membrane" of Robertson; lower part presents the hypothetical model of the inner mitochondrial membrane, proposed by Sjöstrand and Barajas (56) in 1970. The model comprises only those enzymes and coenzymes which were experimentally established to be present in this structure.

is the "unit membrane" proposed by Robertson (53) which is formed by a bimolecular leaflet of phospholipids, surrounded on the outside and the inside by some proteins attached mainly by Coulombic forces; the lower part presents the still hypothetical model of the inner mitochondrial membrane proposed 10 years later by Sjöstrand and Barajas (56), using new methods for preventing the denaturation of proteins. Their model comprises only those enzymes and coenzymes which were experimentally established as being present in this membrane.

The vast number of data obtained by the biochemical approach have been repeatedly summarized by the author in reviews (e.g., Nachmansohn, 39–41,42a,43) and recently in a revised monograph (Nachmansohn and Neumann, 44).

CONTROL OF ION PERMEABILITY BY THE ACH CYCLE

On the basis of biochemical and physicochemical data a concept of the function of ACh emerged entirely different from that originally proposed. ACh is not a neurohumoral transmitter *between* cells; its action is *intramembranous*. An ACh cycle, formed by four proteins, acts *within* all excitable membranes, in its conducting and synaptic parts. ACh, by its action on a specific ACh receptor, induces a conformational change of this protein and thereby triggers a series of reactions leading to increased ion permeability during activity. The cycle proposed in a Harvey lecture in 1953 (Nachmansohn, 37) has since been greatly elaborated. Figure 2 shows the cycle as extended in the last two decades (see, e.g., Nachmansohn, 42a). It indicates how chemical energy is transducted into electrical energy; the action of ACh on the receptor releases Ca^{2+} ions. Their action opens the gateway, the ion

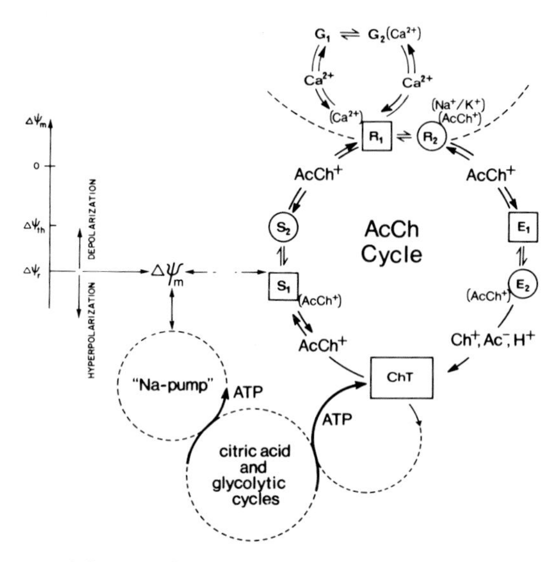

Fig. 2. Scheme of the transduction of chemical into electrical energy; role of the ACh-cycle. (For details see text.)

permeation zone, for the rapid influx of Na^+ ions during the action potential. The release of ACh from the storage protein is attributed to the drop in resting potential. Neumann and Katchalsky (48) and Neumann and Rosenheck (49) have found that an electric field of 15–20 kV/cm (i.e., 15–20 mV/100 Å) may induce a change of conformation of biopolymers with a resulting displacement of counterions surrounding the biopolymer; the repulsive forces in the polymer are thereby increased and the dissociation of charged groups, such as the ACh ion, is facilitated. Since it is known that a drop of 15–20 mV in the membrane resting potential leads to an all-or-none response, the action potential, it suggests that an electrical stimulus effecting such a drop of potential releases ACh from the storage protein and permits its action on the receptor. The ACh released is transduced to the receptor protein (R) to which Ca^{2+} ions are bound. AcCh induces a conformational change of the receptor by which Ca^{2+} ions are released; they act on the ion permeation zone, the gateway G (see Fig. 6). The Ca^{2+} ions induce conformational changes of phospholipids or lipo- or glycoproteins in the gateway, probably producing a transitory aqueous zone of a few angstroms, thereby permitting the rapid Na^+ ion influx leading to the rising phase of the action potential (G open). In the meantime, ACh has been transduced to the enzyme acetylcholinesterase (E), which hydrolyzes the ester, in microseconds, into choline (Ch^+), acetate (Ac^-), and protons (H^+). The removal of ACh from the receptor permits the return to its resting conformation, binding Ca^{2+} ions, and thereby restoring the barrier for the rapid ion movements (G′ closed). The hydrolysis of ACh, the virtually irreversible step of the cycle, is followed by the supply of energy, ATP, to the enzyme choline *O*-acetyltransferase (ChT), which acetylates choline and assures the steady supply of ACh to the storage protein.

The glycolytic and citric acid cycles provide the energy, ATP, both for maintaining the resting (stationary) membrane potential ($\Delta\psi_r$) caused by the asymmetric distribution of various ions across the membrane, and for a steady supply flux of ACh to the storage protein. $\Delta\psi_{th}$ is the threshold potential that evokes an action potential. While the immediate source of energy of the action potential is the concentration gradient of Na^+ ions, maintained by active transport, this potential source of energy becomes available by the ACh cycle.

Two steps of the cycle may be briefly discussed. The hydrolysis of the ester is the virtually irreversible step in the cyclic process and requires input of energy for the synthesis of the ester. When studying the sequence of the energy transformations in the electric organ of *Electrophorus* during electrical activity, in the years 1941 and 1942, the author found a surprisingly high hydrolysis of phosphocreatine during the electric discharge. The concentrations of both phosphocreatine and ATP are very high in electric tissue, in spite of its low protein and high water content, higher than in striated muscle. Assuming that the hydrolysis of phosphocreatine was used for rapid rephosphorylation of the ATP hydrolyzed for providing energy used during the discharge, the author calculated that the ΔG of ATP hydrolysis is more than adequate for providing the energy for acetylation of choline. In fact, there is a high excess of energy released by the ATP hydrolysis which, as was found in the 1950's by many investigators, is used for active transport across cell membranes, a process not specific for excitable membranes but required in all cells. The author prepared cell-free solutions from electric tissue and brain and found a high synthesis of ACh in the presence of choline, acetate, and ATP; addition of NaFl was necessary for the inhibition of ATPase. I also observed the requirement of a coenzyme for the acetylation, which I immediately started to purify. This discovery, in the fall of 1942, was the first demonstration of the use of energy of ATP hydrolysis for acetylation and a biosynthetic process outside the glycolytic cycle, as was recognized by many investigators. At a symposium on "Phosphorus Metabolism," held in 1951 at The Johns Hopkins University, Otto Meyerhof stressed, in his opening address, that this discovery was one of three of the most pertinent contributions to the function of

ATP (Meyerhof, 33). The paper describing this discovery was rejected by three journals. Thanks to the support of John F. Fulton, the paper was finally published, in 1943, in the *Journal of Neurophysiology* (for details, see also the Prefatory Chapter of the Annual Review of Biochemistry, Nachmansohn, 42).

In an historical review, Lipmann (28) recalled the roles of ATP and phosphocreatine in energy transfer, in relation to the work in Meyerhof's laboratory in 1927–1928. Experiments by the author in Meyerhof's laboratory during that period established a direct connection between muscular action and phosphocreatine breakdown (Nachmansohn, 35). Later, the writer proposed and Meyerhof accepted the idea that phosphocreatine breakdown is somehow associated with a special parameter of contraction, namely its speed (Nachmansohn, 36; Meyerhof, 32). No mechanism was proposed at that time in view of the poor information available. The assumption turned out to be correct when Lohmann (28a,b), in his studies on ATP, established, in 1934, that phosphocreatine serves the rapid restoration of hydrolyzed ATP, without loss of energy. These observations provided the explanation of why rapidly contracting muscles have high concentrations of phosphocreatine, while slowly contracting muscles have low concentrations or none at all. Actually, it was on the basis of this historical background that the author first looked for phosphocreatine breakdown during the electric discharge, a process requiring much faster energy supply than muscular contraction.

The second step of the ACh cycle to be briefly discussed is the role of Ca^{2+} ions. For more than a century it was known that Ca^{2+} ions played an essential role in nerve excitability, but the molecular basis was completely obscure. In the 1960's evidence accumulated that Ca^{2+} ions are particularly effective in inducing large conformational changes as, for instance, in muscular contraction, and are particularly efficient in systems that contain regions of a relatively high negative surface charge. In such polyelectric regions the osmotic coefficient of Ca is of the order of 0.01, i.e., about 99% of Ca^{2+} counterions are bound (Katchalsky, 22). The high binding capacity is one of the reasons for the assumption that Ca^{2+} ions play an essential role in maintaining the structural and functional integrity of macromolecules and macromolecular structures.

It thus appeared possible to assume that Ca^{2+} ions may act on the gateway, changing the conformation of phospholipids or lipoproteins and thereby producing a transient aqueous zone permitting the ion flow. However, the action of Ca must be controlled by a specific protein. It was suggested by the writer that Ca^{2+} ions are bound to the receptor and that the conformational change induced by ACh may release Ca (see, e.g., Nachmansohn, 39–41). However, at that time there was no possibility of testing this idea. Even in the isolated excitable membrane many components react with Ca, thus preventing an unequivocal answer. Only when Changeux and his associates succeeded in isolating the receptor protein with the use of the α-toxin of *Naja naja* and by the introduction of α-bungarotoxin for the identification and purification of the protein, did an analysis of the interactions between receptor and Ca become possible (31b). During the last 3 years this problem has been analyzed in depth by Chang and Neumann (Chang and Neumann, 5; Neumann and Chang, 47). The data will be discussed in the paper by Neumann, Rosenberry, and Chang (this volume). Only the biologically most significant fact of their observations may be stressed in the context of theory. It is not the strikingly high absorptive capacity of the receptor molecule that may bind up to 60 Ca^{2+} ions per molecule of 260,000 daltons. It is the ability of ACh, the biological receptor activator, to induce a conformational change and to release two to three Ca^{2+} ions per molecule of ACh. In contrast, subsequent addition of α-bungarotoxin, a receptor inhibitor, leads to a reuptake of two to three Ca^{2+} ions. These opposing actions of activator and inhibitor suggest a more complex interaction between receptor, ACh, Ca, and α-bungarotoxin than direct competition; the interactions presumably involve different conformations, stabilized alternatively by activators and inhibitors. These observations support the postulated function of ACh receptor in nerve excitability, although final evidence requires confirmation by experiments on the intact membrane. Within the membrane the effect per molecule of ACh activating the receptor may be even stronger if, e.g., a Ca^{2+} ion is bound with one valence to the receptor, and the second one to a phospholipid or lipoprotein in the gateway.

It may be mentioned that Ruebsamen *et al.* (55) have found that the activators carbamylcholine and decamethonium displace Ca^{2+} ions from receptor sites which are associated with a Ca dissociation constant (k_{Ca}) of about 1 mM. The k_{Ca} values obtained by these authors are of the same order of magnitude as the data of Chang and Neumann derived from direct ACh and Ca binding experiments.

FACTUAL BASIS OF THE CONCEPT

The vast amount of data accumulated over several decades cannot be described; the reader is referred to the reviews and the monograph mentioned. Only a few aspects may be mentioned to dispel some misunderstandings frequently encountered in the literature.

Acetylcholinesterase (acetylcholine hydrolase: EC 3.1.1.7) is present in all excitable membranes both in their conducting and in their synaptic parts. No exceptions exist. For more than a decade no enzyme was detected in many nerve fibers or even in electric tissue using histochemical techniques and light microscopy, in sharp contrast to the results obtained by chemical determinations. This apparent absence was long used as an argument against the proposed theory. The thickness of the slices used prevented the substrate from reaching the enzyme. Using electron microscopy, the enzyme was found in all excitable membranes. In myelinated axons there was at the beginning some uncertainty, until Brzin (4) added to the incubation mixture a detergent, Triton X-100, thereby demonstrating the presence of the enzyme in the membrane (Fig. 3). Changeux *et al.* (6) did not find any difference between conducting and synaptic parts of the excitable membrane of the electroplax of *Electrophorus*, although the synaptic parts form less than 5% of the total membrane surface. A particularly elegant histochemical staining technique was introduced by Koelle and his associates in which thioacetate and gold sulfide are used for the formation of the dense end product (Koelle *et al.*, 26). It permits one to see more sharply the exact localization of the enzyme. Figure 4 shows the presence of the enzyme in the membrane of a nerve terminal and the conducting membrane of the electroplax of *Electrophorus* (N. Tomas, R. Davis, and G. B. Koelle, unpublished experiment reproduced with the permission of the authors). Figure 5 shows the presence of the enzyme in the pre- and postsynaptic membranes of an intercostal synapse of a mouse (Koelle, 25).

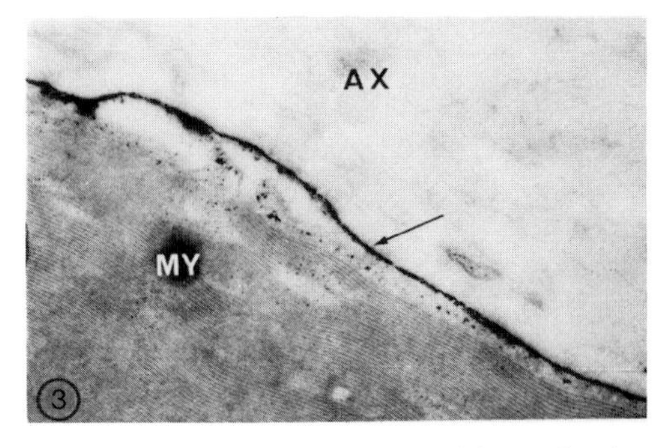

Fig. 3. Myelinated (MY) ventral root axon (AX) of frog. The dense end product is present in the excitable (plasma) membrane (arrow). For details see Brzin (4).

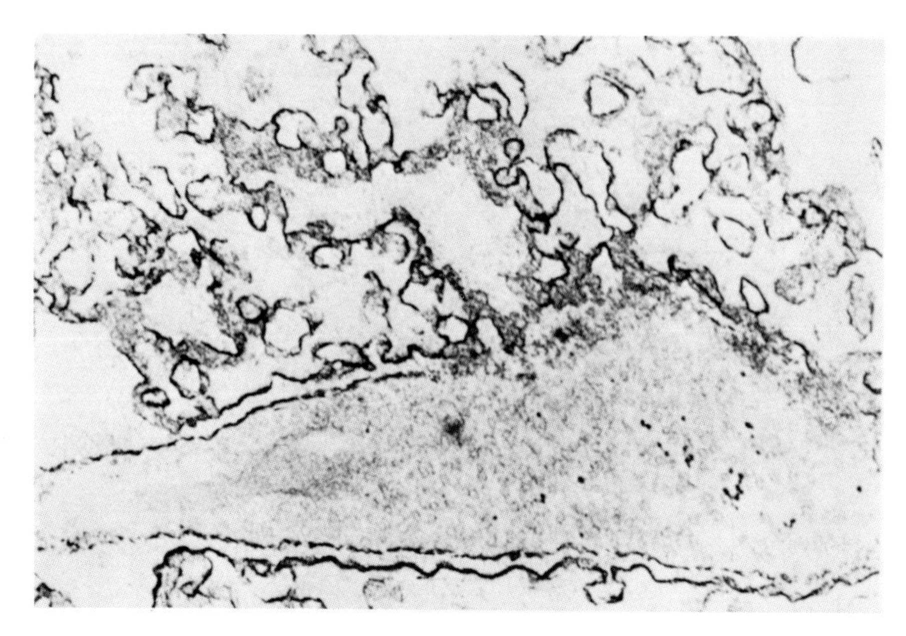

Fig. 4. Electron micrograph of the excitable membrane of *Electrophorus*. The presence of acetylcholinesterase in the membrane is tested by the new method developed by Koelle *et al.* (26). The enzyme is present in the nerve terminal, the postsynaptic and conducting part of the membrane. The circular formations seen in the picture and showing the stain are artifacts owing to the cutting in preparing the slices for examination; they are due to the deep invaginations all along the excitable membrane (N. Tomas, R. Davis, and G. B. Koelle, unpublished material.)

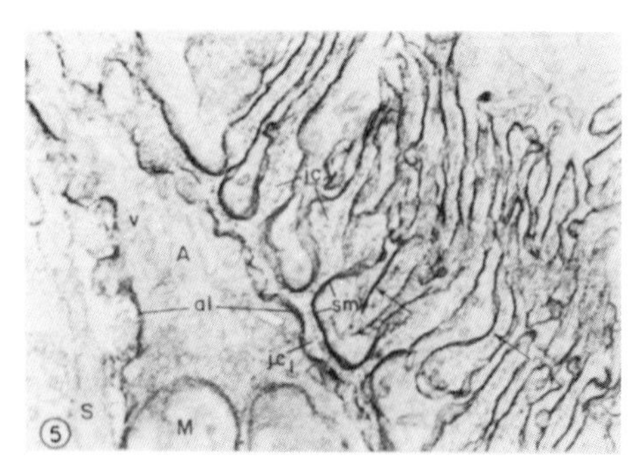

Fig. 5. Electron micrograph showing the histochemical localization of acetylcholinesterase at the motor end plate of mouse intercostal muscle. The dense end product is found in the membrane of the axon terminal (A) and the membrane covering the deep invaginations of the postsynaptic membrane. For details see Koelle (25).

The concentration of the enzyme is extremely high. In the excitable membrane of a single cell (electroplax) of *Electrophorus* 100 billion molecules of enzyme are present. The number of receptor molecules is of the same order of magnitude, as has been found in several laboratories.

However, it must be emphasized that neither the localization nor the concentration of the enzyme is the evidence for the concept presented. It is based upon a great variety of different types of experiments. An essential part of the evidence comes from the effects of powerful and specific inhibitors of either the ACh receptor or the acetylcholinesterase on electrical activity. They have demonstrated unequivocally that these two proteins are inseparably associated with the electrical activity in axonal conduction. Obviously, they must be applied to appropriate preparations and/or under appropriate experimental conditions. Eserine, a potent, specific, and competitive inhibitor of the enzyme affects and eventually blocks axonal conduction. At the nodes of Ranvier of frog sciatic nerve the effects and concentrations required are similar to those at synaptic junctions. Since the compound is a reversible enzyme inhibitor, the effect on electrical activity is readily reversible. Organophosphates are potent and irreversible inhibitors of the enzyme. They phosphorylate the enzyme by forming a P—O bond with the serine oxygen in the active site. These compounds block electrical activity of axons irreversibly. Some nucleophilic compounds are able, in a S_N2 reaction, to detach the phosphoryl group from the oxygen and thereby to reactivate the enzyme. One of the most potent reactivators is 2-pyridine aldoxime methiodide. Under appropriate conditions, electrical activity of axons irreversibly, blocked by organophosphates has been restored by the action of 2-pyridine aldoxime methiodide. Thus, the formation of the P–O bond blocked electrical activity; the specific breaking of the bond restored it. Curare and local anesthetics (structural analogs of ACh) react reversibly with the receptor protein. Both affect and eventually block the electrical activity of axons.

Many efforts have been devoted to test whether it is possible to separate enzyme and electrical activity with the use of organophosphates. These attempts are doomed to failure until completely new methods are developed to overcome the difficulty of determining quantitatively the total concentration of the enzyme in tissue, nerve, muscle, or electric tissue. Until 1965 it was generally assumed, also by the author, that a homogenized suspension permits a quantitative determination. Since then many observations accumulated indicating that simple homogenization is completely inadequate. Adding 1–2 *M* NaCl, detergents, etc., increases the total amount obtained by homogenization three- to fourfold. Whether the values obtained really represent 100% of the enzyme cannot be ascertained. After exposure to organophosphates the difficulties are compounded. It is virtually impossible to remove with certainty all the organophosphate from the tissue prior to homogenization. If a fraction of 1% is retained in the tissue after exposure, it may be released during homogenization. In view of the high potency of the compounds, active in 10^{-8} to 10^{-10} M concentration, the remaining traces would prevent any quantitative determination. A more detailed discussion of this problem may be found in the revised monograph (Nachmansohn and Neumann, 44, pp. 293–303.)

Many apparent contradictions of the early period have been fully explained in the last few years due to new information and to the greatly improved and refined techniques and instruments that have become available during the last 15 years.

A MODEL INTEGRATING BIOCHEMICAL, BIOPHYSICAL, AND THERMODYNAMIC DATA

One of the great pioneers in emphasizing the necessity of applying nonequilibrium thermodynamics to biological systems and particularly to biomembranes was Aharon Katchalsky. More than a decade ago he recognized that the mathematical formalism, offered by Hodgkin and Huxley and based on classical equilibrium thermodynamics, contained too many unknowns and was unable to provide an explanation of the underlying mechanism. The strong heat changes during the action potential, indicating that dissipative energy was involved, excluded a simple diffusion process as assumed by Hodgkin and Huxley. Cole (7), for a long time a strong supporter of the Hodgkin–Huxley theory, also recognized that the Planck ion model was not applicable to biomembranes. Katchalsky was firmly convinced that the ACh cycle provided a solid nucleus for developing a model that would integrate the vast information accumulated by biochemical, biophysical, and thermodynamic data. He and the author started, in 1965, to have many intensive discussions about the various aspects involved. However, a serious attempt at formulating an integral model was only initiated in the spring of 1972, shortly before the tragic death of Katchalsky. Eberhard Neumann, who had spent 3 years in Katchalsky's laboratory and had participated in our discussions, decided, with the strong encouragement of Manfred Eigen, to take up the work on the integral model. A preliminary note appeared in 1973 (Neumann

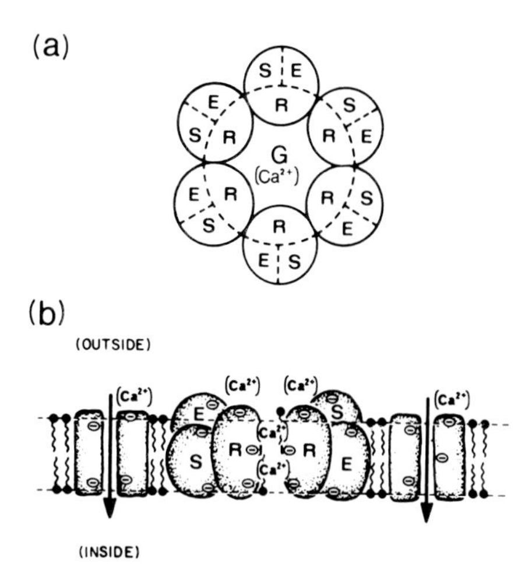

Fig. 6. Scheme of the ACh-controlled gateway (G). (a) Basic excitation unit containing in this example six SRE assemblies, viewed perpendicular to the membrane surface. S, ACh storage site; R, ACh receptor protein; E, acetylcholinesterase. (b) Cross section through a basic excitation unit flanked by two units that model ion passages for K^+ ions; the arrows represent the local electrical field vectors due to partial permselectivity to K^+ ions in the resting stationary state. The minus signs symbolize negatively charged groups of membrane components (Neumann, 46).

et al., 50). Within 2 years Neumann elaborated a tentative integral model that permitted the interpretation of many electrophysiological observations in molecular terms (Neumann, 46); he described the model in the monograph by Nachmansohn and Neumann (44).

Among the many theories and new ideas introduced by Neumann may be mentioned that of the basic excitation units (Fig. 6). According to this theory the gateway, the ion permeation zone, is surrounded not by one, but by several protein assemblies consisting of receptor (R), enzyme (E), and storage protein (S). In Fig. 6 the gateway is surrounded by six protein assemblies. Only when a critical number of receptors is activated and the corresponding number of Ca^{2+} ions are released does the stimulus reach the threshold potential ($\Delta\psi_{th}$) that produces the action potential. Figure 7 indicates the time course of chemical and electrical events and their relationships.

A model of bioelectricity, based on an ACh cycle and a Ca^{2+} cycle, has also been proposed by Dubois and Schoffeniels (15). There are some fundamental similarities between their model and that of Neumann, but there are also some differences that cannot be discussed in the framework of this short paper.

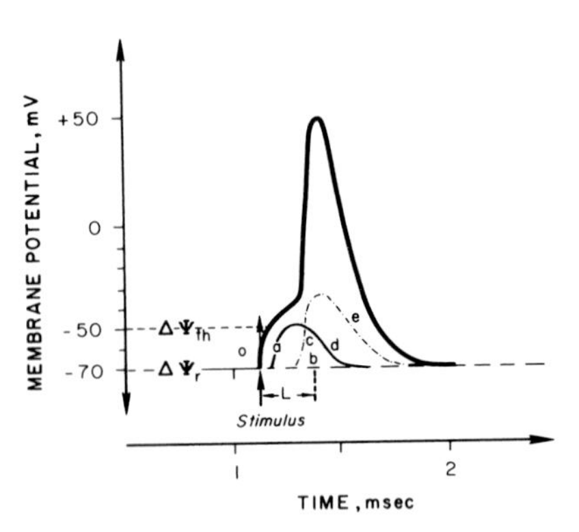

Fig. 7. Schematic representation of the time course of chemical reactions in relation to the action potential (o). Potential change owing to the change of the membrane potential in rest ($\Delta\psi_r$), to the threshold potential ($\Delta\psi_{th}$). (a) and (d), time course of ACh release and hydrolysis, respectively; (b) and (c), time course of Ca^{2+} release from receptor and of gateway opening; (e), time course of Ca^{2+} reuptake and conformational relaxation of the receptor, leading to closure of the gateway (Neumann *et al.*, 50).

REEVALUATION OF THE VOLTAGE CLAMP DATA OF HODGKIN AND HUXLEY

The voltage clamp experiments on squid giant axons by Hodgkin and Huxley (19) provided physical information about the rapid Na^+ and K^+ ion movements across the membranes during the action potential as a function of time at constant voltage. In the quarter of a century that has elapsed since then a large number of investigators have further elaborated the unspecific mathematical models (see, e.g., Cole, 8; Goldman and Schauf, 18; Moore and Cox, 34; Jacobsson, 21; and many others). Goldman and Schauf (18) have applied the voltage clamp technique to *Myxicola* axons using in principle the same equations as Hodgkin and Huxley. All these unspecific mathematical models do not provide a satisfactory specific chemical and molecular interpretation of the rapid permeability changes in the membrane for reasons just discussed above.

Recently, Rawlings and Neumann (52) applied a new method for the analysis of the voltage clamp experiments. They propose a chemical model (cycle of three states) for a dissipative control of ion permeability. One fundamental characteristic of this control model is the association of a small activator molecule (A) with a receptor molecule embedded in the excitable membrane:

$$A + R \rightleftharpoons AR \rightleftharpoons AR'$$

The permeability change ("Na activation") is caused by the structural transition of the receptor complex AR (closed state) of the pathway to a configuration AR′ corresponding to a high permeability arrangement (open state). The temporal limitation of the permeability change is accounted for by a removal mechanism of A, accomplished by a virtually irreversible decomposition catalyzed by an enzyme. Thus the model basically assumes that a correlation exists between the measured conductivity changes g_{Na} (t, V) and the concentration of activator-receptor (AR′):

$$g_{Na}(t,V) = F([AR'])$$

based on the cyclic three state reaction system:

$$\begin{array}{ccccccl} \text{input} \longrightarrow & A_1 + & \boxed{R} & \rightleftharpoons & \boxed{AR} & & \text{closed} \searrow \\ & & \upharpoonleft\downharpoonright & & \downharpoonleft\upharpoonright & & \quad \text{configuration} \\ \text{removed} \longleftarrow & A_2 + & (R') & \rightleftharpoons & (AR') & & \text{open} \nearrow \end{array}$$

A_1 and A_2 stand for the activator molecules in different regions of the membrane. This proposal fully agrees with the control mechanism suggested by the ACh cycle and the integral model elaborated by Neumann. The model is able to reproduce every feature observed by Goldman and Schauf in their voltage clamp experiments. Furthermore, the application of the model to the Hodgkin and Huxley data produces values for the kinetic coefficients which are comparable to those derived from the Goldman and Schauf data.

The basic new feature of the analysis by Rawlings and Neumann is the replacement of the unknowns in the Hodgkin–Huxley equations by chemical factors. The analysis thus introduces chemical reactions into the interpretation of the mechanism of the action potential, i.e., the ion permeability changes; it is not a simple electrodiffusion process. The work of Rawlings and Neumann (52) thus represents a landmark in the transition from descriptive phenomenology to molecular interpretation.

HEAT CHANGES INTERPRETED BY MOLECULAR EVENTS

As mentioned in the Introduction, there is no alternative to the interpretation of the strong heat changes during the action potential by chemical events. As has already been pointed out by Hill and his associates (Abbott *et al.*, 1), ion mixing, Joule heat, etc., can account for only a small fraction of the strong heat changes observed. The heat changes are the result not of one but of a series of chemical reactions taking place in the process and shown in the ACh cycle, as stressed by the author a decade ago (Nachmansohn, 38). However, a computation of the various factors contributing to the heat changes is not an easy problem. It is, therefore, an outstanding contribution to the interpretation of the heat changes that Margineanu and Schoffeniels (30) have made: the first attempt at analyzing the many factors contributing to the complex process, including the molecular events of the ACh cycle and not just in general terms of structural changes. They analyze the variety of factors known to occur during the action potential. Their computation clearly indicates that neither the ionic flows nor the redistribution of electric charges in the membrane, termed the capacitive current, are able to account for the strong heat changes measured. For 20 years after the strong heat changes were found, the interpretations centered only around such processes as condenser theory, local circuit heat, ion mixing, etc., due to the domination of the ionic theory. In contrast, Margineanu and Schoffeniels (30) show the important contributions made by the conformational changes of the proteins of the ACh cycle in the heat changes. The small enthalpy of the hydrolysis of ACh measured by Sturtevant (57) plays a minor role in the recovery process to which this reaction belongs, according to theory. Obviously, there may be other, still-unknown reactions involved, as stated by the two authors. But the agreement between the observed heat changes and those factors computed by the two authors from the known data, including the conformational changes of the proteins, appears quite satisfactory. Thus another step has been accomplished in moving from descriptive phenomenology to molecular interpretation.

THE ROLE OF ACH AT SYNAPTIC JUNCTIONS

REEVALUATION OF THE FACTS SUPPORTING THE TRANSMITTER ROLE OF ACH

The question naturally arises as to the role of ACh at the synaptic junctions in the light of the new information briefly discussed. Let us first consider the three basic facts on which the original hypothesis of neurohumoral transmission rests.

The powerful action of ACh on synaptic junctions in contrast to its complete failure to affect conduction was considered one of its strongest supports. ACh was applied by Dale and his associates to frog sciatic nerve fibers, just as curare was by Claude Bernard more than a century ago. This preparation is surrounded by a heavy sheath of connective tissue, impervious to many compounds. The fibers are formed by several thousand axons, each covered by a heavy myelin sheath, 30,000–50,000 Å thick. Obviously, under such conditions not a trace of ACh or curare, lipid-insoluble quaternary nitrogen compounds, would reach the membrane. Even in the so-called unmyelinated axons the excitable membrane is surrounded by a Schwann cell rich in lipid; in the squid giant axon, e.g., the Schwann cell is 4000 Å thick. However, if one prepares a single axon (see Fig. 8) of a frog sciatic nerve fiber and applies curare to a single node of Ranvier, where the myelin is absent, curare reversibly blocks conduction (Dettbarn, 13). The same applies to eserine, which acts at the Ranvier node in similar concentrations and in a similar way on the action potential of the axon and at the neuromuscular junction (Dettbarn, 14).

When the squid giant axon is exposed to a few μg of phospholipase A for a few minutes, lipid-insoluble quaternary compounds, such as ACh and curare, completely inactive before, affect electrical activity. The concentrations are higher than at the synaptic junction, since the structural barrier is reduced, but not removed; in fact only a superficial outer layer of the Schwann cell is affected, as indicated by electron micrographs. Tertiary compounds act, after exposure to phospholipase A, in concentrations comparable to those acting on the junction (Table I, taken from Rosenberg, 54). Thus the difference between the action of ACh on axons and junctions is due to the structural barriers protecting the axonal, but not the synaptic, membranes.

The second factor on which the hypothesis of neurohumoral transmission was based was the release of ACh from nerve terminals found in the perfusion fluid of junctions after stimulation. However, as has been stressed time and again by Dale and his associates, ACh appears only in the presence of eserine. This compound is a powerful inhibitor of acetylcholinesterase and thus blocks the rapid removal of ACh by hydrolysis; of necessity ACh will come out in the perfusion fluid. The experiments of Otto Loewi on frog heart preparations in which he found, in 1921, the "Vagusstoff" are irreproducible. Loewi tried for more than 10 years, in this country, to repeat his experiments without success. He attributed the failure to a species difference: *Rana pipiens* in the United States and *Rana esculenta* in Europe. In Vienna Brücke and his associates tried for years to repeat Loewi's experiments on *Rana esculenta*, but were also unable to find ACh (personal communication).

The appearance of ACh in the perfusion fluid of the junction was attributed by Dale and his associates (10) to its release from nerve terminals, since no ACh was found after the section and degeneration of

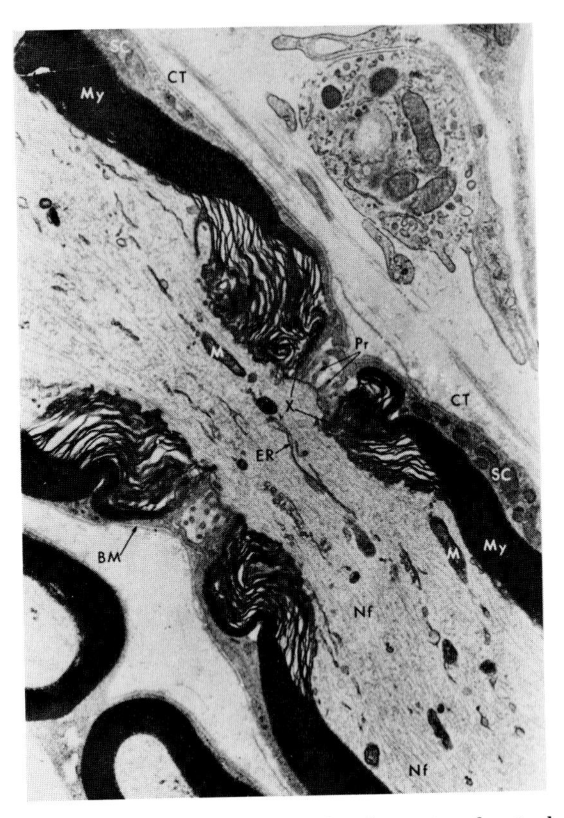

Fig. 8. Electron micrograph showing a node of Ranvier of a single fiber from the sciatic nerve of mouse. The sheath of myelin forms a compact tube (My) over most of the internodal area. In the region of the node, fingerlike processes (Pr) of neighboring Schwann cells (SC) interdigitate and cover the nodal area. A basement membrane (BM) and connective tissue fibers (CT) of the endoneurium complete the wrappings of the fiber. At the node the membrane of the axon is free of myelin and is exposed to the interstitial fluids which diffuse through the basement membrane and between the Schwann cell processes. Axoplasm is rich in neurofilaments (Nf) and contains slender elements of the endoplasmic reticulum (ER) and small number of mitochondria (M). (Porter and Bonneville, 51).

the nerve on direct muscle stimulation. Only a few experiments on dogs were performed. McIntyre (31a), a pupil of Dale, and his associates have convincingly demonstrated in many carefully performed experiments over the years that ACh appears in the perfusion fluid after complete denervation of the nerve terminals when the muscle is stimulated. Appearance of ACh from the cut surface of stimulated axons has been observed by many investigators. Thus the three funda-

TABLE I
Permeability Barriers Protecting Conducting (Axonal) Parts of Excitable Membranes against the Action of Quaternary (But Not of Tertiary) Analogs of Ammonium Derivatives[a]

Compound	Axon (squid)		Synapse (electroplax)
	Untreated	After exposure to phospholipase A	
	Tertiary Compounds		
Atropine	2×10^{-3}	3×10^{-4}	3×10^{-4}
Physostigmine	7×10^{-3}	1×10^{-3}	0.7×10^{-3}
Procaine[b]	3×10^{-3}		1×10^{-3}
Dibucaine[b]	3×10^{-5}		3×10^{-5}
	Quaternary Compounds		
Acetylcholine	$(\geq 10^{-1})$	2×10^{-4}	3×10^{-6}
d-Tubocurarine	$(\geq 10^{-2})$	3×10^{-5}	3×10^{-6}
Benzoylcholine	2×10^{-2}		1×10^{-3}

[a] Data taken from Rosenberg (54).
[b] Local anesthetics (analogs of acetylcholine).

mental facts on which the original hypothesis of neurohumoral transmission was based have lost their validity.

In contrast to the contradictions to the assumption of ACh as a transmitter across junctions, the assumption of a similar role of ACh in both conducting and synaptic parts of the membrane has found increasingly strong experimental support. For many years no electrical activity was detected in nerve terminals, until Hubbard and Schmidt (20) demonstrated action potentials in nerve terminals. These findings were confirmed by Katz and Miledi (23). Efflux of K^+ ions from stimulated axons was demonstrated by Cowan (9). Feldberg and Vartiainen (17) found an efflux of K^+ ions at synaptic junctions following stimulation. Nastuk (45) found that there was no synaptic transmission in the absence of Na^+ ions in the perfusion fluid.

For decades it has been known that ACh, curare, and neostigmine act in a similar way on pre- and postsynaptic membranes and that ACh produces antidromic impulses, which were recorded at the ventral roots. The presence of acetylcholinesterase in both synaptic membranes was described before and shown in Figs. 4 and 5. Recently ACh receptors have been found in both pre- and postsynaptic membranes. Figure 9 shows an electron micrograph prepared by Lentz *et al.* (27); using peroxidase labeled α-bungarotoxin it is seen that the receptor is clearly present in both pre- and postsynaptic membranes. In

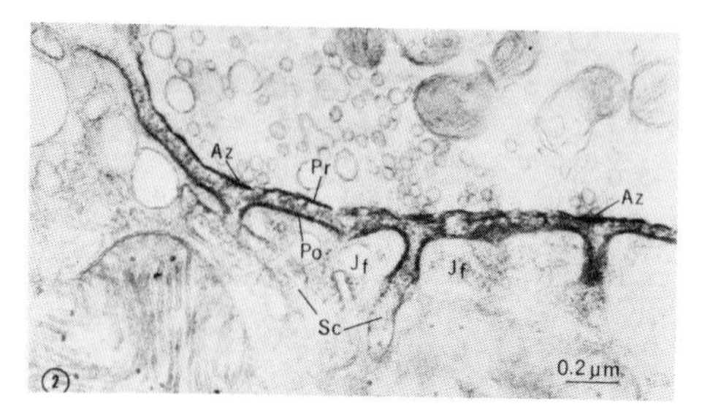

Fig. 9. Neuromuscular junction of mouse diaphragm. Electron micrograph stained by using peroxidase labeled α-bungarotoxin. Postsynaptic activity (Po) occurs in a thick band at the tops of junctional folds (Jf) while the basis of the secondary synaptic clefts (Sc) are unreactive. Presynaptic activity (Pr) is localized to the axolemma, including that overlying the active zones (Az). (Lentz *et al.*, 27).

view of the effects of ACh and analogous structures on the nerve terminal and the action potentials observed there, the demonstration of the presence of the two proteins clearly indicates that the ACh cycle has the same control function as in the axonal membrane. Voltage clamp experiments of Magleby and Stevens (29) show that the time and voltage dependence of the ion conductivity $g(t,V)$ of frog neuromuscular end plates are similar to $g_{Na}(t,V)$ of squid axons. These data support the concept of the basic similarity of the molecular mechanism in synaptic and conducting parts of the membrane.

In the electron micrograph by Lentz *et al.* (Fig. 9) the presence of the receptor seems to be limited to the pre- and postsynaptic membranes. One has to keep in mind the difficulty of obtaining staining, even when using a relatively thin slice, when large molecules such as peroxidase-labeled α-bungarotoxin are used in tissues as well protected as axonal membranes. The long history of failures to show acetylcholinesterase in axonal membranes, and the difficulty of the substrate in reaching the enzyme even in homogenized suspensions should be kept in mind. The presence of acetylcholinesterase in axonal membranes has now been shown not only by chemical methods but also by electron microscopy combined with histochemical methods. The presence of ACh receptors in the axonal membranes has been for many years demonstrated by the action of specific and potent inhibitors of the receptor on electrical activity and in several cases by the production of action potentials by ACh in axons.

In recent years, however, experiments began to accumulate presenting direct evidence for the presence of the receptor protein in axonal membranes. The isolation of a protein from axonal membranes which binds cholinergic ligands and has many characteristics of the ACh receptor has been reported by Denburg (11) and Denburg *et al.* (12) and confirmed by Balerna *et al.* (2). Mautner and his associates (Marquis *et al.*, 31) have performed extensive studies on the interaction of cholinergic ligands, particularly on local anesthetics, with isolated membrane fragments from lobster axons. Isologous local anesthetics containing the ester, thiolester, or selenoester grouping and their quaternary analogs were studied to determine their ability to displace [^{3}H]nicotine from plasma membrane fragments. The relative ability of oxo, thio, and seleno analogs to displace nicotine was the same as their ability to block axonal conduction and synaptic transmission. Among the cholinergic agents choline and aminocholine, previously shown to be inactive as depolarizing agents, were unable to displace nicotine. There was no difference between tertiary and quaternary analogs, thus supporting the view that the relative inactivity of quaternary compounds must be attributed to the presence of structural permeability barriers. The level of α-bungarotoxin binding to these membrane fragments is comparable to that of the nicotine binding. The toxin binding was also found in the supernatant of the preparation from which the membrane fragments were obtained. The chemical nature of this toxic binding compound is under investigation.

In view of all the new information about the biophysical and biochemical processes in excitable membranes, in their conductive and synaptic parts, the alternative interpretation of the role of ACh, postulated for many years, now appears well documented, while the transmitter role is incompatible with all the new data established. The new concept is shown schematically in Fig. 10. The action potential at the nerve terminal, controlled by the ACh cycle in the presynaptic membrane, is associated with the influx of Na^+ and efflux of K^+ ions. Per molecule of ACh released in the membrane, about 20,000 to 40,000 K^+ ions flow to the outside. When 1000 molecules of ACh are released in the membrane of the nerve terminal per impulse, 20 to 40 million K^+ ions would enter, in microseconds, the synaptic cleft of 200–300 Å and of very small diameter. The high concentration of K^+ ions in the cleft would produce a fall of 15–20 mV in the resting potential of the postsynaptic membrane and thereby release ACh there. Some investigators assume a release of 10,000 or even 20,000 molecules per impulse arriving at the nerve terminal. This figure seems excessively large for many reasons. But it may be that the actual figure is 2000–3000 molecules.

Thus the elementary process propagating the impulse along axons and across junctions is basically the same: the electric currents (ion

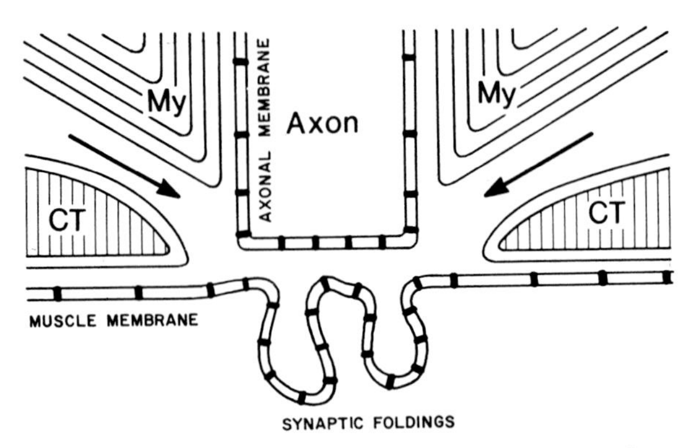

Fig. 10. Scheme of a cross section through a synaptic junction between a neuron and a muscle cell. The bars across the excitable membranes represent cross sections of the suggested basic excitation units (BEU); the density of BEU is assumed to be higher in the synaptic region than in the axonal parts. My, membrane layers of myelin protecting the axonal membrane; CT, protective layers (e.g., connective tissue) of the muscle membrane. The arrows indicate the sites of relatively easy access for external application of chemicals to the excitable membranes of nerve and muscle.

movements) are the propagating agents. The developments of the last decades have fully borne out the fact that the objections of many eminent neurobiologists to the hypothesis of neurohumoral transmission were entirely justified. In addition, they have provided much information about the molecular events underlying nerve excitability and bioelectricity.

However, the view of the universal role of ACh in no way contradicts the existence of many marked differences between synapses and axons. There are striking differences of structure, shape, and environment. The synaptic membranes are unprotected by structural barriers. All drugs, toxins, etc., will primarily act on the junctions. The complex shape of the postsynaptic membrane of the neuromuscular junctions (see Fig. 5) may readily influence the processes by geometric factors. Nothing is known about the internal organization of the different membranes. Most important are the many additional chemical compounds acting at synaptic junctions, such as adrenaline and noradrenaline, the various catecholamines, amino acids, and prostaglandins. As pointed out by von Euler, these compounds may act as modulators or regulators and affect and modify the response of the effector cell to the impulse. We are still far from a real understanding of the extraordinary complexity of the synaptic junctions. But it appears obvious that they offer a much more refined mechanism of modulation than the relatively simple axon cylinders. "Inhibition" or "stimulation" are pictures, they do not reveal the underlying mechanism. ACh acts in some cases as an inhibitory, in others as a stimulatory agent. In the ACh receptor there are S–S groups near the active site (Karlin and Winnick, 21a). Reducing these S–S groups by dithiothreitol drastically changes the effects of ligands and may transform inhibitors into activators or vice versa.

In conclusion, this chapter is aimed at illustrating how the biochemical approach has permitted the analysis of biophysical and thermodynamic data in chemical terms and has moved our understanding of nerve excitability and bioelectricity from descriptive phenomenology to molecular interpretations. The prediction of DuBois Reymond, expressed in 1877, that electric organs may one day help to explain the mechanism of bioelectricity turned out to be a remarkably correct one.

Addendum:

Direct and so far the most convincing biochemical evidence for the presence of the ACh receptor in the axonal membranes has been recently reported (J. K. Marquis, D. C. Hilt, and H. G. Mautner, *Biochem. Biophys. Res. Comm.* **78:** 746, 1977). High affinity binding of ^{125}I-α-bungarotoxin (BgTx) (assumed to be a "nicotinic" antagonist) has a dissociation constant, K_D, of 2.7×10^{-7} M to the membrane fragments (pellet); the maximum binding capacity, B_{max}, was 87 pmoles/mg protein; in the supernatant the K_D was 2.4×10^{-7} M and the B_{max} was 13 pmoles/mg protein. Acetyl-1-^{14}C-choline chloride, in the presence of eserine, had a K_D of 6.7×10^{-6} M. ^{3}H-3-Quinuclidinyl benzilate (QNB) (a "muscarinic" antagonist) was found to be bound only to the membrane fragments at low concentrations (less than 10^{-8} M). Scatchard analysis of dose-response data for QNB show a K_D of 1.1×10^{-9} M and B_{max} of 1.05 pmoles/mg protein. For ^{3}H-atropine K_D of 6.8×10^{-7} M and B_{max} of 59 pmoles/mg protein were found. Neither of these two compounds was bound to the proteins in the supernatant. This direct evidence of the presence of the ACh receptor in the axonal membrane, in combination with the biochemical, biophysical, and thermodynamic data mentioned above, marks an essential and most significant step in support of the view that the function of the ACh cycle is the control of the rapid movements across excitable membranes, both in its axonal and its synaptic parts.

REFERENCES

1. Abbott, B. C., Hill, A. V., and Howarth, J. V. (1958) *Proc. R. Soc. London, Ser. B* **148**, 149.
2. Balerna, M., Fosset, M., Chicheportiche, R., Romey, G., and Lazdunski, M. (1975) *Biochemistry* **14**, 5500.
3. Bender, A. N., Ringel, S. P., and Engel, W. K. (1976) *Neurology* **26**, 477.
4. Brzin, M. (1966) *Proc. Natl. Acad. Sci. U.S.A.* **56**, 1560.
5. Chang, H. W., and Neumann, E. (1976) *Proc. Natl. Acad. Sci. U.S.A.* **73**, 3364.
6. Changeux, J. -P., Gautron, J., Israel, M., and Podleski, T. (1969) *C. R. Hebd. Seances Acad. Sci., Ser. D* **269**, 1788.
7. Cole, K. S. (1965) *Physiol. Rev.* **45**, 340.
8. Cole, K. S. (1968) *In* "Membranes, Ions, and Impulses" (C. E. Tobias, ed.), Univ. of California Press, Berkeley.
9. Cowan, S. L. (1934) *Proc. R. Soc. London, Ser. B* **115**, 216.
10. Dale, H. W., Feldberg, W., and Vogt, M. (1936) *J. Physiol. (London)* **86**, 353.
11. Denburg, J. L. (1972) *Biochim. Biophys. Acta* **282**, 453.
12. Denburg, J. L., Eldefrawi, M. E., and O'Brien, R. D. (1972) *Proc. Natl. Acad. Sci. U.S.A.* **69**, 177.
13. Dettbarn, W. -D. (1960) *Nature (London)* **186**, 891.
14. Dettbarn, W. -D. (1961) *In* "Bioelectrogenesis" (C. Chagas and A. Paes de Carvalho, eds.), pp. 237–261. Elsevier, Amsterdam.
15. Dubois, D. M., and Schoffeniels, E. (1974) *Proc. Natl. Acad. Sci. U.S.A.* **7**, 2858.
16. Erlanger, J. (1939) *J. Neurophysiol.* **2**, 370.
17. Feldberg, W., and Vartiainen, A. (1934) *J. Physiol. (London)* **83**, 103.
18. Goldmann, L., and Schauf, C. L. (1973) *J. Gen. Physiol.* **61**, 361.
19. Hodgkin, A. L., and Huxley, A. F. (1952) *J. Physiol. (London)* **116**, 497; **117**, 500.
20. Hubbard, J. I., and Schmidt, R. F. (1963) *J. Physiol. (London)* **166**, 145.
21. Jakobsson, E. (1976) *Biophys. J.* **16**, 291.
21a. Karlin, A., and Winnick, M. (1968) *Proc. Natl. Acad. Sci. U.S.* **70**, 3636.
22. Katchalsky, A. (1964) *In* "Connective Tissue: Intercellular Macromolecules," p. 9. Little, Brown, Boston, Massachusetts.
23. Katz, B., and Miledi, R. (1965) *Proc. R. Soc. London, Ser. B* **161**, 453.
24. Keynes, R. D., and Aubert, X. (1964) *Nature (London)* **203**, 261.
25. Koelle, G. B. (1971) *Ann. N.Y. Acad. Sci.* **183**, 5.
26. Koelle, G. B., Davis, R., Smyrl, E. G., and Fine, A. Z. (1974) *J. Histochem. Cytochem.* **22**, 252.
27. Lentz, T. L., Chester, J., and Rosenthal, J. (1976) *34th Annu. Proc. Electron Microsc. Soc. Am.* p. 8.
28. Lipmann, F. (1975) *Energy Transform. Biol. Syst., Ciba Found. Symp.* **31** (New Ser.), 3–68.
28a. Lohmann, K. (1934) *Naturwiss.* **22**, 409.
28b. Lohmann, K. (1934) *Biochem. Z.* **271**, 264.
29. Magleby, K. L., and Stevens, C. F. (1972) *J. Physiol. (London)* **223**, 151.
30. Margineanu, D. -G., and Schoffeniels, E. (1977) *Proc. Natl. Acad. Sci. U.S.A.* (in press).
31. Marquis, J. K., Hilt, D. C., Papadeas, V. A., and Mautner, H. G. (1977) *Proc. Natl. Acad. Sci. U.S.A.* **74**, 2278.
31a. McIntyre, A. R. (1959) In "Curare and Curare-like Agents" (D. Bovet, F. Bovet-Nitti, and G. B. Marini-Bettolo, eds.) p. 211, Elsevier, Amsterdam.

31b. Meunier, J.-C., Huchet, M. Boquet, P., and Changeux, J.-P. (1971) *C. R. Acad. Sci., Ser. D* **272,** 117.
32. Meyerhof, O. (1930) "Die chemischen Vorgänge in Muskel und ihr Zusammenhang mit Arbeitsleistung und Wärmebildung." Springer-Verlag, Berlin and New York.
33. Meyerhof, O. (1951) *In* "Phosphorus Metabolism" (W. D. McElroy and B. Glass, eds.), Vol. 1, p. 3. Johns Hopkins Press, Baltimore, Maryland.
34. Moore, J. W., and Cox, E. B. (1976) *Biophys. J.* **16,** 171.
35. Nachmansohn, D. (1928) *Biochem.* Z. **196,** 73.
36. Nachmansohn, D. (1929) *Biochem.* Z. **208,** 237; **213,** 262.
37. Nachmansohn, D. (1955) *Harvey Lect.* **49,** 57.
38. Nachmansohn, D. (1966) *In* "Nerve as a Tissue" (K. Rodahl, ed.), pp. 141–161. McGraw-Hill, New York.
39. Nachmansohn, D. (1969) *J. Gen. Physiol.* **54,** 187S.
40. Nachmansohn, D. (1970) *Science* **168,** 1059.
41. Nachmansohn, D. (1971) *Handb. Sens. Physiol.* **1,** 18–102.
42. Nachmansohn, D. (1972) *Annu. Rev. Biochem.* **41,** 1.
42a. Nachmansohn, D. (1974) In "Biochemistry of Sensory Functions" (L. Jaenicke, ed.), p. 431. Springer-Verlag, Berlin and New York.
43. Nachmansohn, D. (1976) *Proc. Natl. Acad. Sci. U.S.A.* **73,** 82.
44. Nachmansohn, D., and Neumann, E. (1975) "Chemical and Molecular Basis of Nerve Activity." Academic Press, New York (revised).
45. Nastuk, W. L. (1954) *Fed. Proc., Fed. Am. Soc. Exp. Biol.* **13,** 104.
46. Neumann, E. (1974) *In* "Biochemistry of Sensory Functions" (L. Jaenicke, ed.), p. 465. Springer-Verlag, Berlin and New York.
47. Neumann, E., and Chang, H. W. (1976) *Proc. Natl. Acad. Sci. U.S.A.* **73,** 3994.
48. Neumann, E., and Katchalsky, A. (1972) *Proc. Natl. Acad. Sci. U.S.A.* **69,** 993.
49. Neumann, E., and Rosenheck, K. (1972) *J. Membr. Biol.* **10,** 279.
50. Neumann, E., Nachmansohn, D., and Katchalsky, A. (1973) *Proc. Natl. Acad. Sci. U.S.A.* **70,** 727.
51. Porter, K. R., and Bonneville, M. A. (1964) "An Introduction to the Fine Structure of Cells and Tissues." Lea & Febiger, Philadelphia, Pennsylvania.
52. Rawlings, P. K., and Neumann, E. (1976) *Proc. Natl. Acad. Sci. U.S.A.* **73,** 4492.
53. Robertson, J. D. (1960) *In* "Progress in Biophysics" (B. Katz and J. A. V. Butler, eds.), pp. 343–418. Pergamon, Oxford.
54. Rosenberg, P. (1966) *Mem. Inst. Butantan, Sao Paulo* **33,** 477.
55. Ruebsamen, H., Hess, G., Eldefrawi, A. T., and Eldefrawi, M. E. (1976) *Biochem. Biophys. Res. Commun.* **68,** 58.
56. Sjöstrand, F. S., and Barajas, L. (1970) *J. Ultrastruct. Res.* **32,** 293.
57. Sturtevant, J. M. (1972) *J. Biol. Chem.* **247,** 968.

Acetylcholine Receptor-Mediated Ion Flux in Electroplax Membrane Microsacs

JOHN P. ANDREWS[1] AND GEORGE P. HESS
Section of Biochemistry
Cornell University
Ithaca, New York

One of the fascinating problems in biology deals with communication between nerve cells. In many of these cells transmission of a signal involves acetylcholine which binds to a membrane-bound protein, the acetylcholine receptor (1–3). This increases the permeability of the cell membrane to sodium and potassium ions, and creates an electrical signal (4–6). Whether or not the signal is transmitted depends on the magnitude of the voltage change. Although the acetylcholine receptor has been isolated and is being characterized in many laboratories (e.g., 7–12), little is known, on the molecular level, about the relationship between ligand binding and receptor-mediated changes in the permeability of the cell membrane to sodium and potassium ions. In addition, electrophysiological studies (13–17) in which transmembrane potentials and currents are monitored have yielded much useful information concerning macroscopic aspects of the problem, but have elucidated few details of the underlying molecular mechanism. Furthermore, conspicuously absent from such studies is any demonstration of a simple relationship between effec-

[1] Present address: Institute for Cancer Research, The Fox Chase Cancer Center, Philadelphia, Pennsylvania 19111.

ISBN 0-12-398450-5

tive ligand concentration and the resulting voltage changes across the membrane.

Our goal is to systematically investigate the dynamic properties of receptor-mediated processes in a system capable of elucidating, on a molecular level, the relationships between ligand–receptor interactions, the receptor-mediated flux of ions across the nerve membrane, and the concomitant transmembrane potential changes.

Here we will describe the systems and techniques we have developed to investigate the relationships mentioned above, and to summarize the results obtained thus far. Just as the success of experiments of Huxley, Hodgkin, Katz (5,18–23), and others depends to a large extent on the availability of squid giant axon preparations, whose cytoplasm can be replaced with solutions of known composition, so also it would be invaluable to obtain preparations similar to the axons, but suitable for investigating receptor-mediated processes in nerve or muscle cells. One system which appeared promising for studying molecular aspects of neural phenomena utilized preparations obtained from the electric organ of *Electrophorus electricus*, an organ specialized for the generation of electricity to an extent unparalleled in living organisms.

In 1971, Kasai and Changeux (24–26) dissected out the electric organ, disrupted the cellular membranes of the electroplax by homogenization and sonication, and obtained sealed membrane vesicles of 1000 to 2000 Å diameter. The acetylcholine receptor-rich vesicles were then separated from other components by sucrose density gradient centrifugation. These investigators demonstrated that if the vesicles were incubated with $^{22}Na^+$ overnight and then diluted 70-fold into a solution containing nonradioactive sodium chloride, the exchange of hot and cold sodium could be measured by sampling the mixture at timed intervals, collecting the vesicles on Millipore filters, and determining the amount of $^{22}Na^+$ retained by the vesicles. This type of experiment is shown in Fig. 1. The upper curve on the figure represents the isotopic exchange in absence of receptor ligand. The lower curve represents $^{22}Na^+$ efflux in the presence of carbamylcholine, an acetylcholine analogue. As Kasai and Changeux (24–26) observed, the efflux rate, characterized by the half-equilibration time in the presence (τ) and absence (τ_0) of ligand, is slightly increased in the presence of the activator. Several objections were raised as to the validity of relating this *in vitro* system to receptor-mediated phenomena *in vivo*. Among these are: (1) The kinetics of the system are quite complex, involving a minimum of three exponentials in the presence of transmitter. It must be remembered that half-equilibration times are useful for describing rate processes only of first-order events. (2)

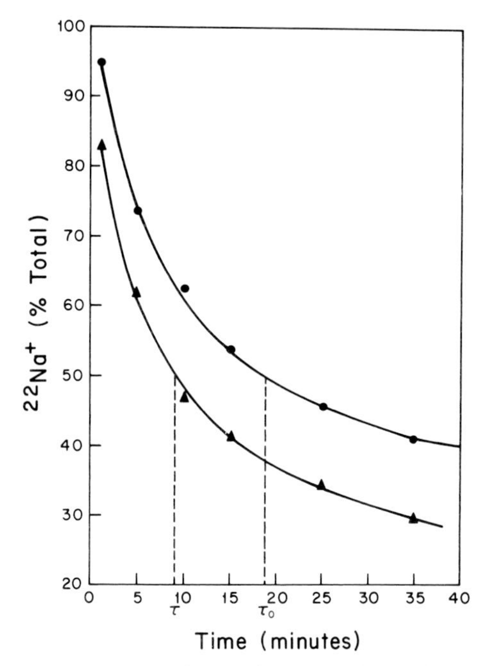

Fig. 1. $^{22}Na^+$ efflux from *Electrophorus electricus* electroplax membrane microsacs, diluted 70-fold according to the procedure of Kasai and Changeux (24), at pH 7.0 and 4°C. The time for half-equilibration of the microsacs with the dilution buffer is given for the control curve (τ_0) and carbamylcholine-mediated flux curve (τ). ●, Efflux in the absence of effector (control); ▲, efflux in the presence of 1×10^{-4} *M* carbamylcholine.

The efficiency of the activator-induced efflux, given as the number of ions which move across the membrane per unit time, appears to be five to six orders of magnitude lower than the number obtained by electrophysiological measurements with nerve or muscle cells (27,28). (3) The values of the half-equilibration time, reflecting in a complex way the efflux rate of ions, varies, depending on the eel preparation.

The observed complexity of the efflux, the apparent inefficiency of the receptor-mediated process, and the variability of the efficiency from preparation to preparation suggested that the parameters measured by this method reflected only partially the underlying primary process. For these reasons, we reinvestigated the efflux of ions from the microsacs, and found that the receptor-mediated flux, which constitutes only a small component of the total observed flux, is obscured by efflux from nonexcitable vesicles. The half-equilibration times reflect both the flux rate constant for unspecific flux and that for the small fraction of excitable microsacs in the preparation. It appeared to us that no meaningful information could be obtained with such a system unless we could ascertain which of the rate processes is affected by chemical transmitters, and in some way separate the specific, receptor-mediated efflux from the unspecific, nonexcitable efflux.

We have accomplished both these objectives (29,30). Our experimental data describing the kinetics of the $^{22}Na^+$ efflux observed with eel electroplax microsacs are given in Table I. The analysis reveals three distinct rate processes, each characterized by a different rate coefficient. The table lists the times for half-equilibration between internal and external solutions. About 85% of the sodium ion efflux is not affected by chemical transmitters, hence the term unspecific microsacs. The half-equilibration times for 35% of the efflux is about 3 min, and for 50% about 35 min. These rates do not change upon addition of chemical activators or inhibitors of neural activity. About 15% of the total observed efflux is affected by chemical transmitters. We call these microsacs specific because they demonstrate receptor-mediated changes in ion efflux rates as will be discussed later. In absence of transmitters the half-time for equilibration is about 330 min. However, in the presence of transmitter the half-equilibration time is reduced to about 3 min, reflecting the increased ion permeability due to receptor–ligand interaction.

These results suggest a method which would allow us to analyze transmitter-induced efflux (specific) without the measurements being obscured by efflux from unspecific microsacs. This was done by diluting the heterogeneous $^{22}Na^+$-filled vesicles and waiting about 2 hr before adding transmitter until the nonexcitable microsacs (unspecific) had equilibrated with the external medium. When we then added receptor ligands, for example carbamylcholine, only trans-

TABLE I
$^{22}Na^+$ Efflux from Electroplax Membrane Vesicles[a]

	Percent of total counts	Half-equilibration time
Unspecific vesicles	35	3 min
	50	35 min
Specific vesicles	15	330 min 3 min in the presence of 1 m*M* carbamylcholine

[a] The values pertain to the data for efflux from a heterogeneous population of microsacs at pH 7.0, 4°C. The procedure for analyzing the efflux has been published (29).

mitter-induced efflux was observed. The data in Fig. 2 illustrate this point. As can be seen, receptor-mediated $^{22}Na^+$ efflux from specific microsacs induced by carbamylcholine follows a single exponential decay:

$$[^{22}Na^+]_t = [^{22}Na^+]_{t=0}\, e^{-k_{obs} t} \qquad (1)$$

In this equation $[^{22}Na^+]_t$ represents the concentration of radioactive ions inside the microsacs as a function of time. From the slope of the line (Fig. 2), one can calculate an observed first-order rate constant, k_{obs}, for the receptor-mediated ion flux through the membrane of the microsacs.

That the ion efflux data represents a first-order rate process indicates an intimate relationship between the measured efflux and receptor–effector interaction. Ion flux from excitable microsacs is, therefore, not a complex kinetic process but can be measured without the measurements reflecting efflux from both excitable and nonexcitable microsacs.

In order to understand acetylcholine-initiated voltage changes in nerve or muscle cells, we need to know the relationship between the binding isotherms of the receptor and activators, and the flux rates for individual ions through nerve or muscle membranes. The questions we asked first were: Is there a simple relationship between ligand binding and the rate at which ions can move? And, if so, what is the effect of the concentration of activators and inhibitors of this process on the flux rate?

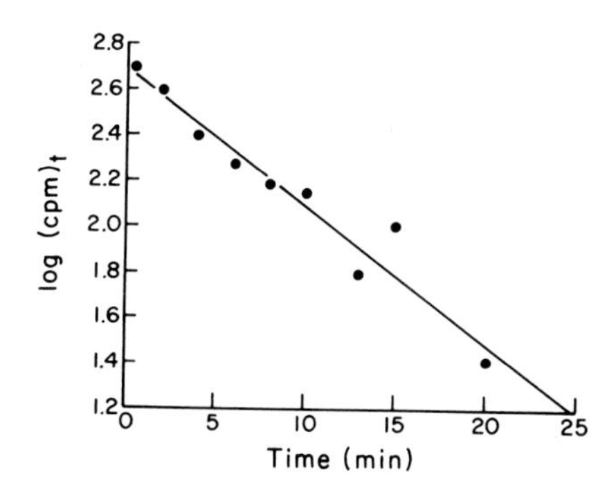

Fig. 2. First-order plot for $^{22}Na^+$ efflux from electroplax microsacs in the presence of 2×10^{-4} M carbamylcholine. The microsacs, containing 10 mM NaCl and 90 mM KCl, were diluted 50-fold into a dilution mixture of identical salt composition, pH 7.0, 4°C. k_{obs} was determined from the slope of the linear least squares fit of the experimental points. The value of the slope was calculated to be -0.06 ± 0.007 min^{-1}, and k_{obs} has a value of 0.14 ± 0.02 min^{-1}.

If the rate of ions moving through the membrane is proportional to the concentration of receptor–transmitter complex, we can determine the rate constant, k_{obs}, for efflux of inorganic ions from the microsacs as a function of ligand concentration. Figure 3 shows the concentration dependence of k_{obs} for decamethonium-induced $^{22}Na^+$ efflux in the presence and absence of *d*-tubocurarine, an inhibitor of transmitter binding. The results are consistent with the simple Michaelis–Menten-type relationship shown in the figure. All the kinetic parameters pertinent to this simple binding mechanism can be determined from the slopes or intercepts of the appropriate curves. k_{max} is the maximal rate constant observed at infinite ligand concentration, [L]. K_D and K_I are the dissociation and inhibition constants for decamethonium and *d*-tubocurarine, respectively. I_0 is the molar concentration of the inhibitor, *d*-tubocurarine. The data pertaining to the uppermost line in the graph were obtained by determining k_{obs} for $^{22}Na^+$ efflux as

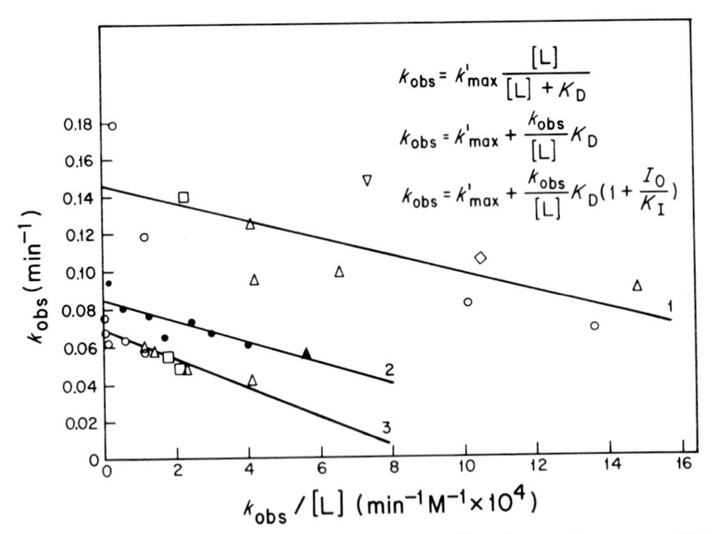

Fig. 3. Acetylcholine receptor-mediated $^{22}Na^+$ efflux from microsacs, pH 7.0, 4°C. The microsacs were equilibrated with 10 m*M* NaCl, 90 m*M* KCl, and 0.4 *M* sucrose, and efflux was measured in a solution of the same composition. Curve 1 represents the dependence of k_{obs} on decamethonium concentration in the absence of *d*-tubocurarine, while curve 2 and curve 3 were in the presence of 0.2 μM and 0.5 μM *d*-turbocurarine, respectively. Different symbols represent membrane preparations from different eels. The data were plotted according to a linear form of the equation shown in the inset: $k_{obs} = k'_{max} - k_{obs} \times K_D \times \text{liter}^{-1}$. The parameters obtained were Curve (1); $K_D = 0.5 \pm 0.15$ μM; $k'_{max} = 0.15 \pm 0.01$ min^{-1}; Curve (2); $K_D = 0.6 \pm 0.1$ μM; $k_I' = 0.08 \pm 0.01$ min^{-1}; Curve (3); $K_D = 0.8 \pm 0.1$ μM; $k_I' = 0.07 \pm 0.002$ min^{-1}. The inhibition constant for *d*-tubocurarine was calculated as 0.3 μM.

a function of ligand concentration in the absence of inhibitor. The two lower, parallel lines were obtained when decamethonium-induced efflux was measured in the presence of various concentrations of curare. The parameters calculated from these data are essentially the same as those obtained from electrophysiological measurements with monocellular electroplax (14,15). The data are inconsistent with a competitive interacting mechanism, but are consistent with a mechanism in which ternary complexes between receptor, transmitter, and inhibitor are formed which do not allow passage of sodium. Since the slope of the lines in not affected, this means that decamethonium binds as well to the receptor in the presence of *d*-tubocurarine as in its absence, indicating separate binding sites for inhibitors and activators of neural activity (30). Earlier work in our laboratory, which directly measured the interaction of activators and inhibitors with the acetylcholine receptor in the same membrane preparation by equilibrium binding techniques, led to the same conclusion (31–33). Identical results were obtained when carbamylcholine was the transmitter or α-bungarotoxin the inhibitor (unpublished results). It is interesting to note that in electrophysiological experiments conducted in a number of laboratories (14,34), curare appears to be a simple competitive inhibitor of acetylcholine- and carbamylcholine-induced voltage changes even though there is no simple relationship between voltage and ligand concentration.

One of the important parameters for a correlation between receptor-mediated ion flux through microsac membranes and the receptor-ligand induced changes in the electrical potential of the membranes of nerve or muscle cells is the number of inorganic ions which pass across the membrane per receptor site per unit time (26–28,35). In order to determine this, we had to know the concentration of receptor molecules in the microsacs demonstrating ligand-induced ion efflux (specific), and the moles of ions diffusing through these excitable microsacs. Since this could only be done by analyzing specific microsacs, we had to develop a method which would enable us to physically separate the 15% excitable microsacs from the 85% unspecific microsacs which contaminate the preparation. The separation procedure (36) is based on a kinetic analysis of the ion efflux observed with the heterogeneous microsac preparation illustrated in Table I. Since microsacs which exhibit receptor-mediated ion flux (specific) are relatively impermeable to ions in the absence of chemical transmitters, compared to microsacs which are not affected by acetylcholine or its analogs, we can use this kinetic distinction to fill the functional microsacs with an NaCl solution while the nonfunctional microsacs are filled with a CsCl solution and to then separate the two entities on the basis of density.

The following protocol for separating specific from unspecific microsacs is based on the kinetic analysis in Table I:

1. A heterogeneous population of microsacs rich in receptor sites and of similar density is collected by centrifugation on a discontinuous sucrose density gradient.

2. The microsacs are equilibrated with 190 m*M* NaCl for 24 hr, long enough for all microsacs to have reached equilibrium (see Table I).

3. Using a Sephadex G-25 column, the 190 m*M* NaCl is exchanged for 190 m*M* CsCl and the microsacs allowed to reequilibrate for about 2 hr. According to the data in Table I, this allows all of the nonspecific microsacs to fill with CsCl ($\tau_{1/2}$ = 3 or 35 min), while the specific microsacs which equilibrate with ions very slowly in the absence of transmitter ($\tau_{1/2}$ = 330 min) still retain most of the NaCl originally present.

4. The NaCl-filled specific microsacs are now separated from nonspecific microsacs filled with heavier CsCl on the basis of their density in a continuous sucrose-190 m*M* CsCl density gradient.

The results of such a density gradient experiment are shown in Fig. 4. The abscissa of the graph gives the molarity of sucrose in the various fractions collected from the continuous gradient. As indicated by the solid circles, most of the membrane protein is found in the denser portion of the gradient, indicative of the heavier CsCl-filled unspecific microsacs. The squares indicate the percent of sodium inside the microsacs whose flux rate is affected by receptor ligands such as carbamylcholine. This value is given by the following:

$$100 \times \frac{{}^{[\text{inorganic ion}]}\text{specific efflux}}{\text{mg protein in functional microsacs}} \div \frac{{}^{[\text{inorganic ion}]}\text{specific and unspecific efflux}}{\text{mg protein in unfractionated microsac preparation}}$$

By this criterion, the fractions which are about 0.8 *M* in sucrose (plus 190 m*M* CsCl present throughout the gradient) contain only microsacs exhibiting ligand-induced changes in ion permeability. Therefore, as expected from the kinetic measurements of efflux of inorganic ions from a mixture of microsacs, we have succeeded in filling the specific microsacs with NaCl while the unspecific microsacs are still filled with CsCl. As a result of this the specific microsacs have floated away from the unspecific microsacs due to their different densities.

An interesting and somewhat unexpected result is that the number of receptor sites (α-bungarotoxin-binding sites) per milligram mem-

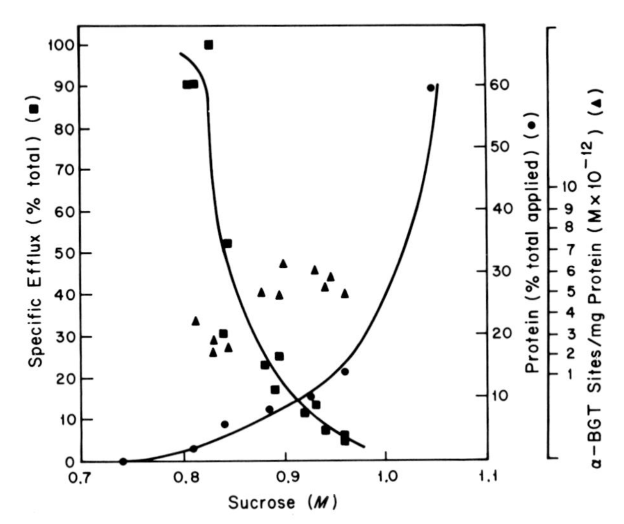

Fig. 4. Purification of functional acetylcholine receptor-rich microsacs by sucrose – 190 m*M* cesium chloride density gradient centrifugation. Four milliliters of acetylcholine receptor-rich microsacs (0.75 mg of membrane protein per ml, 1.1 *M* sucrose, 190 m*M* CsCl, 1 m*M* sodium phosphate buffer, pH 7.0) were placed on the bottom of a continuous gradient (32 ml, 0.7–1.1 *M* sucrose containing 190 m*M* CsCl, 1m*M* sodium phosphate buffer, pH 7.0) and centrifuged in a Beckman SW-27 swinging bucket rotor for 2.5 hr at 4°C. Two-milliliter fractions were collected and analyzed. The abscissa gives the molarity of sucrose in the fraction. The solid lines and closed symbols represent the following: (●) percent of membrane protein applied to gradient; (▲) pmoles of α-bungarotoxin (α-BGT)-binding sites per mg of membrane protein; (■) specific efflux (percent of total); see text for calculations.

brane protein, indicated by the triangles in Fig. 4, are rather uniformly distributed in the preparation. Both specific and unspecific microsacs contain acetylcholine receptor molecules and apparently the presence of receptor sites *per se* is not the only determining factor for excitability in electroplax microsacs. This finding opens up an important area of investigation of receptor-mediated processes: the characterization of membrane components important in the molecular mechanism of chemical excitability. It would be extremely interesting to know why most of the electroplax microsacs are nonexcitable. Do the specific microsacs possibly contain some essential component not measured by α-bungarotoxin, and thus distinct from the receptor, which is missing in nonspecific microsacs? Conversely, is there a structural basis for nonexcitable microsacs reflected, perhaps, in a different lipid composition or lipid/protein ratio than specific microsacs? Research in these areas is now in progress in our laboratory.

Since we can now determine the moles of ions lost only during the receptor-mediated event, k_{max}, the first-order rate constant associated with this process, and the number of receptor sites per milligram membrane protein in functional microsacs, we can calculate the number of ions moving through receptor-formed channels per unit time. We can account for a transport of 10^6 ions per receptor site per minute during receptor-mediated processes (36), a number four orders of magnitude higher than that measured by Kasai and Changeux (26), but still about a factor of 500 less than required by electrophysiological measurements (27,28,37).

There are many reasons why the apparent efficiency of such *in vitro* systems may differ by a factor of 500 from that measured by acetylcholine-induced current changes *in vivo*. One reason may be that the number of ions available per receptor-formed ion channel in a microsac may be several orders of magnitude less than in a nerve or muscle cell. Another reason may be that the receptor-mediated ion transport involves only a small fraction of receptors active in a given time interval even in the presence of saturating amounts of activator (38). Furthermore, an unknown parameter implied in calculations of efficiency is the maximum number of specific ion gates (ionophores) as a function of the molar concentration of receptor sites.

An additional factor which may have to be considered is that the composition of the solution on either side of the membrane has a definite effect on the receptor-mediated flux of inorganic ions, and that k_{max} values higher than those we have reported may be observed. In recent experiments (39) in which we investigated the influence of ion composition inside and outside the microsacs, we noticed a marked effect on the ion efflux kinetics produced by an asymmetrical distribution of inorganic ions. Figure 5 illustrates this point. This graph shows the amount of sodium retained in specific microsacs as a function of time upon addition of carbamylcholine. The squares indicate efflux under conditions which resemble those in nerve cells, high potassium concentration inside and high sodium concentration outside the microsacs. We observe an initial very fast flux rate followed by a slower first-order rate process. Before the first time point can be taken (less than 10 sec), half of the sodium originally present in the microsacs has already effluxed. Any other ion composition, for example, high sodium concentration inside the microsacs and high potassium on the outside, shown by the circles (Fig. 5), gives rise to the much slower single exponential decay without a fast initial flux rate. As far as sodium or potassium ions are concerned, the critical component is sodium on the outside—increasing potassium concentration on the outside decreases the fraction of efflux proceeding by the initial fast process.

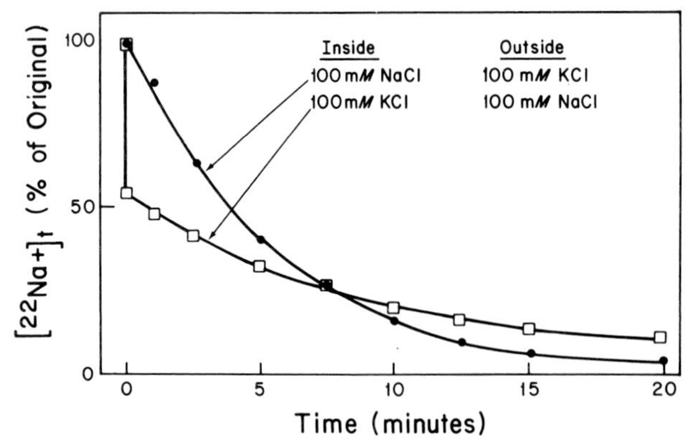

Fig. 5. The effect of asymmetrical distribution of KCl and NaCl on the efflux kinetics from specific electroplax microsacs. The microsacs were either incubated overnight in 100 m*M* NaCl, 0.4 *M* sucrose, 1 m*M* phosphate buffer, pH 7.0 and diluted into 100 m*M* KCl, 0.4 *M* sucrose, 1 m*M* phosphate buffer, pH 7.0 (●), or incubated in 100 m*M* KCl, 0.4 *M* sucrose, 1 m*M* phosphate, pH 7.0 and diluted into 100 m*M* NaCl, 0.4 *M* sucrose, 1 m*M* phosphate, pH 7.0 (□). The ordinate axis represents the amount of $^{22}Na^+$ inside the microsacs (percent of total) as a function of time after addition of 1 m*M* carbamylcholine.

Conversely, varying the molar ratio of sodium and potassium on the inside of the microsacs has no effect on the efflux kinetics. It should be pointed out that although biphasic kinetics are observed under conditions of high external sodium concentration when $^{22}Na^+$ is the tracer ion, identical results have been recently obtained with $^{42}K^+$ or $^{86}Rb^+$ as the radioactive component. Since estimates of efficiency were derived from experiments with microsacs where only the slow efflux rate was observed (36), the determination of the rate constant for the initial rapid flux rate under certain ion compositions should alleviate the discrepancy between the efficiency of *in vitro* and *in vivo* measurements. We are now measuring this initial fast flux rate and preliminarily estimate (39) that it is at least 10 to 100 times faster than the slower efflux process, which is probably sufficient to account for the acetylcholine-induced current changes in electrical experiments. Such studies have relevance concerning the phenomenon of desensitization (16–17,38), the asymmetric nature of the membrane-bound acetylcholine receptor, and the distinct processes involved in receptor-controlled ion translocation.

In summary, we have available a relatively simple and reproducible procedure for obtaining kinetically homogeneous excitable microsacs and for measuring receptor-mediated efflux without the measurements being obscured by efflux from nonexcitable microsacs. The rate parameters of the ion flux and the effect of ions and pharmacologically interesting compounds on this flux can be conveniently measured. When the outer membrane of the microsacs is surrounded by appropriate concentration of sodium and potassium ions, biphasic efflux kinetics are observed. This can account for both the efficiency of the receptor-mediated process and also other observations made in electrophysiological experiments with nerve and muscle cells. The purified microsac preparation may also be useful in identifying membrane components other than the receptor important in chemical excitability.

Since there appears to be a very close relationship between the formation of receptor–transmitter complexes, manifested by the binding of receptor ligands, and the flux of ions through the neural membrane, we can now investigate the central question of the relationship between receptor ligand concentration and the concomitant changes in membrane potential. Our research goals are now directed toward this end. Using multinucleated myotubes in culture, which contain acetylcholine receptors, we are attempting to relate the passive mobility of inorganic ions, the Na^+–K^+ ATPase-mediated movement of ions through the membrane, the ligand-induced rate coefficients for the receptor-mediated process, and the resultant steady-state transmembrane potential. It is anticipated that such studies will shed light on more detailed molecular aspects of the acetylcholine receptor-mediated communication between nerve and muscle cells.

REFERENCES

1. Nachmansohn, D. (1955) *Harvey Lect.* **49,** 57–99.
2. Nachmansohn, D. (1974) In "Biochemistry of Sensory Functions" (L. Jaenicke, ed.), pp. 431–464. Springer-Verlag, Berlin and New York.
3. Nachmansohn, D., and Neumann, E. (1975) "Chemical and Molecular Basis of Nerve Activity" Academic Press, New York.
4. Fatt, P., and Katz, B. (1951) *J. Physiol. (London)* **115,** 320–370.
5. Hodgkin, A. L., and Huxley, A. F. (1952) *J. Physiol. (London)* **117,** 500–544.
6. Katz, B., and Miledi, R. (1972) *J. Physiol. (London)* **224,** 665–699.
7. Klett, R. P., Fulpius, B. W., Cooper, D., Smith, M., Reich, E., and Possani, L. D. (1973) *J. Biol. Chem.* **247,** 6841–6853.
8. Biesecker, G. (1973) *Biochemistry* **12,** 4403–4409.
9. Karlin, A., and Cowburn, D. (1973) *Proc. Natl. Acad. Sci. U.S.A.* **70,** 3636–3640.
10. Meunier, J.-C., Sealock, R., Olsen, R., and Changeux, J.-P. (1974) *Eur. J. Biochem.* **45,** 371–394.
11. Chang, H. W. (1974) *Proc. Natl. Acad. Sci. U.S.A.* **71,** 2113–2117.
12. Maelicke, A., and Reich, E. (1975) *Cold Spring Harbor Symp. Quant. Biol.* **40,** 231–235.

13. Schoeffeniels, E., and Nachmansohn, D. (1957) *Biochim. Biophys. Acta* **26,** 1–15.
14. Higman, H. B., Podleski, T. R., and Bartels, F. (1963) *Biochim. Biophys. Acta* **75,** 187–193.
15. Changeux, J.-P., and Podleski, T. R. (1968) *Proc. Natl. Acad. Sci. U.S.A.* **59,** 944–950.
16. Lester, H. A., Changeux, J.-P., and Sheridan, R. E. (1975) *J. Gen. Physiol.* **65,** 799–816.
17. Sheridan, R. E., and Lester, H. A. (1975) *Proc. Natl. Acad. Sci. U.S.A.* **72,** 3496–3500.
18. Baker, P. F., Hodgkin, A. L., and Shaw, T. I. (1962) *J. Physiol. (London)* **164,** 330–354.
19. Hodgkin, A. L. (1964) "The Conduction of the Nervous Impulse." C. C. Thomas, Springfield, Illinois.
20. Baker, P. F., Hodgkin, A. L., and Ridgway, E. B. (1971) *J. Physiol. (London)* **218,** 709–755.
21. Hodgkin, A. L., and Keynes, R. D. (1955) *J. Physiol. (London)* **128,** 28–60.
22. Mullins, L. J., and Brinley, F. J. (1967) *J. Gen. Physiol.* **50,** 2333–2355.
23. Cole, K. S. (1965) *Physiol. Rev.* **45,** 340–365.
24. Kasai, M., and Changeux, J.-P. (1971) *J. Membr. Biol.* **6,** 1–23.
25. Kasai, M., and Changeux, J.-P. (1971) *J. Membr. Biol.* **6,** 24–57.
26. Kasai, M., and Changeux, J.-P. (1971) *J. Membr. Biol.* **6,** 58–80.
27. Katz, B., and Miledi, R. (1972) *J. Physiol. (London)* **224,** 665–699.
28. Rang, H. P. (1974) *Q. Rev. Biophys.* **7,** 283–399.
29. Hess, G. P., Andrews, J. P., Struve, G. S., and Coombs, S. E. (1975) *Proc. Natl. Acad. Sci. U.S.A.* **72,** 4371–4375.
30. Hess, G. P., Andrews, J. P., and Struve, G. S. (1976) *Biochem. Biophys. Res. Commun.* **69,** 830–837.
31. Bulger, J. E., and Hess, G. P. (1973) *Biochem. Biophys. Res. Commun.* **54,** 677–684.
32. Fu, J.-j. L., Donner, D. B., and Hess, G. P. (1974) *Biochem. Biophys. Res. Commun.* **60,** 1072–1080.
33. Hess, G. P., Bulger, J. E., Fu, J.-j L., Hindy, E. F., and Silberstein, P. J. (1975) *Biochem. Biophys. Res. Commun.* **64,** 1018–1027.
34. Podleski, T. R., and Bartels, E. (1963) *Biochim. Biophys. Acta* **75,** 387–396.
35. Catterall, W. A. (1975) *J. Biol. Chem.* **250,** 1776–1781.
36. Hess, G. P., and Andrews, J. P. (1977) *Proc. Natl. Acad. Sci. U.S.A.* **74,** 482–486.
37. Anderson, C. R., and Stevens, C. F. (1973) *J. Physiol. (London)* **235,** 655–691.
38. Katz, B., and Thesleff, S. (1957) *J. Physiol (London)* **138,** 63–80.
39. Lipkowitz, S. P., Struve, G. S., and Hess, G. P. (1978) In preparation.

Acetylcholine Receptor: Accelerated Dissociation of Receptor–Ligand Complexes

ALFRED MAELICKE
Max-Planck-Institut für Ernährungsphysiologie
Dortmund, Rheinlanddamm, West Germany

MARJORIE McCONNELL
The Rockefeller University
New York, New York

INTRODUCTION

Although the time resolution of electrophysiological techniques permits certain inferences about the kinetics of excitation at chemical synapses (1,2), a full understanding of the underlying chemical events will have to await the independent determination of all rate constants involved. Since binding, dissociation, and inactivation of acetylcholine at the neuromuscular junction take place in the millisecond time range, the experimental techniques for the study of these molecular events will ultimately require the use of fast kinetics based on ligands with suitable spectroscopic properties. Such studies require considerable amounts of purified receptor (molar concentrations in the range of the equilibrium dissociation constant of the ligand employed) and they depend critically on the pharmacological characteristics of the modified ligand. The specific structural criteria that must be met for agonist or antagonist action (3) severely constrain the chemical synthesis of cholinergic probes, and studies involving spectroscopically labeled ligands, while in progress in several laboratories including ours, are at present only in their infancy.

The availability of a class of tightly binding ligands with very slow

ISBN 0-12-398450-5

dissociation rates, namely the neurotoxins from venoms of elapid snakes, has prompted us to analyze the responses of the solubilized acetylcholine receptor to a variety of drugs in a time scale extending from minutes to several days but with a degree of accuracy comparable to that achieved with enzyme kinetics (4,5). In these studies we employed a filter paper assay (6) to measure the concentration of receptor–toxin complexes, the effects of competing acetylcholine and structurally related small ligands, and the equilibrium concentration and dissociation kinetics of these complexes. From these studies the nicotinic receptor emerged as a protein with a wide range of responses in time scale, in affinity for ligands, and, inferentially, in a corresponding conformational plasticity (4). Because membrane receptors have not been accessible for quantitative analysis until recently, some of the reaction mechanisms observed in these studies may be of more general interest, particularly with respect to peptide hormone–receptor interactions. In this paper we consider one of these mechanisms, namely the kinetics of ligand displacement and its effect on the time resolution of the particular receptor system.

Consider a solution containing receptor at equilibrium with a particular ligand A, to which a second competing ligand B is added. Ultimately this system will reach a new equilibrium state defined by the concentration of receptor, and by the concentration of the two ligands and their respective affinites. The transition from the initial to the final equilibrium state could proceed by way of several different pathways, for example: (1) binding of B might occur at a rate proportional to the dissociation rate of A, i.e., binding of A and B is mutually exclusive; (2) B might bind to existing complexes of the type (receptor–A) yielding ternary complexes (A–receptor–B) from which A and B could dissociate individually. Such a mechanism could accelerate the rate of dissociation of A and hence might result in a faster displacement of turnover of initially bound ligand. The complexity of such a mechanism appears at first sight to limit its attractiveness, but it provides one means of designing a system for a rapid and repetitive response. Furthermore, it deserves consideration because, as described below, we have in fact observed (4) that the dissociation of receptor–toxin complexes was strongly accelerated at high concentrations of competing ligand. A detailed analysis then showed that, in analogy to mechanism (2), this effect was mediated by the formation of transient ternary complexes of the type neurotoxin–receptor–ligand. The formation of these complexes and, hence, the acceleration of toxin dissociation occurred only at very high ligand concentrations, since ternary complexes were formed with much lower affinity than secondary ones.

In view of the implications of such a mechanism for receptor action, and for potential therapeutic applications on drug combinations, we have begun to investigate other soluble receptor systems to test for the generality of an accelerating mechanism for ligand dissociation from previously formed complexes. In the one case so far explored—the cytoplasmic estrogen receptor of rat uterus—no rate acceleration has been found.

METHODS

The preparation and characterization of the acetylcholine receptor from *Electrophorus electricus* and of [^{3}H]monopyridoxamine phosphate α-neurotoxin from cobra venom have been described previously (4,5,7,8). Binding of toxin to receptor was measured by the DEAE-filter paper assay (6) which is based on the fact that the receptor and receptor–toxin complexes are strongly anionic and adsorb to DEAE-cellulose filter paper, whereas free toxin is strongly cationic and does not. Determination of 10^{-13} moles of bound toxin can be performed with an accuracy of better than $\pm 6\%$ with this procedure (350 ± 20 cpm for monolabeled toxin of specific activity 4 Ci/mmole; 30% counting efficiency) (4). The time resolution of the assay was approximately 0.5 min.

The preparation of cytoplasmic estrogen receptor and the hydroxylapatite binding assay will be published in detail elsewhere (M. McConnell, A. Maelicke, and E. Reich, in preparation). Generally, uteri from prepubertal female rats were excised, stripped of fat, rinsed in ice-cold buffer, homogenized at 4°C and centrifuged for 90 min at 200,000 *g*. The supernatant, fat-free cytosol was used in kinetic and binding studies. Determination of 2×10^{-14} moles of bound 6,7-[^{3}H]estradiol can be achieved with an accuracy of better than $\pm 10\%$ (400 ± 40 cpm) for [^{3}H]estradiol of specific activity 47.9 Ci/mmole, 25% counting efficiency. The time resolution of the assay was approximately 1 min.

RESULTS

We have applied two basically different sets of experimental conditions to investigate the effects of free ligands on the dissociation of receptor–ligand complexes; the first approach measures only the effect of ligand competition, while the second measures the combined effects of chemical dilution and ligand competition on the dissociation rate of receptor–ligand complexes. In the first, aliquots of a solution of radioactive receptor–ligand complexes at equilibrium were exposed to different concentrations of competing, unlabeled ligands under conditions that excluded significant spontaneous dissociation due to dilution. As a result of competition of the two ligands, the concentration of labeled original complexes decreased as new complexes were formed with unlabeled ligand. This changing concentration of initial complexes was then monitored as a function of time. In the second, aliquots of a solution of preformed, radioactively labeled complexes at equilibrium were diluted into large volumes of buffer containing different concentrations of unlabled competing ligand, and the decreasing concentration of labeled complexes was determined in the same way.

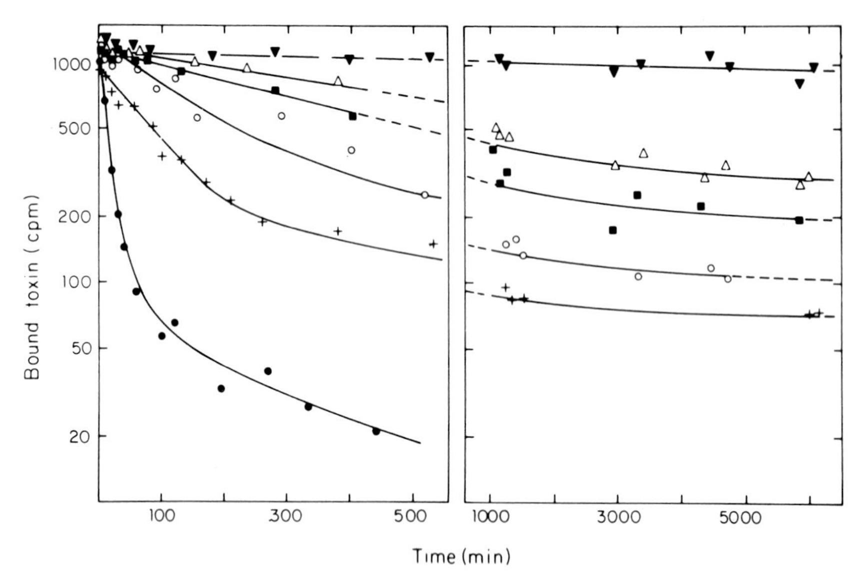

Fig. 1. Dissociation of ^{3}H–toxin–receptor complexes in the presence of benzoquinonium. In a total volume of 5.0 ml, receptor (4.0×10^{-10} moles) and toxin (1.4×10^{-10} moles) were incubated in standard buffer for 20.5 hr at 21°C. The resulting receptor saturation was 28% and, hence, receptor–toxin complexes were of the high affinity type (RT)* (for details see (4)). For each experiment, 500 μl of this reaction mixture were added to 50 ml of a benzoquinonium solution in standard buffer, and 2.5-ml aliquots were analyzed for their content of remaining receptor–toxin complexes by filtration through DEAE-filter discs at the indicated times. The molar concentrations of receptor and toxin after dilution were 8×10^{-10} and 2.9×10^{-10} *M*, respectively. Hence, spontaneous dissociation of receptor–toxin complexes due to dilution is negligible. The applied benzoquinonium concentrations were: ▼ no benzoquinonium added; △, 2.0×10^{-7} *M*; ■, 6.7×10^{-7} *M*; ○, 2.0×10^{-6} *M*; +, 6.7×10^{-6} *M*; ●, 2.2×10^{-4} *M*, respectively.

NICOTINIC ACETYLCHOLINE RECEPTOR

Figure 1 shows the dissociation of ^{3}H–toxin–receptor complexes in the presence of benzoquinonium, a high-affinity antagonist of acetylcholine at the neuromuscular junction [($K_I = 6.3 \times 10^{-8}$ *M* with solubilized receptor (4)]. Since spontaneous dissociation of receptor toxin complexes due to dilution was negligible in this experiment, the observed accelerating effect is quantitatively related to the concentration of competing ligand. As seen in Fig. 1, significant acceleration of receptor–toxin dissociation occurred only at benzoquinonium concentrations well above the equilibrium dissociation constant (K_I) for the binding of this drug alone. All dissociation curves leveled off in time, reflecting the approach to a new equilibrium state defined by the concentrations of receptor, neurotoxin, benzoquinonium, and their respective complexes in the reaction medium. Since the initial rate of dissociation was a function both of the initial concentrations of receptor–toxin complexes and competing ligand benzoquinonium, the dissociation reaction seemed to be second order, rather than first order, directly implying a reaction of the type

$$RT + B \longleftrightarrow RTB \longleftrightarrow RB + T$$

A plot of the initial rates of receptor–toxin complex dissociation as a function of benzoquinonium concentration is presented in Fig. 2. A typical saturation curve was obtained from which $C\ (\frac{1}{2}k_{max}) = 2 \times 10^{-5}M$ was extrapolated as the benzoquinonium concentration required for half-maximal acceleration.

The final equilibrium values reached after incubation of receptor–toxin complexes with benzoquinonium (Fig. 1) were ana-

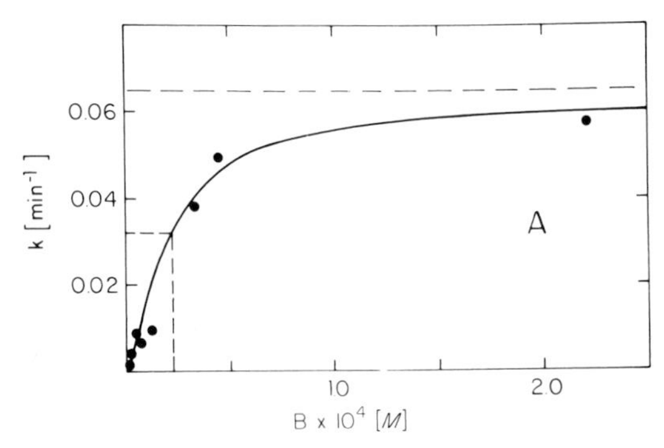

Fig. 2. Initial rate constants k for various concentrations of benzoquinonium under comparable experimental conditions. For original data see Fig. 1.

$k_{max} = 0.065\ \text{min}^{-1}$; $C\ (\frac{1}{2}\,k_{max}) = 2.4 \times 10^{-5}$ *M*

lyzed in terms of the competing affinites K_D (toxin) and K_I (benzoquinonium) by a new plot (Fig. 3), originally designed for competition binding experiments and outlined in detail elsewhere (4,9). The slope $n = 0.52$ yielded the number of benzoquinonium sites per toxin binding sites and was consistent with results previously obtained from equilibrium binding experiments (4). The same held true for the extrapolated equilibrium binding constant for benzoquinonium $K_I = 1.3 \times 10^{-8}$ M. The data thus indicated that acceleration of receptor–toxin complexes at high benzoquinonium concentrations was due to the formation of a ternary complex: receptor–toxin–benzoquinonium. The affinity of receptor–toxin complexes for benzoquinonium [C ($\frac{1}{2}k_{max}$) $= K_I = 2 \times 10^{-5}$ M] was approximately 500-fold lower than that of free receptor; the probability of formation of ternary complexes at equilibrium was therefore low (Fig. 3).

Figure 4 compares the effects of benzoquinonium, with and without additional dilution, on dissociation of receptor–toxin complexes. It is apparent that without dilution the phase of rapid dissociation soon approached a new equilibrium state characterized by a constant but lower concentration of receptor-toxin complexes. In contrast, when

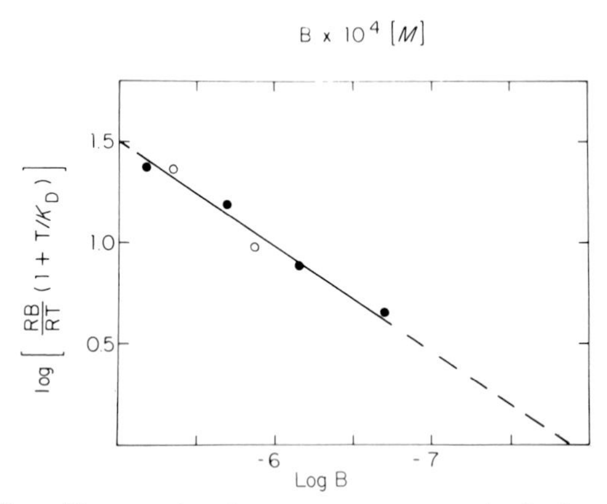

Fig. 3. Effect of benzoquinonium concentration on the final equilibrium concentration of remaining receptor–toxin complexes. ●, data taken from Fig. 1, initial receptor saturation by toxin, 28%; ○, data taken from an experiment with initially 54% receptor saturation. Data were calculated according to the equation

$$\log \left[\frac{(RI_n)}{(RT)}\left(1 + \frac{T}{K_D}\right)\right] = n \log I - n \log K_I$$

Ratio of benzoquinonium per toxin binding sites; $n = 0.52$, dissociation constant $K_I = 1.3 \times 10^{-8}$ M.

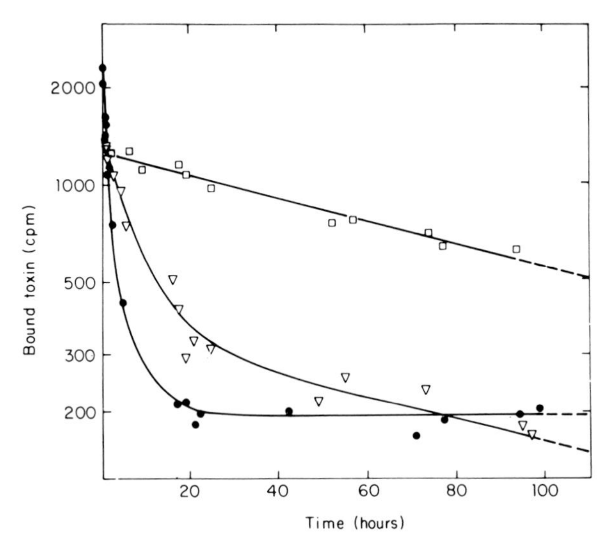

Fig. 4. Dissociation of ^{3}H–toxin–receptor complexes in presence of benzoquinonium. ●, equilibrium shift by addition of benzoquinonium. Experimental conditions are as described in the legend to Fig. 1. Concentrations of receptor, toxin, and benzoquinonium were 8×10^{-10}, 2.9×10^{-10}, and 4.5×10^{-6} *M*, respectively. Rate constant of initial linear part, $k = 8.67 \times 10^{-3}$ min^{-1}; equilibrium concentration of bound toxin, $c_{eq} = 2.4 \times 10^{-11}$ *M*. ▽, equilibrium shift by dilution and addition of benzoquinonium. Receptor (1.2×10^{-11} moles) and toxin (9×10^{-12} moles) in a total volume of 3.1 ml were incubated for 3 hr at 21°C, and 2000 ml of buffer (8×10^{-8} *M* in benzoquinonium) were then added. Aliquots of 50 ml were taken at the indicated times and analyzed by filtration through DEAE-filter discs. Rate constant of initial linear part, $k = 1.6 \times 10^{-3}$ min^{-1}; rate constant of final linear part, $k_1 = 1.6 \times 10^{-4}$ min^{-1}. □, equilibrium shift by dilution only. Experimental conditions are as described above, except that standard buffer without benzoquinonium was used for dilution. $k_1 = 1.3 \times 10^{-4}$ min^{-1}.

the addition of benzoquinonium coincided with dilution, the rapid initial phase of benzoquinonium induced accelerated dissociation was followed by the slow, dilution determined intrinsic dissociation of receptor–toxin complexes. In Fig. 4, the rapid initial phase lasted for approximately 30 hr, with approximately 80% of the initial receptor–toxin complex dissociated, while the slow second phase paralleled the normally observed dilution dependent dissociation with half-times in the order of 70–200 hr. It follows that a high concentration of benzoquinonium increased the rate of toxin dissociation only during the first rapid phase, when the concentration of receptor–toxin complexes available to form ternary complexes was high. Benzoquinonium did not alter the intrinsic dissociation rate of receptor–toxin complexes during the second phase, when the concentration of receptor–toxin complexes was lowered and the effects of dilution became the rate-determining factor. The above data conform to Scheme (1). The scheme is simplified in the following respects: (1) it disregards the potential existence of more than one kind of receptor–toxin complex with different affinities; and (2) it does not take into account the different number of binding sites for toxin and small ligand at the receptor (4). Since accurate integration of the differential rate laws of scheme (1) cannot be performed, one or both of the following approximations may help to define the boundary conditions of the system:

$$
\begin{array}{ccccc}
 & & (K_D) & & \\
 & R + T & \underset{k_1}{\overset{k_2}{\rightleftharpoons}} & RT & \\
 & + & & + & \\
 & B & & B & \\
(K_I) & \downarrow\uparrow & & k_+ \downarrow\uparrow k_- & (K_I') \\
 & RB + T & \underset{k_7}{\overset{k_8}{\rightleftharpoons}} & RTB & \\
 & & (K_D') & &
\end{array}
$$

Fast Equilibrium Approximation for RT ⇌ RTB. This approximation assumes that neither k_1 nor k_7 affects the equilibrium between RT and RTB. It leads to the integrated rate law shown in Eq. (1).

$$
\begin{aligned}
[(RT) + (RTB)]_t &= [(RT) + (RTB)]_0 \, e^{-k_{obs} t} \\
k_{obs} &= \frac{k_1(K_I' + k_7)B}{B + K_I'}
\end{aligned}
\tag{1}
$$

For high concentrations of B (benzoquinonium), the observed rate constant k_{obs} approaches k_7. Hence, the asymptotic value of k in a plot of k versus B (Fig. 2) is k_7 ($k_7 = 0.065 \text{ min}^{-1}$). With known k_7, the equilibrium dissociation constant, K_I', can be calculated. The dissociation rate experiments of Fig. 1 gave an average value $K_I' = 2.7 \times 10^{-5}\, M$, in good agreement with $C(\frac{1}{2}k_{max})$, the benzoquinonium concentration for half-maximal, accelerated dissociation rate constant (Fig. 2).

Steady State Approximation for RTB. In the second approximation we assume that the rate of ternary complex dissociation is entirely determined by the rate of formation of this complex. This implied that the concentration of RTB remained insignificantly small during the course of the reaction, and, hence, RTB, k_7 and k_8 could be neglected.

The reaction accordingly degenerates to Scheme (2)

$$RT + B \underset{k_-}{\overset{k_+}{\rightleftharpoons}} RB + T \tag{2}$$

Applying the integrated rate law of Scheme (2), the experimental data of Fig. 1 yielded an average forward rate constant $k_+ = 0.0018\ M^{-1}\ \text{min}^{-1}$. Knowing K_I and k_+, the dissociation rate constant was then calculated to $k_- = 0.036\ \text{min}^{-1}$. These calculations, summarized in Table I, show that the dissociation rate constants of the ternary complex k_7 and k_- are of the same order and that very high concentrations of small ligand are therefore needed to increase the probability of formation of this complex and the related accelerated dissociation of neurotoxin.

In the same way we analyzed the effects of high concentrations of dimethyl-*d*-tubocurarine, hexamethonium, carbamylcholine, and decamethonium on the rate of dissociation of receptor–toxin complexes. The results were qualitatively identical to those obtained with benzoquinonium and showed that formation of ternary complexes was of much lower probability than formation of binary ones, and usually occurred only transiently to a significant extent at the concentrations of receptor, toxin and small ligand applied.

CYTOPLASMIC ESTROGEN RECEPTOR

We have examined the dissociation of complexes of the cytoplasmic estrogen receptor from uteri of prepubertal rats over a wide range of

TABLE I
Rate Constants k and Equilibrium Dissociation Constants K Calculated on the Basis of Scheme (1)[a]

Association k (M^{-1} min^{-1})	Dissociation k (min^{-1})	Equilibrium K (M)
—	—	$K_I = 6.3 \times 10^{-8}$ [b]
—	—	$K_D = 4 \times 10^{-10}$ [b]
$k_8 = 7 \times 10^{6}$ [c]	$k_7 = 0.065$ [c]	$K_I' = 2.7 \times 10^{5}$ [c]
$k_+ = 1.8 \times 10^{3}$ [e]	$k_- = 0.036$ [e]	$K_D' = 2 \times 10^{-7}$ [d]

[a] For experimental details see Maelicke *et al.* (4).
[b] Experimentally determined (1).
[c] Calculated assuming fast equilibration between RT and RTB.
[d] Calculated knowing K_I, K_D, and K_I'.
[e] Calculated on the basis of a steady state assumption for the ternary complex RTB.

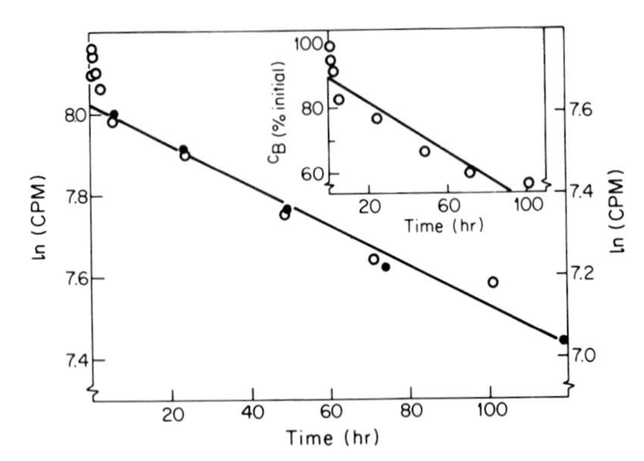

Fig. 5. Dissociation of receptor–[^{3}H]estradiol complex at 4°C. Receptor ($R_0 = 2 \times 10^{-10}$ *M*), and [^{3}H]estradiol ($E_0 = 2.17 \times 10^{-9}$ *M*) were incubated at 4°C for 18 hr. Equilibrium concentration of receptor–[^{3}H]–estradiol was $\bar{x} = 1.98 \times 10^{-10}$ *M* (calculated with a $K_D = 2 \times 10^{-11}$ *M*), prior to dilution with 10^{-6} *M* unlabeled ligand (○). Percent bound E_2 versus time for the same experiment is plotted (insert). Receptor ($R_0 = 3.96 \times 10^{-10}$ *M*) and estradiol ($E_0 = 4.95 \times 10^{10}$ *M*) were incubated at 4°C for 18 hr to attain $\bar{x} = 3.48 \times 10^{-10}$ *M* prior to dilution by volume (200-fold). Final equilibrium concentration of complex was $\bar{x} = 2.05 \times 10^{-13}$ *M* following volume dilution (●). For both procedures at given times following dilution the concentration of complexes was assayed and corrected for nonspecific binding. The dissociation rate constant was identical for isotope and for chemical dilutions, $k_- = 8.04 \times 10^{-5}$ min^{-1}, half time = 144.4 hr.

concentrations and temperatures with the following ligands: estradiol, estriol, estrone, 11α-ethynylestradiol (R 16117) and 11α-methoxy-17α-ethynylestradiol (RU 2858). As an example, a representative experiment employing both chemical and isotope dilution to initiate complex dissociation is shown in Fig. 5. Both methods yielded identical dissociation curves for each ligand tested. In addition, none of the ligands was able to accelerate the dissociation of complexes with another ligand beyond the intrinsic dissociation rate characteristics of the particular system. In general, we observed only monophasic, first-order dissociation patterns independent of receptor saturation, type of ligand, and ligand concentration, and this was not modified by changes in temperature or incubation time.

DISCUSSION

We have described here the new and, at first view, puzzling finding that the rate of dissociation of receptor–neutrotoxin complexes is not independent of the concentration of cholinergic ligands present but instead can be accelerated several hundred fold above its intrinsic value by addition of high concentrations of ligand. Our analysis showed (1) that no acceleration is observed at concentrations around the equilibrium dissociation constant for each ligand; hence mutually exclusive binding is assured in this concentration range; and (2) that the acceleration is due to the formation of ternary complexes of much lower affinity for each ligand. Hence, as the concentration of initial receptor–toxin complexes decreases by accelerated dissociation, the probability of ternary complexes also diminishes and the slow intrinsic rate of complex dissociation is again predominant (see Fig. 1). This effect, even if only confined to a few specific ligands, provides the acetylcholine receptor with an enormous plasticity of response in time range and affinity, factors that could be necessary to regulate more complex neuronal functions. Without being too speculative, we can only list a few more obvious consequences of such a mechanism:

(1) The capability of forming ternary complexes in addition to secondary ones might enable the receptor to recognize effector substances that could modulate the response to transmitter. This may be compared to another finding which also results in an expanded range of response, namely, the anticooperative response to agonists, in which receptor affinity to a given ligand decreases as a function of the concentration of the same previously bound ligand.

(2) If the ultimate response is proportional in intensity and speed to the rate of transmitter dissociation from receptor after binding, then accelerated dissociation may result in faster response (faster rise time). The high concentration of acetylcholine per impulse in the synaptic cleft (10) makes it an attractive hypothesis that ternary complexes and their rate constants may determine the time constants of the system. This would result in faster frequency response than anticipated from dissociation rates of binary complexes. "Ternary" complexes, in this case, would involve the binding of at least two identical, small ligands to a single receptor element.

(3) The formation of ternary complexes may be a general phenomenon that could be explored in different ways for regulatory functions. Several other receptor systems have been reported to have biphasic dissociation kinetics consistent with the formation of complexes consisting of at least two ligands with receptor and/or anticooperative binding. In the case of the insulin receptor, DeMeyts *et al.* (11) have found that increasing concentrations of insulin can accelerate the dissociation of previously bound radioactive insulin. Their finding may relate to our observation that neurotoxin itself is also capable though less efficiently of acceleration the dissociation of receptor–toxin

complexes (12). Similar reports on the cytoplasmic estrogen receptor, prompted us to reanalyze its interaction with estrogenic ligands. In this case we were not able to substantiate a mechanism of accelerated dissociation. This seems to agree with the physiologically slow changes of cytoplasmic estrogen levels the molar concentrations of which generally do not significantly exceed the equilibrium binding constant.

ACKNOWLEDGMENTS

This work was supported in part by Grant CA 08290-11 from the National Institute of Health, United States Public Health Service, and NATO Research Grant No. 932 (d. 1984).

REFERENCES

1. Stevens, C. F. (1976) *Cold Spring Harbor Symp. Quant. Biol.* **40,** 169–173.
2. Katz, B., and Miledi, R. (1970) *Nature (London)* **226,** 962–963; (1971) *Nature (London), New Biol.* **232,** 124–126.
3. Beers, W. H., and Reich, E. (1970) *Nature (London)* **228,** 917–922.
4. Maelicke, A., Fulpius, B. W., Klett, R. P., Reich, E., and Dumaguing, E. (1977) *J. Biol. Chem.* **252,** 4811–4830.
5. Klett, R. P., Fulpius, B. W., Cooper, D., Smith, P., Reich, E., and Possani, L. D. (1973) *J. Biol. Chem.* **248,** 6841–6851.
6. Fulpius, B. W., Cha, S., Klett, R. P., and Reich, E. (1972) *FEBS Lett.* **24,** 323–326.
7. Cooper, D., and Reich, E. (1972) *J. Biol. Chem.* **247,** 3008–3013.
8. Fulpius, B. W., Maelicke, A., Klett, R. P., and Reich, E. (1975) *In* "Cholinergic Receptors" (P. Waser, ed.). Raven Press, New York.
9. Maelicke, A., Fulpius, B. W., and Reich, E. (1977) *Hand. Physiol., Sect. 1: Nerv. Syst.* 493–519.
10. Collier, B. (1977) *Hand. Physiol., Sect. 1: Nerv. Syst.* 463–492.
11. DeMeyts, P., Bianco, A. R., and Roth, J. (1976) *J. Biol. Chem.* **251,** 1877–1888.
12. Maelicke, A., and Reich, E. (1976) *Cold Spring Harbor Symp. Quant. Biol.* **40,** 231–235.

Elementary Chemical Reactions of Acetylcholine with Receptor and Esterase: Relationship to Neuronal Information Transfer

EBERHARD NEUMANN
Max-Planck-Institut für Biochemie, D-8033
München, West Germany

TERRONE L. ROSENBERRY AND HAI WON CHANG
Departments of Neurology and Biochemistry
College of Physicians and Surgeons
Columbia University, New York, New York

I. INTRODUCTION

This chapter examines some conceptual problems involving neuronal information transfer mediated by acetylcholine. As is well known, acetylcholine is crucially involved in the control of ionic conductivities of nerve and muscle cell membranes. These membranes are intrinsically associated with two proteins which are essential for the cholinergic control of ion flows: (1) The acetylcholine receptor system "translates" the binding of acetylcholine into permeability changes (opening and closing of ion pathways, e.g., ion channels) in excitable membranes. (2) The enzyme acetylcholinesterase limits the duration of the acetylcholine action by hydrolytic removal of the activator from the membrane environment.

Mechanistic details of the coupling of acetylcholine reactions with these proteins to the membrane permeability changes are not known.

ISBN 0-12-398450-5

However, a useful hypothesis of the coupling mechanism was introduced by David Nachmansohn some 30 years ago (1). Central to this hypothesis was Nachmansohn's proposal in 1953 that the binding of acetylcholine induces a conformation change in the membrane-bound acetylcholine receptor (1–5). The conformation change was postulated to release receptor-bound Ca^{2+} ions which subsequently triggered a conductance increase through specific ion pathways in the membrane (4). The proposed conformation change may be represented by the reaction scheme in Fig. 1 The receptor form R corresponds to the closed or nonconducting state and the form R′, to the open or conducting state. In the absence of activator A, the closed conformation R is dominant; the ratio of the concentrations of receptor forms [R′]/[R] is very small, thus accounting for the extremely small conductance of the membrane in the resting steady state. When activator A is present, receptor sites bind A such that $[AR']/[AR] > [R']/[R]$. The resulting increase of forms AR′ plus R′ corresponding to the conducting state initiates the conductivity increase. The presence of the esterase insures rapid removal of the activator acetylcholine and thus quickly restores the initial closed state. The reaction scheme in Fig. 1 is analogous to others that have been formulated previously to describe the synaptic action of acetylcholine (see, for example, Colquhoun, 6). In 1957, del Castillo and Katz (7) introduced the explicit reaction scheme which is the upper path ($A + R \rightleftharpoons AR \rightleftharpoons AR'$) of the scheme shown in Fig. 1. As a general activator–receptor model, this scheme can be used successfully to model the transient Na^+ ion conductivity changes during excitation of axonal membranes (8–10).

In this article we discuss the functional implications of recent kinetic data on isolated acetylcholine receptors and acetylcholines-

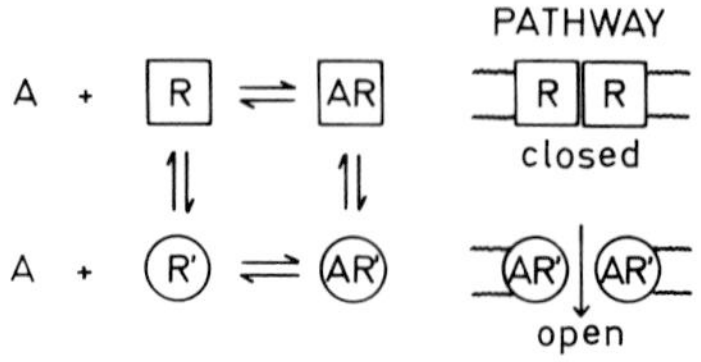

Fig. 1. Reaction scheme for the structural transition induced by acetylcholine A in the acetylcholine receptor binding sites: R, closed conformation and R′, open conformation. On the right is a schematic view of the receptor-mediated permeability change in the membrane.

terase obtained from the electric organs of electric fish. These organs are phylogenetically derived from muscle and provide excitable membranes rich in receptor and esterase which are thought to be closely analogous to mammalian excitable membranes. The kinetic differences between the two isolated proteins appear to complicate a molecular description of the close functional relationship between receptor and esterase indicated by electrophysiological data. We discuss various models and touch briefly several unsolved problems concerning acetylcholine-mediated information transfer.

II. LOCALIZATION OF ACETYLCHOLINE RECEPTOR AND ACETYLCHOLINESTERASE

Conditions required for the extraction of acetylcholine receptor and acetylcholinesterase from excitable membranes indicate that both proteins are predominantly membrane bound (11,12; also see Rosenberry, 13). Detergents are required for solubilization of the receptor, thus characterizing it as an integral protein of phospholipid membrane. Acetylcholinesterase is extracted from electric organ membranes at high ionic strength in the absence of detergent, although in several mammalian tissues the addition of detergent increases the amount solubilized (14,15). The esterase thus may be classified as a peripheral membrane protein, and recent evidence suggests that at synapses this enzyme is incorporated in the extracellular basement membrane matrix (16,17).

The histochemical localization of acetylcholinesterase in excitable membranes has long been established (see Koelle, 18,19,20) and is based on the deposition of esterase hydrolysis products by metal ion precipitation. A more quantitative measure of the concentration of active sites of receptor and esterase can be obtained by autoradiography with the use of radiolabeled ligands which bind to the active sites with virtual irreversibility. Autoradiographic studies of mouse sternomastoid neuromuscular junctions by Fertuck and Salpeter (21) with ^{125}I-labeled α-bungarotoxin suggest particularly high receptor concentrations in the juxtaneuronal postsynaptic membrane. Relatively few receptors appear to extend into the depths of the postsynaptic folds. Similar studies of acetylcholinesterase with [^{3}H]diisopropylfluorophosphate suggest a more uniform distribution along the synaptic membranes (22,23). It is noteworthy that the resolution of the autoradiographs in these studies is not sufficient to specify the distribution of receptor and esterase between pre- and postsynaptic membranes (21). Electron microscopy involving either immunoperoxidase techniques (24) or peroxidase-labeled α-bungarotoxin (25) reveal both a postsynaptic and a presynaptic receptor localization. However, it is clear from the cited autoradiographic studies that the apparent membrane concentrations of receptor and esterase are much lower in extrajunctional regions than within the junction.

Several reports have indicated that the ratio of total active sites of receptor and esterase is about 1 both in electric organ and in muscle (26–29), although the ratio appears to increase after denervation of rat diaphragm (14,30). In rat diaphragm there are about 4×10^7 receptor sites per end plate (28,31) and about the same number of acetylcholinesterase sites (32), although the determination of acetylcholinesterase sites is uncertain by perhaps a factor of two because some diisopropylfluorophosphate-labeled sites may not correspond to acetylcholinesterase (32). If one assumes an exclusive and homogeneous postsynaptic localization, this number corresponds to about 10^4 sites/μm^2 (33). However, postsynaptic receptors do not appear to be distributed homogeneously, as noted in the preceding paragraph, and maximum receptor densities of 3×10^4 sites/μm^2 have been estimated for the juxtaneuronal postsynaptic membrane of mouse sternomastoid muscle (21). This estimate is quite close to that for receptor densities in the subsynaptic membrane of eel electroplax (34) and suggests very high membrane concentrations which approach maximum values calculated for close packing of receptors in the membrane (33).

As suggested by the morphological evidence, electrophysiological data reveal a close functional relationship between receptor and esterase in controlling the action of acetylcholine. Ionic currents in postsynaptic membrane were shown to be highly sensitive to inhibitors which blocked the access of acetylcholine to the active sites either of receptor or of esterase (35,36). More recently, Magleby and Stevens (37) presented evidence that the decay of end plate currents (epcs) in frog sartorius neuromuscular junction is longer than the estimated lifetime of the neurally evoked acetylcholine available to the receptors. The estimated time dependence of the free (unbound) acetylcholine concentration in their report was determined indirectly from the time course of the epcs and is indicated in line A of Fig. 2. Also shown as line B in Fig. 2 is the comparatively longer duration of miniature end plate currents (mepcs) is observed in toad neuromuscular

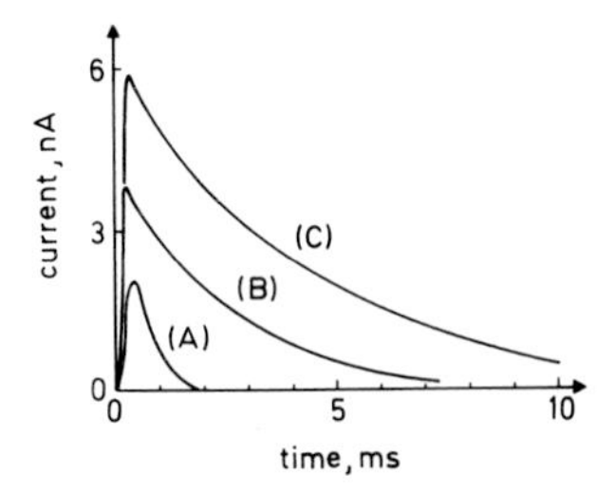

Fig. 2. Miniature end plate currents (mepcs; inward current positive) reflecting conductivity changes in a voltage-clamped toad muscle fiber at 22°C (redrawn from Gage and McBurney, 38); line B, in standard Ringer solution; line C, after incubating for 30 min in 1 mg/liter neostigmine. Line A represents the estimated concentration (in arbitrary units) of acetylcholine available to synaptic receptors following neural triggering of an end plate current (epc) (37). The similarity of the decay time constants and their voltage dependence for both epcs (37) and mepcs (38) justifies the application of epc estimates for acetylcholine to mepcs.

junctions by Gage and McBurney (38). The slow decay of the mepc in line B is exponential; and the time constant, voltage dependence, and temperature dependence of the decay is about the same as that observed for the decay of both neurally evoked epcs and acetylcholine-induced single channel openings by Stevens and his colleagues (37–39). The equivalence of these decay time constants supports the contention of Magleby and Stevens (37) that channel closing [or agonist dissociation (see Kordas, 40)] is rate limiting during epc (or mepc) decay such that free acetylcholine is no longer in equilibrium with the receptor.

In the presence of an acetylcholinesterase inhibitor, both the amplitude and the decay time of mepcs are increased by about 50%, as indicated in line C of Fig. 2, while the growth phase is virtually unaffected (38). Similar effects are seen with epcs (37,40,41). Thus esterase inhibition appears to result in activation of a greater number of receptors and an increase in the lifetime of free acetylcholine such that its removal from the cleft by diffusion contributes to the decay time constant (41). This diffusion appears to be slowed by the binding of acetylcholine to receptors, and addition of receptor inhibitors reduces receptor binding and restores the decay time constant to close to its original value in the absence of both esterase and receptor inhibitors (42). We may thus conclude that the effect of acetylcholinesterase inhibitors on epcs and mepcs particularly demonstrates the close functional as well as spatial proximity of receptor and esterase proteins.

III. DO RECEPTOR AND ESTERASE COMPETE FOR ACETYLCHOLINE?

In view of the close spatial and functional proximity of receptor and esterase, one may ask the question: Is the access of acetylcholine to these two proteins regulated in order to enhance their functionally sequential roles, such that acetylcholine first interacts with receptor and then with esterase? In the neurotransmitter theory of synaptic acetylcholine action (43), it is assumed that acetylcholine is released from the nerve terminal into the synaptic cleft. Receptor and esterase are then presumed to compete for the available acetylcholine, and it is evident that sufficient acetylcholine must bind to receptor to account for the observed conductance increase in the postsynaptic membrane. In the following sections we present recent kinetic data on the interaction of acetylcholine and its analogs with acetylcholine receptor and acetylcholinesterase. These studies suggest that, with the solubilized proteins from eel and torpedo electric organs, the esterase binds acetylcholine at least 10 times (and perhaps 100 times) more rapidly than the receptor. Such a difference appears to place the receptor at a considerable competitive disadvantage. We consider the implications of this disadvantage in a simple quantitative description of competitive acetylcholine action at the synapse. We also describe alternative models, including a sequential mechanism in which acetylcholine has access first to receptor and then to esterase. Such a sequential mechanism is included in a previous hypothesis of a partially intramembranous action of acetylcholine in excitable membranes (1–5,8–10).

IV. KINETIC ANALYSES

The presentation of our analyses of the interaction of acetylcholine (A) with receptor (R) and esterase (E) will focus on the reactions in Eqs. (1) and (2). Of particular relevance are the bimolecular reaction

$$\mathrm{A} + \mathrm{R} \underset{k_{-1}^{\mathrm{R}}}{\overset{k_1^{\mathrm{R}}}{\rightleftharpoons}} \mathrm{AR} \tag{1}$$

$$\mathrm{A} + \mathrm{E} \underset{k_{-1}^{\mathrm{E}}}{\overset{k_1^{\mathrm{E}}}{\rightleftharpoons}} \mathrm{AE} \tag{2}$$

rate constants k_1^{R} and k_1^{E} for acetylcholine binding to receptor and esterase, respectively. One might anticipate that both bimolecular reactions are close to diffusion controlled; that is, nearly every collisional encounter between acetylcholine and an R or E binding site leads to binding. In practical terms this implies that the bimolecular reactions are very rapid (in the μsec or msec time range) and require special rapid kinetic methods. Furthermore, the analysis of rapid kinetic reactions is greatly facilitated when the reaction systems are homogeneous. Thus we have so far applied rapid kinetic techniques only to solubilized receptor or esterase of high purity.

A powerful method for the determination of rate constants of rapid chemical reactions is chemical relaxation spectrometry (44,45). The principle of this method is the perturbation of a chemical equilibrium or a steady-state by a rapid change in a physical variable, for example, temperature, followed by a measurement of a rate of concentration change as the components adjust to their new equilibrium or steady-state concentrations. Generally the concentration of one component is monitored by spectrophotometric or spectrofluorometric techniques. For small physical perturbations, the concentration change associated with a single elementary reaction such as those in Eqs. (1) and (2) has an exponential time dependence and is thus characterized by a relaxation time and a relaxation amplitude. A simple theoretical analysis (44) predicts that this relaxation time τ for the reaction in Eq. (1), for instance, will depend on the reactant concentrations according to Eq. (3),

$$\tau = [k_1^{\mathrm{R}}([\mathrm{A}] + [\mathrm{R}]) + k_{-1}^{\mathrm{R}}]^{-1} \tag{3}$$

where [A] and [R] are equilibrium concentrations. Usually [A] and/or [R] cannot be directly measured; and it is convenient to express Eq. (3) in terms of the total concentrations $[\mathrm{A}^0]$ and $[\mathrm{R}^0]$, where $[\mathrm{A}^0] = [\mathrm{A}] + [\mathrm{AR}]$ and $[\mathrm{R}^0] = [\mathrm{R}] + [\mathrm{AR}]$, as shown in Eq. (4) (see Winkler-Oswatitsch, 46).

$$\tau = [k_1^{\mathrm{R}}[\mathrm{R}^0]\sqrt{(1 + p + [\mathrm{A}^0]/[\mathrm{R}^0])^2 - 4[\mathrm{A}^0][\mathrm{R}^0]}]^{-1} \tag{4}$$

In Eq. (4) $p = K/[\mathrm{R}^0]$ and $K = k_{-1}^{\mathrm{R}}/k_1^{\mathrm{R}}$. Equation (4) is readily rearranged to Eq. (5) (see Rosenberry and Neumann, 47).

$$\tau^{-2} = \alpha + \beta[\mathrm{A}^0] + \alpha[\mathrm{A}^0]^2 \tag{5}$$

where $\alpha = (k_1^{\mathrm{R}})^2(K + [\mathrm{R}^0])^2$, $\beta = 2(k_1^{\mathrm{R}})^2(K - [\mathrm{R}^0])$, and $\gamma = (k_1^{\mathrm{R}})^2$. Equations 4 and 5 have been written with apparent asymmetry of $[\mathrm{A}^0]$ and $[\mathrm{R}^0]$ in anticipation of experimental measurements of τ in which $[\mathrm{R}^0]$ is constant while $[\mathrm{A}^0]$ is varied. Under these conditions it is readily shown that τ has a maximum value (τ^{-2} a minimum) when $[\mathrm{A}^0] = [\mathrm{R}^0] - K$ provided that $[\mathrm{R}^0] > K$, i.e., $p < 1$ [see Winkler-Oswatitsch (46) and Neumann and Chang (48)].

While measurement of the reaction rate constants of acetylcholine with receptor and esterase defined in Eqs. (1) and (2) by means of Eqs. (4) and (5) thus would appear straightforward, direct measurements have not yet been possible. In the receptor case, no suitable optical signal for monitoring the reaction in Eq. (1) itself has been found. However, this reaction can be coupled to Ca^{2+}-binding equilibria involving the receptor (48,49). Recently, multiple relaxations in this coupled system have been observed, and corresponding extensions of Eq. (4) permitted estimates both of several rate constants including k_1^R in Eq. (1) and of receptor site normalities (48,49; see Section VI). In the esterase case, the complex AE in Eq. (2) is an intermediate which can also react along a hydrolytic pathway with such speed that equilibrium relaxation measurements are not possible [see Eq. (6)]. However, a minimum estimate of k_1^E in Eq. (2) is available from steady-state kinetic data (see Section V).

For both receptor and esterase, the relaxation kinetics of specific fluorescent ligand binding at the active site have been studied (47,50). The fluorescent ligands used in these studies are shown in Fig. 3. They are highly fluorescent when free in solution but totally quenched on binding to the active site, and this difference in fluorescence intensity allows monitoring of concentration changes during temperature-jump relaxation studies. These ligands appear to act as specific analogs of acetylcholine and have provided valuable information about bimolecular reaction rate constants for both proteins, which is discussed in the following sections.

V. ACETYLCHOLINESTERASE

A. STRUCTURE

Several forms of the esterase, characterized by sedimentation coefficients of 18 S, 14 S, 8 S, and 11 S, have been purified from eel electric organ extracts by affinity chromatography (13,17). Electron microscopic (51,52) and biochemical (16,17) studies indicate that the 18 S, 14 S, and 8 S species correspond, respectively, to 3, 2, and 1 catalytic subunit tetramers attached to a 50 nm collagenlike tail structure by disulfide bonds. The 11 S form corresponds to a single catalytic subunit tetramer devoid of the tail structure. Esterase at rat diaphragm end plates appears to have a similar tail structure (14). The tail structure has little effect on the catalytic activity (53) but has been suggested to be responsible for the esterase membrane attachment (11,16). Acetylcholinesterase at synapses may be localized in the extracellular basement membrane (11,16,54,55).

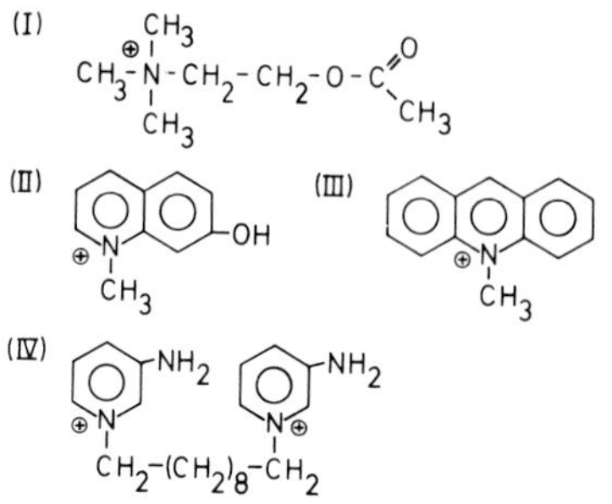

Fig. 3. Chemical formula of acetylcholine (I), 1-methyl-7-hydroxyquinolinium (II), *N*-methylacridinium (III), and bis(3-aminopyridinium)-1, 10-decane (IV).

B. STEADY-STATE KINETICS

Numerous studies have demonstrated that a minimal mechanism for the hydrolysis of acetylcholine by acetylcholinesterase is given by the reaction in Eq. (6) (see Rosenberry, 13).

$$\mathrm{A} + \mathrm{E} \underset{k_{-1}^{\mathrm{E}}}{\overset{k_1^{\mathrm{E}}}{\rightleftharpoons}} \mathrm{AE} \xrightarrow[\downarrow \text{ choline}]{k_2} \text{acetyl E} \xrightarrow[\uparrow \ \mathrm{H_2O}]{k_3} \mathrm{E} + \text{acetate} + \mathrm{H}^+ \tag{6}$$

Under steady-state conditions ($[\mathrm{A}] \gg [\mathrm{E}^0]$), the velocity ($v$) of the acetylcholine hydrolysis is given by Eq. (7).

$$v = \frac{k_{\mathrm{cat}}[\mathrm{E}^0]}{1 + K_{\mathrm{app}}/[\mathrm{A}]} \tag{7}$$

where $k_{\mathrm{cat}} = k_2k_3/(k_2 + k_3)$ and $K_{\mathrm{app}} = k_{\mathrm{cat}}(k_{-1}{}^{\mathrm{E}} + k_2)/k_1{}^{\mathrm{E}}k_2$. At high acetylcholine concentrations ($[\mathrm{A}] > K_{\mathrm{app}} \cong 10^{-4}\ M$), v becomes first order in $[\mathrm{E}^0]$; and values of the first-order rate constant $k_{\mathrm{cat}} = 1.6 \times 10^4\ \mathrm{sec}^{-1}$ (0.1 M ionic strength, pH 8.0, 25°C) have consistently been measured (see Rosenberry, 13). The relevance of this extremely high rate constant to acetylcholine-mediated neuronal information transfer was first recognized by Nachmansohn (56a). With acetylcholine as substrate, k_{cat} is thought to approximate k_3 (13), and k_2 has been estimated to be about $10^5\ \mathrm{sec}^{-1}$ (56). At low acetylcholine concentrations v becomes second order, and the second-order rate constant $k_{\mathrm{cat}}/k_{\mathrm{app}}$ has been measured as $1.6 \times 10^8\ M^{-1}\mathrm{sec}^{-1}$ under the same experimental conditions (13). According to Eq. (6), the second order rate constant is given by Eq. (8),

$$\frac{k_{\mathrm{cat}}}{K_{\mathrm{app}}} = k_1{}^{\mathrm{E}}\left(\frac{k_2}{k_{-1}{}^{\mathrm{E}} + k_2}\right) \tag{8}$$

and thus it is apparent that k_{cat}/K_{app} establishes a minimum value for $k_1{}^E$. Detailed kinetic studies suggest that the actual esterase mechanism is somewhat more complicated than that in Eq. (6) (57). Even in this more complicated mechanism, however, k_{cat}/K_{app} would still underestimate $k_1{}^E$.

At very high acetylcholine concentrations ($\geq 10^{-2}$ *M*) substrate inhibition of acetylcholine hydrolysis may be detected (see Augustinsson, 58). While some controversy about the mechanism of substrate inhibition exists (59), strong evidence indicates that this inhibition arises from the binding of acetylcholine to the active site in the *acetylenzyme* with consequent inhibition of deacylation (60,61).

C. RELAXATION KINETICS

Two cationic ligands which have been used in temperature jump studies of acetylcholinesterase are *N*-methylacridinium and 1-methyl-7-hydroxyquinolinium (47; see Fig. 3). Both ligands bind with high specificity to the esterase active site. The interaction of *N*-methylacridinium with acetylcholinesterase was analyzed according to Eq. (5) and is shown in Fig. 4. Bimolecular reaction rate constants and equilibrium dissociation constants for both ligands are given in Table I. The observed bimolecular reaction rate constants of some-

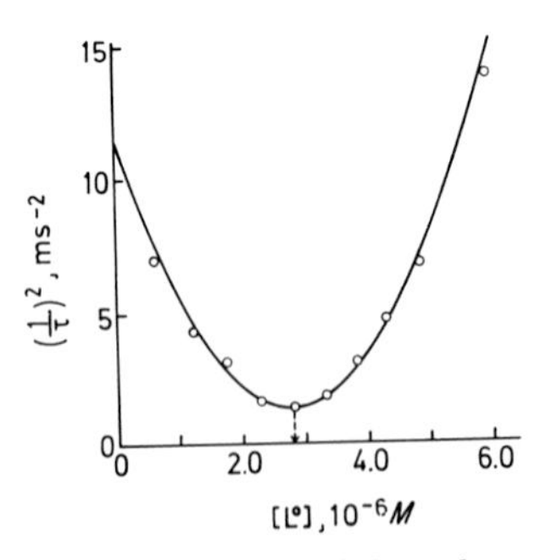

Fig. 4. Dependence of the mean values of the relaxation times, τ, observed with acetylcholinesterase and *N*-methylacridinium on total ligand concentration, $[L^0]$, in 0.1 *M* sodium phosphate at pH 8.0 and 23°C (47). Initial concentration of esterase active sites $[E^0] = 2.92 \times 10^{-6}$ *M*. Data are plotted according to Eq. (5). The solid line was calculated from a weighted least-squares analysis based on a second-order polynomial in $[L^0]$. From the position of the minimum, the value of $[E^0] = [L^0]_{min} - K = 2.94(\pm 0.04) \times 10^{-6}$ *M* can be obtained independently from the kinetic titration; it is consistently the same as the initial concentration of esterase sites determined by thermodynamic techniques.

TABLE I
Equilibrium Dissociation Constants K and Rate Constants for the Interaction of Acetylcholinesterase and Cationic Ligands [Eq. (2)][a]

Compound[b]	k_1^E (M^{-1} sec^{-1})	K (M)	k_{-1}^E (sec^{-1})
(I)	$\geq 1.6\ (\pm 0.1) \times 10^8$		
(II)	$2.18\ (\pm 0.15) \times 10^9$	$2.03\ (\pm 0.3) \times 10^{-7}$	4.4×10^2
(III)	$1.18\ (\pm 0.03) \times 10^9$	$1.49\ (\pm 0.03) \times 10^{-7}$	1.8×10^2

[a] From Rosenberry and Neumann (47).
[b] (I), Acetylcholine in 0.1 M ionic strength at 25°C, pH 8.0; (II), 1-Methyl-7-hydroxyquinolinium in 0.1 M sodium phosphate at 23°C, pH 7.0; (III), N-methylacridinium in 0.1 M sodium phosphate at 23°C, pH 8.0.

what greater than $10^9\ M^{-1}$ sec^{-1} are unusually high for enzyme–ligand interactions (see Rosenberry and Neumann, 47). Recent data show a very high ionic strength dependence of k_1^E for these fluorescent ligands consistent with an "effective" negative charge on the enzyme active site of about -6 (62). Virtually the same ionic strength dependence is observed for k_{cat}/K_{app} for acetylthiocholine [see Eq. (8)], a substrate whose structure and kinetic properties are very similar to those of acetylcholine. Thus k_1^E values for several cationic ligands, including acetylcholine, appear to be unusually high because of the large electrostatic interaction between ligand and esterase. Several fixed negative charges near the active site may contribute to the high effective negative charge on the esterase, thereby creating a "binding surface," involved in trapping acetylcholine, that is considerably larger than the catalytic site itself.

VI. ACETYLCHOLINE RECEPTOR

A. STRUCTURE

While isolation of the various electric organ acetylcholinesterase species poses no major problems, the purification of native acetylcholine receptor is still a difficult task. Conventional homogenization procedures may result in chemical modification of the receptor even prior to its extraction from the membrane, as the following observations suggest. Solubilized receptor purified from torpedo electric organ exists in two major forms (63): a heavy (H) form (13 S) and a light (L) form (9 S). It has been recently established that the H form is a dimer of L forms linked by an intermolecular disulfide bond involving the 67,000-dalton subunits of the receptor and that, without precautions, the apparently native dimeric H form is split by disulfide reduction into monomeric L forms during homogenization of torpedo electric organ (64). This cleavage may be prevented by homogenization in the presence of *N*-ethylmaleimide, a sulfhydryl alkylating agent. In crude extracts, the receptor H form appears to bind acetylcholine more tightly than the L form, the respective equilibrium dissociation constants (K_d) being $(3 \pm 1) \times 10^{-9}\,M$ and $(2 \pm 1) \times 10^{-8}\,M$. After purification of the H or L forms by affinity chromatography, however, the binding affinity of acetylcholine to either form is partially converted to a lower value ($K_d \cong 10^{-6}\,M$) (64). The conversion of H to L forms by endogenous reducing agents as well as these variations in acetylcholine affinities serve to remind us that, in general, extrapolation of protein properties in solution to those *in vivo* should be done with caution.

B. Ca^{2+}-BINDING PROPERTIES

Detergent-solubilized isolated receptor binds large amounts of Ca^{2+} ions (49,65). The Ca^{2+} binding isotherm shows two extended linear regions in Scatchard plots, suggesting at least two types of independent Ca^{2+} binding sites (49). Data on the stoichiometry and affinity of Ca^{2+} binding are summarized in Table II. As noted in Section I, Nachmansohn has proposed that the binding of acetylcholine to the receptor causes the release of receptor-bound Ca^{2+} ions (4). A recent test of this proposal has demonstrated that isolated receptor does indeed

TABLE II
Apparent Equilibrium Dissociation Constants K_{Ca} and Maximum Number B^0 of Ca Binding Sites per 380,000 (±20,000) Daltons of the Isolated Acetylcholine Receptor from *Torpedo californica* in 0.1 *M* NaCl, 0.05 *M* Tris HCl, 0.1% Brij, pH 8.5 at 20°C[a,b]

Region	K_{Ca} (*M*)	B^0
(1)	$3.3 (\pm 0.3) \times 10^{-4}$	44 (± 4)
(2)	$\leq 2.5 (\pm 0.5) \times 10^{-6}$	34 (± 4)

[a] From Chang and Neumann (49).
[b] The data were obtained from a Scatchard plot where two extended linear regions suggest at least two types of independent Ca^{2+} binding sites. The overall acetylcholine equilibrium constant of the receptor preparation was $10^{-6}\,M$.

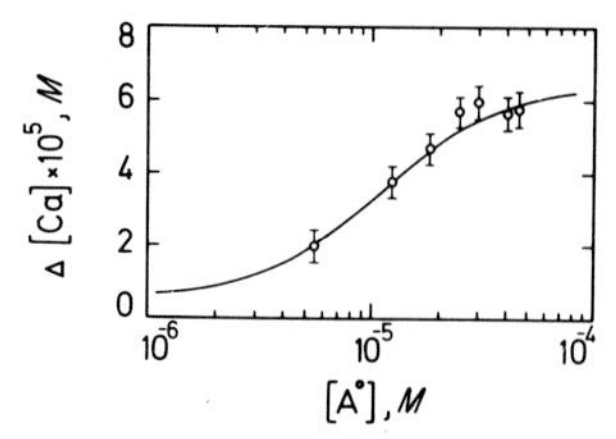

Fig. 5. The change in concentration of free Ca^{2+} ions reflecting release of bound Ca^{2+}, Ca_b^{2+} ($\Delta[Ca^{2+}] = -\Delta[Ca_b^{2+}]$), from isolated acetylcholine receptor of *Torpedo californica* (in 0.1 *M* NaCl, 0.05 *M* Tris HCl, 0.1% Brij, 0.00 12 *M* Ca, pH 8.5, at 20°C) as a function of the total acetylcholine concentration [A^0] (49). The receptor concentration is 2.6 mg/ml.

release Ca^{2+} ions upon binding acetylcholine (48,49). As shown in Fig. 5 there is progressive release of Ca^{2+} ions from the receptor on addition of acetylcholine until an apparent saturation level is reached. The Ca^{2+} release curves can be quantitatively analyzed in terms of the overall reaction in Eq. (9)

$$nA + RCa_x \rightleftharpoons A_nR + xCa \tag{9}$$

where $n = 2$ is the number of acetylcholine ions bound to the receptor (H form), x is the maximum number of Ca^{2+} ions which can be released by acetylcholine binding, and A_nR represents the receptor conformations with bound acetylcholine. The analysis indicates that at 1.2 m*M* [Ca^{2+}], $x = 5$ ($\pm$ 1); in other words, two to three Ca^{2+} ions are released per bound acetylcholine. Furthermore, subsequent addition of α-bungarotoxin to the receptor solutions displaces the bound acetylcholine and leads to reuptake of the Ca^{2+} ions originally released. It thus seems that receptor activators and inhibitors have opposing effects on the Ca^{2+} binding of receptors (49).

C. Relaxation Kinetics

As noted in Section IV, no direct method of rapidly monitoring acetylcholine reactions with the isolated receptor is currently available. Therefore, the binding of acetylcholine has been analyzed by its coupling with Ca^{2+} release from the receptor (48). The kinetic data suggest that the receptor is equilibrated among at least three conformations ($R \rightleftharpoons R'' \rightleftharpoons R'''$). When acetylcholine is present, at least two of these states contribute in a characteristic manner to the chemical relaxation spectrum. It appears that the main reaction path for the interaction with acetylcholine is $A + R \rightleftharpoons AR \rightleftharpoons AR''$, indicating at least one intramolecular (conformational) change influenced by the bind-

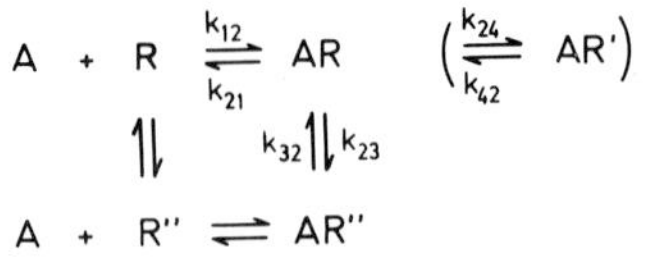

$$\begin{array}{ccccc} A + R & \underset{k_{21}}{\overset{k_{12}}{\rightleftharpoons}} & AR & \left(\underset{k_{42}}{\overset{k_{24}}{\rightleftharpoons}}\right. & \left. AR' \right) \\ \upharpoonleft\downharpoonright & & k_{32}\upharpoonleft\downharpoonright k_{23} & & \\ A + R'' & \rightleftharpoons & AR'' & & \end{array}$$

Fig. 6. Reaction scheme for the interaction of acetylcholine with isolated receptor from *Torpedo californica*, suggested by kinetic studies in which the release of Ca^{2+} ions is used as an indicator for acetylcholine binding. The observed main reaction path is $A + R \rightleftharpoons AR \rightleftharpoons AR''$, with $[R''] \ll [R]$. The $AR \rightleftharpoons AR''$ relaxation is slow and well separated from the initial binding step. The bimolecular rate constant k_{on} is k_{12} [equivalent to k_1^R in Eq. (1)]; the dissociation rate constant k_{off} is k_{21} [equivalent to k_{-1}^R in Eq. (1)] or, if a step $AR \rightleftharpoons AR'$ is rapidly coupled to the observed bimolecular reaction, $k_{off} = k_{21}k_{42}(k_{42} + k_{42})^{-1}$(see Neumann and Chang, 48).

ing of activator. This reaction path is included in a reaction scheme suggested by the relaxation kinetic data in Fig. 6. Within the experimental accuracy there was no evidence for cooperativity between the two acetylcholine binding sites in the receptor macromolecule, and thus this scheme is simply expressed in terms of binding sites. Data from the relaxation kinetic studies are summarized in Table III.

Although the schemes dipicted in Figs. 1 and 6 are formally quite similar, the time range calculated for the reaction step $AR \rightleftharpoons AR''$ in Fig. 6 is 20 to 50 msec and thus falls outside the physiologically relevant domain of 1 to 10 msec observed for the relaxation times of receptor-mediated conductivity changes (66) modeled by the scheme in Fig. 1. Since the kinetic data on isolated acetylcholine receptor do not exclude the presence of a rapidly coupled structural transition $AR \rightleftharpoons AR'$ (see Appendix), this step is included in Fig. 6 to model the channel activation in the scheme shown in Fig. 1.

It is apparent from Table III that the rate constant $k_1^R = 2.4 \times 10^7$ M^{-1} sec^{-1} for the association of acetylcholine to receptor is relatively

TABLE III

Kinetic and Thermodynamic Parameters of the Interaction of Acetylcholine with Isolated Acetylcholine Receptor from *Torpedo californica*, for the Main Reaction Path $A + R \rightleftharpoons AR \rightleftharpoons AR''$[a,b]

$A + R \rightleftharpoons AR$	$AR \rightleftharpoons AR''$
$k_{on} = 2.4\ (\pm\ 0.5) \times 10^7\ M^{-1}$ sec^{-1}	$k_{23} = 43.5$ sec^{-1}
$k_{off} = 140$ sec^{-1}	$k_{32} = 6.5$ sec^{-1}
$K_1 = 0.6 \times 10^{-5}\ M$	$K_2 = 6.7$

[a] From Neumann and Chang (48).

[b] The solvent is composed of 0.1 *M* NaCl, 0.1% Brij, 0.001 *M* Ca, 0.05 *M* Tris HCl, pH 8.5, at 23°C. The overall acetylcholine equilibrium constant $\overline{K} = K_1(1 + K_2)^{-1}$ was 10^{-6} *M*, where $K_1 = k_{off}/k_{on}$ and $K_2 = k_{23}/k_{32}$.

low compared to k_1^E values. It is noteworthy that recent stopped-flow experiments involving receptor-rich membrane fragments of *Torpedo marmorata* and the dication suberyldicholine have yielded a bimolecular rate constant of $1.0 \times 10^7 M^{-1} sec^{-1}$ (F. Barrantes, personal communication), comparable to the rate constant k_1^R for the binding of acetylcholine to isolated receptor in Table III. On the other hand, recent relaxation kinetic experiments with the dicationic inhibitor bis(3-aminopyridinium)-1, 10-decane (DAP) (see Fig. 3), and the isolated receptor from *Torpedo marmorata* have shown that this ligand has a bimolecular rate constant of $\sim 10^8 M^{-1} sec^{-1}$ (0.1 *M* ionic strength, pH 7.0, 20°C). The ionic strength dependence of the association rate constant for DAP suggests an "effective charge" of -3 ($\pm$ 1) on the binding site of the protein. This value is somewhat less negative than that indicated for the acetylcholinesterase active site. However, it seems that in both proteins there are large electrostatic contributions to the rate with which cationic ligands like acetylcholine are bound.

Independent information about acetylcholine interactions with *in vivo* receptor has recently been obtained from electrophysiological experiments by Sheridan and Lester (66). Applying voltage-jump perturbations, postsynaptic current relaxation times in eel electroplax could be evaluated as a function of the steady-state concentration of externally applied acetylcholine. Within the limited concentration range of 10^{-5} to 10^{-4} *M*, the relaxation times of the measured currents appeared to be bimolecularly controlled by acetylcholine; and the bimolecular rate constant was estimated to be $10^7 M^{-1} sec^{-1}$. The apparent dissociation rate constant was strongly dependent on clamp voltage and spanned the range from 10^2 to 10^3 sec^{-1}. These values are comparable to the rate constants obtained for the isolated receptor. In particular, the similarity between the values of $k_{on} = 10^7 M^{-1} sec^{-1}$ from current relaxations and $k_1^R = 2.4 \times 10^7 M^{-1} sec^{-1}$ from kinetic studies on isolated receptor suggests that the rate of coupled Ca^{2+} release not only reflects the rate of acetylcholine binding to isolated receptor, but also may represent the rate-limiting step for the conductivity increase in the membrane.

A second important indication from this electrophysiological study arose from the dependence of the relaxation current amplitude on acetylcholine concentration. The current data suggested that at least two acetylcholine molecules must bind to receptor to open a single channel conductance unit (66). This suggestion that the active receptor unit is dimeric may be related to the fact that the H form of detergent-solubilized receptor binds two acetylcholine molecules.

The stoichiometry of the acetylcholine binding and the various re-

$$
\begin{array}{ccccccc}
2A & + & R & \underset{k_{-1}}{\overset{2k_1}{\rightleftharpoons}} & AR & + \; A & \underset{2k_{-1}}{\overset{k_1}{\rightleftharpoons}} & A_2R \\
 & & \upharpoonleft\downharpoonright & & \upharpoonleft\downharpoonright & & & \upharpoonleft\downharpoonright \\
2A & + & R' & \rightleftharpoons & AR' & + \; A & \rightleftharpoons & A_2R' \\
 & & \upharpoonleft\downharpoonright & & \upharpoonleft\downharpoonright & & & \upharpoonleft\downharpoonright \\
2A & + & R^{++} & \rightleftharpoons & AR^{++} & + \; A & \rightleftharpoons & A_2R^{++}
\end{array}
$$

Fig. 7. Reaction scheme for the interaction of acetylcholine with *in vivo* receptor as suggested by electrophysiological studies. The three receptor states correspond to the R (closed), R′ (open), and R^{++} (desensitized) states. The acetylcholine binding sites are assumed to be equivalent and independent, as indicated by the rate coefficients k_1 and k_{-1} with their appropriate statistical factors.

ceptor states indicated by electrophysiological studies may be summarized in the general reaction scheme depicted in Fig. 7. In this scheme the association–dissociation steps are represented horizontally and the conformational transitions between three receptor states are given vertically. These three states correspond to the R (closed), R′ (open), and R^{++} (desensitized) states. The desensitized state is an inactive receptor form which can be detected in the continued presence of externally applied acetylcholine (67). Under *in vivo* conditions it appears that $[R'] + [R^{++}] \ll [R]$. Thus, under various experimental conditions, only a few of all the possible reactions depicted in the scheme in Fig. 7 may contribute to a measurable extent to the observed phenomena. For instance, neurally triggered receptor activation does not lead to desensitization; thus the state R^{++} seems uninvolved in the determination of neurally triggered epc's.

VII. COMPARISONS BETWEEN COMPETITIVE AND SEQUENTIAL REACTIONS OF ACETYLCHOLINE AT THE SYNAPSE

The electrophysiological characteristics of impulse transmission at neuromuscular junctions establish, as we noted in Section II, a close functional relationship between receptor and esterase which is probably based on a close spatial proximity of these two proteins. We now wish to incorporate the kinetic data presented on the interactions between acetylcholine and these proteins after isolation with the structural localization of the proteins in the synapse. Predictions of the rates and extents of acetylcholine interactions thus can be made and compared with the electrophysiological data. This task is complicated by the assumptions necessary for a quantitative analysis. The foremost assumption is that rate constants obtained with the isolated proteins in solution are applicable to the membrane-bound proteins in the synapse. The rate constants of greatest interest here, the bimolecular association constants for acetylcholine, probably satisfy this assumption rather well, although additional electrostatic contributions by the membrane environment and an altered acetylcholine diffusion rate in the synaptic gap are possible sources of alterations. The close correspondence of k_1^R from the kinetic (48) and electrophysiological (66) studies noted above support the use of this assumption. The second assumption involves an approximation of the geometry, topology, and homogeneity of the reaction space within the synapse. This approximation may involve local concentration gradients either of the proteins or of acetylcholine. Two alternatives regarding the homogeneity of the reaction space are the competitive versus the sequential modes of acetylcholine interaction noted in Section III. We consider these two alternative modes in the following sections with full awareness of the reaction space approximations required.

A. COMPETITION MODELS

Localization data in Section II indicate 4×10^7 receptor sites for α-neurotoxin per rat diaphragm end plate and nearly an equal number of esterase sites. Furthermore, there appears to be two toxin sites per acetylcholine site on the receptor (64). Direct measurements of acetylcholine release from esterase-inhibited rat diaphragm end plates during nerve stimulation lead to estimates of 3 to 6×10^6 acetylcholine molecules released per end plate potential (68,69). For the calculations that follow we assume simply that both the proteins and acetylcholine are homogeneously distributed. This homogeneous reaction space assumption prohibits concentration gradients over the duration of the end plate potential. It thus does not consider the proposal of acetylcholine release from spatially discrete resides; the possibility of acetylcholine diffusion from the synaptic cleft; and any inhomogeneity in receptor or esterase distributions. We also assume acetylcholine release is essentially instantaneous. This assumption is not very good for epcs (70) but is probably much better for the mepcs shown in Fig. 2. These two assumptions reduce the kinetic description of epcs to the chemical reactions in Fig. 1 and Eq. (6). A quantitative solution to the differential equations arising from this kinetic description is given in the Appendix. The solution is greatly simplified by noting that, within the homogeneous reaction space assumption, the concentrations of both receptor and esterase active sites are about fivefold in excess of the total initial acetylcholine concentration. Under this condition, the free active site concentrations are approximately given by the total active site concentrations: $[R] \cong [R^0]$ and $[E] \cong [E^0]$. Several important features of the Appendix solution become apparent by considering the association fluxes J of the receptor and esterase reactions with acetylcholine in Eqs. (1 and 2). When the dissociation fluxes are negligible, these fluxes are sufficient to account for the distribution of acetylcholine between receptor and enzyme, as shown in Eqs. (10 and 11).

$$J^{R} \equiv k_1^{R}[A][R] \cong k_1^{R}[A][R^0] \cong \frac{d[AR]}{dt} \tag{10}$$

$$J^{E} \equiv k_1^{E}[A][E] \cong k_1^{E}[A][E^0] \cong \frac{d[AE]}{dt} \tag{11}$$

Integration under the initial condition that at $t = 0$, $[A] = [A^0]$ leads to Eq. (12).

$$\frac{[AR]}{[A^0]} = \frac{k_1^{R}[R^0]}{(k_1^{R}[R^0] + k_1^{E}[E^0])} \{1 - \exp[-k_1^{R}[R^0] + (k_1^{E}[E^0])t]\} \tag{12}$$

With values of $k_1^{R} = 2 \times 10^7 M^{-1} \sec^{-1}$ and $k_1^{E} = 2 \times 10^8 M^{-1} \sec^{-1}$ given in Sections V and VI, together with the condition $[R^0] = [E^0]$, the maximum value of $[AR]/[A^0]$ obtained from Eq. (12) is 0.1. The more extensive treatment in the Appendix gives a similar $[AR']_{max}/[A^0]$ value of 0.082. If one AR′ corresponds to one open ion channel, then this $[AR']_{max}/[A^0]$ ratio indicates that somewhat less than 10% of the total released acetylcholine activates about 1% of the total receptors (recall $[R^0] \cong 5[A^0]$ during an epc, in reasonable agreement with values estimated electrophysiologically from epc peak amplitudes (see Colquhoun, 6). If, however, as recent electrophysiological data (66) summarized in Fig. 7 suggest, only a dimeric A_2R' corresponds to one open channel and if acetylcholine binding at both sites is characterized by the k_1^{R} given above, then $[A_2R']_{max}/[R^0] \leq 10^{-4}$ [note that $[A_2R']/[R^0] = \frac{1}{2}[AR']/[R^0]^2$, see Eq. (A15)]. This is a 100-fold lower value than the electrophysiological estimate. In fact, to achieve an activation of 1% of the total receptors from dimeric A_2R' within the homogeneous reaction space assumption, nearly all the released acetylcholine would have to react with receptor before it reacted with esterase.

Because J^{E} is considerably larger than J^{R}, Eq. (12) also predicts that the epc peak amplitudes as well as the epc growth times should be quite sensitive to esterase inhibitors. When Eq. (12) is extended to include the dissociation fluxes in Eqs. (1 and 2), 99% esterase inhibition is predicted to increase the epc peak amplitudes by a factor of 8.1 in a monomeric receptor scheme (Fig. 1) and by a factor of 65 in a dimeric receptor scheme (Fig. 7) and to increase the time to peak amplitude from about 220 μsec to 2.0 msec in either model (see Appendix). In contrast, the observed growth times for mepc's in Fig. 2 are virtually unaffected by esterase inhibition and peak amplitudes are increased only about 50%. Only slightly larger esterase inhibition effects are seen on epc's (71).

Despite the fact that the numerical estimates can be altered somewhat by assuming some variation in $[R^0]/[E^0]$ ratios, these comparisons lead us to conclude that the competition model with the homogeneous reaction space assumption is probably inappropriate for a monomeric receptor scheme and certainly inappropriate for a dimeric receptor scheme when the entire duration of the epc is being simulated. This model may be appropriate for the kinetics of the epc decay phase (see Magleby and Stevens, 37) under conditions in which acetylcholine diffusion from the synaptic cleft is not of major significance. In this respect it is noteworthy that the model predicts that 90% esterase inhibition would increase the decay rate constant by a factor of only two (see Appendix), a value consistent with electrophysiological observations (37).

One may consider alternatives to the homogeneous reaction space assumption in either competitive or sequential models. A quantitative treatment of these alternatives is beyond the scope of this chapter, but features which overcome shortcomings inherent in the homogeneous reaction space assumption can be noted.

An important alternative competitive model involves the assumption of a spatially nonhomogeneous acetylcholine concentration. This assumption applies to a vesicular release of acetylcholine, as currently proposed in the neurotransmitter theory (43). One may assume, for example, that acetylcholine released at the endplate by nerve stimulation is initially confined to volume elements corresponding to only 1% of the total potential reaction space. If receptor and esterase remain homogeneously distributed in the reaction space, then the initial acetylcholine concentration in these volume elements is twentyfold in excess of the total receptor or esterase concentrations. Under these conditions local saturation of receptor and enzyme would quickly occur (the time to half-saturation of receptors would be of the order of 30 μsec and of the esterase, about 3 μsec) but would be counterbalanced by acetylcholine dilution arising from diffusion into the entire reaction space. Model calculations thus must consider both diffusion and chemical reactions. While this model qualitatively would appear to result in a more favorable competition of receptor for acetylcholine than in the homogeneous reaction space model above (i.e., a greater $[AR']_{max}/[A^0]$), the quantitative predictions of such a model are not evident simply by inspection.

B. SEQUENTIAL MODELS

Sequential processing of acetylcholine can occur if receptor and esterase are topologically arranged such that the receptor sites for the acetylcholine binding are closer to the sites of neurally triggered acetylcholine release. Such a nonhomogeneous protein distribution is involved in a spatial separation model, which proposes receptors clustered in the juxtaneuronal part of postsynaptic membranes and esterase distributed uniformly within the synaptic cleft (21,33). This spatial separation model also would suggest greater acetylcholine binding to receptor than in the homogeneous reaction space model but may conflict with the close coupling of receptor and esterase indicated by electrophysiological data. A quantitative treatment of this model is hampered by the lack of structural details on the exact localization of esterase relative to the receptor.

Quite a different line of thinking is involved in a *translocation* model for acetylcholine processing (9,72). This approach is based on a general acetylcholine theory of nerve excitation originally proposed and developed by Nachmansohn (1–5; see article by Nachmansohn in this volume). According to this model the reactions of acetylcholine with receptor and esterase are strictly organized, and close proximity of both proteins is assumed. Recently, explicit separation of the total reaction space into "microreaction spaces" has been introduced into the model (8,9). According to this concept, acetylcholine released by a nerve impulse first has access to receptor in a reaction space 1. The structural transition in the initial receptor–acetylcholine complex induced by acetylcholine binding translocates the bound acetylcholine ion to another reaction space 2 where acetylcholine dissociates and esterase activity prevents the return of acetylcholine to the receptor. Esterase activity is restricted to reaction space 2 and is thus an integral part of this sequential mechanism, insuring practically unidirectional flow of acetylcholine through the receptor system. This nonequilibrium aspect of the translocation model may be summarized in the flow scheme with separated reaction spaces shown in Fig. 8. The model may be applied both to conduction along excitable membranes and to transmission at the synapse (1–5, 8–10). At the synapse, presynaptic nerve stimulation causes a transient increase of K^+ ions in the synaptic gap. Since the postsynaptic membrane potential is sensitive to K^+, such an increase must lead to a potential

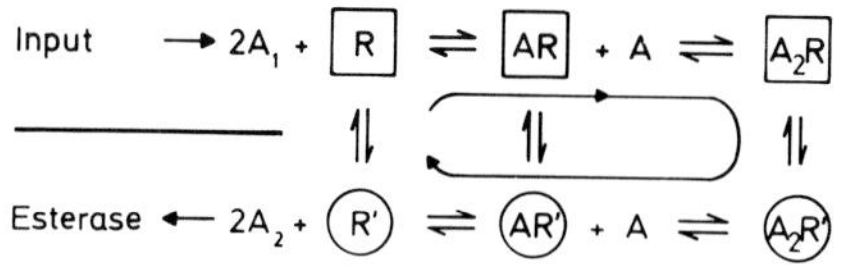

$$\text{Input} \longrightarrow 2A_1 + \boxed{R} \rightleftharpoons \boxed{AR} + A \rightleftharpoons \boxed{A_2R}$$

$$\text{Esterase} \longleftarrow 2A_2 + (R') \rightleftharpoons (AR') + A \rightleftharpoons (A_2R')$$

Fig. 8. Flow scheme for neurally triggered acetylcholine (input) in the sequential translocation model. The curved arrow indicates the flow of acetylcholine A_1 from a reaction space 1 through the closed (R) and open (R′) receptor states to reaction space 2 where also esterase has access to acetylcholine A_2.

change in the postsynaptic membrane. It is this change of membrane potential which has been proposed to induce a transient increase in the acetylcholine concentration in the (probably intramembraneous) reaction space 1 and thus to amplify the flow of acetylcholine along the reaction path $R \rightarrow A_2R \rightarrow A_2R' \rightarrow R$ (see curved arrow in Fig. 7). An essential role of K^+ ions at synapses is also emphasized by von Euler (see article by von Euler in this volume). Acetylcholine, once translocated into the (probably extramembranous) reaction space 2, is exposed to virtually irreversible hydrolysis by the esterase. Thus neural activity drives the schematic "receptor cycle" essentially clockwise in one direction. The postulated separation of receptor and esterase reactions insures optimal use of available acetylcholine and avoids problems arising from the slower association of acetylcholine with the receptor than with the esterase. The sequential character of the flow scheme would also account for the observation that the growth time of miniature end plate currents is independent of esterase inhibition (see Fig. 2). Finally, if the acetylcholine reaction with the receptor in reaction space 1 occurs intramembranously, locally high concentrations of acetylcholine should lead to local receptor saturation. However, as mentioned in the discussion of the various other models for the *in vivo* association of acetylcholine with receptor and esterase, a quantitative analysis of the translocation model must await the elucidation of further organizational and functional details of the receptor and esterase system.

Other unresolved problems of acetylcholine-mediated neuronal information transfer include the relevance of the phenomenon of pharmacological desensitization (67) and the functional role of presynaptic and extrasynaptic receptor and esterase. The neurotransmitter theory does not explicitly consider pre- and extrasynaptic cholinergic proteins; and the vesicle hypothesis, modeling synaptic vesicles as the exclusive source of acetylcholine released during excitation, does not incorporate the observation of nonpostsynaptic acetylcholine receptors. On the other hand, the postulate of an intramembranous processing of acetylcholine by receptors in all excitable membranes offers a functional role also for pre- and extrajunctional and axonal receptors (1–5).

While the quantitative estimates from the homogeneous reaction space assumption discussed above have suggested that the reaction space at the synapse is nonhomogeneous, there is currently no unequivocal evidence to differentiate between any of the alternative competitive or sequential models proposed. Thus the close functional relationship between receptor and esterase and the coupling of acetylcholine reactions to membrane permeability changes remain objects for experimental and theoretical studies.

APPENDIX: QUANTITATIVE SIMULATION OF NEURALLY EVOKED END PLATE CURRENTS ASSUMING A HOMOGENEOUS REACTION SPACE*

The general solutions to the differential equations arising from the receptor reaction scheme in Fig. 1 and the esterase reaction mechanism in Eq. (6) are too complex to be useful in this analysis. Simplifications and conditions introduced in Section VII will be assumed here: a homogeneous reaction space at the synapse; and the total concentrations $[R^0] \cong]E^0] \cong 5[A^0]$ estimated at a rat diaphragm end plate during a neurally triggered end plate current (epc). It follows that $[R] \cong [R^0]$ and $[E] \cong [E^0]$ during the entire duration of the epc (see Section VII). Additional simplifications in the chemical reaction schemes are indicated in the following paragraphs.

Electrophysiological data suggest that perturbations of receptor–acetylcholine equilibria in the end plate (e.g., by voltage-jump) result in epc relaxations that are characterized by a single exponential time course (66), and temperature-jump kinetic studies involving isolated receptor and acetylcholine show single exponential relaxations in the time range which corresponds to *in vivo* epcs (48). These observations suggest that the scheme of Fig. 1 can be reduced to the overall reaction shown in Eq. (A1).

$$A + R \underset{k_{-1}^{R*}}{\overset{k_1^{R*}}{\rightleftharpoons}} AR' \tag{A1}$$

In Eq. (A1), k_1^{R*} and k_{-1}^{R*} are observed composite rate constants containing rate constant terms from each reaction in Fig. 1. This reduction of the scheme in Fig. 1 can arise from several alternative physical situ-

* By T. L. Rosenberry.

ations. Examples include the case in which species R′ is negligible as a reaction partner and the equilibrium AR ⇌ AR′ is rapid; and the case in which R′ and AR are present only at low concentration in a steady-state and R′ makes only a small contribution as a reaction partner. A situation assumed in other treatments (37,66), that R′ is negligible and A + R ⇌ AR is rapid, could be modeled by an extension of the following calculations and would explicitly require the value of the rapid equilibrium dissociation constant.

Reduction of the acetylcholinesterase mechanism in Eq. (6) to that in Eq. (A2) follows simply from the stipulation that $[E] \cong [E^0]$.

$$\mathrm{A} + \mathrm{E} \underset{k_{-1}^{\mathrm{E}}}{\overset{k_1^{\mathrm{E}}}{\rightleftharpoons}} \mathrm{AE} \xrightarrow{k_2} \text{acetyl E} \tag{A2}$$

Because [E] is not determined by the extent of acetyl enzyme formation or by the rate of its hydrolysis, the deacetylation portion of the mechanism [k_3 in Eq. (6)] does not effect the time course of acetylcholine removal. This would eliminate, for example, any effect of substrate inhibition of deacetylation on the simulation of epcs below. The reaction in Eq. (A2) can be further simplified directly from the value of $k_2 \cong 10^5\ \mathrm{sec}^{-1}$ cited in Section V. This value indicates that a rapid steady-state between A + E and AE is achieved prior to the time course relevant to epcs.

The rate equations following from these reduced and simplified chemical equations are given in Eqs. (A3) and (A4),

$$\frac{d[\mathrm{AR}']}{dt} \cong k_1^{\mathrm{R}^*}[\mathrm{R}^0][\mathrm{A}] - k_{-1}^{\mathrm{R}^*}[\mathrm{AR}'] \tag{A3}$$

$$\begin{aligned}\frac{d([\mathrm{A}] + [\mathrm{AE}])}{dt} &\cong \left(1 + \frac{[\mathrm{E}^0]}{K_\mathrm{m}}\right)\frac{d[\mathrm{A}]}{dt} \\ &\cong -(k_1^{\mathrm{R}^*}[\mathrm{R}^0] + k^{\mathrm{E}^*}[\mathrm{E}^0])[\mathrm{A}] + k_{-1}^{\mathrm{R}^*}[\mathrm{AR}']\end{aligned} \tag{A4}$$

where $k^{\mathrm{E}^*} \equiv k_2/K_m$ and $K_m \equiv (k_{-1}^{\mathrm{E}} + k_2)/k_1^{\mathrm{E}}$ (see Section V). Equations (A3 and A4) contain only two time-dependent variables [AR′] and [A] and can be solved simultaneously by matrix methods (73) to yield the two time constants τ_I and τ_II which characterize the system. The reciprocal time constants, or reciprocal relaxation times, are given by Eq. (A5)

$$\tau^{-1} = \tfrac{1}{2}b[1 \pm \sqrt{1 - (4c/b^2)}] \tag{A5}$$

where τ_I^{-1} corresponds to the positive sign and τ_II^{-1}, to the negative sign. The constant terms b and c in Eq. (A5) are expressions involving the individual rate constants in Eqs. (A3) and (A4) and are defined below.

Although no further simplification is necessary for a precise mathematical description of the time dependence of [AR′] and [A], two further approximations are suggested by the magnitudes of the individual rate constants which simplify the expressions. These approximations require an estimate of the reaction space volume; this estimate is 450 μm^3 for the rat diaphragm end plates (33). Thus for 2×10^7 active sites for both receptor and esterase, the total active site concentration of each protein is 0.75×10^{-4} *M* within the homogeneous reaction space assumption. The first simplifying assumption is that the quantity $[E^0]/K_m < 1$ and hence is negligible in Eq. (A4). This is equivalent to assuming a negligibly low steady-state [AE]. This assumption is justified by values of $K_{app} \cong 10^{-4}$ *M*, $k_2 \cong 10^5$ sec^{-1} and $k_3 \cong 2 \times 10^4$ sec^{-1} in Section V, from which one can estimate K_m to be about 6×10^{-4} *M* and $[E^0]/K_m$ to be about 0.12. With this assumption *b* and *c* are given by Eqs. (A6) and (A7).

$$b \cong k_1{}^{R}\,[R^0] + k^{E}\,[E^0] + k_{-1}{}^{R} \tag{A6}$$

$$c \cong k^{E}\,[E^0]k_{-1}{}^{R} \tag{A7}$$

sec^{-1} in Sections V–VII, the values of all terms in Eqs. (A6) and (A7) except $k_{-1}{}^{R^*}$ are determined. An estimate of $k_{-1}{}^{R^*} = 0.5 \times 10^3$ sec^{-1} from electrophysiological data will be assumed (37,38,66). The second simplifying assumption is that the quantity $4c/b^2 < 1$ such that τ^{-1} in Eq. (A5) can be approximated by the first two terms of a power series as in Eq. (A8).

$$\tau^{-1} \cong \tfrac{1}{2}b[1 \pm (1 - 2c/b^2)] \tag{A8}$$

This assumption is justified by noting the values of $b = 2 \times 10^4$ sec^{-1} and $c = 8 \times 10^6$ sec^{-2}. The time constants τ_I and τ_{II} are now given by Eqs. (A9) and (A10).

$$\tau_I{}^{-1} \cong b - (c/b) \cong b \tag{A9}$$

$$\tau_{II}{}^{-1} \cong c/b \tag{A10}$$

Completing the matrix method solution with the boundary condition that at time zero $[A] = [A^0]$, one obtains Eq. (A11) for [AR′].

$$\frac{[AR']}{[A^0]} = \frac{k_1^{R^*}[R^0]}{\tau_I^{-1} - \tau_{II}^{-1}}(e^{-t/\tau_I} - e^{-t/\tau_{II}}) \quad (A11)$$

The smaller rate constant τ_{II}^{-1} determines the decay phase and according to Eq. (A10) and Eq. (A7) ff. is approximately $k_{-1}^{R^*}$. The maximum value of [AR′] is obtained by differentiating Eq. (A11) and determining the time t_p to peak amplitude [Eq. (A12)].

$$t_p = \frac{\ln(\tau_{II}/\tau_I)}{\tau_I^{-1} - \tau_{II}^{-1}} \quad (A12)$$

The calculated value of t_p is about 220 μsec. Substitution of t_p into Eq. (A11) gives $[AR']_{max}/[A^0] = 0.082$.

The reduced receptor reaction in Eq. (A1) can be expanded to include a dimeric A_2R' as the only state which corresponds to an open channel (see Fig. 7) as shown in Eq. (A13).

$$2\,A + R \underset{k_{-1}^{R*}}{\overset{2k_1^{R*}}{\rightleftharpoons}} AR' + A \underset{2k_{-1}^{R*}}{\overset{k_1^{R*}}{\rightleftharpoons}} A_2R' \quad (A13)$$

If, as indicated by the relative rate constants in Eq. (A13), both acetylcholine binding sites are equivalent and independent, then Eq. (A11) still holds, with the exception that AR′ in Eq. (A11) must be replaced by the total receptor-bound acetylcholine, defined as $[A_b] \equiv [AR'] + 2[A_2R']$. Since $[R^0] \gg [AR']$, to a good approximation $[AR'] \gg [A_2R']$. Then $[A_b] \cong [AR']$ and the rate equation for $[A_2R']$ is given in Eq. (A14)

$$\frac{d[A_2R']}{dt} \cong k_1^{R^*}[A][A_b] - 2k_{-1}^{R^*}[A_2R'] \quad (A14)$$

and integration gives Eq. (A15).

$$\frac{[A_2R']}{[A^0]} = \frac{(k_1^{R^*})^2[A^0][R^0]}{(\tau_I^{-1} - \tau_{II}^{-1})^2}[\tfrac{1}{2}e^{-2t/\tau_I} + \tfrac{1}{2}e^{-2t/\tau_{II}} - e^{-t(\tau_I^{-1}+\tau_{II}^{-1})}] \quad (A15)$$

It is noteworthy that Eqs. (A11) and (A15) still hold when $[E^0]$ is greatly reduced by an esterase inhibitor. The estimated $[A^0] \cong 1.5 \times 10^{-5}$ *M* is sufficiently below the esterase $K_{app} \cong 10^{-4}$ *M* that the initial approximation $[E] \cong [E^0]$ is still valid when $[E^0]$ is small. If $[E^0]$ is reduced to 1% of its initial value, $b = 2 \times 10^3$ sec^{-1} and $c = 8 \times 10^4$ sec^{-2}. The calculated t_p is 1970 μsec and $[AR']_{max}/[A^0] = 0.66$.

The calculated epc decay rate constant corresponds to τ_{II}^{-1} in Eq. (A11) and to $2\,\tau_{II}^{-1}$ in Eq. (A15). When 99% of the esterase is inhibited,

τ_{II}^{-1} becomes 35 sec^{-1}, somewhat smaller than the rate of diffusion from the synaptic cleft (see Section II); in this case the homogeneous reaction space assumption is not applicable. However, when 90% of the esterase is inhibited, τ_{II}^{-1} becomes 0.21×10^3 sec^{-1}, about half its original value. This calculation appears consistent with electrophysiological observations (37) and suggests that the homogeneous reaction space assumption can be applied to epc decay rate constants at moderate levels of esterase inhibition.

ACKNOWLEDGMENTS

The authors are indebted to Professor David Nachmansohn for stimulating our interest in this field. We also thank Ute Wolfänger for technical help.

This work was supported in part by the Stiftung Volkswagenwerk (Grant 112072) and by the Deutsche Forschungsgemeinschaft (Grant NE 227/1); also by the National Science Foundation (Grants PCM74-08394 and PCM73-00744) and the National Institutes of Health (Grant NS-11766).

REFERENCES

1. Nachmansohn, D. (1955) *Harvey Lect.* **49,** 57–99.
2. Nachmansohn, D. (1959) "Chemical and Molecular Basis of Nerve Activity." Academic Press, New York (revised, 1975).
3. Nachmansohn, D. (1971) *Handb. Sens. Physiol.* **I,** 18–102.
4. Nachmansohn, D. (1968) *Proc. Natl. Acad. Sci. U.S.A.* **61,** 1034–1041.
5. Nachmansohn, D. (1969) *J. Gen. Physiol.* **54,** 197S–224S.
6. Colquhoun, D. (1975) *Annu. Rev. Pharmacol.* **15,** 307–320.
7. del Castillo, J., and Katz, B. (1957) *Proc. R. Soc. London, Ser. B* **146,** 369–381.
8. Rawlings, P. K., and Neumann, E. (1976) *Proc. Natl. Acad. Sci. U.S.A.* **73,** 4492–4496.
9. Neumann, E., Nachmansohn, D., and Katchalsky, A. (1973) *Proc. Natl. Acad. Sci. U.S.A.* **70,** 727–731.
10. Neumann, E., and Bernhardt, J. (1977) *Annu. Rev. Biochem.* **46,** 117–141.
11. Dudai, Y., and Silman, I. (1974) *J. Neurochem.* **23,** 1177–1187.
12. Changeux, J.-P. (1975) *Handb. Psychopharmacol.* **6,** 235–301.
13. Rosenberry, T. L. (1975) *Adv. Enzymol.* **43,** 103–218.
14. Hall, Z. W. (1973) *J. Neurobiol.* **4,** 343–361.
15. McIntosh, C. S. H., and Plummer, D. T. (1973) *Biochem. J.* **133,** 655–665.
16. Lwebuga-Makasa, J. S., Lappi, S., and Taylor, P. (1976) *Biochemistry* **15,** 1425–1434.
17. Rosenberry, T. L., and Richardson, J. (1977) *Biochemistry* **16,** 3550–3558.
18. Koelle, G. B., ed. (1963) "Cholinesterases and Anticholinesterase Agents." Springer-Verlag, Berlin and New York.
19. Bloom, F. E., and Barrnett, R. J. (1966) *J. Cell Biol.* **29,** 475–495.
20. Brzin, M. (1966) *Proc. Natl. Acad. Sci. U.S.A.* **56,** 1560–1563.

21. Fertuck, H. C., and Salpeter, M. M. (1976) *J. Cell Biol.* **69,** 144–158.
22. Salpeter, M. M., Plattner, H., and Rogers, A. W. (1972) *J. Histochem. Cytochem.* **20,** 1059–1068.
23. Rogers, A. W., Darzynkiewicz, Z., Salpeter, M. M., Ostrowski, K., and Barnard, E. A. (1969) *J. Cell Biol.* **41,** 665–685.
24. Ringel, S. P., Bender, A. N., Festoff, B. W., Engel, W. K., Vogel, Z., and Daniels, M. P. (1975) *Nature (London)* **225,** 730–731.
25. Lentz, T. L., Mazurkiewicz, J., and Rosenthal, J. (1977) *Brain Res.* **132,** 423–442.
26. Changeux, J.-P., Kasai, M., and Lee, C. Y. (1970) *Proc. Natl. Acad. Sci. U.S.A.* **67,** 1241–1247.
27. Karlin, A., Prives, J., Deal, W., and Winnik, M. (1971) *J. Mol. Biol.* **61,** 175–188.
28. Miledi, R., and Potter, L. T. (1971) *Nature (London)* **233,** 599–603.
29. Porter, C. W., Chiu, T. H., Wiechowski, J., and Barnard, E. A. (1973) *Nature (London), New Biol.* **241,** 3–7.
30. Berg, D. K., Kelly, R. B., Sargent, P. B., Williamson, P., and Hall, Z. W. (1972) *Proc. Natl. Acad. Sci. U.S.A.* **69,** 147–151.
31. Fambrough, D. M., and Hartzell, H. C. (1972) *Science* **176,** 189–191.
32. Barnard, E. A., and Rogers, A. W. (1971) *In* "Cholinergic Ligand Interactions" (D. J. Triggle, J. F. Morgan, and E. A. Barnard, eds.), p. 175. Academic Press, New York.
33. Salpeter, M. M., and Eldefrawi, M. E. (1973) *J. Histochem. Cytochem.* **21,** 769–778.
34. Bourgeois, J.-P., Kyter, A., Menez, A., Fromageot, P., Boquet, P., and Changeux, J.-P. (1972) *FEBS Lett.* **25,** 127–133.
35. Fatt, P., and Katz, B. (1951) *J. Physiol. (London)* **115,** 320–370.
36. Nastuk, W. L., and Alexander, J. T. (1954) *J. Pharmacol. Exp. Ther.* **111,** 302–328.
37. Magleby, K. L., and Stevens, C. F. (1972) *J. Physiol. (London)* **223,** 173–197.
38. Gage, P. W., and McBurney, R. N. (1975) *J. Physiol. (London)* **244,** 385–407.
39. Anderson, C. R., and Stevens, C. F. (1973) *J. Physiol. (London)* **235,** 655–691.
40. Kordas, S. M. (1972) *J. Physiol. (London)* **224,** 317–332.
41. Katz, B., and Miledi, R. (1973) *J. Physiol. (London)* **231,** 549–557.
42. Magleby, K. L., and Terrar, D. A. (1975) *J. Physiol. (London)* **244,** 467–495.
43. Katz, B. (1969) "The Release of Neural Transmitter Substances." Liverpool Univ. Press, Liverpool.
44. Eigen, M., and DeMaeyer, L. (1963) *Tech. Org. Chem.* **8,** Part 2, 895–1054.
45. Eigen, M., and DeMaeyer, L. (1973) *Tech. Chem. (N.Y.)* **6,** Part 2, 63–146.
46. Winkler-Oswatitsch, R. (1969) Thesis, Göttingen and Vienna.
47. Rosenberry, T. L., and Neumann, E. (1977) *Biochemistry* **16,** 3870–3878.
48. Neumann, E., and Chang, H. W. (1976) *Proc. Natl. Acad. Sci. U.S.A.* **73,** 3994–3998.
49. Chang, H. W., and Neumann, E. (1976) *Proc. Natl. Acad. Sci. U.S. A.* **73,** 3364–3368.
50. Neumann, E., and Chang, H. W. (1978) In preparation.
51. Rieger, F., Bon, S., Massoulié, J., and Cartaud, J. (1973) *Eur. J. Biochem.* **34,** 539–547.
52. Dudai, Y., Herzberg, M., and Silman, I. (1973) *Proc. Natl. Acad. Sci. U.S.A.* **70,** 2473–2476.
53. Massoulié, J., and Rieger, F. (1969) *Eur. J. Biochem.* **11,** 441–455.
54. Hall, Z. W., and Kelly, R. (1971) *Nature (London), New Biol.* **232,** 62–63.
55. Betz, W., and Sakmann, B. (1973). *J. Physiol. (London)* **230,** 673–688.
56. Wilson, I. B., and Cabib, E. (1956) *J. Am. Chem. Soc.* **78,** 202–207.
56a. Rothenberg, M. A., and Nachmansohn, D. (1947) *J. Biol. Chem.* **168,** 223–231.
57. Rosenberry, T. L. (1975) *Proc. Natl. Acad. Sci. U.S.A.* **72,** 3834–3838.
58. Augustinsson, K. B. (1963) *In* Cholinesterases and Anticholinesterase Agents" (G. B. Koelle, ed.), p. 89. Springer-Verlag, Berlin and New York.
59. Aldridge, W. N., and Reiner, E. (1969) *Biochem. J.* **115,** 147–162.

60. Krupka, R. M., and Laidler, K. J. (1961) *J. Am. Chem. Soc.* **83**, 1445–1460.
61. Rosenberry, T. L., and Bernhard, S. A. (1972) *Biochemistry* **11**, 4308–4321.
62. Nolte, H. J., Rosenberry, T. L., and Neumann, E. (1978) In preparation.
63. Gibson, R. E., O'Brien, R. D., Edelstein, S. J., and Thompson, W. R. (1976) *Biochemistry* **15**, 2377–2382.
64. Chang, H. W., and Bock, E. (1977) *Biochemistry* **16**, 4513–4520.
65. Eldefrawi, M. E., Eldefrawi, A. T., Penfield, L. A., O'Brien, R. D., and Van Campen, D. (1975) *Life Sci.* **16**, 925–935.
66. Sheridan, R. Z., and Lester, H. A. (1977) *J. Gen. Physiol.* **70**, 187–219.
67. Katz, B., and Thesleff, S. (1957) *J. Physiol. (London)* **138**, 63–80.
68. Mitchell, J. F., and Krnjevic, K. (1961) *J. Physiol. (London)* **155**, 246–262.
69. Potter, L. T. (1970) *J. Physiol. (London)* **206**, 144–166.
70. Katz, B., and Miledi, R. (1965) *Proc. R. Soc. London, Ser. B* **161**, 483–496.
71. Takeuchi, A., and Takeuchi, N. (1959) *J. Neurophysiol.* **22**, 395–411.
72. Neumann, E. (1974) *In* "Biochemistry of Sensory Functions" (L. Jaenicke, ed.), pp. 465–510. Springer-Verlag, Berlin and New York.
73. Perrin, C. L. (1970) "Mathematics for Chemists," pp. 279–282. Wiley (Interscience), New York.

PART III

AMINO ACID SYSTEMS

Roles of GABA in Neurons in Information Processing in the Vertebrate CNS

EUGENE ROBERTS
Division of Neurosciences
City of Hope National Medical Center
Duarte, California

INTRODUCTION

γ-Aminobutyric acid (GABA) was the first amino acid shown to function as a neurotransmitter in both vertebrate and invertebrate nervous systems. Much of the key evidence for this role of GABA has been obtained at a few relatively accessible synaptic sites, i.e., the crayfish stretch receptor sensory neuron, the mammalian cerebellar Purkinje cell, and the neuromuscular junction of the lobster, where release of GABA related to nerve stimulation has been detected. Whether released from neurons or externally applied, GABA most often exerts inhibitory or hyperpolarizing effects. Recent data, however, suggest a greater versatility for GABA, since it also appears to have excitatory or depolarizing actions. In this paper no attempt will be made to summarize the vast literature dealing with GABA function and metabolism. This has been done in books and reviews, and several representative ones can be found in the reference list (1–10). Instead, a personalized and selective view of a few of the cutting edges that eventually may be referable to the role of GABA neurons in information processing will be given.

The demonstration that a synapse is a GABA-releasing one is not sufficient evidence to identify it as an inhibitory synapse. Supporting physiological evidence is always necessary for such a functional assignment to be made. However, in almost all instances adequately

ISBN 0-12-398450-5

studied to date the overall effects of GABA, where GABA synapses are known to exist, have been found to be inhibitory either at pre- or post-synaptic sites.

GABA typically produces an increase in membrane permeability to chloride ions that is measured as an increase in membrane conductance. Chloride ions then tend to distribute across the membrane according to its equilibrium potential, which usually is similar to the resting potential of the cell. The resultant effect is to "clamp" the membrane potential near the equilibrium level for chloride ions. Because the latter potential usually is more negative than the resting potential, the action of GABA most often decreases the sensitivity of the membrane to ongoing or subsequent depolarizing stimuli. Thus, in most instances studied, GABA has been shown to exert a hyperpolarizing or inhibitory effect via the above mechanism. Recent evidence suggests that GABA may be the transmitter mediating presynaptic inhibition in the spinal cord and other regions in the vertebrate CNS and that it acts by producing depolarization of primary afferent terminals, resulting in a decreased probability of release of quanta of excitatory transmitter from the excitatory nerve endings. GABA also has been reported to have a depolarizing action on cell bodies of primary afferent neurons located in sensory ganglia. This may result from the cell body having receptors similar to those of synaptic endings. When producing depolarization, GABA also acts by increasing permeability of membranes to Cl^-. The decreases in membrane potential produced by GABA action in these latter instances probably are attributable to relatively high intracellular Cl^- concentrations (11).

It should be kept in mind that, where they are found, GABA neurons could cause excitation of other neurons that release GABA or other transmitter substances. Indeed, recently it has been reported that GABA causes excitation of cholinergic motoneurons, which in turn cause the contraction of the muscle fibers of sea urchin tube feet (12). This further emphasizes the importance of detailed physiological analysis in ascribing roles to GABA neurons in any region of the nervous system. This is particularly important and difficult in the nonlaminar neostriatum, where densely packed, local-circuit GABA and cholinergic neurons seem to bear complex relationships to each other, to the axon terminals of fibers entering from the substantia nigra, cortex, and thalamus, and to the dendrites and somata of GABA and substance P-containing neurons whose processes leave the neostriatum to enter the substantia nigra and globus pallidus.

A consideration of the biochemical, pharmacological, and physiological data available on the function of GABA and nervous system function suggested that, in general, the major neuronal system exerting tonic inhibition on pacemaker neurons might be the system of inhibitory neurons utilizing GABA as transmitter (13–15). Of course, GABA neurons perform a myriad of other functions in nervous system information processing, some of which will be discussed in relation to the results of our immunocytochemical studies. GABA neurons are present ubiquitously in the CNS of vertebrate species and, on a quantitative basis, GABA is more extensively and more evenly distributed throughout the various brain regions than the neuronal systems that employ other known neurotransmitters such as acetylcholine, the catecholamines, or serotonin. Biochemical analytical measurements have shown the presence of glutamic acid decarboxylase (GAD) and GABA in many regions of the vertebrate CNS. With newly developed immunocytochemical techniques, various aspects of the normal morphology and connectivity of GABA neurons are being worked out in regions of the CNS. Eventually it even may be possible to determine whether or not deficiencies might exist in the relative number of GABA neurons or whether defects may occur in their relationships to other types of neurons in pathologic states in humans (e.g., Huntington's chorea, schizophrenia, epilepsy).

DISINHIBITION AS A MAJOR ORGANIZING PRINCIPLE

In order to achieve some insight into the principles by which normal systems work, it is important to construct progressively more adequate theoretical and frankly speculative frameworks. An integration of the information coming in at an ever-accelerating rate from various pertinent disciplines eventually may enable us to comprehend the continuity that exists "from the couch to the molecule" (13,15–26).

A major tenet of the writer's *current view* is that in behavioral sequences, innate or learned, genetically preprogrammed circuits are released to function at varying rates and in various combinations largely by the disinhibition of pacemaker neurons whose activities are under the control of tonically active inhibitory command neurons, many of which may use GABA as transmitter. In this connection, it is of great interest that recent experiments show that at the neuromuscular junction of the crab there is tonic release of inhibitory transmitter (probably GABA) that acts both presynaptically and postsynaptically (27). Such circuits may be released by inhibition of the neurons which are tonically holding in check pacemaker cells with capacity for spontaneous activity. If the pacemaker neurons are triggering a circuit related to the regulation of a vital function (e.g., heart action or respiration), the inhibitory neurons might act in such a way as to vary the rate of the discharge of the pacemaker neurons. On the other hand, pacemaker neurons in circuits in behavioral sequences involving the voluntary movements of the limb muscles might be held in complete check by the tonic action of local circuit inhibitory neurons and might be allowed to discharge in a graded manner only on demand. According to this view, excitatory input to pacemaker neurons would have largely a modulatory role (28).

> Thus, disinhibition, acting in conjunction with intrinsic pacemaker activity and often with modulatory excitatory input, appears to be one of the major organizing principles in nervous system function. Disinhibition may act as a switch, turning on a specific coherent neuronal pattern which is otherwise actively and continuously inhibited, as well as play a role in the organization of sequential and alternating discharges among separate groups of elements (28).

For the sake of simplicity, let us suppose that in a simple linear series of three neurons and a muscle fiber, a neuron, A, controls through a single interneuron, B, the activity of a motor neuron, C, which, if left alone, could discharge spontaneously at a rapid rate causing the muscle fiber to contract. Let us also suppose that the interneuron, B, is a tonically active inhibitory neuron from which, in the absence of input from the first neuron in the series, A, an inhibitory chemical transmitter substance is liberated at such a rate that the membrane potential of the motor neuron is clamped at a level below the firing level, and the muscle fiber does not contract. If the first neuron in the series, A, is inhibitory, an increase in its rate of discharge upon the interneuron, B, will decrease the inhibition from the interneuron on the motor neuron. As a result, the motor neuron, C, will fire; this, in turn, will cause contraction to take place. There is evidence that a simple circuit, similar in principle to that described above, may operate in the control of insect flight and leg muscles and that, at least in the case of the flight system, the inhibitory command neuron uses GABA as a transmitter (29).

Let us now substitute for the muscle fiber in the above model an entire genetically preprogrammed neuronal circuit. The pacemaker for the firing of the preprogrammed circuit would then be analogous to the motor neuron, C, in the preceding model. The tonically active inhibitory interneuron, B, would be the command neuron for the circuit, and the inhibitory neuron, A, acting on the latter interneuron, would be the disinhibiting or releasing neuron coming from a neuronal circuit higher in the control hierarchy or from one preceding it in a temporal sequence. There could be multiple excitatory and inhibitory inputs onto both the pacemaker and command neurons. However, the model requires that, in most instances, decrease or cessation of the inhibitory signal from the command neuron would be a necessary but not always sufficient condition for the firing of a pacemaker neuron. Excitatory input to the pacemaker neuron may be required for it to depolarize to the firing level even when the tonic inhibitory influence on it has been completely removed.

Most of the activity within the stomatogastric ganglion in the lobster is integrated by mechanisms involving inhibition and disinhibition rather than by direct excitation, whereas the final motor messages to the stomach muscles are excitatory (28,30–33). The cerebellar cortex has two known excitatory inputs, the climbing fibers to the Purkinje cells and mossy fiber endings on the granule cells. All of the known interneurons in the cerebellar cortex (stellate, basket, and Golgi type II cells) are inhibitory, as are the sole output neurons, the Purkinje cells (34). Immunocytochemical work in our laboratory (see Table I) (35–61) has shown that probably all of the latter cells use GABA as transmitter. Inhibitory neurons interact with other inhibitory neurons regardless of the transmitter which they employ. The cerebellar Purkinje cells, GABA-releasing neurons, are inhibited by basket and stellate cells, which also are GABA-releasing neurons; Purkinje cells also may be inhibited, possibly nonspecifically, through the widely ramifying norepinephrine (NE)-releasing endings of nerve fibers which have their cells of origin in the locus coeruleus (62). Thus, inhibitory neurons utilizing GABA as a transmitter can be inhibited by other GABA neurons and by noradrenergic neurons. In the complex arrangements of various regions of the CNS, various combinations of inhibitory neurons can act upon each other (15).

Indigenous spinal circuits in the cat can be released for action, at least in part, by the disinhibitory action of descending NE fibers originating from cells lying in the "mesencephalic locomotor region" (63–65). In the spinal cord, iontophoretically administered NE has been shown to have inhibitory effects (66). NE-mediated inhibition in spinal trigeminal neurons has been found to originate in the locus coeruleus (67). Acute spinal cats ordinarily show neither postural nor locomotor activity. However, after intravenous administration of clonidine, a drug that specifically stimulates central α-noradrenergic receptors and that passes the blood brain barrier, it was possible to elicit walking behavior on a moving treadmill with a speed that can be adjusted by the speed of the treadmill. In the best preparations "this locomotion looks normal to the eye with smooth alternating movements

TABLE I

Development of the Immunocytochemistry of GABA-Related Enzymes

Steps along the way	Date	References
1. Purification and Properties		
GAD		
Purification and characterization of glutamate decarboxylase from mouse brain	1973	Wu, Matsuda, and Roberts (35)
Electrophoresis of glutamic acid decarboxylase from mouse brain in sodium dodecyl sulfate polyacrylamide gels	1973	Matsuda, Wu, and Roberts (36)
Properties of brain L-glutamate decarboxylase: inhibition studies	1974	Wu and Roberts (37)
GABA-T		
Purification and characterization of the 4-aminobutyrate-2-ketoglutarate transaminase from mouse brain	1973	Schousboe, Wu, and Roberts (38)
Subunit structure and kinetic properties of 4-aminobutyrate-2-keto glutarate transaminase purified from mouse brain	1974	Schousboe, Wu, and Roberts (39)
SUMMARY		
Purification, characterization, and kinetic studies of GAD and GABA-T from mouse brain	1976	Wu (40)
3. Immunocytochemical Approaches (continued)		
The fine structural localization of glutamate decarboxylase in developing axonal processes and presynaptic terminals of rodent cerebellum	1975	McLaughlin, Wood, Saito, Roberts, and Wu (48)
Immunocytochemical localization of glutamate decarboxylase in rat spinal cord	1975	McLaughlin, Barber, Saito, Roberts, and Wu (49)
Immunocytochemical localization of glutamate decarboxylase in the substantia nigra of the rat	1976	Ribak, Vaughn, Saito, and Barber (50)
Immunocytochemical localization of glutamate decarboxylase in rat substantia nigra	1976	Ribak, Vaughn, Saito, Barber, and Roberts (51)
Immunocytochemical localization of glutamate decarboxylase (GAD) in the olfactory bulb	1976	Ribak, Vaughn, and Saito (52)
Glutamate decarboxylase (GAD) localization in neurons of the olfactory bulb	1977	Ribak, Vaughn, Saito, Barber, and Roberts (53)
Immunocytochemical localization of GAD in somata and dendrites of	1976	Ribak and Vaughn (54)

2. Immunological Studies		
GAD		
Immunochemical studies on glutamic decarboxylase from mouse brain	1973	Matsuda, Wu, and Roberts (41)
Immunochemical comparisons of vertebrate glutamic acid decarboxylase	1974	Saito, Wu, Matsuda, and Roberts (42)
Immunochemical studies of brain glutamate decarboxylase and GABA-transaminase of six inbred strains of mice	1974	Wong, Schousboe, Saito, Wu, and Roberts (43)
GABA-T		
Some immunochemical properties and species specificity of GABA-α-ketoglutarate (also see ref. 43)	1974	Saito, Schousboe, Wu, and Roberts (44)
SUMMARY		
Immunochemical studies of glutamate decarboxylase and GABA-α-ketoglutarate transaminase	1976	Saito (45)
3. Immunocytochemical Approaches		
GAD		
Immunohistochemical localization of glutamate decarboxylase in rat cerebellum	1974	Saito, Barber, Wu, Matsuda, Roberts, and Vaughn (46)
The fine structural localization of glutamate decarboxylase in synaptic terminals of rodent cerebellum	1974	McLaughlin, Wood, Saito, Barber, Vaughn, Roberts, and Wu (47)
GABAergic neurons following colchicine treatment		
The immunocytochemical localization of GAD within stellate neurons of rat visual cortex	1976	Ribak (55)
Immunocytochemical localization of glutamic acid decarboxylase in neuronal somata following colchicine inhibition of axonal transport	1978	Ribak, Vaughn, and Saito (56)
GABAergic terminals are presynaptic to primary afferent terminals in the substantia gelatinosa of the rat spinal cord: Morphological substrates for presynaptic modification of cutaneous afferent activity	1978	Barber, Vaughn, Saito, McLaughlin, and Roberts (57)
Immunocytochemical localization of GAD in electron microscopic preparations of rodent CNS	1976	Wood, McLaughlin, and Vaughn (58)
GABA-T		
See Wood *et al.* (58)		
SUMMARIES		
Light microscopic visualization of GAD and GABA-T in immunocytochemical preparations of rodent CNS	1976	Barber and Saito (59)
Immunochemistry of the GABA system—a novel approach to an old transmitter	1976	Roberts (60)
Immunocytochemical identification of GABAergic neurons	1977	Saito, Roberts, and Barber (61)

in all joints" (68). Thus, stimulation of nonadrenergic receptors on neurons in the cord, combined with stimulation by a treadmill, can release the expression of neuronal programs for coordinated postural control and locomotion that are located entirely in the cord.

My view, then, of a basic nervous system is one in which genetic programs are translated via derepression and repression of the synthesis of specific proteins during development into the laying down of mainline neural circuits that, by themselves, could give rise only to stereotypical behavioral expression. It would seem that once circuits like those proposed above had arisen originally, they would eventually have been "printed" repeatedly in newly developed portions of the nervous system as a result of gene duplication, mutation, and selection. In the newer regions of the nervous system, the relations of the old, or original circuits, to each other and to more recently developed ones would be contextually different than before, and more complex. Ever more subtle integration of information about events within the organism and outside of it would become possible, leading to greater capacity for adaptive behavior. At some time in evolutionary history, possibly coincidentally with the appearance of various types of local circuit neurons, there arose the capacity of nervous systems to undergo plastic changes (increases or decreases in synaptic connectivity; see Roberts and Mathysse, 18) so that, as a result of experience, there existed an increased probability of using some of the genetically preprogrammed circuits ("hard-wired") in combinations and/or sequences which themselves may not be genetically determined.

Nervous systems are not permissive or democratic; they are hierarchical. In a hierarchical segmental system, such as has been found in crustacea and analyzed in the case of the system involved in control of swimmeret movement in the crayfish (69,70), the activity of an inhibitory command neuron of a particular segment is controlled to a considerable extent by the neuronal activities of the segments above it in the hierarchy, with the head ganglion or brain exerting the highest level of control. If the communication between the segments is interrupted by cutting the connectives, command neurons within each particular segment assume control of the activity of the segment. Segmental pacemaker neurons, like the circuits they activate, are largely controlled by local inhibitory command neurons and the degree of inhibition is controlled from above. A decrease in inhibition allows the pacemaker neurons to fire, thereby releasing the preprogrammed circuits over whose activity they preside. Striking instances of this are the release of the highly coordinated stereotypical sexual behavior of the male praying mantis when his head is bitten off by the female (71) and the once-familiar sight of a headless chicken running.

The easiest behavioral sequences to observe and study are the most primitive, stereotypical ones. It is surprising how much of the so-called normal activity even of human beings consists of this type of behavior, clear demonstrations of which may be the stereotypical postural and movement effects and the paranoia released by overdoses of amphetamines (72) or seen in some types of mental disorders. Paranoid thinking may be a complicated, but stereotypical, genetically preprogrammed process that can be disinhibited or released by skillful demagogues as well as by drugs—and most effectively by a combination of both. Some of our deepest and most cherished emotions may be the phenotypic of expression of genetically preprogrammed circuits, which, once disinhibited or "turned on," follow an invariant and stereotypical course in a particular individual. Learning may not be possible within such circuits, but what must be learned is the context within which the circuits are switched on.

GABA NEURONS AND PROBLEMS OF FUNCTIONAL COORDINATION IN THE NERVOUS SYSTEM

The successful or adaptive operation of a nervous system, such as discussed above, requires a coordination of neuronal activity which can determine the ability of an individual to prevent the too-frequent firing of preprogrammed circuits of behavioral options spontaneously or maladaptively and, under a variety of environmental circumstances, internal and external, to maintain within physiologic limits the rates of operation of continuously needed neuronal circuits, such as those required for cardiac function, respiration, and maintenance of blood pressure. When gross malfunctions of the coordination of inhibitory and disinhibitory neuronal systems occur, there may result lethal effects either through generalized seizures or cessation of operation of some vital function; alternatively, some obviously severe neurological dysfunctions may result. Of course, the coordinative capacity of a nervous system must, in the long run, enable an organism to survive physically in whatever environment it exists and to reproduce sufficiently to ensure continuity of the species.

When there is incoordination between the GABA system and other neurotransmitter systems, for whatever reason, the defect might be restricted to a local brain region, might include several regions, or might be global throughout the CNS. Under relatively simple environmental conditions, the nervous system in such individuals could function in an apparently adequate adaptive manner, which might appear to be in the normal range. As the complexity and intensity of environmental inputs is increased, there would be a correlated increased degree of incoordination. Then, those systems in the nervous system that are most poorly controlled will tend to break down under the stress and produce symptoms that are consequent to such a breakdown. Most individuals have an Achilles heel, a physiological breaking point that starts from a relatively poorly compensated region in the CNS. In this respect, it is interesting that among individuals in whom there is a maladaptive response to stress, there are those who respond to perceived environmental pressures with gastrointestinal symptoms, cardiac problems, skin outbreaks, respiratory ailments, etc. There, no doubt, may be strong hereditary factors as well as learning factors involved in the development of so-called "psychosomatic" illnesses.

Let us suppose that for some reason in the entire brain or in specific regions, the inhibitory GABA neurons have a considerably lower-than-normal effectiveness on their recipient neurons, which themselves are normally effective. As the complexity and intensity of environmental inputs is increased, there would be an increase of excitatory influences on pacesetter neurons, possibly to a considerable extent via the monoaminergic systems. Since the activities of many catecholamine neurons also probably are powerfully inhibited by intersystem GABA neurons, as are the nigral dopamine neurons, this could lead to a vicious cycle of relative hyperfunction of the monoaminergic system and hypofunction of the GABA system. More-than-normal numbers of behavioral options or inappropriate ones would be released (behavior disorders, mania, schizophrenia, etc.); choreic movements, seizures, or spasticity might occur; there might be hypersensitivity to pain, etc.; and greater-than-normal degrees of changes in responses would be observed in autonomic functions. For instance, if special hypothalamic regions were affected, greater-than-normal degrees of changes in responses might be observed in emotional reactivity, cardiac and respiratory functions, blood pressure, food and water intake, sweating, galvanic skin response, insulin secretion, liberation of gastric acid, motility of the colon, etc. Recent experimental results suggest that GABA neurons may play an important role in control mechanisms in the hypothalamic feeding and satiety centers (73). In a similar fashion, GABA neurons may play important roles in the regulation of other hypothalamic neural functions and in the release of a variety of hypothalamic hormones. On the other hand, if the GABA neurons function normally but the monoaminergic neurons are inadequate, then one might expect evidence of hypoactivity (Parkinson's disease, depression, etc.). Rational pharmacological approaches to correcting imbalances between the GABA and monoaminergic systems should include use of combinations of drugs and procedures that specifically can block or amplify their activities.

IDENTIFYING GABA-RELEASING NEURONS IN REGIONS OF THE VERTEBRATE CNS

Until quite recently, the localization of GABA neurons has been inferred by correlating microchemical, electrophysiological, pharmacological, and iontophoretic studies with what was known of the cytoarchitecture of specific regions of brain and spinal cord (1,2,5). A common approach has been to study a particular biochemical variable in whole brain or in some grossly defined regions of brain or spinal cord. Analyses of GABA contents and GAD activities were performed in almost all identifiable brain structures and in the spinal cord. Some studies have combined biochemical analyses with various types of lesioning procedures in attempts to correlate specific neural degenerations with losses of GAD and GABA. The distributions of the components of the GABA system also were studied extensively by subcellular fractionation techniques in preparations from whole brain or selected regions (74). Interpretation of results from the above types of analyses always suffered from the lack of definition attributable to the presence of millions of cells of different types in any dissected region, and definitive conclusions were not possible about specific synaptic connections. Individual cell bodies of large neurons, such as Purkinje cells, also were dissected out and subjected to microanalytical analyses. Even in the latter instance there were serious questions, since adhering to the neuronal somata were presynaptic endings from the axons of other neurons, and it was not possible to estimate the proportions of a particular measured variable contributed by somata or presynaptic endings. Furthermore, the technical difficulties involved precluded the study of large numbers of neurons in this manner. None of the above approaches made it possible to obtain a definitive understanding of how GABA neurons might participate in information processing in different parts of the vertebrate CNS. To begin to achieve this minimally, direct visualization of GABA neurons and nerve endings at histological and cytological levels was necessary. The purifica-

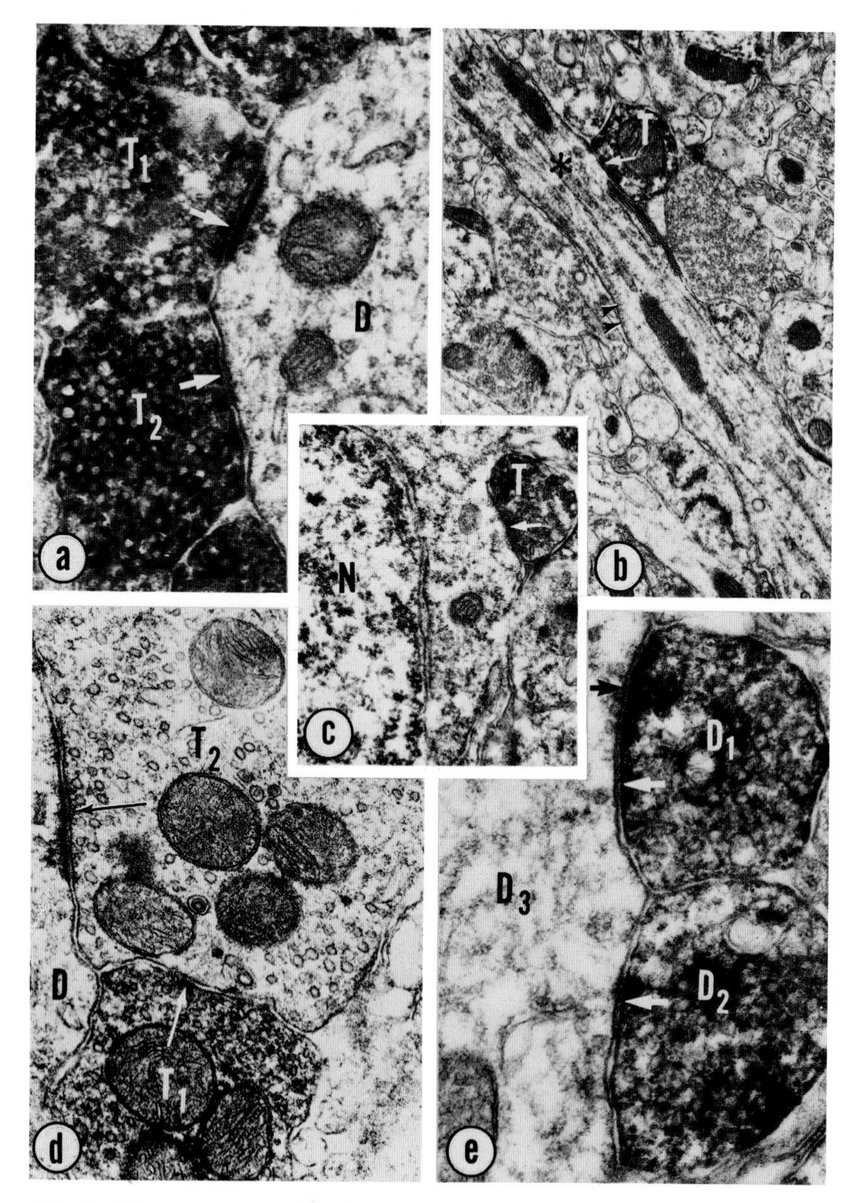

Fig. 1 Electron micrographs of various types of synaptic junctions formed by presynaptic terminals which contain glutamate decarboxylase (GAD), the enzyme that synthesizes the neurotransmitter γ-aminobutyric acid (GABA). All specimens were obtained from rat CNS, and all were prepared according to immunoperoxidase procedures developed for the ultrastructural localization of GAD (49,51). (a) Axodendritic synapses in the substantia nigra. Two axon terminals (T_1 and T_2) filled with electron opaque,

tion of mouse brain GAD, the enzyme that catalyzes the formation of GABA from glutamic acid, and the preparation of antibodies to it now have provided a means for the direct visualization of GABA neurons and their endings at the light and electron microscopic levels through the use of immunocytochemical peroxidase labeling procedures. The basic strategy employed by us and the chronology of its achievement can be seen from Table I, in which are listed the titles of the relevant papers that have been published to date or are in press. These publications can be consulted for relevant procedural details.

One of the crucial tests for determining whether a compound is a neurotransmitter is the direct demonstration of a synthetic capacity to form the compound at its site of action, the synapse. It is believed that the major information processing units in the nervous system are synapses. Therefore, if one is to attempt to elucidate the role of GABA in information processing one must be able to visualize the synaptic arrangements in which GABA neurons participate. Some types of probable GABA-releasing synapses are illustrated in Fig. 1. GABA neurons have been found to form axodendritic, axosomatic, axoaxonic, and dendrodendritic synapses in the various regions of rat CNS studied to date. In almost all instances several, if not all, of these types of GABA synapses are found in close proximity to each other. Employing even relatively refined dissection and sampling techniques, portions of tissue removed for chemical analysis probably contain a complex mixture of somata and nerve endings of such GABA-releasing neurons. Since in most instances the physiological consequences of

---

GAD-positive reaction product are shown to synapse with a dendritic shaft (D) in the pars reticulata. One of the terminals (T_1) forms an asymmetric synaptic junction (arrow), while the other terminal (T_2) forms a symmetric synapse (arrow). ×44,000. (b) An axoaxonal synapse in the cerebral cortex. A GAD-positive axon terminal (T) is shown forming a symmetric synapse (arrow) with an axon initial segment identified by a dense undercoating of the axolemma (arrow heads) and a fasciculation of microtubules (e.g., asterisk). ×20,000. (c) An axosomatic synapse in the dorsal horn of the spinal cord. A probable synaptic junction (arrow) is shown between a GAD-positive terminal (T) and a neuron (N) in the substantia gelatinosa. ×26,000. (d) An axoaxonal synapse in the dorsal horn of the spinal cord. A synaptic junction (white arrow) is shown between the GAD-positive presynaptic terminal (T_1) and another synaptic terminal (T) which is not GAD-positive. In addition, T_2 is the presynaptic component of another synaptic junction (black arrow) with a dendrite (D). ×38,000. (e) Dendrodendritic synapses in the glomerular layer of the olfactory bulb. Two GAD-positive gemmules (D_1, D_2) from dendrites of periglomerular neurons form synapses with a mitral/tufted dendritic shaft (D_3). One gemmule (D_1) appears to form a reciprocal synapse and the other gemmule (D_2) appears to be presynaptic only. ×54,000. Directions of synaptic transmission are indicated by arrows in a–e. Electron micrographs provided by R. P. Barber, B. J. McLaughlin, C. E. Ribak, and J. E. Vaughn.

GABA release from particular endings still are not known, it follows that in such cases measurements of GABA content or turnover and/or GAD activity, or changes in them resulting from experimental manipulations, largely would be uninterpretable and add little to our basic understanding of information processing in a particular region of the CNS. However, gross regional changes in the above parameters may be usefully correlatable with important phenomena that accompany changes in overall regional activity that occur with altered functional demands or in pathological states, such as seizures, Huntington's disease, etc. Although accurate, specific, cytological localization of GABA neurons and their processes in physiologically undefined settings might not be particularly informative, it could still serve as a guide for the design of further physiological investigations at the cellular level.

CEREBELLUM

We chose first to attempt to visualize GAD-containing nerve endings in the rat cerebellum. The cerebellum has been by far the most favorable site for the investigation of possible substances which may mediate the activity of neurons with inhibitory functions because more extensive correlative neuroanatomical and neurophysiological analyses have been made of the cerebellum than of any other structure in the vertebrate brain (34,75). The overall function of the cerebellar cortex probably is entirely inhibitory. The only output cells of the cerebellar cortex, the Purkinje cells, inhibit monosynaptically in Deiters' and intracerebellar nuclei. Cells that lie entirely in the cerebellar cortex, the basket, stellate and Golgi II cells, are believed to play inhibitory roles within the cerebellum. The basket cells make numerous powerful inhibitory synapses on the somata, axon hillocks, and initial axon segments of the Purkinje cells. The superficial stellate cells form inhibitory synapses on the dendrites of Purkinje cells. The Golgi II cells make inhibitory synapses on the dendrites of the granule cells. Afferent excitatory inputs reach the cerebellum via the climbing and mossy fibers, which excite the dendrites of the Purkinje and granule cells, respectively. The latter are believed to be the only cells with an excitatory function that lie entirely within the cerebellum.

Even our first comprehensive biochemical laminar analyses of the GABA system suggested the possibility that all of the inhibitory cells of the cerebellum (Purkinje, basket, stellate, and Golgi) might use

GABA as transmitter (5). Subsequently, evidence was adduced for the occurrence of both GAD and GABA in high concentrations in the deep cerebellar nuclei, where the Purkinje cell axons terminate (76–78). Electrophysiological and pharmacological studies suggested strongly that Purkinje cell terminals use GABA as transmitter (79–81). The first application of the immunoperoxidase technique at the light level showed an intense punctate deposition of reaction product around the Purkinje cells and around the neurons of the deep cerebellar nuclei, cells known to receive an inhibitory synaptic input from the Purkinje cells (46), suggesting the impingement of many nerve terminals containing GAD upon these neuronal surfaces. It then was possible to extend our studies to the electron microscopic level (47). GAD appeared to be highly localized in certain synaptic terminals in close association with the membranes of synaptic vesicles and mitochondria, but not within these organelles. GAD-positive terminals, presumably largely from Purkinje cells, were seen on the somata and proximal dendrites of neurons in the deep cerebellar nuclei. Similarly, terminals presumably arising from basket, stellate and Golgi type II cells also were strongly positive for the enzyme. Thus, all of the cerebellar cortical cells known to be inhibitory were shown probably to use GABA as transmitter.

A disturbing feature of the earlier results was that it was not possible to detect any GAD-positive reaction product in the somata or dendrites of the cells whose terminals were strongly positive, since the synthesis of GAD is believed to occur mainly in the somata from which the enzyme probably is translocated to the terminals via axoplasmic transport. Presumptive evidence of the latter was furnished by the observation of GAD-positive product on smooth membrane cisternae in the preterminal axons of basket cells (47). Since one of the possible explanations for the failure to detect somal and dendritic GAD was that the concentrations were too low because of rapid somatofugal transport of the somally synthesized enzyme, direct injections of colchicine were made into the cerebellar cortex in an attempt to disrupt axoplasmic transport (54). In the colchicine-injected rats, but not in those similarly injected with the inactive lumicolchicine or with saline, the proximal dendrites and somata of Purkinje and Golgi type II neurons and the somata of basket and stellate cells were shown to contain detectable accumulations of GAD-positive reaction product. The GAD-positive reaction product appeared to be concentrated around the cisternae of the Golgi apparatus and was not seen in nuclei or nucleoli. The latter results appear to forge the necessary, but still somewhat circumstantial, link between the presence of GAD in the terminals of all of the known inhibitory neurons in the cerebellar cortex and the synthesis and transport of the enzyme in these cells.

More probing questions can be asked and answered by the immunocytochemical approach currently than by other available techniques. For example, it was interesting to know whether or not developing nerve terminals have the transmitter-forming enzymes and, therefore, the potential capacity to synthesize neurotransmitters. If a developing presynaptic terminal has this capacity prior to the early stages of synaptic junction formation, the possibility then exists that the passage of transmitter molecules or of the transmitter-forming enzyme itself to receptors on potential postsynaptic membranes might be part of a recognition process that allows for synaptic differentiation of contacts between specified cell types. If, on the other hand, transmitter-synthesizing enzyme appears within a presynaptic terminal after a protosynaptic contact is formed, it is possible that the signal for enzyme synthesis may come from the postsynaptic element and that the transmitter enzyme or transmitter molecules may not play a role in synaptic recognition mechanisms. Applying the immunocytochemical method for localization of GAD in a study of developing rat cerebellum, it was shown that GAD is present in growing neurites in close association with small vesicles prior to the time the neurites make protosynaptic contacts, and that differentiation of these contacts results in a sequestering of GAD into synaptic terminals (48). The data suggest that the initial signal for synthesis probably predates the establishment of contacts between pre- and post-synaptic elements of a developing synapse.

SPINAL CORD

We next were led to an immunocytochemical examination of the spinal cord (49) because a number of preceding biochemical studies in several species had shown GABA and GAD to be distributed in a dorsoventral gradient (82–84); and physiological studies had suggested that GABA may be the depolarizing transmitter of spinal interneurons that mediate presynaptic inhibition of primary afferent terminals (84–88), that GABA-releasing interneurons might be involved in postsynaptic inhibition of second-order neurons that receive primary afferent terminals (84–88), and that GABA-releasing interneurons might be involved in postsynaptic inhibition of motoneurons (89,90). Light microscopic localization of GAD in the rat lumbosacral spinal cord showed heavy, punctate GAD-positive reaction product in the dorsal horn laminae I–III. Moderately heavy reaction product was also seen in the deeper dorsal horn laminae IV–VI, the medial aspect of the intermediate gray (lamina VII), and the region around the central canal (lamina X). A moderately light concentration of GAD-positive reaction product was observed in the ventral horn, and punctate deposits of reaction product also were seen on motoneuron cell bodies. The punctate distribution of GAD-positive reaction product in both ventral and dorsal horns, as visualized by light microscopy, corresponded to GAD-positive synaptic terminals seen by electron microscopy in comparable regions of the spinal gray (49). Many more GAD-positive terminals were observed in dorsal horn laminae I–III than in deeper laminae IV–VI. GAD-containing terminals in the dorsal horn were presynaptic to dendrites and cell bodies. GAD-positive terminals that were presynaptic to other axon terminals, which were more numerous in laminae II and III, also were observed. In the motor nuclei, GAD-positive knobs were presynaptic to large and small dendrites and motoneuron somata. In addition, small GAD-containing terminals also were presynaptic to larger axonal terminals which were in turn presynaptic to motoneuron somata. The observation of GAD-positive terminals presynaptic to dendrites and cell bodies in both dorsal and ventral horns is compatible with the evidence suggesting that GABA terminals may mediate postsynaptic inhibition of spinal interneurons and motoneurons. The finding of GAD-positive terminals presynaptic to other axonal terminals in the dorsal horn and motor nuclei is consistent with the evidence that GABA also may be the transmitter mediating presynaptic inhibition via axoaxonal synapses in the spinal cord.

However, the above findings were only a good beginning and numerous questions remained to be answered. For example, it was important to know whether the GAD-containing terminals discussed above come from nearby GABA interneurons, from supraspinal structures, or from both. It was necessary to determine with certainty whether some of the GAD-containing terminals are presynaptic to primary afferent terminals. Improvements in our staining techniques, together with suitable surgical ablation procedures, made it possible to begin to answer these questions.

Multiple dorsal rhizotomies were performed unilaterally at lumbar levels L1–L4 in adult rats, and the spinal cords were examined 24–48 hr later (57). At the light microscopic level, large numbers of degenerating terminals, probably entirely from cutaneous afferents, were observed in the ipsilateral substantia gelatinosa, but not contralaterally. However, the distribution of GAD-positive reaction product, most intense within laminae II and III, appeared to be normal on both sides of the cord. Electron microscopically, primary afferent terminals were found in various stages of degeneration on the side of the rhizotomies, and GAD-positive axon terminals were found to be presynaptic to degenerating primary afferent terminals in the substantia gelatinosa. The data furnish a chemomorphological basis for the conclusion that the presynaptic inhibition of primary afferents is mediated by axoaxonal synapses formed between GABA-releasing interneurons and primary sensory neurons. A detailed analysis of the various synaptic relationships of GAD-positive terminals (57) led to reasonable hypotheses about how release of GABA from such terminals could participate in such presynaptically modulated phenomena as primary afferent depolarization (91–96), the dorsal root reflex (91,97), and primary afferent hyperpolarization (98).

OLFACTORY BULB

Morphologic and physiologic aspects of the mammalian olfactory bulb have been studied extensively (99). In addition, high levels of GAD and GABA were found in the external plexiform (EPL), glomerular (GL), and granule cell (GRL) layers of this laminar structure (100). The mitral and tufted cells, which receive impulses from the olfactory nerves and from extrabulbar sources, are inhibited via reciprocal dendrodendritic synapses on their dendrites in the external plexiform and glomerular layers formed with the indigenous granule and periglomerular cells (99,101). Pharmacologic studies suggested that both of the above interneurons are GABAergic (102,103). GAD has now been localized in the olfactory bulb by immunocytochemical methods at the light and electron microscopic levels (53). The light microscopic results demonstrated GAD-positive puncta throughout all layers of the olfactory bulb with the greatest concentration in the external plexiform layer and in the glomeruli of the glomerular layer. The cytoplasm of many neuronal somata in the granule and glomerular cell layers was GAD-positive, but not the cytoplasm of mitral and tufted cell somata. The GAD-positive staining of presumed granule and periglomerular neuronal somata also extended into their dendrites for many microns. Immunochemical evidence at the light level suggests that some of the periglomerular cells also may be dopaminergic (104).

Electron microscopic observations confirmed the presence of GAD-positive reaction product within the cytoplasm of granule and periglomerular neurons. Also, in the external plexiform layer, reaction product filled many of the granule cell gemmules which form reciprocal dendrodendritic synapses with mitral cell dendrites. The presence of GAD within granule and periglomerular cells provides further evidence that these inhibitory interneurons use GABA as their neurotransmitter. GAD-positive cell bodies also have been observed in other CNS regions where dendrodendritic synapses are known to occur, such as the lateral and medial geniculate nuclei and the superior colliculus. It was only after blocking axoplasmic transport by suitable intracerebellar injections of colchicine that marked accumulations of GAD-positive reaction product were observed in the somata and dendrites of Purkinje, Golgi, basket, and stellate cells of the cerebellum (54).

BASAL GANGLIA

The nigrostriatal–pallidal system is concerned to a considerable extent with processing information related to proprioceptive, vestibular, and visual stimuli in the service of coordinating mechanisms involved in the physical orientation of an organism in its perceived space–time continuum. The caudate nucleus, putamen, and substantia nigra exchange fibers with each other, as do the substantia nigra and globus pallidus. The globus pallidus and substantia nigra receive inputs from the caudate and putamen and appear to have two-way communication with the subthalamic nucleus. There also are thalamic, cortical, and midbrain inputs to the caudate and putamen. Most of the final results of the computations in the basal ganglia are sent out via a fiber system from the globus pallidus to the nuclei of the thalamus and thence largely to the motor cortex. There are some nigrothalamic connections as well. In addition, there probably are connections between the globus pallidus and the midbrain tegmentum through which descending influences may be mediated (105). In this regard, it is of considerable interest that facilitation of the γ-motor neurons can be achieved by stimulation of a midbrain region close to termination of the fibers from the globus pallidus, as well as by stimulation of the caudate nucleus. Normal relations within and between the above structures must minimally involve a coordinated functioning of different groups of intra- and intersystem neurons whose transmitters may be GABA, acetylcholine, dopamine, serotonin, norepinephrine, and possibly still unidentified excitatory transmitters, one of which may be the polypeptide substance P (106–109).

The basal ganglia may contain preprogrammed neuronal circuits for patterned postural and motor controls. In the case of the neostriatum, in which there are numerous interneurons, excitatory pacemaker neurons (possibly indigenous cholinergic neurons) may be held in tonic inhibition by indigenous, inhibitory, GABA command neurons (14,110–113). There is a tremendous convergence of largely excitatory inputs onto striatal neurons (114), presumably both on the excitatory pacemakers as well as onto the inhibitory command and local circuit neurons. However, the chief switching mechanisms for finally turning on the patterned activities within the striatal regions may be the fibers emanating from neurons in the substantia nigra, some of which release dopamine and others a still unknown excitatory transmitter, possibly glutamate or substance P (111). The activity of the nigral inputs acting together with those from the cortex, thalamus, and other regions results in a release of specific coded neuronal patterns in a sequential manner. The richness of the interneuronal population in the neostriatum suggests that plastic changes may take place in it and that it might be the learning center of the basal ganglia. The results of this activity in the striatum are communicated monosynaptically to the globus pallidus, in which there is a relative paucity of short-axon interneurons, where the striatal efferents project radially in a topographic manner upon pallidal cells, with the medial and lateral segments of the globus pallidus receiving fibers from the corresponding parts of the striatum (105). Many of the strionigral and striopallidal efferent neurons are undoubtedly inhibitory, and much more presumptive evidence suggests strongly that they are GABAergic (112), and some of them probably are excitatory and release substance P (34,115). Neural patterns that are activated in the striatum may disinhibit the analogous patterns in the globus pallidus, and the result of this activity is communicated to the regions in the thalamus where integration with other incoming information takes place. A recent study has shown that pallidothalamic fibers exert exclusively inhibitory effects (monosynaptic IPSPs) on thalamic neurons (116). The final instructions for posture and movement then are elaborated in the cerebral cortex where, after further refinement, the activities of appropriate pyramidal neurons in the motor areas are released to signal the effectors. Circuits that fire in the striatum may inform appropriate pallidal and nigral neurons about their activity via intersystem inhibitory fibers employing GABA (110,112,113) thus preventing their own further activation until the need arises again. Both local circuit GABA neurons and long-axon extrinsic GABA neurons appear to play decisive roles in the function of basal ganglia. Recently it has been suggested that Parkinsonian symptoms may be alleviated by blocking GABA action in the globus pallidus and that dyskinesias might be helped by increasing pallidal GABA (117).

As a first step in the analysis of some of the above relationships at a cytochemical level, GAD was localized by both light and electron microscopy in the substantia nigra by the immunoperoxidase procedure (51). Large amounts of GAD-positive reaction product were seen throughout the substantia nigra in light microscopic preparations, and it appeared to be localized in punctate structures that were apposed to dendrites and somata. Electron microscopic studies revealed that most of the axon terminals in the substantia nigra were filled with GAD-positive reaction product and formed both axodendritic and axosomatic synapses. Many dendrites were extensively surrounded by GAD-positive terminals which most commonly formed symmetric synaptic junctions, although some formed asymmetric synaptic junctions. The results were consistent with biochemical, pharmacologic, and physiologic data which previously had indicated that neurons of the neostriatum and globus pallidus exerted a GABA-mediated, postsynaptic inhibition upon the neurons of the substantia nigra.

INTERACTIONS AMONG NEUROTRANSMITTER SYSTEMS

In the preceding discussion some reference was made to possible interactions between GABA neurons and those liberating other transmitters or neuromodulators. One of the major objectives of current neurobiological research is to delineate the relationships of various neuronal cell types to each other (118). Our work in tracing the complexities of the synaptic relationships of GABA neurons has raised some serious questions about the conceptual utility of formulating detailed hypotheses about information processing in the whole brain or in specific regions strictly on the basis of "classical" biochemical analytical approaches, by observing behavioral changes produced by lesions or pharmacological manipulations, or by a combination of both. The latter approaches currently are giving utilitarian information that is immensely important in devising effective drugs and in characterizing disease processes. However, just as physiologic recordings from neurons must be carried out in morphologically characterized regions before they can reveal secrets of information processing, so eventually it will be necessary to perform such studies in more adequately described settings. It seems obvious to me that it is necessary to begin to develop detailed chemomorphologic maps of various brain regions in order to understand how neurons liberating the various putative transmitters, known and still unknown, are related to each other. Further refinement of immunocytochemical techniques, which are still in their infancy, will be required. It will be necessary to develop procedures that can be applied to ultrathin sections and to visualize two or more antigens on one electronmicroscopic section, so that three-dimensional reconstructions will be possible.

It probably is advisable to make a distinction between at least two major classes of neurons in the vertebrate central nervous system. It appears that some neurons, such as GABA- and acetylcholine-releasing ones, may largely be involved in direct point-to-point information transmittal. In other words, release of transmitter from their presynaptic endings affects postsynaptic sites in such a way that in a fraction of a millisecond either GO (excitatory) or NO GO (inhibitory) information is transmitted, recognized, and the signaling substance removed. There is another class of neurons, such as those which release catecholamines, serotonin, and peptides, which chiefly may play different roles. Current evidence suggests to me that in most instances these latter neurons may act by liberating their transmitter more generally into a region which may contain not only postsynaptic endings, but also presynaptic endings of other neurons as well as glial cells and blood vessels, and that in this region as a whole these substances exert longer lasting effects that may have metabolic and trophic consequences. It is striking that when the substantia nigra is stimulated, physiologically recorded signals in the corpus striatum do not seem to be greatly altered when the nigrostriatal dopamine neurons are destroyed by 6-OH-dopamine or when the action of dopamine is blocked completely by large doses of haloperidol. This suggests that the physiologically relevant signals are carried by fibers of still uncharacterized nondopaminergic neurons and that the effects of dopamine released from the dopaminergic fibers may not be informational in the strictest sense of the word. A phenomenon related to the above is described in many anecdotal accounts about Parkinsonian patients, obviously suffering from a defective functioning of the nigrostriatal dopaminergic neurons, who can fully mobilize normal and adaptive physical activity in an emergency but who relapse into the typically inactive Parkinsonian state as soon as the emergency is over. The above and the therapeutic effects of exogenously supplied L-dopa in Parkinsonism suggests that the neuronal circuitry in the neostriatum is potentially available and that the communication lines are clear, but that the dopamine ordinarily released from the dopaminergic neurons furnishes the "oil" required for the neuronal machinery to function smoothly. The above effects of dopamine may be analogous to that of squirting oil into inadequately lubricated, but intact, machinery, the parts of which will not move if sufficient oil is not furnished. However, oil is not a part of the actual machinery. Roger Guillemin has coined the word "cybernenes" to describe substances which serve to optimize nervous system function without themselves being involved in specific information transmittal. I would like to suggest that in most instances in which they act in the CNS, the catecholamines, serotonin, and neurally released peptides may be cybernenes.

"WET" NEUROBIOLOGY AND CYBERNETICS

As discussed in a preceding section, neurophysiologic studies based upon detailed morphologic analyses of the cerebellum have shown that the Purkinje, basket, stellate, and Golgi type II cells of the cerebellar cortex are all inhibitory, and the basic communication patterns among the above cell types and the excitatory mossy and climbing fiber inputs and the excitatory, indigenously occurring, parallel fiber systems of granule cell origin have been thoroughly explored. On the basis of the above "wet" observations several notable theoretical formulations of cerebellar functions have been made (20,21,23–25). Neurochemical and pharmacologic observations, carefully built onto the neurophysiologic observations, suggested that all of the above inhibitory cells might use GABA as transmitter. The latter supposition now has been confirmed by our immunocytochemical observations. In addition, studies have shown that norepinephrine-containing fibers originating in cells of the locus coeruleus may synapse on Purkinje cell dendrites in the molecular layer (62). Attempts are now being made to identify the transmitters employed by the excitatory cells in the cerebellum (119). It may be assumed that the existing and developing technology will make it possible eventually to visualize and identify neurochemically in three-dimensional reconstructions most of the connections in the cerebellar cortex. The question arises as to whether the latter type of information will add any necessary elements to the understanding of the principles of information processing (20,21,23–25). The answer will not be certain until the data are available and someone with an understanding of biochemistry and molecular biology retraces the paths. It may be that the chemical data will not add any more to the effort than the knowledge of the kind of solder used does to an analysis of an electrical wiring diagram. On the other hand, a knowledge of the neurotransmitters and of the cellular consequences of their impingement on neural, glial, and vascular elements may reveal hitherto unsuspected superdimensionality.

ACKNOWLEDGMENTS

This work was supported by USPHS grants NS-12116 and NS-1615 from the NINCDS, and grant 22438 from the NIMH.

REFERENCES

1. Roberts, E., Baxter, C. F., Van Harreveld, A., Wiersma, C. A. G., Adey, W. R., and Killam, K. F., eds. (1960) "Inhibition in the Nervous System and Gamma-Aminobutyric Acid." Pergamon, Oxford.
2. Roberts, E., Chase, T. N., and Tower, D. B., eds. (1976) "GABA in Nervous System Function." Raven Press, New York.
3. Roberts, E., and Eidelberg, E. (1960) *Int. Rev. Neurobiol.* **2,** 279–332.
4. Kravitz, E. A. (1967) *In* "The Neurosciences" (G. C. Quarton, T. Melnechuk, and F. O. Schmitt, eds.), Vol. 1, pp. 433–444. Rockefeller Univ. Press, New York.
5. Roberts, E., and Kuriyama, K. (1968) *Brain Res.* **8,** 1–35.
6. Takeuchi, A., and Takeuchi, N. (1972) *Adv. Biophys.* **3,** 45–95.
7. Roberts, E. (1974) *Biochem. Pharmacol.* **23,** 2637–2649.
8. Curtis, D. R., and Johnston, G. A. R. (1974) *Ergeb. Physiol., Biol. Chem. Exp. Pharmakol.* **69,** 97–188.
9. Krnjević, K. (1974) *Physiol. Rev.* **54,** 418–540.
10. Roberts, E., and Hammerschlag, R. (1976) *In* "Basic Neurochemistry" (G. J. Siegel *et al.,* eds.), pp. 218–245. Little, Brown, Boston, Massachusetts.
11. Obata, K. (1976) *In* "GABA in Nervous System Function" (E. Roberts, T. N. Chase, and D. B. Tower, eds.), pp. 283–286. Raven Press, New York.
12. Florey, E., Cahill, M. A., and Rathmayer, M. (1975) *Comp. Biochem. Physiol. C* **51,** 5–12.
13. Roberts, E. (1972) *Neurosci. Res. Program, Bull.* **10,** 468–482.
14. Fahn, S. (1976) *In* "GABA in Nervous System Function" (E. Roberts, T. N. Chase, and D. B. Tower, eds.), pp. 169–186. Raven Press, New York.
15. Roberts, E. (1976) *In* "GABA in Nervous System Function" (E. Roberts, T. N. Chase, and D. B. Tower, eds.), pp. 515–539. Raven Press, New York.
16. Roberts, E. (1966) *Brain Res.* **1,** 117–166.
17. Roberts, E. (1966) *Brain Res.* **2,** 109–144.
18. Roberts, E., and Matthysse, S. (1970) *Annu. Rev. Biochem.* **39,** 777–820.
19. Roberts, E., Wein, J., and Simonsen, D. G. (1964) *Vitam. Horm.* (*N.Y.*) **22,** 503–559.
20. Marr, D. (1969) *J. Physiol.* (*London*) **202,** 437–470.
21. Blomfield, S., and Marr, D. (1970) *Nature* (*London*) **227,** 1224–1228.
22. Marr, D. (1970) *Proc. R. Soc. London, Ser. B* **176,** 161–234.
23. Gilbert, P. F. C. (1974) *Brain Res.* **70,** 1–18.
24. Pellionisz, A., and Szentágothai, J. (1973) *Brain Res.* **49,** 83–99.

25. Pellionisz, A., and Szentágothai, J. (1974) *Brain Res.* **68**, 19–40.
26. Szentágothai, J. (1975) *Brain Res.* **95**, 475–496.
27. Parnas, I., Rahamimoff, R., and Sarne, Y. (1975) *J. Physiol. (London)* **250**, 275–286.
28. Maynard, D. M. (1972) *Ann. N.Y. Acad. Sci.* **193**, 59–72.
29. Ikeda, K., Hori, N., and Tsuruhara, T. (1975) *Fed. Proc., Fed. Am. Soc. Exp. Biol.* **34**, 359.
30. Mulloney, B., and Selverston, A. I. (1974) *J. Comp. Physiol.* **91**, 1–32.
31. Mulloney, B., and Selverston, A. I. (1974) *J. Comp. Physiol.* **91**, 53–78.
32. Selverston, A. I., and Mulloney, B. (1974) *J. Comp. Physiol.* **91**, 33–51.
33. Selverston, A. I., Russell, D. F., Miller, J. P., and King, D. G. (1976) *Prog. Neurobiol.* **7**, 215–290.
34. Eccles, J. C., Ito, M., and Szentágothai, J., eds. (1967) "The Cerebellum as a Neuronal Machine." Springer-Verlag, Berlin and New York.
35. Wu, J.-Y., Matsuda, T., and Roberts, E. (1973) *J. Biol. Chem.* **248**, 3029–3034.
36. Matsuda, T., Wu, J.-Y., and Roberts, E. (1973) *J. Neurochem.* **21**, 167–172.
37. Wu, J.-Y., and Roberts, E. (1974) *J. Neurochem.* **23**, 759–767.
38. Schousboe, A., Wu, J.-Y., and Roberts, E. (1973) *Biochemistry* **12**, 2868–2873.
39. Schousboe, A., Wu, J.-Y., and Roberts, E. (1974) *J. Neurochem.* **23**, 1189–1195.
40. Wu, J.-Y. (1976) *In* "GABA in Nervous System Function" (E. Roberts, T. N. Chase, and D. B. Tower, eds.), pp. 7–55. Raven Press, New York.
41. Matsuda, T., Wu, J.-Y., and Roberts, E. (1973) *J. Neurochem.* **21**, 159–166.
42. Saito, K., Wu, J.-Y., Matsuda, T., and Roberts, E. (1974) *Brain Res.* **65**, 277–285.
43. Wong, E., Schousboe, A., Saito, K., Wu, J.-Y., and Roberts, E. (1974) *Brain Res.* **68**, 133–142.
44. Saito, K., Schousboe, A., Wu, J.-Y., and Roberts, E. (1974) *Brain Res.* **65**, 287–296.
45. Saito, K. (1976) *In* "GABA in Nervous System Function" (E. Roberts, T. N. Chase, and D. B. Tower, eds.), pp. 103–111. Raven Press, New York.
46. Saito, K., Barber, R., Wu, J.-Y., Matsuda, T., Roberts, E., and Vaughn, J. E. (1974) *Proc. Natl. Acad. Sci. U.S.A.* **71**, 269–273.
47. McLaughlin, B. J., Wood, J. G., Saito, K., Barber, R., Vaughn, J. E., Roberts, E., and Wu, J.-Y. (1974) *Brain Res.* **76**, 377–391.
48. McLaughlin, B. J., Wood, J. G., Saito, K., Roberts, E., and Wu, J.-Y. (1975) *Brain Res.* **85**, 355–371.
49. McLaughlin, B. J., Barber, R., Saito, K., Roberts, E., and Wu, J.-Y. (1975) *J. Comp. Neurol.* **164**, 305–321.
50. Ribak, C. E., Vaughn, J. E., Saito, K., and Barber, R. (1976) *In* "The Basal Ganglia" (M. D. Yahr, ed.), pp. 205–211. Raven Press, New York.
51. Ribak, C. E., Vaughn, J. E., Saito, K., Barker, R., and Roberts, E. (1976) *Brain Res.* **116**, 287–298.
52. Ribak, C. E., Vaughn, J. E., and Saito, K. (1976) *Anat. Rec.* **184**, 512–513.
53. Ribak, C. E., Vaughn, J. E., Saito, K., Barber, R., and Roberts, E. (1977) *Brain Res.* **126**, 1–18.
54. Ribak, C. E., and Vaughn, J. E. (1976) *Neurosci. Abstr.* **2**, 796.
55. Ribak, C. E. (1977) *Anat. Rec.* **187**, 692–693.
56. Ribak, C. E., Vaughn, J. E., and Saito, K. (1978) *Brain Res.* 315–332.
57. Barber, R., Vaughn, J. E., Saito, K., McLaughlin, B. J., and Roberts, E. (1978). *Brain Res.* 35–55.
58. Wood, J. G., McLaughlin, B. J., and Vaughn, J. E. (1976) *In* "GABA in Nervous System Function" (E. Roberts, T. N. Chase, and D. B. Tower, eds.), pp. 133–148. Raven Press, New York.

59. Barber, R., and Saito, K. (1976) *In* "GABA in Nervous System Function" (E. Roberts, T. N. Chase, and D. B. Tower, eds.), pp. 113–132. Raven Press, New York.
60. Roberts, E. (1976) *In* "Neurotransmitters, Hormones, and Receptors: Novel Approaches" (J. A. Ferrendelli, B. S. McEwen, and S. H. Snyder, eds.), pp. 123–138. Soc. Neurosci., Bethesda, Maryland.
61. Saito, K., Roberts, E., and Barber, R. (1977) *In* "Structure and Function of Synapses" (K. Kuriyama, ed.), pp. 143–157. Ishiyaku Shuppan Publ. Co., Tokyo.
62. Bloom, F. E., and Hoffer, B. J. (1973) *In* "Frontiers in Catecholamine Research" (S. H. Snyder and E. Usdin, eds.), pp. 637–642. Pergamon, Oxford.
63. Fuxe, K., Hökfelt, T., and Ungerstedt, U. (1970) *Int. Rev. Neurobiol.* **13,** 93–126.
64. Livett, B. G. (1973) *Br. Med. Bull.* **29,** 93–99.
65. Steeves, J. D., Jordan, L. M., and Lake, N. (1975) *Brain Res.* **100,** 663–670.
66. Biscoe, T. J., Curtis, D. R., and Ryall, R. W. (1966) *Int. J. Neuropharmacol.* **5,** 429–434.
67. Sasa, M., Munekiyo, K., Ikeda, H., and Takaori, S. (1974) *Brain Res.* **80,** 443–460.
68. Grillner, S. (1975) *Physiol. Rev.* **55,** 247–304.
69. Ikeda, K., and Wiersma, C. A. G. (1964) *Comp. Biochem. Physiol.* **12,** 107–115.
70. Wiersma, C. A. G., and Ikeda, K. (1964) *Comp. Biochem. Physiol.* **12,** 509–525.
71. Roeder, K. D., Tozian, L., and Weiant, E. A. (1960) *J. Insect Physiol.* **4,** 45–62.
72. Randrup, A., and Munkvad, I. (1970) *In* "International Symposium on Amphetamines and Related Compounds" (E. Costa and S. Garattini, eds.), pp. 695–713. Raven Press, New York.
73. Kuriyama, K., and Kimura, H. (1976) *In* "GABA in Nervous System Function" (E. Roberts, T. N. Chase, and D. B. Tower, eds.), pp. 203–216. Raven Press, New York.
74. Kuriyama, K. (1976) *In* "GABA in Nervous System Function" (E. Roberts, T. N. Chase, and D. B. Tower, eds.), pp. 187–196. Raven Press, New York.
75. Llinas, R., ed. (1969) "Neurobiology of Cerebellar Evolution and Development." AMA-ERF Inst. Biomed. Res., Chicago, Illinois.
76. Fonnum, F., Storm-Mathisen, J., and Walberg, F. (1970) *Brain Res.* **20,** 259–275.
77. Fonnum, F., and Walberg, F. (1973) *Brain Res,* **54,** 115–127.
78. Fonnum, F., and Walberg, F. (1973) *Brain Res.* **62,** 577–579.
79. Curtis, D. R., Duggan, A. W., and Felix, D. (1970) *Brain Res.* **23,** 117–120.
80. Obata, K., Ito, M., Ochi, R., and Sato, N. (1967) *Exp. Brain Res.* **4,** 43–57.
81. Obata, K., and Takeda, K. (1969) *J. Neurochem.* **16,** 1043–1047.
82. Albers, R. W., and Brady, R. O. (1959) *J. Biol. Chem.* **234,** 926–928.
83. Graham, L. T., Jr., and Aprison, M. H. (1969) *J. Neurochem.* **16,** 559–566.
84. Miyata, Y., and Otsuka, M. (1972) *J. Neurochem.* **19,** 1833–1834.
85. Eccles, J. C., Schmidt, R., and Willis, W. D. (1963) *J. Physiol. (London)* **168,** 500–530.
86. Schmidt, R. F. (1964) *Prog. Brain Res.* **12,** 119–134.
87. Barker, J. L., and Nicoll, R. A. (1972) *Science* **176,** 1043–1045.
88. Otsuka, M., and Konishi, S. (1975) *In* "GABA in Nervous System Function" (E. Roberts, T. N. Chase, and D. B. Tower, eds.), pp. 197–202. Raven Press, New York.
89. Curtis, D. R., Hösli, L., Johnston, G. A. R., and Johnston, I. H. (1968) *Exp. Brain Res.* **5,** 235–258.
90. Curtis, D. R. (1969) *Prog. Brain Res.* **31,** 171–189.
91. Barker, J. L., and Nicoll, R. A. (1972) *Science* **176,** 1043–1045.
92. Barker, J. L., Nicoll, R. A., and Padjen, A. (1975) *J. Physiol. (London)* **245,** 537–538.

93. Davidoff, R. A., (1972) *Science* **175,** 331–333.
94. Davidson, N., and Southwick, C. A. P. (1971) *J. Physiol. (London)* **219,** 689–708.
95. DeGroat, W. C., Lalley, P. M., and Saum, W. R. (1972) *Brain Res.* **44,** 273–277.
96. Levy, R. A. (1974) *Brain Res.* **76,** 155–160.
97. Bell, J. A., and Anderson, E. G. (1972) *Brain Res.* **43,** 161–169.
98. Levy, R. A., and Anderson, E. G. (1974) *Brain Res.* **76,** 71–82.
99. Shepherd, G. M. (1972) *Physiol. Rev.* **52,** 864–917.
100. Graham, L. T. (1973) *Life Sci.* **12,** 443–447.
101. Getchell, T. V., and Shepherd, G. M. (1975) *J. Physiol. (London)* **251,** 523–548.
102. McLennan, H. (1971) *Brain Res.* **29,** 177–184.
103. Nicoll, R. A. (1971) *Brain Res.* **35,** 137–149.
104. Hökfelt, T., Hálsz, N., Lungdahl, Å., Johansson, O., Goldstein, M., and Park, D. (1975) *Neurosci. Lett.* **1,** 85.
105. Kemp, J. M., and Powell, T. P. S. (1971) *Philos. Trans. R. Soc. London, Ser. B* **262,** 441.
106. Cheramy, A., Nieoullon, A., Michelot, R., and Glowinski, J. (1977) *Neurosci. Lett.* **4,** 105–109.
107. Hong, J. S., Yang, H. Y. T., Racagni, G., and Costa, E. (1977) *Brain Res.* **122,** 541–544.
108. Kanazawa, I., and Gessel, T. (1976) *Brain Res.* **117,** 362–367.
109. Kanazawa, I., Emson, P. C., and Cuello, A. C. (1977) *Brain Res.* **119,** 447–453.
110. Hornykiewciz, O., Lloyd, K. G., and Davidson, L. (1976) *In* "GABA in Nervous System Function" (E. Roberts, T. N. Chase, and D. B. Tower, eds.), pp. 479–485. Raven Press, New York.
111. Krnjević, K. (1974) *Adv. Neurol.* **5,** 145–152.
112. McGeer, P. L., and McGeer, E. G. (1976) *In* "GABA in Nervous System Function" (E. Roberts, T. N. Chase, and D. B. Tower, eds.) pp. 487–495. Raven Press, New York.
113. Okada, Y. (1976) *In* "GABA in Nervous System Function" (E. Roberts, T. N. Chase, and D. B. Tower, eds.), pp. 235–243. Raven Press, New York.
114. Kocsis, J. D., Sugimori, M., and Kitai, S. T. (1977) *Brain Res.* **124,** 403–413.
115. Kanazawa, I., Miyata, Y., Toyokura, Y., and Otsuka, M. (1973) *Brain Res.* **51,** 363–365.
116. Uno, M., and Yoshida, M. (1975) *Brain Res.* **99,** 377–380.
117. Pycock, C., Horton, R. W., and Marsden, C. D. (1976) *Brain Res.* **116,** 353–359.
118. Garattini, S., Pujol, J. F., and Samanin, R., eds. (1978) "Interactions between Putative Neurotransmitters in the Brain." Raven Press, New York.
119. Young, A. B., Oster-Granite, M. L., Herndon, R. M., and Snyder, S. H. (1974) *Brain Res.* **73,** 1–13.

An Evaluation of the Proposed Transmitter Role of Glutamate and Taurine

ROGER A. NICOLL AND EDGAR T. IWAMOTO
Departments of Pharmacology and Physiology
University of California
San Francisco, California

INTRODUCTION

A remarkably long time elapsed between the finding that the brain contained large amounts of free amino acids and the appearance of solid experimental evidence that amino acids play a major role in neurotransmission. The established transmitter role for GABA, both at the crustacean neuromuscular junction (1) and in the vertebrate CNS (2), has resulted in a tendency to uncritically group a number of amino acids, e.g., glutamate, aspartate, glycine, taurine, and proline into the category "amino acid neurotransmitters." However, with the possible exception of glycine (3), the evidence for such optimism is often rudimentary or conflicting. In this chapter we will critically examine the evidence that the excitatory amino acids, glutamate and aspartate, and the inhibitory amino acid, taurine, are neurotransmitters in the CNS. For the excitatory amino acids emphasis will be placed on two systems, the spinal primary afferents and the excitatory pathways in the hippocampal formation. For taurine, emphasis will be placed on the frog spinal cord and the retina.

Three factors have been of major importance in establishing GABA as a neurotransmitter in the CNS. First, GABA appears to be localized and synthesized almost exclusively by the neurons which are thought

ISBN 0-12-398450-5

to have an inhibitory function. The other amino acids clearly have functions unrelated to neurotransmission and are present and synthesized by a variety of nonneuronal cells. Second, a number of relatively specific GABA antagonists exist, which have been extremely helpful in providing neuropharmacological evidence that a particular pathway utilizes GABA as a transmitter. For the excitatory amino acids, a number of compounds have been proposed as antagonists but, as will be discussed below, the low potency and lack of specificity makes these compounds of marginal value. Third, inhibitory synapses are generally located on the soma, so that an accurate comparison can be made between the action of GABA and the natural transmitter. For excitatory synapses technical difficulties make it very difficult to demonstrate that the ionic mechanism underlying the generation of a particular excitatory postsynaptic potential is the same as that of excitatory action of putative transmitters. This is because (1) the reversal potential for excitation is far removed from the resting potential and therefore subject to considerable error in measurement and (2) excitatory synapses are generally located on the dendrites and therefore errors are introduced when measuring the reversal potential with a microelectrode located in the soma.

EXCITATORY AMINO ACIDS

SPINAL PRIMARY AFFERENT SYNAPSES

Mechanisms of Action of Primary Afferents. It is important to bear in mind that primary afferents are very heterogeneous populations of fibers. From physiological studies a number of classes of fibers, subserving transmission of different sensory modalities and having different diameters, have been found. Recently, this physiological heterogeneity has been found to have a biochemical counterpart. Thus, Hökfelt *et al.* (4,5) have found that there are two distinct populations of small afferent neurons, one which reacts with antisera to substance P and another which reacts with antisera to somatosatin. The possibility that different classes of primary afferents may utilize different transmitters suggests that different ionic mechanisms may underlie their postsynaptic action.

The first study which examined the ionic mechanism of the EPSP derived from Ia afferent fibers in mammalian motoneurons was done by Coombs *et al.* (6). They found that the reversal potential for the EPSP varied in different motoneurons from +3 to +10 mV. For the

EPSP shown in Fig. 1 the reversal potential was +3 mV. They noted that the amplitude of the Ia EPSP was very insensitive to hyperpolarizing current. The existence of a reversal potential is a property of all chemically mediated potentials and thus the demonstration of a reversal potential for the EPSP, and for spinal IPSP's formed the basis for Eccles' conversion from belief in electrical transmission to acceptance of chemical transmission in the CNS. However, although similar findings were obtained by Marshall and Engberg (7) a number of

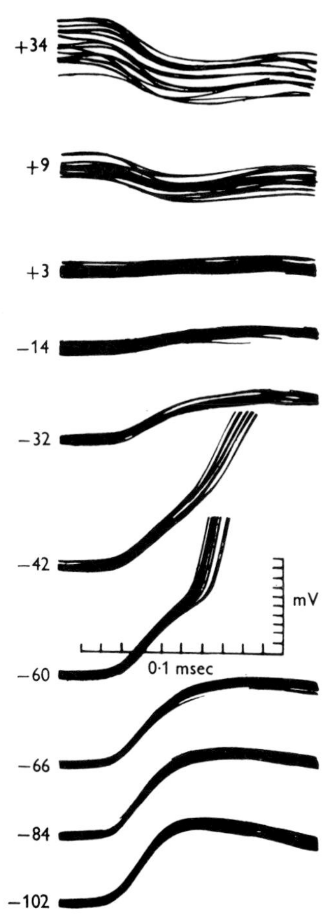

Fig. 1. EPSP's set up in a cat biceps-semitendinosus motoneuron at various levels of membrane potential. Each record is formed by the superimposition of about 20 faint traces. The membrane was shifted to the indicated values from its resting value of −66 mV by steady currents through the other barrel of the double microelectrode (Coombs, Eccles, and Fatt, 6).

other studies have failed to reverse the Ia EPSP, especially its early phase (*8–11*). The failure to reverse the EPSP is not due to the synapses being remote from the recording electrode; in fact, the time courses of the EPSPs studied indicated that the synapses were close to the soma. Furthermore, currents which failed to reverse the early phase of the Ia EPSP were sufficient to reverse EPSPs derived from a variety of other pathways (11). In Fig. 2 76 nA of depolarizing current completely reversed the EPSP derived from stimulating spinal interneurons and also caused some reversal of the later part of the Ia EPSP. But the early phase failed to reverse. This reversal of the latter part of the EPSP has been observed in all studies that have used composite EPSP's. When unitary Ia EPSP's are used, even the late phase does

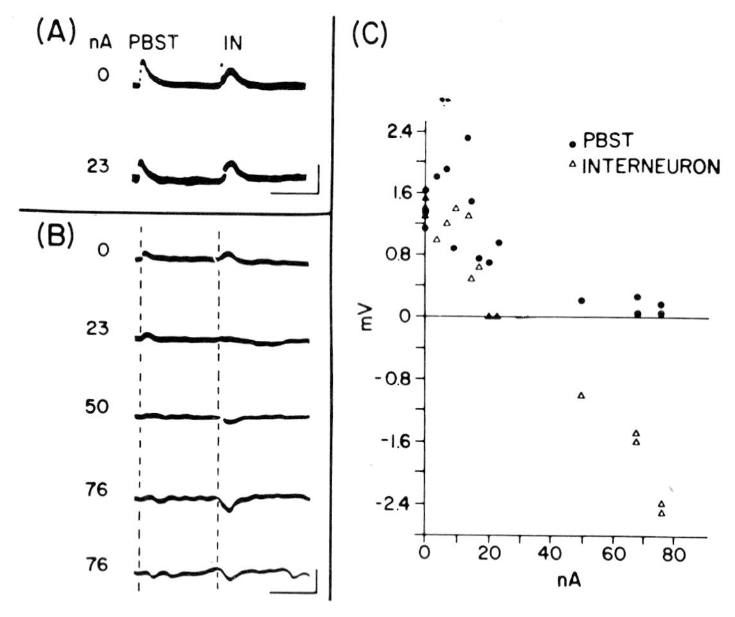

Fig. 2. Non-Ia EPSP's are more sensitive to current than Ia EPSP's. A: effects of hyperpolarization. Sixteen sweeps averaged at 1 Hz of a PBST Ia EPSP followed by an IN EPSP triggered by a 0.2 msec, 10 μA pulse in a high spinal cat with only one dorsal root filament intact to the ipsilateral lumbosacral cord; KCl electrode; 40 nA hyperpolarization produced a 12% decrease in amplitude of the PBST EPSP and a 16% increase in the IN EPSP. Immediately post-injection, these EPSPs returned to control levels. Calibration: 20 msec, 2 mV. B: single sweeps of the same EPSP's in the same cell showing the effects of depolarization. Lines indicate time of onset of EPSP's. Calibration: 20 msec, 5 mV. C: plot of the effect of depolarizing current on the amplitudes of PBST EPSP (●) and an IN EPSP (△) at the time of control maximums (Werman and Carlen, 11).

not reverse (10). Electrical coupling has been proposed as one possible explanation for the lack of a reversal potential by all of these investigators. The basis for these negative findings is not clear. One possibility is that in these later studies, the membrane potential was not monitored during passage of depolarizing current and it could be argued that the reversal potential for the Ia EPSP had not been reached. Moreover, the anatomical evidence is clearly in support of chemical transmission. Figure 3 shows an electron micrograph of a

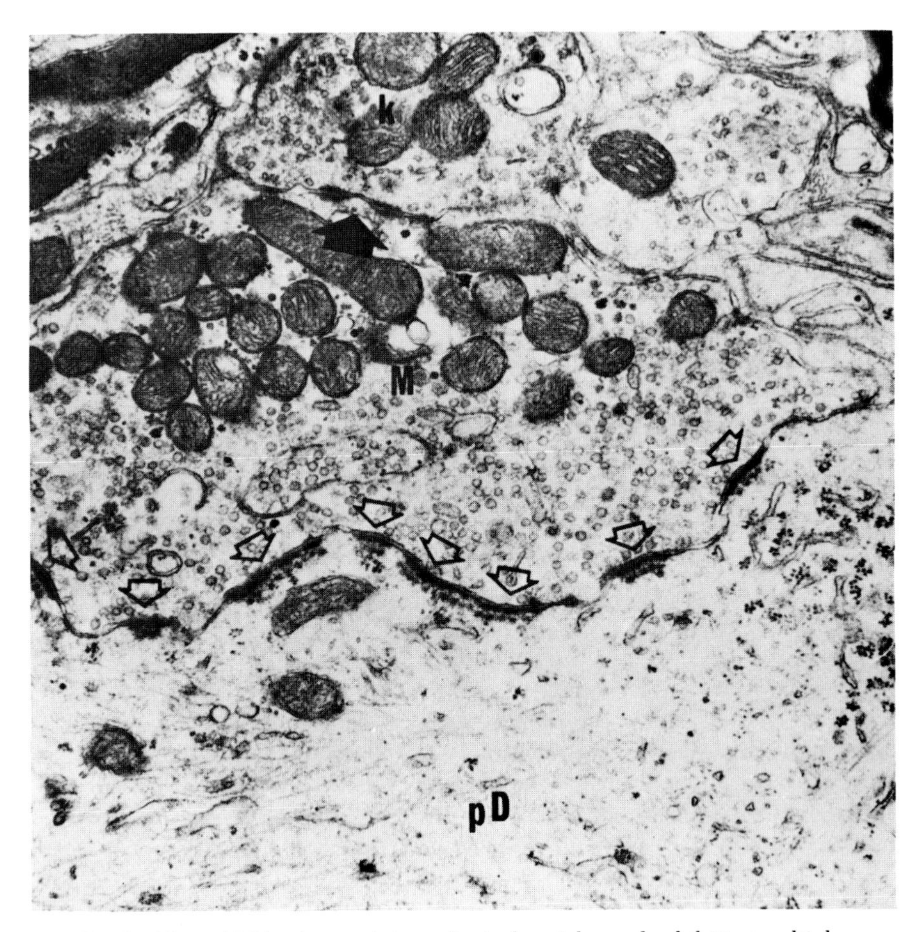

Fig. 3. Normal M knob containing spherical vesicles and exhibiting multiple synaptic complexes or "active" zones with a proximal dendrite (pD). These "active" zones (open arrows) are characterized by many subsynaptic dense bodies. A smaller knob (k), containing pleomorphic vesicles, is seen to make an adhesivelike contact (closed arrow) with the M knob (McLaughlin, 13).

synaptic profile ending on a motoneuron dendrite that is presumed, from degeneration studies, to be derived from a primary afferent. It has all the features typically associated with chemically transmitting excitatory synapses, including round vesicles in the terminal and a synaptic cleft with asymmetrical membrane thickening. Although there are problems in conclusively demonstrating that a particular synaptic profile is of primary afferent origin, anatomical studies have failed to find any synapses in the ventral horn between terminals and dendrites with gap junctions (12–15). Werman and Carlen (11) have proposed a combined electrical–chemical synaptic action, where the electrical coupling would be extracellular and not require specialized membrane appositions. This would explain the reversal of the late phase of the EPSP, but is in conflict with the negative results obtained with unitary EPSP's.

Kuno (16,17) has presented evidence that transmission at Ia primary afferent synapses is quantal in nature, a finding which would be expected at a chemically transmitting synapse. However, in recent experiments Edwards *et al.* (18,19) were unable to demonstrate quantal transmission and concluded that transmission at a single Ia terminal is all-or-none.

Thus, our present knowledge of the ionic mechanism of the most studied synapses in the mammalian CNS is embarrassingly confused and recent evidence raises the possibility of some type of electrical coupling, while the anatomy clearly favors chemical transmission at Ia primary afferent synapses. Synaptic potentials derived from other types of primary afferents have not been studied and it would be interesting to know if they also demonstrate the same unusual physiological properties. Primary afferent transmission in the newborn rat (20) and frog (21) spinal cord does appear to be chemical. This is based on the finding that perfusion of these isolated preparations with a low Ca^{2+} high Mg^{2+} Ringer solution abolishes synaptic transmission. Calcium dependence is a universal finding at chemically transmitting synapses, but is not a feature of electrical synapses.

Mechanism of Glutamate Action. The iontophoretic application of glutamate appears to excite all or almost all neurons in the CNS. The few instances in which inhibition has been observed can be explained in terms of an indirect excitation of inhibitory interneurons (22,23). This universality of action is not a compelling reason for rejecting this substance as a neurotransmitter and, indeed, neurons which are devoid of synapses, e.g., dorsal root ganglion cells, lack any sensitivity to glutamate (24). Application of glutamate causes a depolarization of the membrane and an increase in membrane conductance (Fig. 4). The response appears to have a reversal potential of about 0 to −30 mV (25–27), but there is considerable uncertainty in these measurements. Such a reversal potential, which is in the same range as that seen for the late phase of the Ia EPSP (11,25) and for nonprimary afferent EPSP's, suggests that sodium is the major ion involved (cf. 28) but also suggests that potassium is involved. The dependence of glutamate action in frog mononeurons on the presence of extracellular sodium (29) supports this conclusion. In addition, the action of glutamate is not blocked by tetrodotoxin (27) and, therefore, resembles excitatory transmitter action in other systems. The depolarizing action of aspartate has not been analyzed in detail, but in general aspartate has properties similar to glutamate.

Receptors and Antagonists for Excitatory Amino Acids. It is unclear whether glutamate and aspartate cause their effects by activating the same receptors. Virtually all neurons are excited by both amino

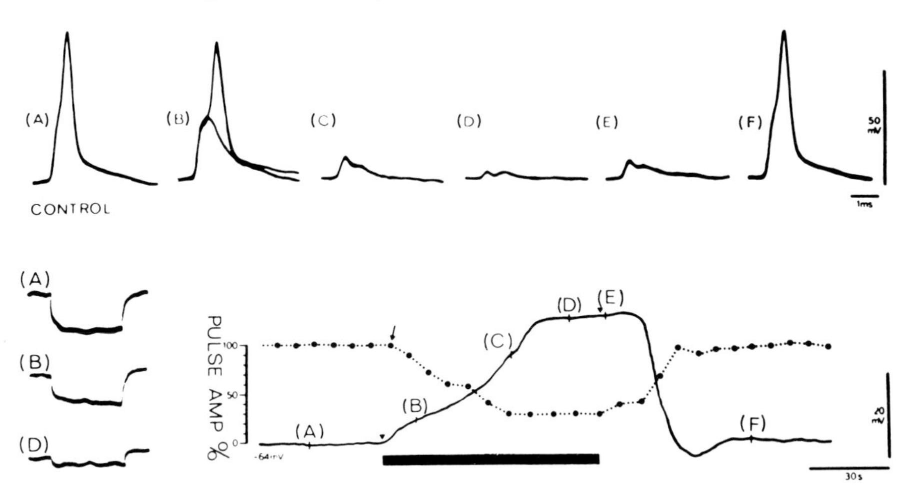

Fig. 4 Intracellular recording from a biceps-semitendinosus motoneuron. 200 mA of GLUT was applied. Intertip distance, 85 μm. An antidromic spike is evoked (two traces superimposed). A, control; B–D, recordings taken at different levels of depolarization caused by GLUT; E–F, during recovery. Note that a depolarization has already occurred before the point (arrow) where the conductance begins to change. Bottom right: penwriter recording of the membrane potential; letters refer to the recordings above. Bar indicates period of application. Dotted line shows simultaneous measurements of conductance changes (%). The amplitude of four consecutive current pulses were averaged. Bottom left: hyperpolarizing test pulses (duration 20 msec). A, B, D taken before the corresponding antidromic spikes. Resting potential, −64 mV; initial membrane resistance, 1.2 *M*. Stimulus frequency, 1/sec (Zieglgansberger and Puil, 26).

acids, but aspartate is generally less potent. It has been found that the relative potency of these two amino acids does differ on different populations of defined neurons. Thus Renshaw cells, which receive input from excitatory interneurons, but not from primary afferents, are more sensitive to aspartate than to glutamate, while dorsal horn interneurons, which receive direct input from primary afferents, are more sensitive to glutamate (30,31). This differential sensitivity suggests that there may be two populations of receptors and supports the proposal, based on neurochemical evidence, that aspartate may be an excitatory transmitter for spinal interneurons, while glutamate may be released from primary afferents (32).

Recently it has been found that brain membranes bind kainic acid, a potent glutamate agonist (33). The binding and displacement parameters are generally consistent with known postsynaptic glutamate receptors. Aspartate is about 50 times less potent than L-glutamate in displacing kainic acid, but this evidence is of little help in clarifying whether these amino acids utilize different receptors, since aspartate is usually also less potent neurophysiologically. The lack of affinity of D-glutamate in this assay is disturbing, since neurophysiological studies show that D-glutamate is only slightly less potent than L-glutamate. More detailed binding studies are needed before they will be of value in establishing a transmitter function for the excitatory amino acids.

There have been a number of reports during the past 5 years in which a number of compounds have been proposed as glutamate antagonists. The major problem in this area is establishing selectivity. Most studies have used extracellular recording and it is difficult to exclude direct effects on membrane excitability, especially if the spontaneous activity is low or absent. Furthermore, the only other excitatory substance that has been used as a control for specificity is acetylcholine, and since there is evidence that it may act through a different ionic mechanism (34), it may not be an appropriate control. The antagonist that has been studied in greatest detail is glutamic acid diethyl ester (GDEE) (35). It has been found to block both glutamate and aspartate responses and also the synaptic action of primary afferents in the cuneate and spinal cord. However, this compound has direct effects on cat spinal motoneurons (36) and in the frog there is no antagonism of amino acid or synaptic responses up to concentrations of 10^{-3} M. Higher concentrations cause direct depolarizations (Fig. 5). Thus neither the potency nor the specificity of this antagonist seem sufficient to help substantially in clarifying the role of excitatory amino acids.

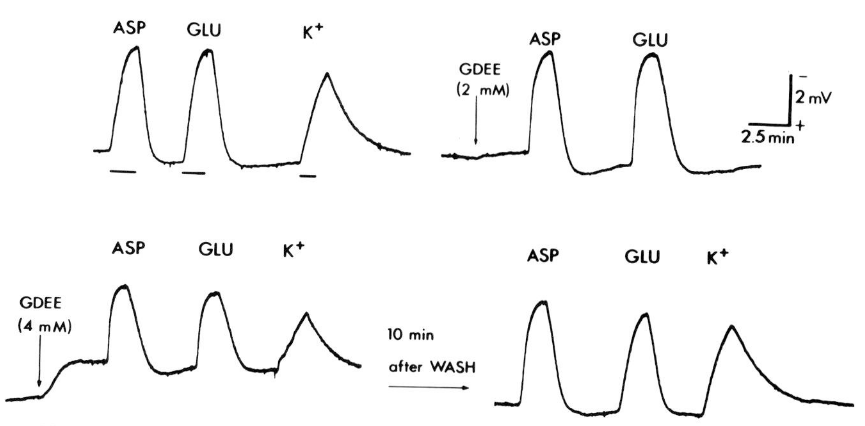

Fig. 5. Effect of glutamic acid diethyl ester (GDEE) on amino acid responses from frog motoneurons. 2 m*M* GDEE has no effect on the aspartate (0.5 m*M*) or glutamate (0.5 m*M*) depolarization recorded with sucrose gap from the ventral root. 4 m*M* GDEE directly depolarizes the motoneurons and depresses the amino acid and potassium (8 m*M*) responses to the same extent. The direct membrane effects of GDEE are quickly reversible (R. A. Nicoll, unpublished observations).

Presence. As mentioned in the Introduction, glutamate and aspartate have a variety of metabolic functions besides their proposed neurotransmitter role and appear to be present in all neurons. It might be expected that in those neurons which utilized one of these amino acids as a neurotransmitter the concentration of the amino acid might be higher and, in addition, one might expect the concentration to fall in an area containing these neurons following neuronal degeneration. In this regard it has been found that the concentration of glutamate in the dorsal root is 1.2 to 1.9 times higher than in the ventral root (37–41). Since the ventral root contains axons of cholinergic neurons, the glutamate concentration in this tissue presumably represents the nonsynaptic metabolic pool and thus the excess of glutamate in the dorsal root might represent a true transmitter pool. The distribution of glutamate in dorsal sensory neurons has also been examined (38–40). The concentration is highest in the dorsal horn, and is higher in the dorsal root between the ganglion and spinal cord than in the dorsal root peripheral to the ganglion (Fig. 6). These findings suggest that there is a selective transport of glutamate toward the spinal cord although no transport of radiolabeled material could be detected following injection of [^{14}C]glucose into dorsal root ganglia (41). Another finding which questions the significance of these results concerning a transmitter role for glutamate is that following dorsal root ligation there is no fall in glutamate concentrations on the side of the tie

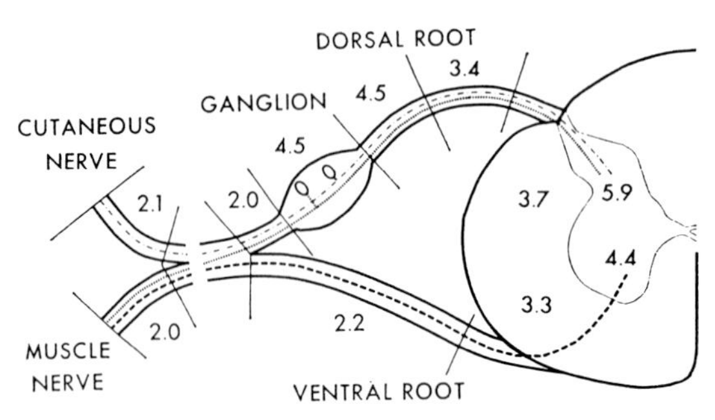

Fig. 6. Diagrammatic representation of the levels of free glutamate, in μmoles/g wet tissue, in the lumbasacral spinal cord, dorsal and ventral root ganglia, and peripheral nerves of the cat (Duggan and Johnston, 39).

nearest the cord (42) and dorsal root section causes no fall in glutamate concentrations in the dorsal horn (42,43). On the other hand, when the thoracic spinal cord is sectioned, glutamate levels in the lumbar cord decline (44), suggesting that descending fibers, whose EPSP's in motoneurons have a reversal potential similar to that of glutamate (11), may utilize this amino acid.

Uptake. It has been found that isolated nerve endings from spinal cord and cerebral cortex possess a high-affinity uptake system for glutamate in addition to a low-affinity uptake system (cf. 45). Aspartate has been found to share the same uptake system. It has been argued that the high-affinity system represents uptake into nerve terminals that utilize glutamate or aspartate as neurotransmitters and represents a means of terminating transmitter action, while the low affinity is a general process which might subserve the metabolic role for these amino acids. Examination of glutamate uptake, then, might shed light on its role in primary afferent transmission. Indeed, it has been found that dorsal root ganglia do possess both the high and low uptake systems (46) and that uptake is greater in the dorsal root compared to the ventral root (47). However, autoradiography (48) has demonstrated that this uptake is exclusively into the satellite glial cells, there being no label concentrated over primary afferent neurons or axons (Fig. 7). It might be argued that only the nerve terminals would have this uptake system and one might be able to demonstrate this by comparing uptake into intact dorsal spinal cord tissue to that from an animal in which the primary afferents have been sectioned. When such a comparison is made, no difference in uptake can be found (43). Thus uptake studies have been of no value in providing evidence that glutamate is a transmitter in primary afferents.

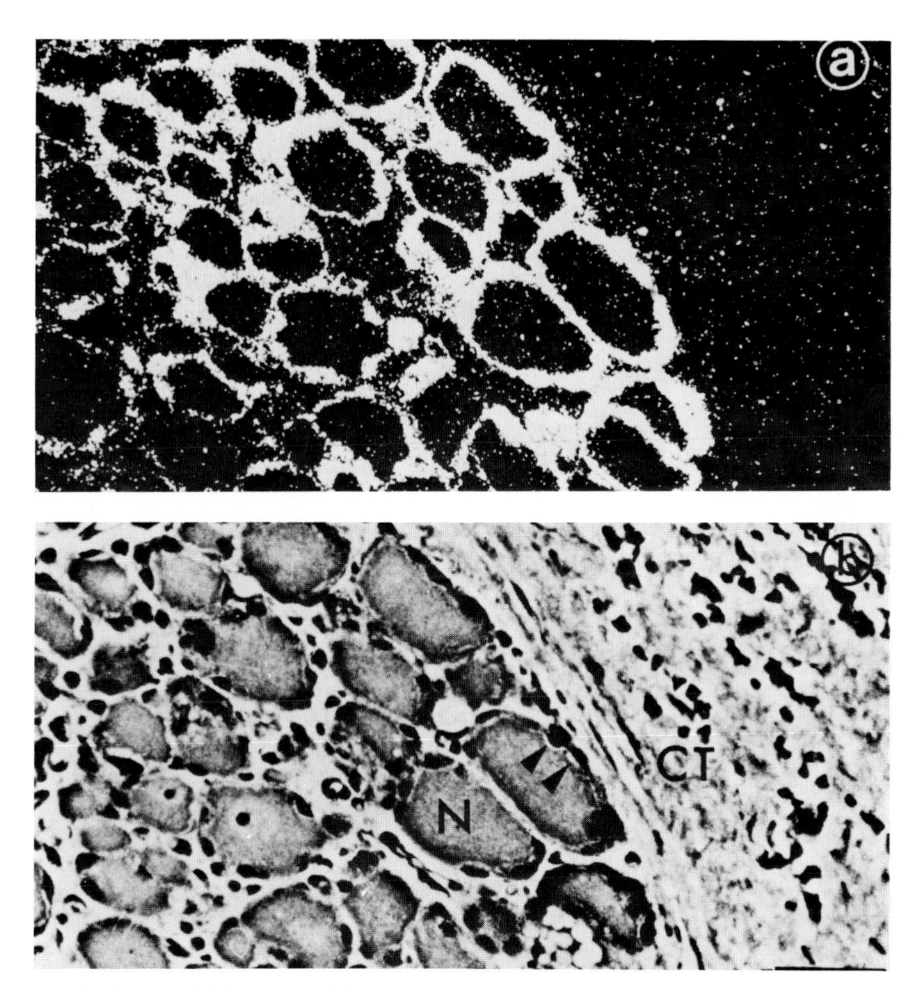

Fig. 7. (a) and (b) Dark-field autoradiograph and corresponding phase-contrast field of rat sensory ganglia incubated with 1.75×10^{-5} *M* [^{3}H]DL-glutamic acid. Silver grains are predominantly located over satellite glial cells (indicated by arrowheads). The connective tissue sheath (CT) and neuronal cell bodies (N) were relatively free of labeling. Exposure time, 4 weeks; calibration bar, 20 μm (Schon and Kelly, 48).

Release. It has been found that depolarizing stimuli will release [^{14}C]glutamate and endogenous glutamate from brain tissue (49–54) and the release, in some studies, was shown to be calcium dependent. Although a calcium-dependent release must be demonstrated for a substance which is considered to be a transmitter, a number of problems exist in these studies. It is not known which fibers are releasing the substance. Amino acids can be released from glial cells and this release shows some dependence on calcium (55,56). The failure to demonstrate release may be of little significance because the released substance may be taken up by the tissue without overflow. Figure 8 shows that, in the isolated frog spinal cord, dorsal root stimulation fails to accelerate the release of [^{14}C]glutamate, but lateral column stimulation does (54). Roberts (53) has studied the release of [^{14}C]glutamate and endogenous glutamate from the cuneate and gracilis nuclei *in vivo*. The nuclei were superfused and the effects of dorsal column stimulation examined. It was found that both labeled and endogenous glutamate were released during stimulation and that this release was abolished in the absence of calcium ions in the perfusion medium. This release appeared to be specific since the efflux of other endogenous amino acids, except GABA, was unaffected. Since medial lemniscal stimulation increased the efflux of GABA but not glutamate it is unlikely that the release of glutamate occurred from recurrent collaterals of the relay neurons.

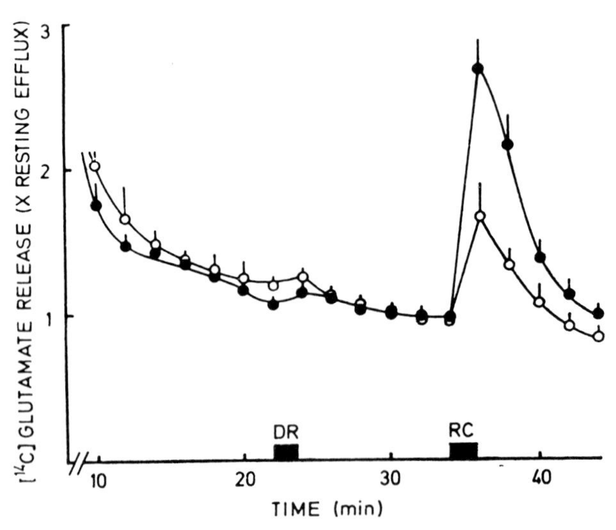

Fig. 8. The effect of electrical stimulation of the dorsal roots (DR) and rostral cord (RC) on the efflux of [C^{14}]L-glutamate from the spinal cord in normal medium (●) and calcium-free medium (○). Each point represents the radioactivity released in each 2-min collection period expressed as a ratio to the release occurring during the steady spontaneous efflux stage of each experiment (mean ± SEM, seven experiments) (Roberts and Mitchell, 52).

The release experiments in the dorsal column nuclei provide the only solid evidence that glutamate may function as a transmitter at primary afferents, at least at those that synapse in the dorsal column nuclei. We have no evidence (except for the questionable results with the "antagonist" glutamic acid diethyl ester) that glutamate is the transmitter in primary afferents that end in the spinal cord. There are two alternatives for this large body of negative results. First, glutamate may not be the transmitter released from any spinal primary afferents, or, alternatively, the experiments have been based on assumptions that are incorrect and that one can expect negative results even though glutamate is the transmitter in this system.

The significance of these negative results would be greatly increased if it were possible to demonstrate that the same experiments gave positive results in another system. Indeed, recent results in the hippocampal formation would suggest that the experimental approaches used in the spinal cord are on a firm conceptual framework.

EXCITATORY SYNAPSES IN THE HIPPOCAMPAL FORMATION

Anatomy and Physiology of Excitatory Synapses. The ordered and layered structure of the hippocampal formation provides a particularly favorable area for identifying neurotransmitters for specific types of neurons (57). At the simplest level the hippocampal formation consists of a trisynaptic circuit (Fig. 9). Fibers from the entorhinal cortex form the perforant path and make excitatory synapses on the dendrites of granule cells in the dentate area. The axons of granule cells give rise to the giant mossy fiber terminals which form excitatory synapses on CA3 pyramidal cells. The CA3 pyramidal cells send axonal branches, termed Schaffer collaterals, to the stratum radiatum of CA1 which form excitatory synapses onto the apical dendrites of pyramidal cells. The axons of CA3 pyramidal cells also leave the hippocampal formation via the fimbria and project to the contralateral side to form excitatory synapses on the dendrites of CA1–3 pyramidal cells in stratum oriens and stratum radiatum. The excitatory synapses for all these fibers (perforant mossy, commissural, and Schaffer collateral) have a dendrite location and form asymmetrical synapses with round synaptic vesicles in the terminals (58).

The dendritic location of these excitatory synapses has limited the analysis of the ionic mechanism of the EPSP's. However, the dependence on the calcium–magnesium ratio of the extracellularly recorded EPSP in granule cells derived from stimulating the perforant pathway (59) provides additional evidence that transmission is chemical at this

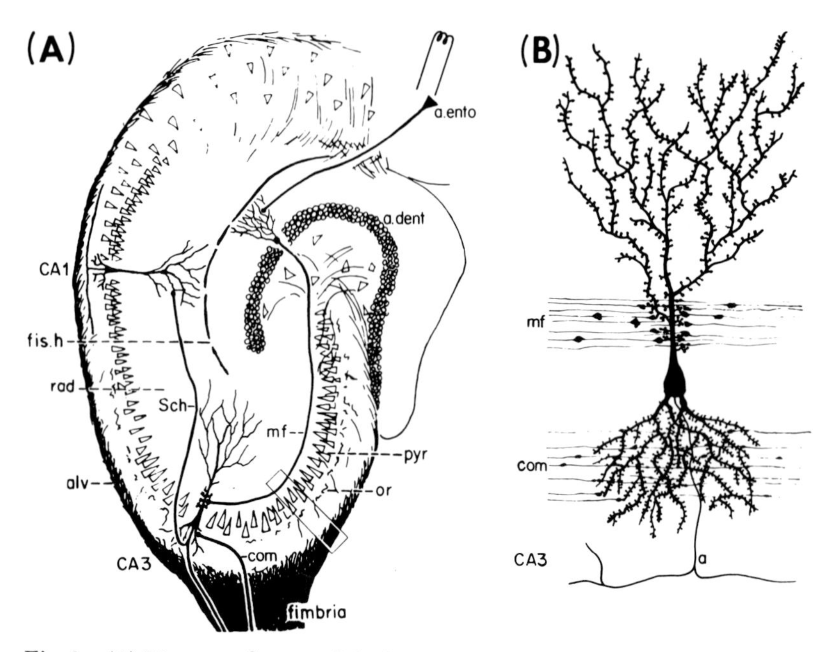

Fig. 9. (A) Diagram of a part of the hippocampal region based on a horizontal section of the rat brain but valid for other species with regard to the structures dealt with in this paper. Only a few pathways have been indicated. a. dent, the dentate area; a. ento, entorhinal area; alv, the alveus; com, commissural afferents; fis. h, hippocampal fissue; mf, mossy fibers, or stratium oriens; pyr, stratum pyramidale; Sch, Schaffer collateral from CA3 pyramidal cell. The rectangular area in CA3 indicates the position of the zone shown in Fig. 6. (B) Diagram of CA3 pyramidal cell. a: the axon dichotomizing in the alveus, com: commissural afferents, mf: mossy fibers (Andersen *et al.*, 58).

site. Furthermore, it has been found that the size of the EPSP derived from Schaffer collateral stimulation is increased by membrane hyperpolarization, suggesting that there is an increase in conductance accompanying the EPSP (60). However, the reversal potential for the EPSP's is unknown.

Action of Excitatory Amino Acids and the Effect of Antagonists. The firing rate of granule and pyramidal cells is increased following the iontophoretic application of glutamate to the soma of these neurons (61–65). Aspartate appears to have approximately the same potency as glutamate. Iontophoresis of glutamate to pyramidal cell dendrites indicates that receptors are present on the dendrites (66–68) and in one study it was reported that the dendrites were more sensitive than the cell bodies (68). This excitation is associated with depolarization of the cell body (60), but the ionic mechanism of this depolarization has not been studied. Segal (65) has compared the sensitivity of CA1 neurons to aspartate and acetylcholine in normal rats and in rats in which the commissural pathway has been lesioned. Following removal of the commissural pathway, the CA1 pyramidal cells exhibited an increased sensitivity to aspartate but not to acetylcholine. It is unclear whether this change results from an increased sensitivity of the cell membrane to aspartate or is secondary to the removal of barriers and/or uptake sites.

Glutamic acid diethyl ester (GDEE) has been reported to block the responses of both glutamate and aspartate with minimal effects on acetylcholine responses when low iontophoretic currents are used (63,64). However, with slightly higher current it has a potent direct inhibitory effect (63). This direct effect complicates the interpretation of results obtained with parenteral administration of this drug. However, it was claimed that following parenteral administration, GDEE reduced the field potential elicited by commissural stimulation but had no effect on the field potential elicited by perforant path stimulation. This selectivity is surprising in that there is neurochemical evidence that glutamate may also be the transmitter in this commissural pathway (see below).

Presence, Uptake, and Release of Excitatory Amino Acids from Hippocampal Formation. Crawford and Connor (69) found that the levels of glutamate were about twice as high in samples dissected from the CA3 region, so as to include the mossy fiber layer, as in samples dissected from the CA1 region. Aspartate concentrations were also higher in the mossy fiber layer. No other studies are available on the distribution and localization of glutamate and aspartate in the hippocampal formation and no lesion experiments have been performed to demonstrate that these amino acids are concentrated in fibers serving an excitatory function. However, glutamate uptake into hippocampal slices has been examined and light and electronmicroscopic autoradiography indicates that the uptake of [^{3}H]glutamate is predominantly into excitatory nerve endings (70,71). In addition, removal of the excitatory input to CA1, which is derived from the ipsilateral and contralateral projection of CA3 pyramidal cells, results in an 80–90% loss of glutamate uptake into stratum oriens and stratum radiatum. There was no loss of glutamic acid decarboxylase activity, the enzyme which synthesizes GABA, indicating that the short-axoned inhibitory neurons were left intact. Following removal of the excitatory perforant path to dentate granule cells there was also a marked fall in glutamate uptake in the molecular layer of dentate gyrus where these excitatory fibers terminate. Nadler *et al.* (72) have reported similar results in the dentate gyrus. These experiments suggest that glutamate is specifically accumulated by excitatory nerve endings. It is puzzling that glial uptake of glutamate, which has been reported in numerous areas of the CNS (48,74–78; see Fig. 7) appears to be minimal in the hippocampal formation. Nadler *et al.* (72) also studied the effect of removing excitatory fibers on the calcium dependent release of glutamate and aspartate from the hippocampal formation exposed to high potassium levels. It was found that removal of the perforant path resulted in a 50% reduction in calcium-dependent glutamate efflux from the dentate gyrus but no change in the CA1 region of the hippocampus. Aspartate release was not decreased by the lesion. On the other hand, removal of the commissural fibers, which project both to CA1 and the dentate gyrus, resulted in a fall in both aspartate and glutamate release. Although these results were not corrected for the loss of tissue volume which is produced by these lesions, the results suggest that glutamate release is associated with the fibers of the perforant path and that aspartate and glutamate release is associated with commissural fibers. Crawford and Connors (73) also demonstrated a release of glutamate from the hippocampal formation during perforant path stimulation, but did not examine the calcium dependence of this release or the effects of lesions on this release.

SUMMARY

A marked disparity exists between the results obtained with primary afferents and with the hippocampal formation. The only evidence suggesting that glutamate functions as an excitatory transmitter at spinal primary afferents is the slightly higher levels of this substance in dorsal versus ventral root and the dubious results with GDEE. It has often been reasoned in the past that since glutamate and aspartate have the most potent excitatory action of any endogenous substance and, aside from acetylcholine, are the only endogenous substances with such an action, it is only a matter of time before their transmitter role is established at excitatory synapses. However, this exclusive position no longer exists, since the discovery that substance P has a more potent action than these amino acids on spinal neurons. Although substance P appears to be localized only in a small fraction of primary afferents (4), its potent excitatory action emphasizes that other as yet undiscovered excitatory substances may prove to be the transmitters at those spinal primary afferents which do not contain substance P. Hence the evidence for glutamate's transmitter role at spinal primary afferent synapses is meager.

On the other hand, results in the hippocampal formation, although incomplete, all more clearly support the hypothesis that glutamate, and possibly aspartate, are neurotransmitters released from excitatory synapses. Additional studies are needed in the cellular localization of these amino acids and the discovery and use of more potent and selective antagonists of the excitatory amino acids would greatly strengthen experimental evidence for their existence as neurotransmitters.

TAURINE

Of all the naturally occurring amino acids taurine is certainly one of the most puzzling. Because of its ubiquitous nature and presence in most forms of invertebrates and vertebrates, taurine has received widespread attention, and has even been the subject of a symposium (79). Yet, its precise role either in neuronal or nonneuronal tissue remains enigmatic. It has long been suspected that taurine might be a neurotransmitter, since it has potent effects on neuronal excitability. The areas in which this possibility has received the most attention are the retina and frog spinal cord. Thus emphasis will be placed on the possible role of taurine in synaptic events in these two areas.

FROG SPINAL CORD

Receptors and Antagonists for Taurine. The action of taurine on neurons of the frog spinal cord has been examined by numerous investigators (80–84). Taurine suppresses reflex activity and silences spontaneous neuronal activity. This is accompanied by a hyperpolarization of the motoneurons which has a considerably slower time course than the responses to other amino acids. The hyperpolarization is not blocked by conditions which abolish synaptic transmission, and therefore is presumably a direct action on the motoneurons. Taurine is the most potent amino acid on frog motoneurons, being approximately twice as potent as GABA. This high apparent potency may result to some degree from the lack of a high affinity uptake system for taurine in the frog spinal cord (see below). The mechanism of action of taurine appears to be the same as that for the other neutral amino acids involving a conductance increase to chloride ions. This is shown in Fig. 10 in which replacement of extracellular chloride with the imper-

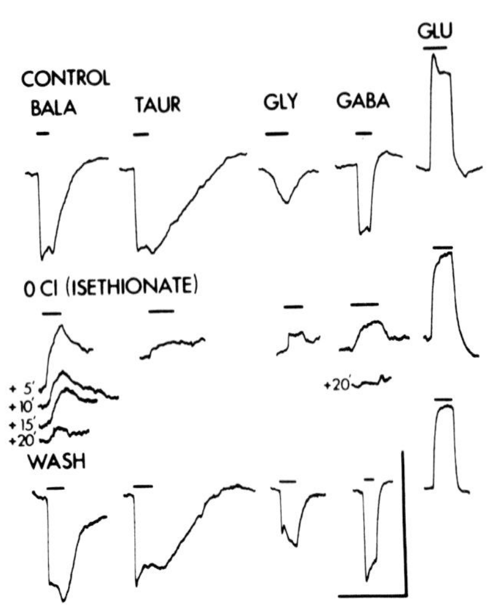

Fig. 10. Effect of chloride-free Ringer's solution on the amino acid responses. Replacement of chloride with isethionate reversed the hyperpolarizations, which decreased in size with time (indicated in minutes at the left of the β-alanine and GABA responses). The glutamate depolarization was unaffected in this preparation. Return to normal Ringer's (WASH) restored all of the responses. All drugs applied in concentration of 1 m*M*. Calibration: 5 mV for all records except GLU which is 10 mV; 2.5 min (Nicoll *et al.*, 82).

meant anion, isethionate, converts the hyperpolarizations of all the amino acids to small depolarizations.

On primary afferents GABA has been found to have a depolarizing action (81,85) and is thought to be the transmitter in presynaptic inhibition. Taurine also has a depolarizing action (Fig. 11), but, unlike GABA, there is often a small hyperpolarizing component. The response has a slower time course than GABA and is approximately as potent as GABA. Although it was initially proposed that the GABA depolarization was due to a sodium mechanism (86), recent evidence suggests that chloride may be the predominant ion involved (85). The fact that the GABA response is depolarizing is presumably due to an unusually high intracellular concentration of chloride ions in the primary afferent fibers so that the equilibrium potential for chloride is in the depolarizing direction. Although similar studies have not been performed for taurine, it is probable that the depolarization has a mechanism similar to that of GABA.

The hyperpolarizing action of taurine on motoneurons along with that of β-alanine and glycine are blocked by strychnine (Fig. 12), while GABA responses are unaffected. Unlike the glycine response,

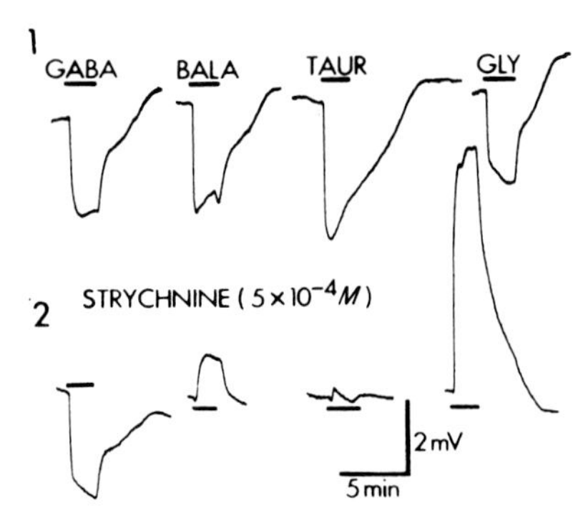

Fig. 11. Effect of strychnine on amino acid responses of ventral roots. (1) Control hyperpolarizing responses to 2.5 m*M* concentration of four amino acids. (2) Shows that a relatively high concentration of strychnine converted β-alanine and glycine responses into depolarizations, and abolished taurine responses, while not affecting the GABA hyperpolarizations (Nicoll *et al.*, 82).

which has a strychnine-resistant, depolarizing component, there does not appear to be any strychnine-resistant component to the taurine response. The action of the GABA antagonists picrotoxin and bicuculline on the strychnine-sensitive amino acid response is quite variable and often these responses are more readily blocked than GABA.

Although specific inhibitory pathways have not been elucidated in the frog, the pronounced seizure activity produced by strychnine in all probability results from a block of postsynaptic inhibition. The question which remains to be answered is which of the strychnine sensitive amino acids is the inhibitory transmitter. The weak and variable action of glycine in the frog cord when compared to taurine would certainly favor taurine as the postsynaptic inhibitory transmitter.

On primary afferents the depolarizing action of taurine and β-alanine is completely blocked by picrotoxin and strychnine, while the action of GABA is only partially blocked by picrotoxin (Fig. 12). Interestingly the dorsal root potential derived from ventral root stimulation is also completely blocked by both picrotoxin and strychnine (87,88). Thus, on pharmacological grounds there is evidence that either taurine or β-alanine is the transmitter in this pathway. The only reservation to this interpretation concerns the site of action of strychnine in blocking the dorsal root potential. It is known that this pathway contains a cholinergic synapse (89) and it is possible that strychnine, which has an anticholinergic action (90), is blocking the pathway at this site, rather than at the final synapse onto the primary afferents.

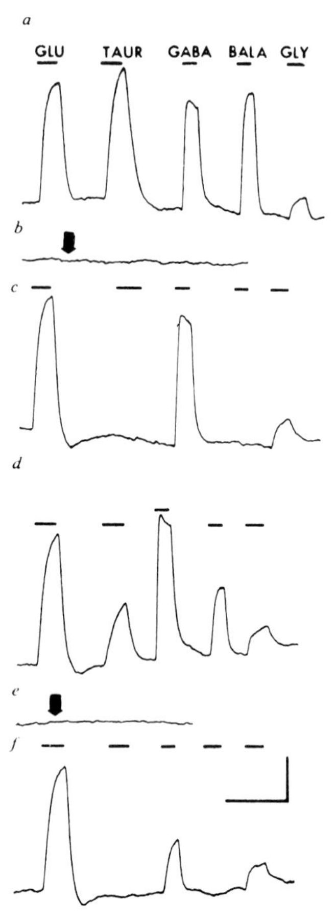

Fig. 12. Effect of strychnine and picrotoxin on amino acid induced depolarizations of primary afferents. (a) Control responses to glutamic acid (GLU), taurine (TAUR), GABA, β-alanine (BALA), and glycine (GLY) (all drugs 10^{-3} *M* concentration); (b) strychnine (10^{-4} *M*) added to the perfusate; (c) the responses obtained 30 min after starting the strychnine; (d) responses obtained 2 hr after removing strychnine from the Ringer's; (e) picrotoxin (10^{-4} *M*) added to the Ringer's solution; (f) responses repeated 20 min after starting the picrotoxin. Calibration, 2 mV, 8 min. (Nicoll and Barker, 87).

Presence and Uptake of Taurine. The concentration of taurine (2.29 μmoles/g wet weight) is higher than that of any other free amino acid and is twice the concentration of glycine. Although a high affinity, sodium-dependent uptake of taurine has been found in mammalian brain tissue (91) such a process does not appear to exist in the frog spinal cord (92,93). This lack of an uptake process might explain in part the high apparent potency of taurine and its slow time course of action. While the failure to demonstrate the existence of a high affinity uptake for taurine raises doubts concerning its candidacy as a transmitter in the frog spinal cord it is possible that diffusion alone is sufficient for terminating transmitter action.

RETINA

Presence. Although taurine is the predominant free amino acid in the retina (94–98), little physiologic understanding has derived from measurements of whole retinal taurine content. For example, in the frog retina, where taurine concentration (12 μmoles/g wet weight) is 3 times as great as glutamate, 17 times that of aspartate, 4.5 times that of GABA, and almost 7 times the concentration of glycine, large differences in states of light and dark adaptation have yielded little alteration of any amino acid level (98). Taurine appears to be concentrated in the outer photoreceptor regions of retina (99–101) and this is supported by experiments in which the interneurons and ganglion cells but not photoreceptors or Müller glial cells are selectively destroyed by chronic glutamate treatment (101). Although there is a severe loss of most putative neurotransmitters and their synthetic enzymes, there is no change in the level of taurine. The 60% diminution of taurine levels observed in the mouse and cat with photoreceptor dystrophy (97,102) further suggests that taurine is localized, at least in part, within the photoreceptors.

Uptake. Unlike the frog spinal cord, isolated retinae are capable of concentrating radiolabeled taurine against a gradient in a manner which requires the presence of sodium and energy (103,104). After careful examination of previous literature and recalculation of taurine uptake kinetic parameters in isolated retinal tissue, Neal (105) was able to support his previous observation of the presence of two components of taurine uptake consisting of a "high-affinity" process with an apparent K_m ranging between 2 and 43 μM and another "low-affinity" process with an apparent K_m on the order of 0.5 to 1 mM (106). The presence of a high-affinity, high-capacity retinal uptake process for taurine, in addition to an absence of significant taurine metabolism (103,107), suggests that taurine may be taken up and stored in a stable transmitter pool. However, autoradiographic studies suggest that taurine uptake may reside with Müller glial cells (107) which span the depths between the outer and inner limiting membrane (108) and possibly also in amacrine cells (109). The significance of this glial uptake of taurine to synaptic transmission remains unclear.

Release. Pasantes-Morales *et al.* (110–112) have observed enhanced efflux of both endogenous and labeled taurine from isolated, perfused chicken retinae after stimulation with light flashes. Interestingly, under similar conditions endogenous glutamate, glycine, alanine, GABA, and lysine efflux were unaffected, although transmural electrical stimulation released both radiolabeled taurine and GABA. Surprisingly, 30 m*M* and 60 m*M* potassium media did not affect release of taurine. Release of [^{35}S]taurine from isolated retinae is apparently calcium dependent as incubation in Ca^{2+}-free medium abolishes light-stimulated release and incubating with a Ca^{2+}-free plus 2 m*M* EDTA medium decreased electrically stimulated efflux by 65%. It is unclear from which cells [^{35}S]taurine is released. Presumably it is not from Müller glial cells because, although the rise in extracellular potassium following light stimulation does depolarize Müller cells (113), high-potassium-containing media fail to release [^{35}S]taurine.

Receptors and Antagonists. Both taurine and GABA have been shown to depress the amplitude of the b-wave of the electroretinogram (ERG) (114). The effect of taurine, but not GABA, is blocked by the administration of low doses of strychnine. Cunningham and Miller (115) have examined in detail the effects of taurine on the isolated perfused retina-eyecup preparation of rabbits. They found that taurine (1) produces characteristic changes in the receptive fields of ganglion cells, abolishing surrounding excitation in on-center cells, while center-on-discharge in these cells persisted; no spontaneous or evoked responses could be obtained from off-center ganglion cells in the presence of taurine; (2) horizontal cells were unaffected by taurine; (3) the off response of the proximal negative response, which is a reflection of amacrine activity, is abolished. Based on this data and the known physiological organization of the retina, they reasoned that taurine either blocks the hyperpolarizing bipolar cell directly or blocks the postsynaptic activity dependent on the hyperpolarizing bipolar pathway.

Since strychnine completely blocks the effects of taurine in the retina (114,115), any synaptic activity generated by the release of taurine should be blocked by strychnine. Unfortunately, concentrations of strychnine which readily block the action of taurine have no specific effect on the ERG or on the tectal evoked response in the chicken (114). Rather, high concentrations appear to have a facilitatory effect on the proximal negative response (116). However, the precise synaptic locus at which strychnine acts to produce this effect is unclear.

SUMMARY

Although taurine is present in high amounts in the retina, is accumulated by retinal tissue by a high-affinity process, is released by a calcium-dependent mechanism, and has potent effects on retinal cells, it still remains questionable whether taurine has an important transmitter role in the retina. This scepticism is based on the distribution of endogenous taurine and on the generally negative effects of strychnine on retinal function. The localization of taurine in the photoreceptor layer suggests that if it were a transmitter in the retina it would be released from the photoreceptors. However, horizontal cells which receive input from photoreceptors are unaffected by taurine and strychnine does not appear to block the synaptic action of photoreceptors. It is possible that taurine may function as a transmitter in some amacrine cells, but the failure to demonstrate any fall in taurine levels following degeneration of amacrine cells (101) certainly raises doubts about its role as a transmitter at this level of the retina.

The role of taurine in the frog spinal cord is also far from clear. A major problem in this system is that the basic organization of the interneuronal pathways is poorly understood. Thus, although the dorsal root potential derived from ventral root stimulation has pharmacological properties similar to taurine's action, the interneurons in this pathway have yet to be identified. In addition, studies are needed on the regional and cellular localization of taurine and on the release of taurine from the frog spinal cord.

CONCLUSION

It could be argued that the present review is unduly negative and reveals more about the authors' bias than an accurate appraisal of the current status of the proposed transmitter role for glutamate and taurine. It is inevitable that each investigator will place different emphasis on different criteria for transmitter identification and on the reliability of various approaches and techniques to establish a particular criterion. However, in the case of glutamate, a number of experiments which gave negative results when tested on primary afferents have yielded positive results in the hippocampus. The optimism in regard to the results in the hippocampus is due to the fact that it has been possible to correlate these positive findings to specific excitatory pathways. Similar correlations have also been possible for glutamate and the excitatory granule cells in the cerebellum (117).

This correlation has not been possible with the results on taurine in the retina. Thus, although the retina does contain many processes for taurine which are usually associated with transmitter molecules, these processes have not been linked to a particular type of synapse. This is suprising because the organization of the retina is well understood and a particularly good taurine antagonist, strychnine, is available. Until it can be shown that a specific type of synapse is blocked by strychnine, taurine's role as a synaptic transmitter in the retina will remain in doubt. The same arguments apply for the frog spinal cord. However, in addition, in this system the neuronal organization is poorly understood. Thus, the role of taurine in the frog spinal cord will depend on advances in our understanding of the physiology of this system.

REFERENCES

1. Otsuka, M., Iversen, L. L., Hall, Z. W., and Kravitz, E. A. (1966) *Proc. Natl. Acad. Sci. U.S.A.* **56,** 1110–1115.
2. Roberts, E., this symposium.
3. Curtis, D. R., and Johnston, G. A. R. (1974) *Ergeb. Physiol., Biol. Chem. Exp. Pharmakol.* **69,** 97–188.
4. Hökfelt, T., Kellerth, J. O., Nilsson, G., and Pernow, B. (1975) *Brain Res.* **100,** 235–252.
5. Hökfelt, T., Elde, R., Johansson, O., Luft, R., Nilsson, G., and Arimura, A. (1976) *Neuroscience* **1,** 131–136.
6. Coombs, J. S., Eccles, J. C., and Fatt, P. (1955) *J. Physiol. (London)* **130,** 374–395.
7. Marshall, K. C., and Engberg, I. (1973) *Physiol. Can.* **4,** 188.
8. Smith, T. G., Wuerker, R. B., and Frank, K. (1967) *J. Neurophysiol.* **30,** 1072–1096.
9. Shapavalov, A. I., and Kurchavcji, G. C. (1974) *Brain Res.* **82,** 49–67.
10. Edwards, F. R., Redman, S. J., and Walmsley, B. (1976) *J. Physiol. (London)* **259,** 705–723.
11. Werman, R., and Carlen, P. L. (1976) *Brain Res.* **112,** 395–401.
12. Conradi, S. (1969) *Acta Physiol. Scand., Suppl.* **332.**
13. McLaughlin, B. J. (1972) *J. Comp. Neurol.* **144,** 429–460.
14. McLaughlin, B. J. (1972) *J. Comp. Neurol.* **144,** 461–474.
15. Ralston, H. J., personal communication.
16. Kuno, M. (1964) *J. Physiol. (London)* **175,** 81–99.
17. Kuno, M. (1971) *Physiol. Rev.* **51,** 647–678.
18. Edwards, F. R., Redman, S. J., and Walmsley, B. (1976) *J. Physiol. (London)* **259,** 665–688.
19. Edwards, F. R., Redman, S. J., and Walmsley, B. (1976) *J. Physiol. (London)* **259,** 689–704.
20. Otsuka, M., and Konishi, S. (1975) *Cold Spring Harbor Symp. Quant. Biol.* **40,** 135–144.
21. Dambach, G. E., and Erulkar, S. D. (1973) *J. Physiol. (London)* **228,** 799–817.
22. McLennan, H. (1971) *Brain Res.* **29,** 177–184.

23. Nicoll, R. A. (1971 *Brain Res.* **35**, 137–149.
24. De Groat, W. C., Lalley, P. M., and Saum, W. R. (1972) *Brain Res.* **44**, 213–217.
25. Curtis, D. R. (1965). "Studies in Physiology (D. R. Curtis and A. K. McIntyre, eds.), pp. 34–42. Springer-Verlag, Berlin and New York.
26. Zieglgansberger, W., and Puil, E. A. (1973) *Exp. Brain Res.* **17**, 35–49.
27. Curtis, D. R., Duggan, A. W., Felix, D., Johnston, G. A. R., Tebecis, A. K., and Watkins, J. (1972) *Brain Res.* **41**, 283–301.
28. Harvey, J. A., and McIlwain, H. (1968) *Biochem. J.* **108**, 269–274.
29. Nicoll, R. A., Padjen, A., and Barker, J. L. (1976) *Neuropharmacology* **15**, 45–53.
30. Duggan, A. W. (1974) *Exp. Brain Res.* **19**, 522–528.
31. Briscoe, J. J., Headley, P. M., Lodge, D., Martin, M. R., and Watkins, J. C. (1976) *Exp. Brain Res.* **26**, 547–551.
32. Davidoff, R. A., Graham, L. T., Shank, R. P., Werman, R., and Aprison, M. H. (1967) *J. Neurochem.* **14**, 1025–1031.
33. Simon, J. R., Contrero, J. F., and Kuhar, M. J. (1976) *J. Neurochem.* **26**, 141–149.
34. Krnjević, K., Puman, R., and Renaud, L. (1971) *J. Physiol. (London)* **215**, 247–268.
35. McLennan, H. (1972) *Handb. Psychopharmacol.* **4**, 211–228.
36. Zieglgansberger, W., and Puil, E. A. (1973) *Naunyn-Schmiedeberg's Arch. Pharmacol.* **277**, Suppl., R89.
37. Graham, L. T., Shank, R. P., Werman, R., and Aprison, M. H. (1967) *J. Neurochem.* **14**, 465–472.
38. Johnson, J. L., and Aprison, M. H. (1970) *Brain Res.* **24**, 285–292.
39. Duggan, A. W., and Johnston, G. A. R. (1970) *J. Neurochem.* **17**, 1205–1208.
40. Duggan, A. W., and Johnston, G. A. R. (1970) *Comp. Gen. Pharmacol.* **1**, 127–128.
41. Roberts, P. J., Keen, P., and Mitchell, J. F. (1973) *J. Neurochem.* **21**, 199–209.
42. Takahashi, T., and Otsuka, M. (1975) *Brain Res.* **87**, 1–11.
43. Roberts, P. J., and Keen, P. (1974) *Brain Res.* **74**, 333–337.
44. Rizzoli, A. A. (1968) *Brain Res.* **11**, 11–18.
45. Logan, W. J., and Snyder, S. H. (1972) *Brain Res.* **42**, 413–431.
46. Roberts, P. J., and Keen, P. (1974) *J. Neurochem.* **23**, 201–209.
47. Roberts, P. J., and Keen, P. (1973) *Brain Res.* **57**, 234–238.
48. Schon, F., and Kelly, J. S. (1974) *Brain Res.* **66**, 275–288.
49. Mulder, A. H., and Snyder, S. H. (1974) *Brain Res.* **76**, 297–308.
50. Hopkin, J., and Neal, M. J. (1971) *Br. J. Pharmacol.* **42**, 215–223.
51. Bradford, H. F. (1970) *Brain Res.* **19**, 239–247.
52. Roberts, P. J., and Mitchell, J. F. (1972) *J. Neurochem.* **19**, 2473–2481.
53. Roberts, P. J. (1974) *Brain Res.* **67**, 419–428.
54. Arnfred, T., and Hertz, L. (1971) *J. Neurochem.* **18**, 259–265.
55. Minchin, M. C. W., and Iversen, L. L. (1974) *J. Neurochem.* **23**, 533–540.
56. Roberts, P. J. (1974) *Brain Res.* **74**, 327–332.
57. Storm-Mathisen, J. (1977) *Prog. Neurobiol.* **8**, 119–181.
58. Andersen, P., Blackstad, T. W., and Lomo, T. (1966) *Exp. Brain Res.* **1**, 236–248.
59. Bliss, T. V. P., and Richards, C. D. (1971) *J. Physiol. (London)* **214**, 7P–9P.
60. Schwartzkroin, P. A. (1975) *Brain Res.* **85**, 423–436.
61. Biscoe, T. J., and Straughan, D. W. (1966) *J. Physiol. (London)* **183**, 341–359.
62. Salmoiraghi, G. C., and Stefanis, C. N. (1965) *Arch. Ital. Biol.* **103**, 705–724.
63. Segal, M. (1976) *Br. J. Pharmacol.* **58**, 341–345.
64. Spencer, H. J., Gribkoff, V. K., Cotman, C. W., and Lynch, G. S. (1976) *Brain Res.* **105**, 471–481.
65. Segal, M. (1977) *Brain Res.* **119**, 476–479.

66. Dudar, J. D. (1974) *Neuropharmacology* **13**, 1083–1089.
67. Schwartzkroin, P. A., and Anderson, P. (1975) *Adv. Neurol.* **12**, 45–51.
68. Schwartzkroin, P. A., Skrede, K. K., Storm, J., and Andersen, P. (1974) *Int. Congr. Physiol. Sci.* [*Proc.*], *26th, 1974* Vol. 11, p. 391.
69. Crawford, I. L., and Connor, J. D. (1973) *Nature (London)* **244**, 442–443.
70. Storm-Mathisen, J. (1977) *Brain Res.* **120**, 379–386.
71. Iversen, L. L., and Storm-Mathisen, J. (1976) *Acta Physiol. Scand.* **96**, 22A–23A.
72. Nadler, J. V., Vaca, K. W., White, W. F., Lynch, G. S., and Cotman, C. W. (1976) *Nature (London)* **260**, 538–540.
73. Crawford, I. L., and Connor, J. D. (1973) *Nature (London)* **244**, 442–443.
74. Bruun, A., and Ehinger, B. (1974) *Exp. Eye Res.* **19**, 435–447.
75. Henn, F. A., Goldstein, M. N., and Hamberger, A. (1974) *Nature (London)* **249**, 663–664.
76. Hökfelt, T., and Ljungdahl, A. (1972) *Adv. Biochem. Psychopharmacol.* **6**, 1–36.
77. Kennedy, A. J., Voaden, M. J., and Marshall, J. (1974) *Nature (London)* **252**, 50–52.
78. McLennan, H. (1976) *Brain Res* **115**, 139–144.
79. Huxtable, R., and Barbeau, A., eds. (1976). "Taurine." Raven, New York.
80. Curtis, D. R., Phillis, J. W., and Watkins, J. C. (1961) *Br. J. Pharmacol. Chemother.* **16**, 262–283.
81. Barker, J. L., Nicoll, R. A., and Padjen, A. (1975) *J. Physiol. (London)* **245**, 521–536.
82. Nicoll, R. A. Padjen, A., and Barker, J. L. (1976) *Neuropharmacology* **15**, 45–53.
83. Nistri, A., and Constanti, A. (1976) *Neuropharmacology* **15**, 635–641.
84. Evans, R. H., and Watkins, J. C. (1975) *Br. J. Pharmacol.* **55**, 519–526.
85. Nishi, S., Minota, S., and Karczmar, A. G. (1974) *Neuropharmacology* **13**, 215–219.
86. Barker, J. L., and Nicoll, R. A. (1973) *J. Physiol. (London)* **228**, 259–277.
87. Nicoll, R. A., and Barker, J. L. (1973) *Nature (London), New Biol.* **246**, 224–225.
88. Barker, J. L., Nicoll, R. A., and Padjen, A. (1975) *J. Physiol. (London)* **245**, 537–548.
89. Kiraly, J. K., and Phillis, J. K. (1961) *Br. J. Pharmacol. Chemother.* **17**, 224–231.
90. Alving, B. O. (1961) *Arch. Int. Pharmacodyn. Ther.* **131**, 123–150.
91. Kaczmarek, L. K., and Davison, A. N. (1972) *J. Neurochem.* **19**, 2355–2362.
92. Davidoff, R. A., and Adair, R. (1976) *Brain Res.* **110**, 392–398.
93. Muller, W. E., and Snyder, S. H. (1978) *Brain Res.* **143**, 487–498.
94. Kubicek, R., and Dolenk, A. (1958) *J. Chromatogr.* **1**, 266–268.
95. Brotherton, J. (1962) *Exp. Eye Res.* **1**, 246–252.
96. Pasantes-Morales, H., Klethi, J., Ledig, M., and Mandel, P. (1972) *Brain Res.* **41**, 494–497.
97. Cohen, A. I., McDaniel, M., and Orr, H. (1973) *Invest. Ophthalmol.* **12**, 686–693.
98. Starr, M. S. (1973) *Brain Res.* **59**, 331–338.
99. Kennedy, A. J., and Voaden, M. J. (1974) *Biochem. Soc. Trans.* **2**, 1256–1258.
100. Orr, H. T., Cohen, A. I., and Lowry, O. H. (1976) *J. Neurochem.* **26**, 609–611.
101. Lund Karlsen, R., and Fonnum, F. (1976) *J. Neurochem.* **27**, 1437–1441.
102. Hayes, K. C., Carey, R. E., and Schmitt, S. Y. (1975) *Science* **188**, 949–950.
103. Starr, M. S., and Voaden, M. J. (1972) *Vision Res.* **12**, 1261–1269.
104. Pasantes-Morales, H., Klethi, J., Urban, P. F., and Mandel, P. (1972) *Physiol. Chem. Phys.* **4**, 339–348.
105. Neal, M. J., (1976) *Gen. Pharmacol.* **7**, 321–332.
106. Neal, M. J., Peacock, P. J., and White, R. D. (1973) *Br. J. Pharmacol.* **47**, 656–657.
107. Ehinger, B. (1973) *Brain Res.* **60**, 512–516.
108. Dowling, J. E. (1970) *Invest. Opthalmol.* **9**, 655–680.
109. Kennedy, A. J., and Voaden, M. J. (1976) *J. Neurochem.* **27**, 131–137.

110. Pasantes-Morales, H., Urban, P. F., Klethi, J., and Mandel, P. (1973) *Brain Res.* **51,** 375–378.
111. Pasantes-Morales, H., Klethi, J., Urban, P. F., and Mandel, P. (1974) *Exp. Brain Res.* **19,** 131–141.
112. Pasantes-Morales, H., Salceda, R., and Lopez-Colome, A. M. (1976) *In* "Taurine" (R. Huxtable and A. Barbeau, eds.), pp. 191–201. Raven, New York.
113. Miller, R. F. (1973) *J. Neurophysiol* **36,** 28–38.
114. Bonaventure, N., Wioland, N., and Mandel, P. (1974) *Brain Res.* **80,** 281–289.
115. Cunningham, R., and Miller, R. F. (1976) *Brain Res.* **117,** 341–345.
116. Burkhardt, D. A. (1972) *Brain Res.* **43,** 246–249.
117. Young, A. B., Oster-Granite, Herndon, M. L., and Snyder, S. H. (1974) *Brain Res.* **73,** 1–13.

PART IV

BRAIN PEPTIDES AND OPIATE SYSTEM

Biologically Active Peptides in the Brain

MICHEL J. BROWNSTEIN
Section on Pharmacology
Laboratory of Clinical Science
National Institute of Mental Health
National Institutes of Health
Bethesda, Maryland

INTRODUCTION

In the late 1920's and early 1930's Scharrer (1–4) described several populations of neurons with "morphologic aspects of secretory activity." Until recently, neurobiologists paid relatively little attention to neurosecretory or hormone-producing cells, but concentrated, instead, on their nonpeptidergic neighbors. The characterization of several biologically active neuropeptides and the discovery of their widespread distribution in the nervous system has aroused great interest in them, however. The youth and vigor of the field of peptide research makes it a difficult one to review; much of the data are of a preliminary nature and many of the currently held theories lack refinement. The following progress report must be read in the context of this apology.

BIOLOGICALLY ACTIVE PEPTIDES

A number of biologically active peptides have been shown to be present in the mammalian central nervous system. Many of these are not unique to the nervous system but are also found in the pituitary, pancreas, gut, or skin, emphasizing the common neuroectodermal origin of elements in these tissues (5). In addition to the neuropeptides that are found in warm-blooded vertebrates, there are a number of related and unrelated peptides secreted by neurons of cold-blooded vertebrates and invertebrates.

ISBN 0-12-398450-5

PEPTIDES IN THE MAMMALIAN BRAIN

Five "hypothalamic hormones" have been isolated from the brains of mammals: luteinizing-hormone-releasing hormone (LH-RH) (6,7), thyrotropin releasing hormone (TRH) (8,9), growth hormone release inhibiting hormone (somatosatin) (10–12), antidiuretic hormone (vasopressin) (13), and oxytocin (14). The structures of these hormones appear in Table I. The first three are released into the hypophysial portal vessels and regulate the secretion of trophic factors by cells of the anterior pituitary. Vasopressin and oxytocin are made by hypothalamic cells whose axons traverse the median eminence and terminate in the posterior pituitary. Beside the five peptides listed above, there are several hypothalamic hormones, the existence of which is accepted but the identities of which are unknown: corticotropin releasing factor, prolactin releasing factor, prolactin-release-inhibiting factor, and growth hormone releasing factor.

The brain contains a number of peptides that are not primarily involved in regulating hypophysial function. Their roles remain to be determined. Several of these peptides are present in both the digestive and nervous systems: substance P (15), neurotensin (16), the enkephalins (17), vasoactive intestinal protein (VIP) (18), gastrinlike protein (19), and angiotensin (20). Others appear to be synthesized both by cells of the brain and the pituitary: adrenocorticotropic hormone (ACTH) (21), β-lipotropin (22), β-endorphin (22), growth hormone (23), and prolactin (24).

TABLE I
Peptides Found in Mammalian Brain

LH-RH	pGlu-His-Trp-Ser-Tyr-Gly-Leu-Arg-Pro-Gly-NH_2
TRH	pGlu-His-Pro-NH_2
Somatostatin	H-Ala-Gly-Cys-Lys-Asn-Phe-Phe-Trp
	| |
	HO-Cys-Ser-Thr-Phe-Thr-Lys
Vasopressin	H-Cys-Tyr-Phe
	| |
	NH_2-Gly-Arg-Pro-Cys-Asn-Glu
Oxytocin	H-Cys-Tyr-Ileu
	| |
	NH_2-Gly-Leu-Pro-Cys-Asn-Gln
Substance P	H-Arg-Pro-Lys-Pro-Gln-Gln-Phe-Phe-Gly-Leu-Met-NH_2
Neurotensin	pGlu-Leu-Tyr-Glu-Asn-Lys-Pro-Arg-Arg-Pro-Tyr-Ileu-Leu-OH
Met-enkephalin	H-Tyr-Gly-Gly-Phe-Met-OH
Leu-enkephalin	H-Tyr-Gly-Gly-Phe-Leu-OH

INVERTEBRATE AND COLD-BLOODED VERTEBRATE PEPTIDES

Many biologically active peptides have been discovered in cold-blooded vertebrates and invertebrates. The peptides isolated from the skin of cold-blooded vertebrates have been divided into four groups by Bertaccini (25): bradykinins, tachykinins, caeruleinlike peptides, and bombesinlike peptides. The reason for calling attention to these agents in a review intended for neuroscientists is that the skin of cold-blooded vertebrates has been such a rich source of neuropeptides. It is not unlikely that the mammalian brain contains peptides which structurally and/or pharmacologically resemble the biologically active peptides in skin.

Many invertebrates appear to use peptides as neurotransmitters or neuroendocrine mediators (26). These peptides have a variety of functions: they alter the color of the animal's body by concentrating or dispersing pigments in chromatophores; they cause muscles in the heart or gut to contract or relax; they participate in salt and water regulation; and they are involved in reproduction, growth, and development.

MAPPING BIOLOGICALLY ACTIVE PEPTIDES IN THE BRAIN (TABLE II) (18,19,27–30)

Two complementary methods have been employed to localize peptidergic perikarya and to determine the distribution of their processes in the central nervous system. Some investigators have measured the peptides in samples of tissue from normal and lesioned brains. Others have used immunocytochemistry. While the immunocytochemical technique allows one to visualize peptides in specific neurons, it is not quantitative. The microanalytical methods are quantitative and, furthermore, can be used to detect low concentrations of peptides that are present in large pools of tissue. In addition, microchemical methods can be used unambiguously to identify the peptides that are being measured. Unfortunately, too little attention has been paid to date to the validation of immunoanalytical and immunocytochemical techniques (31,32).

Peptide-containing neuronal cell bodies have been visualized in many areas of the mammalian brain (33–36). For example, LH-RH, TRH, somatostatin, substance P, neurotensin, and angiotensin are present in perikarya in the hypothalamus and preoptic area. Somatostatin is also found in cells in the amygdala, hippocampus, pyriform

TABLE II
Distribution of Selected Peptides in the Mammalian Central Nervous System[a]

	TRH[b]	LH-RH[c]	Somatostatin[d]	Substance P[e]	Neurotensin[f]	VIP[g] (dog)	Gastrinlike protein (human)	Met-Enk[i]	Leu-Enk[i]
Hypothalamus	100	100	100	100	100	100	100	100	100
Septum and preoptic area	7	−5	30	79	88	—	—	—	—
Striatum	—	—	2.4	47	2.3	—	433	192	188
Thalamus	7	—	7.1	31	29	3	—	—	—
Midbrain	—	—	2.8	91	34	5	—	23	19
Brainstem	9	—	2.4	75	23	3	130	54	38
Cerebellum	0.8	—	0.9	1.1	4	3	410	7.5	19
Cerebral cortex	1.6	—	1.4	6.3	22	69	2167	20	25
Olfactory bulb	—	—	0.9	10	11	—	—	—	—

[a] Except as noted, these data are for the rat. The values are percentages of the level found in hypothalamus, which was set at 100.
[b] Winokur and Utiger (27).
[c] Palkovits, M., Brownstein, M., Arimura, A., Schally, A. V., unpublished.
[d] Brownstein, M., Arimura, A., Sato, H., Schally, A. V., and Kizer, J. S. (28).
[e] Brownstein, M., Mroz, E., Kizer, J. S., Palkovits, M., Leeman, S. (29).
[f] S. E. Leeman (unpublished).
[g] Said and Rosenberg (18).
[h] Van der Hagghen *et al.* (19).
[i] Yang, H.-Y., Hung, J. S., Costa, E. (30).

cortex, neocortex, and entopeduncular nucleus. Substance-P-containing cell bodies have been seen in the dorsal tegmental nucleus, interpeduncular nucleus, medial habenular nucleus, bed nucleus of the stria terminalis, and amygdala. Gastrin and VIP have been seen in cells of the hippocampus and amygdala, respectively.

Axons and nerve terminals stained by means of antipeptide antibodies have been found in most parts of the brain. Neuronal processes seem to be easier to visualize than cell bodies because the former have higher levels of peptides. It is also possible that the antibodies that are available have little affinity for large peptide precursor molecules, or that the antibodies penetrate storage sites in the cell body less well than storage sites in the processes.

Microanalytical studies have confirmed and extended immunocytochemical ones (37,38). For example, the substance-P-containing cell bodies in the medial habenula, which were mentioned earlier, have been shown to innervate the region of the interpeduncular nucleus. Lesions that destroy the habenula or that sever its connection with the interpeduncular nucleus cause a 70% decrease in substance P in the interpeduncular nucleus (39). Similarly, knife cuts that separate the substantia nigra from the basal ganglia deplete the former structure of almost 90% of its substance P (40). By making a number of different lesions in the basal ganglia, we have shown that almost all of the substance P in the substantia nigra is in neuronal processes of cells located in the anterior striatum. The majority of these cells are rostral to GABAergic neurons which also innervate the substantia nigra. Although it is possible to demonstrate substance P in axons in the substantia nigra immunocytochemically, it has not yet proven possible, unequivocally, to localize substance-P-containing perikarya in the striatum (41).

BIOSYNTHESIS AND DEGRADATION OF PEPTIDES

It is undeniably true that many biologically active peptides are present in the brain, but little is known about how they are synthesized and stored there. Some of the small neuropeptides are made enzymatically by one or more "synthetases." It is likely that the larger peptides are synthesized ribosomally as parts of precursor molecules which are cleaved after their translation.

Examples of both ribosomal and nonribosomal modes of synthesis can be found in the literature. For example, carnosine (β-alanylhistidine), homocarnosine (γ-amino-n-butyrylhistidine), glutathione (γ-glutamylcysteinylglycine), and opthalmic acid (γ-glutamyl-α-aminobutyrylglycine), are synthesized from their precursor amino acids enzymatically, that is, on "protein templates" (42,43). TRH may also be synthesized this way.

Another mechanism for peptide bond formation has features in common with both the protein template (enzymatic) and nucleic acid template (ribosomal) mechanisms (44,45). There are a group of enzymes which catalyze the transfer of the aminoacyl moiety of certain aminoacyl-tRNA's to the NH_2-terminus of acceptor peptides and proteins. While this process is dependent on amino acid activation by adenylation and aminoacyl-tRNA formation, as is the nucleic acid template mechanism, peptide bond formation is independent of mRNA, ribosomes, GTP, or other components of ribosomal protein synthesis. Thus far only a few amino acids have been shown to be transferred to acceptor proteins.

Proteolytic enzymes have been shown to catalyze peptidyl transferase reactions (46). Apparently the aminoacylated enzyme can undergo attack by an exogenous nucleophilic amino acid or peptide to give rise to a new peptide. Whether these peptidyl transferase reactions of peptidases are important *in vivo* or are *in vitro* artifacts remains to be learned.

The biosynthesis of vasopressin, oxytocin, and their "carrier proteins," neurophysins, is the best model for studying ribosomally mediated biosynthesis of neuropeptides. Sachs and his co-workers demonstrated that vasopressin is synthesized by neurons in the supraoptic nucleus (47–49). The hormone is made in the perikarya and transported intraaxonally to nerve endings in the posterior pituitary. Sachs suggested that vasopressin was made as part of a large protein which was also a precursor for neurophysin. Gainer and his collaborators have provided direct evidence for the existence of two large neurophysin precursor molecules—one for the vasopressin-associated neurophysin and another for the oxytocin-associated neurophysin (50–53). These two 20,000 MW precursors seem to "mature" into the 12,000 MW neurophysins (via 17,000 MW intermediates) while they are being transported to the neurohypophysis. The vasopressin-associated neurophysin's precursor and intermediate appear to react with antivasopressin antibody, suggesting that the precursor does, indeed, contain both the hormone and its carrier. The remainder of the molecule (approximately 7,000 daltons) may be inactive or may have biological actions that are not appreciated yet.

ACTH, β-lipotropin, β-endorphin, and the enkephalins appear to be synthesized from a single, large precursor just as neurophysin and vasopressin may be (54,55). Which of the many potential products of degradation of a precursor are formed and released probably depends upon which of several peptidases are packaged with it. Clearly, the regulation of the synthesis and secretion of biologically active peptides cannot be studied until more is know about the mechanisms involved in their manufacture.

DEGRADATION

The actions of peptides seem to be terminated principally by their proteolysis; reuptake of the peptides by the nerve endings which release them does not appear to play an important role in inactivation. A large number of peptidases appear to be present in the brain (56). Some of these are, no doubt, involved in liberating active neuropeptides from precursor molecules; others are responsible for metabolizing proteins and peptides. There are five broad classes of peptidases: exopeptidases (N-terminal and C-terminal peptidases), thiol proteinases, acid proteinases, serine proteinases, and unclassified peptidases (including renin and cathepsin M). Both exo- and endopeptidases, which may participate in degrading neuropeptides, are found in the brain. LH-RH, for example, appears to be cleaved internally by a neutral endopeptidase. This is followed by sequential degradation by conventional peptide hydrolases. LH-RH can also undergo removal of its C-terminal glycineamide.

Somatostatin and substance P are cleaved internally, while neurotensin, vasopressin, and oxytocin seem to be metabolized by carboxypeptidases. The latter two peptides can also be inactivated by reductive scission of their disulfide rings followed by aminopeptidase cleavage. TRF can be degraded either by a pyroglutamyl peptidase or by a C-terminal deamidase. When the peptidases that are involved in terminating the actions of neuropeptides are purified and characterized, it may be possible to find pharmacological agents that specifically inhibit them and that prolong their physiological half-lives.

PEPTIDE RECEPTORS IN THE CNS

Two lines of evidence support the idea that peptides which are released from one neuron can modify the activity of another by occupying receptors on its surface (i.e., postsynaptic receptors). First, a number of peptides (the enkephalins, neurotensin, and angiotensin among them) bind to membranes recovered from nervous tissue with high affinity and specificity (57). Second, when they are applied to the brain iontophoretically, TRH, LH-RH, somatostatin, substance P, neurotensin, and the opiatelike peptides alter the firing rates and membrane properties of neurons (58,59).

There may be presynaptic receptors for the peptides as well as post-synaptic ones. By acting upon a presynaptic receptor, a peptide may alter the release of another neurotransmitter. Thus, the potassium-evoked release of substance P from nerve terminals in the rat trigeminal nerve nucleus is suppressed by opiates or by endorphins. This supression is reversed by naloxone, a narcotic antagonist (60). Unlike the opiates, somatostatin appears to facilitate the release of transmitter from neurons which innervate (and activate) motoneurons in the spinal cord (61).

PHARMACOLOGICAL PROPERTIES OF PEPTIDES

As neuropeptides have become easier to obtain from commercial sources, more and more data have been collected relating to their pharmacology (62,63). Various peptides have been implicated in the regulation or modification of such diverse processes as release of trophic factors from the pituitary, mating behavior, thermoregulation, thirst, learning, and memory.

CONCLUDING REMARKS

The addition of the neuropeptides to the list of putative transmitters in the central nervous system has, almost overnight, doubled this list's size. While many of the techniques that have been used to study more conventional-neurotransmitters—acetylcholine, the monoamines, or GABA—can be used to learn more about peptides, many new methods and approaches must be developed. The addition of immunocytochemistry to the neurobiologist's armamentarium has been of great importance. Immunocytochemical and analytical approaches have been used to determine the central topography of several peptidergic systems, but the gross topography and ultrastructure of peptidergic neurons are still poorly known. Unlike acetylcholine or norepinephrine, many peptides are probably synthesized in the cell body of the neuron as parts of larger precursors. These precursors are then packaged, transported down the axon, and converted into the active products that are finally released. The amount and nature of these products depend on at least two factors: the rate of transcription of the precursor, and the character and activity of peptidases that are responsible for the maturation process. Since all of the peptide is made in the cell body, it cannot immediately be replaced by newly synthesized material when it is released, and, theoretically, a nerve ending can be exhausted of its supply of transmitter. For this reason, it seems most likely that peptides are either released in small amounts chronically or in large amounts on special occasions, but not in large amounts over relatively long periods. Perhaps, because they can be depleted more easily than transmitters that are synthesized in terminals, it is appropriate (1) that the affinities of peptide receptors for their agonists are relatively great (so that only a tiny amount of peptide has to be released in order to produce a physiological effect) and (2) that the effects of peptides on follower cells are often rather prolonged. The variety of specific and potent actions that peptides have on the central nervous system has excited the interest of investigators in several fields, and the elucidation of the central and peripheral roles of these potent molecules may provide us with new keys to understanding normal and abnormal brain function.

REFERENCES

1. Scharrer, E. (1928) *Z. Vergl. Physiol.* **7,** 1–38.
2. Scharrer, E. (1930) *Z. Vergl. Physiol.* **11,** 767–773.
3. Scharrer, E. (1932) *Z. Vergl. Physiol.* **17,** 491–509.
4. Scharrer, E. (1956) "Neurosecretion, Fifth Annual Report on Stress," pp. 185–192. MD Publications, Inc., New York.
5. Pearse, A. G. E. (1968) *Proc. R. Soc. London, Ser. B* **170,** 71–80.
6. Baba, Y., Matsuo, H., and Schally, A. V. (1971) *Biochem. Biophys. Res. Commun.* **44,** 459–463.
7. Matsuo, H., Baba, Y., Nair, R. M. G., Arimura, A., and Schally, A. V. (1971) *Biochem. Biophys. Res. Commun.* **43,** 1334–1339.
8. Bøler, J., Enzmann, F., Folkers, K., Bowers, C. Y., and Schally, A. V. (1969) *Biochem. Biophys. Res. Commun.* **37,** 705–710.
9. Burgus, R., Dunn, T. F., Desiderio, D., and Guilleman, R. (1969) *C. R. Hebd. Seances Acad. Sci., Ser. D* **12,** 1870.
10. Brazeau, P., Vale, W., Burgus, R., Ling, M., Butcher, J., Rivier, J., and Guilleman, R. (1973) *Science* **179,** 77–79.
11. Burgus, R., Ling, N., Butcher, M., and Guilleman, R. (1973) *Proc. Natl. Acad. Sci. U.S.A.* **70,** 684.
12. Ling, N., Burgus, R., Rivier, J., Vale, W., and Brazeau, P. (1973) *Biochem. Biophys. Res. Commun.* **52,** 782.
13. du Vigneaud, V., Lawler, H. C., and Popenoe, A. (1953) *J. Am. Chem. Soc.* **75,** 4880–4881.
14. du Vigneaud, V., Ressler, C., Swan, J. M., Roberts, C. W., Katsoyannis, P. G., and Gordon, S. (1953) *J. Am. Chem. Soc.* **75,** 4879–4880.
15. Chang, M. M., and Leeman, S. (1970) *J. Biol. Chem.* **245,** 4784–4790.

16. Carraway, R. E., and Leeman, S. E. (1973) *J. Biol. Chem.* **248,** 6854–6861.
17. Hughes, J., Smith, T. W., Kosterlitz, H. W., Fothergill, L. A., Morgan, B. A., and Morris, H. R. (1975) *Nature (London)* **258,** 577–579.
18. Said, S. I., and Rosenberg, R. N. (1976) *Science* **192,** 907–908.
19. Van der Hagghen, J. J., Signeau, J. C., and Gepts, W. (1975) *Nature (London)* **257,** 604–605.
20. Fuxe, K., Ganten, D., Hökfelt, T., and Bolme, P. (1976) *Neurosci. Lett.* **2,** 229–234.
21. Krieger, D., Liotta, A., and Brownstein, M. J. (1977) *Proc. Natl. Acad. Sci. U.S.A.* **74,** 648–652.
22. Krieger, D., Liotta, A., Suda, T., Palkovits, M., and Brownstein, J. (1977) *Biochem. Biophys. Res. Commun.* **76,** 930–936.
23. Pacold, S. T., Lawrence, A. M., and Kirsteins, L. (1977) *Clin. Res.* **24,** 563A.
24. Fuxe, K., Hökfelt, T., Eneroth, P., Gustafsson, J. A., and Skett, P. (1977) *Science* **196,** 899–900.
25. Bertaccini, G. (1977) *Pharmacol. Rev.* **28,** 127–177.
26. Frontali, N. and Gainer, H. (1977) *In* "Peptides in Neurobiology" (H. Gainer, ed.), pp. 259–294. Plenum, New York.
27. Winokur, A., and Utiger, R. D. (1974) *Science* **185,** 265.
28. Brownstein, M. J., Arimura, A., Sato, H., Schally, A. V., and Kizer, JS. (1975) *Endocrinology* **96,** 1456.
29. Brownstein, M. J., Mroz, E., Kizer, J. S., Palkovits, M., and Leeman, S. E. (1976) *Brain Res.* **116,** 299.
30. Yang, H.-Y., Hung, J. S., and Costa, E. (1977) *Neuropharmacology* **16,** 303.
31. Straus, E., and Yalow, R. S. (1977) *In* "Peptides in Neurobiology" (H. Gainer, ed.), pp. 39–60. Plenum, New York.
32. Leeman, S. E., Mroz, E. A., and Carraway, R. E. (1977) *In* "Peptides in Neurobiology" (H. Gainer, ed.), pp. 107–108. Plenum, New York.
33. Sternberger, L. A. (1977) *In* "Peptides in Neurobiology" (H. Gainer, ed.), pp. 61–98. Plenum, New York.
34. Zimmerman, E. A. (1976) *In* "Frontiers in Neuroendocrinology" (L. Martini and W. F. Ganong, eds.), Vol. 4, pp. 25–62. Raven, New York.
35. Hökfelt, T., Johansson, O., Fuxe, K., Löfström, A., Goldstein, M., Park, D., Ebstein, R., Fraser, H., Jefcoate, S., Efendic, S., Luft, R., and Arimura, A. (1976) *Proc. Int. Congr. Pharmacol. 6th, 1975* Vol. 3, 93–110.
36. Hökfelt, T. (1978) *In* "Neurobiology of Peptides" (L. L. Iversen, R. A. Nicoll, and W. Vale, eds.) M.I.T. Press.
37. Browstein, M. J., Palkovits, M., Saavedra, J. M., and Kizer, J. S. (1976) *In* "Frontiers in Neuroendocrinology" (L. Martini and W. F. Ganong, eds.), Vol. 4, pp. 1–23. Raven, New York.
38. Browstein, M. J. (1977) *In* "Peptides in Neurobiology" (H. Gainer, ed.), pp. 145–170. Plenum, New York.
39. Mroz, E., Brownstein, M. J., and Leeman, S. (1976) *Brain Res.* **113,** 597–599.
40. Mroz, E., Brownstein, M. J., and Leeman, S. (1977) *Brain Res.* **125,** 305–312.
41. Brownstein, M. J. Mroz, E. A., Tappaz, M., and Leeman, S. E. (1977) *Brain Res.* **135,** 315–323.
42. Reichelt, K. L., and Edminson, P. D. (1977) *In* "Peptides in Neurobiology" (H. Gainer, ed.), pp. 171–181. Plenum, New York.
43. McKelvy, J. F. (1977) *In* "Hypothalamic Peptide Hormones and Pituitary Regulation" (J. C. Porter, ed.), pp. 77–88. Plenum, New York.
44. Soffer, R. L. (1973) *Mol. Cell. Biochem.* **2,** 3–14.
45. Soffer, R. L. (1974) *Adv. Enzymol.* **40,** 91–140.

46. Mycek, M. J. (1970) *In* "Methods in Enzymology" (G. E. Perlman and L. Lorand, eds.), Vol. 19, pp. 285–315. Academic Press, New York.
47. Sachs, H., and Takabatake, Y. (1964) *Endocrinology* **75**, 934–938.
48. Sachs, H., Fawsett, P., Takabatake, Y., and Portanova, R. (1969) *Recent Prog. Horm. Res.* **25**, 447–491.
49. Sachs, H., Saito, S., and Sunde, D. (1971) In "Subcellular Organization and Function in Endocrine Tissues" (H. Heller and K. Lederis, eds.), pp. 325–336. Cambridge University Press.
50. Gainer, H., Sarne, Y., and Brownstein, M. J. (1977) *Science* **195**, 1354–1356.
51. Gainer, H., Sarne, Y., and Brownstein, M. J. (1977) *J. Cell Biol.* **73**, 366–381.
52. Brownstein, M. J., and Gainer, H. (1977) *Proc. Natl. Acad. Sci. U.S.A.* **74**, 4046–4049.
53. Brownstein, M. J., Robinson, A., and Gainer, H. (1977) *Nature (London)* **269**, 259–261.
54. Mains, R. E., and Eipper, B. A. (1976) *J. Biol. Chem.* **251**, 4115–4120.
55. Mains, R. E., Eipper, B. A., and Ling, N. (1977) *Proc. Natl. Acad. Sci. U.S.A.* **74**, 3014–3018.
56. Marks, N. (1977) *In* "Peptides in Neurobiology" (H. Gainer, ed.), pp. 221–258. Plenum, New York.
57. Snyder, S. H., and Bennett, J. P., Jr. (1976) *Annu. Rev. Physiol.* **38**, 153–175.
58. Nicoll, R. A. (1975) *Handb. Psychopharmacol.* **4**, 229–263.
59. Barker, J. L. (1977) In "Peptides in Neurobiology" (H. Gainer, ed.), pp. 295–344. Plenum, New York.
60. Iversen, L. L. (1978) *In* "Neurobiology of Peptides" (L. L. Iversen, R. A. Nicoll, and W. Vale, eds.) M.I.T. Press.
61. Nicoll, R. A. (1978) *In* "Neurobiology of Peptides" (L. L. Iversen, R. A. Nicoll, and W. Vale, eds.) M.I.T. Press.
62. Vale, W., Rivier, C., Brown, M., and Rivier, J. (1977) *In* "Hypothalamic Peptide Hormones and Pituitary Regulation" (J. C. Porter, ed.), pp. 123–156.
63. de Wied, D., and Gispen, W. H. (1977) *In* "Peptides in Neurobiology" (H. Gainer, ed.), pp. 397–448. Plenum, New York.

Opioid Peptides

JOHN HUGHES
Department of Biochemistry
Imperial College of Science and Technology
London, England

INTRODUCTION

Kosterlitz and Hughes (18) originally suggested that the enkephalins might be inhibitory neurotransmitters or neuromodulators. Recent progress in this rapidly advancing field and particularly in the immunofluorescent localization of the enkephalins has supported our original concept. However, the apparent multiplicity of opioid peptides and of opioid peptide receptors has required a modification of the original concept of one endogenous ligand for the opiate receptor (Hughes, 14; Kosterlitz and Hughes, 18).

At present the following peptides have been shown to occur in the brain or pituitary: methionine enkephalin; leucine enkephalin; and α-, β-, and γ-endorphin (Fig. 1). All these peptides have opioid activity as evidenced by bioassay or radioreceptor assay. In addition there are a number of unidentified opioid substances that have been detected in the pituitary (Gentleman *et al.*, 10), brain (Ross *et al.*, 29a; Hughes *et al.*, 16), and cerebrospinal fluid (Terenius and Wahlström, 35). Some of these uncharacterized substances may be related to larger precursors of leucine enkephalin but there is no evidence for this at present.

This chapter will concentrate on those points relating to the putative neurotransmitter role of the enkephalins. However, it should be noted that the use of the term "neurotransmitter" is becoming increasingly suspect when applied to centrally acting peptides or amines. The problem is a very real one, as evidenced by reports of very large synaptic gaps for catecholamine neurons and by the possibility of more than one putative neurotransmitter being stored in a single nerve terminal (Mroz *et al.*, 27; Hökfelt *et al.*, 12). A neurotransmitter

ISBN 0-12-398450-5

Sequence	Peptide
61 Tyr-Gly-Gly-Phe-Met- 65	Met-Enkephalin
Thr-Ser-Glu-Lys-Ser-Gln-Thr-Pro-Leu-Val-Thr- 76	α-Endorphin
77 Leu-	γ-Endorphin
Phe-Lys-Asn-Ala-Ile-Val-Lys-Asn-Ala-His-Lys-Lys-Gly-Gln-OH 91	β-Endorphin

Fig. 1. Amino acid sequences of known opioid peptides. The numbers refer to the amino acid positions in the parent protein β-lipotropin.

may be considered as the primary agent of information transfer from one neuron to another. This information transfer is commonly regarded as being involved over short distances (20–200 nm) and consisting of excitation or inhibition of neural activity. However, actions involving subtle changes in cellular metabolism and agents acting over larger distances may fall outside this definition. In order to avoid introducing ill-defined terms such as "neuromodulator," it may be best to define a neurotransmitter as a substance which is released from a neuron and which acts on an adjacent neuron or the same neuron to effect a change in cellular activity.

TABLE I
Actions of Opioid Peptides[a,b,c]

Effect	Morphine	Met-enkephalin	β-Endorphin
1. Inhibition of adrenergic transmission			
a. Mouse vas deferens	1	30	7
b. Rat cerebral cortex	+	+	NT
2. Inhibition of cholinergic transmission			
a. Guinea pig ileum	1	0.8	1
b. Rat hippocampus	+	+	+
3. Inhibition of dopaminergic transmission			
a. Rat basal ganglia	+	+	+
4. Inhibition of substance P release	+	+	+
5. Inhibition of adenyl cyclase	1	160	NT
a. Neuroblastoma x glioma cells			
b. Striatum	+	+	+
6. Increase cGMP levels			
a. Striatum	+	+	NT

[a] The values are approximate molar potencies relative to morphine where calculation is possible.

[b] +, positive effect; 0, no effect; NT, not tested.

[c] Key references include Waterfield *et al.* 39a, Taube *et al.* (34); Minneman and Iversen (26); Wahlström *et al.* (38); Subramanian *et al.* (33); Jessel and Iversen (17).

PHARMACOLOGICAL ACTIVITY OF OPIOID PEPTIDES

The biological actions of the enkephalins and β-endorphin have received the greatest attention to date. In general the peptides have qualitatively the same spectrum of activity (Tables I and II). However, it is apparent that β-endorphin is much more potent in the intact organism and it produces a wide spectrum of effects, including analgesia, catatonia, and behavioral disturbances (Bloom *et al.*, 3; Loh *et al.*, 19; Meyerson and Terenius, 24).

It is likely that most but not all of the differences between β-endorphin and enkephalin are due to the rapid breakdown of the latter by tissue peptidases. The biological half-life of enkephalin is approximately 1–2 min while it is 3–4 hr for β-endorphin. A primary site of enkephalin inactivation is removal of the N-terminal tyrosine

TABLE II
Actions of Opioid Peptides[a,b,c]

	Morphine	Met-enkephalin	β-Endorphin
1. Inhibit brain opiate receptor binding of			
a. ^{3}H-Naloxone	1	0.8	2-8
b. ^{3}H-Dihydromorphine	1	0.5	NT
c. ^{3}H-Leu-enkephalin	1	350	500
d. ^{125}I-(D-Ala)$_2$-Leu-enkephalin	1	7	20
2. Neuronal cell firing rate			
Cerebral cortex	↓	↓	↓/↑
Thalamus	↓	↓	↓
Caudate nucleus	↓	↓	↓
Brainstem	↓/↑	↓	↓
Hippocampus	↑	↑	↑
Substantia gelatinosa	↓	↓	NT
Renshaw cells	↑	↑	NT
3. Produces analgenia			
a. intracerebral injection	1	0.01	50
b. intravenous injection	1	0	4
4. Cross tolerance with morphine	+	+	+
5. Produces catatonia	+	0	+++
6. Growth hormone and prolactin release	+	+	+

[a] Values are potency ratios relative to morphine.

[b] +, positive effect; 0, no effect; NT, not tested; ↑, increase; ↓, decrease.

[c] Key references include Waterfield *et al.* (39*a*), *Lord et al.* (21); Wahlström *et al.* (38); Miller *et al.* (25); Duggan *et al.* (7); Nicol *et al.* (28); Bradley *et al.* (5); Zieglgansberger *et al.* (40); Frederickson and Norris (9); Loh *et al.* (19,20); Cocchi *et al.* (6).

by aminopeptidase type enzymes (Hambrook *et al.*, 11; Meek *et al.*, 23). However, experiments with enzyme inhibitors in our laboratory suggest that C-terminal hydrolysis may also play a role in the inactivation of enkephalin particularly if N-terminal hydrolysis is prevented. Marks *et al.* (22) have also shown that enkephalins are subjected to both N- and C-terminal hydrolysis by rat and mouse brain extracts.

The importance of N-terminal hydrolysis in limiting the biological activity of the enkephalins was illustrated by the synthesis of the stable analogs of enkephalin Tyr–D–Ala–Gly–Phe–Leu or Met (Pert *et al.*, 28a Miller *et al.*, 25). These compounds are resistant to aminopeptidase and, unlike the enkephalins, are as potent as β-endorphin in producing analgesia when injected intracerebrally.

It has been suggested that α- and γ-endorphin and Met-enkephalin might be artifacts resulting from the breakdown of β-endorphin (Austen *et al.*, 2). However, these results were obtained under extremely artificial conditions of prolonged incubation for 4 hr under acidic conditions. The contention of the Mill Hill group may be discounted for a number of reasons including the histochemical data now available (see below) and the fact that β-endorphin has been shown to be stable under conditions used for extracting the enkephalins (Hughes *et al.*, 16). Furthermore, it has been shown that *in vivo* fixation of brain peptidases by formaldehydehyde perfusion (Hughes *et al.*, 16) or by microwave irradiation (Yang *et al.*, 37) does not decrease the yield of enkephalin but may actually increase it.

MULTIPLE OPIATE RECEPTORS

Differences in the rate of metabolism may not be the sole reason for differences between the endorphins, enkephalins, and opiate alkaloids. Recent evidence suggests that there are different types or subgroups of opiate receptors, just as there are multiple types of adrenergic receptors. Opiate receptors may be subdivided into at least three subgroups denoted by the subscripts μ, κ, and σ (Lord *et al.*, 21). Parallel assay of a series of opiate alkaloids and opioid peptides has revealed variations in the rank order of potency as measured in the mouse vas deferens and guinea pig ileum bioassays and in the opiate receptor binding assay (Table III). Such variations in the order of potency is strong but not conclusive evidence for multiple opiate receptors. However, in the mouse vas deferens more conclusive evidence is provided by the measurement of the affinity constant (K_e) for naloxone as an antagonist of morphine and the opioid peptides. In this

TABLE III
Parallel Bioassay of Opioid Alkaloids and Peptides[a]

Mouse vas deferens	Le > ME > α-END > β-END > Morphine
Guinea pig ileum	Morphine = β-END ≧ ME > α-END > LE
^{3}H-LE binding	ME = β-END > LE > α-END ≫ Morphine
^{3}H-Naloxone binding	β-END > Morphine = ME > α-END > LE

[a] Le, Leu-enkephalin; ME, Met-enkephalin; α-END and β-END, endorphins. Binding assays at 4°C on guinea pig brain homogenate.

tissue, naloxone has a K_e of 2 nM against morphine and other opiate alkaloids but this value increases to 20 nM against the enkephalins and endorphins. Thus the adrenergic neurons, which are the site of opiate action, of the mouse vas possess receptors for morphine (μ-receptor) distinct from those for the opioid peptides (δ-receptor).

Further advances in this area will depend on the development of more selective antagonists. However, the concept of multiple receptors fits in well with the presence of numerous opiate ligands. We cannot as yet assign specific peptides or physiological functions to a specific receptor type but this is a real possibility in the future. β-Endorphin may perhaps be viewed as the prototype opioid peptide, interacting well with several if not all opiate receptors. The shorter peptides, on the other hand, may have evolved for more specific functions. They aquired a different receptor specificity from β-endorphin and also became sensitive to proteolytic destruction. This "evolution" of β-endorphin thus led to peptides with characteristics more fitted for a neurotransmitter role of a rapid and transient nature. This hypothesis forms the bulk of the remaining discussion.

ENKEPHALINS AS NEUROTRANSMITTERS

DISTRIBUTION

In contrast to β-endorphin, the enkephalins are widely distributed in the brain, spinal cord, gastrointestinal tract, and peripheral autonomic nerves (Hughes *et al.*, 16), but are hardly detectable in the pituitary which contains enormous (>30 nmoles/g) quantities of β-endorphin. Biochemical studies have revealed a close correspondence between the regional brain distribution of opiate receptor binding sites and endogenous enkephalin levels (Simantov *et al.*, 31).

Perhaps the most important studies to date are those involving the immunofluorescent localization of enkephalin-containing neurons with specific antibodies (Elde *et al.*, 8; Simantov *et al.*, 31; Hökfelt *et al.* (13). These have confirmed the presence of "enkephalinergic" neurons throughout the brain, spinal cord, and gastrointestinal tract. Areas with a particularly dense innervation include the brainstem nuclei, periaqueductal gray, zona compacta of the substantia nigra, medial lemniscus, nucleus parateniatis, globus pallidue, nucleus accumbens, several hypothalamic nuclei, laminae I and II of spinal cord, substantia gelatinosa of the caudal nucleus of nerve V, and the vagal nucleus of the medulla. Lesion experiments indicate that enkephalin neurons are interneurons with short processes in the spinal cord dorsal horn. A number of cell bodies have been observed in different brain areas including the periaqueductal gray, the nucleus raphe magnus, the marginal layer, and the substantia gelatinosa of the spinal trigeminal nucleus.

It is of particular interest that enkephalin-rich areas overlap in many cases with substance-P-containing neurons and also with serotonin-containing neurons as in the raphe nucleus. Substance P has been implicated as a primary afferent sensory transmitter in small-diameter fibers and it has been shown that morphine, β-endorphin, and enkephalin inhibit the release of substance P from the rat trigeminal nucleus (Jesel and Iversen, 17). Serotonin-containing fibers have also been implicated in the antinociceptive effect of electrical stimulation of the periaqueductal gray (Akil and Liebeskind, 1).

The immunohistochemical methods have yet to attain the specificity required to separately visualize Met-enkephalin- and Leu-enkephalin-containing neurons. Biochemical studies (Hughes *et al.*, 16) have shown that, although there is constant ratio of 4:1 (Met-enkephalin : Leu-enkephalin) in the whole brains of several laboratory animals, there is a considerable variation in this ratio in different brain areas (Table IV). This suggests that the two enkephalins may be associated with different neuronal systems. Indeed it is difficult to see why they should be contained within the same neurons although this point obviously requires further attention.

Finally it has been shown by subcellular fractionation that the enkephalins are stored within the synaptosomal fraction of brain homogenates (Smith *et al.*, 1976; Simantov *et al.*, 30). The synaptosomal stores of enkephalin appear to be protected from hydrolytic enzymes and these stores may be maintained for several hours with only a slow loss of enkephalin when synaptosomes are incubated under physiological conditions.

TABLE IV
Variation in Enkephalin Ratios in Different Areas

Guinea pig	Ratio ME/LE
Cortex	1.3
Hippocampus	2.1
Striatum	4.2
Pons–medulla	6.9
Thalamus	7.4
Hypothalamus	8.4
Cerebellum	>20.0
Ileal myenteric plexus	2.7
Ileal articular muscle	4.7

RELEASE OF ENKEPHALINS

Indirect evidence for the neuronal release of enkephalin has been presented by several groups. The first evidence was provided by Waterfield and Kosterlitz (39), who showed that opiate antagonists stereoselectively enhanced the release of acetylcholine from the guinea pig myenteric plexus during nerve stimulation. This agrees with the concept that the enkephalins may act as inhibitory neuroregulators in the intestine. Other workers have shown that naloxone can facilitate the peristaltic reflex of a fatigued segment of intestine (Van Neuten *et al.*, 36) or enhance the recovery of cholinergic nerve activity after high-frequency electrical stimulation of the guinea pig myenteric plexus (Puig *et al.*, 29).

We have obtained direct evidence for the release of Met-enkephalin and Leu-enkephalin from isolated brain slice and synaptosome preparations (Henderson *et al.*, 11a). Destruction of the enkephalins was prevented by adding the dipeptides Tyr–Tyr, Leu–Gly, and Leu–Leu to the superfusion medium (1 m*M* each). These dipeptides appear to prevent the breakdown of the enkephalins by competitive inhibition of proteolytic enzymes. Small amounts of enkephalin activity were detected in the superfusate from a layer of crude synaptosomes prepared from the rabbit striatum. The release of enkephalin was markedly increased on increasing the potassium concentration of the medium from 1.19 m*M* to 50 m*M* (Table V). This potassium-evoked release was enhanced in the presence of raised calcium levels and could be blocked by emitting calcium from the medium (Table V). The origin of the enkephalin released into the medium was unlikely to be due to the extracellular breakdown of β-endorphin since no enke-

TABLE V
Potassium-Evoked Release of Enkephalin[a]

Calcium (mM)	Potassium (mM)	n	Fractional release (%)
2.54	1.19	11	0.4 ± 0.2
5.08	1.19	4	0.5 ± 0.2
2.54	50.00	4	1.9 ± 0.3
5.08	50.00	4	4.4 ± 0.2
0 (+EDTA 0.5 mM)	50.00	3	not detectable

[a] The P_2 (crude synaptosomal) fraction of rabbit striatum (0.8–1 g) was layered on a 1-cm filter and superfused with Kreb's solution at 36°C. The basal release was determined over a 30-min collection period and potassium-evoked release over a 15-min period. Fractional release refers to the total enkephalin activity (measured as Met-enkephalin) released into the superfusate and as expressed as a percentage of the tissue content.

phalin activity could be detected when this peptide was added to the superfusing medium.

The effect of potassium as a depolarizing agent is not specific for neurons. Veratridine is a more specific stimulus and we were able to show that this alkaloid (50 μM) also caused the release of enkephalins from superfused guinea pig striated slices. Perfusion with veratridine-containing medium for 5 min caused the release of 5 to 7% of the total enkephalin store into the medium. This effect could be reversibly blocked with tetrodotoxin (1.6 μM). Further analysis of the peptides released by veratridine showed the presence of both Met-enkephalin and Leu-enkephalin in the ratio of 3.4 to 1. Analysis of the tissue stores showed the Met: Lew ratio to be 3.8 to 1 and thus the enkephalins are released in proportion to their tissue content.

BIOGENESIS OF ENKEPHALINS

It has been assumed but not proven that the enkephalins are derived from proteolytic cleavage of precursor proteins. In the case of Met-enkephalin this precursor may well be β-lipotropin. At present there is no information as to the nature of the precursor for Leu-enkephalin. We have studied the incorporation of labeled amino acids into the enkephalins using high-pressure liquid chromatography and thin layer chromatography to isolate the pure labeled peptides (Sosa *et al.*, 32). In both the isolated guinea pig myenteric plexus and striatal

TABLE VI
Incorporation of ^3H-Tyrosine into Enkephalin Stores of Guinea Pig Myenteric Plexus[a]

	Met-enkephalin (dpm/g tissue)	Leu-enkephalin (dpm/g tissue)	Protein (dpm/mg)
Untreated	3756 ± 255	1426 ± 62	24561 ± 2422
Puromycin	317 ± 57	295 ± 127	1529 ± 335
Cyclohexamide	544 ± 160	197 ± 72	2100 ± 100

[a] The isolated guinea pig myenteric plexus was incubated with 3 μl/ml of ^3H-tyrosine (80 liters/mmol) for 4 hr in the presence or absence of puromycin or cyclohexamide (0.1 m*M*). The enkephalins were then extracted from the tissue with 0.1 *M* HCl and purified by high-pressure liquid chromatography and thin layer chromatography (Sosa *et al.*, 32). Results are the means and standard errors of four experiments.

brain slices there is a lag period of up to 1 hr in the incorporation of ^3H-tyrosine into the pentapeptides. Incorporation then proceeds linearly for several hours. This incorporation can be blocked by the inclusion of cyclohexamide or puromycin in the incubating medium (Table VI). These results support the hypothesis that the enkephalins are derived from a ribosomally synthesized protein which is then cleaved to form the pentapeptides. *In vivo* studies with the intracisternal injection of ^3H-tyrosine also show incorporation of the label into the enkephalins. Our preliminary studies suggest that after a single intracisternal injection the endogenous stores are maximally labeled within 2–4 hr but that the levels of labeled enkephalin do not show a significant decline for up to 12 hr, indicating a rather slow turnover rate.

CONCLUDING REMARKS

The current pace of research precludes any final conclusions regarding the physiological significance of the opioid peptides. Undoubtedly a number of unidentified opioid substances need to be characterized before the chemical picture is complete and there is the unexplained mystery of the Leu-enkephalin precursor. Originally it seemed as though the enkephalains would fall neatly into the role of neurotransmitters while the pituitary location of β-endorphin and its chemical stability would make it an ideal candidate for having an endocrine role. However, recent results (Bloom *et al.*, 4) indicate that there is a widespread neuronal system, distinct from enkephalin, containing β-endorphin in the brain. Innervation seems most intense in the ventral septum, preoptic hypothalamus, periaqueductal gray, substantia nigra, and locus coeruleus.

It thus seems that there may be a fast, transient, opioid peptide neurotransmitter system (enkephalins) and a neurotransmitter system containing β-endorphin which may produce slower but long-term effects on brain activity. The possible role, if any, of all the other opioid factors remains to be investigated.

REFERENCES

1. Akil, H., and Liebeskind, J. C. (1975) *Brain Res.* **94,** 279–296.
2. Austen, B. M., Smythe, D. C., and Snell, C. R. (1977) *Nature* (*London*) **269,** 618–619.
3. Bloom, F., Battenburg, E., Rossier, J., Ling, N., Leppaluoto, J., Vargo, T. M., and Guillemin, R. (1976) *Science* **194,** 630–632.
4. Bloom, F., Rossier, J., Battenburg, E., Vargo, T., Minick, S., Ling, N., and Guillemin, R. (1977) *Soc. Neurosci.* (in press).
5. Bradley, P. B., Gayton, R. J., and Lambert, L. A. (1978) *In* "Centrally Acting Peptides" (J. Hughes, ed.), pp. 215–229. Macmillan, New York.
6. Cocchi, D., Santagostino, A., Gil-Ad, I., Ferri, S., and Muller, E. E. (1977) *Life Sci.* **20,** 2041–2046.
7. Duggan, A. W., Hall, J. G., and Headley, P. M. (1976) *Nature* (*London*) **264,** 456–458.
8. Elde, Hökfelt, T., Johansson, O., and Terenius, L. (1976) *Neuroscience* **1,** 349–351.
9. Frederickson, R. C. A., and Norris, F. H. (1976) *Science* **194,** 440–442.
10. Gentleman, S., Ross, M., Lowney, L. I., Cox, B. M., and Goldstein, A. (1976) *In* "Opiates and Endogenous Opioid Peptides" (H. W. Kosterlitz, ed.), pp. 27–34. Elsevier, Amsterdam.
11. Hambrook, J. M., Morgan, B. A., Rance, M. J., and Smith, C. F. C. (1976) *Nature* (*London*) **262,** 782–783.

11a. Henderson, G., Hughes, J., and Kosterlitz, H. W. (1978) *Nature* (*London*) **271,** 677–679.

12. Hökfelt, T., Elfin, L. G., Elde, R., Schultzberg, M., Goldstein, M., and Luft, R. (1977) *Proc. Natl. Acad. Sci. U.S.A.* **74,** 3587–3591.
13. Hökfelt, T., Ljungdahl, A., Terenius, L., Elde, R., and Nilsson, G. (1977) *Proc. Natl. Acad. Sci. U.S.A.* **74,** 3081–3085.
14. Hughes, J. (1975) *Brain Res.* **88,** 295–308.
15. Hughes, J., Smith, T. W., Kosterlitz, H. W., Fothergill, L. A., Morgan, B. A., and Morris, H. R. (1975) *Nature* (*London*) **258,** 577–579.
16. Hughes, J. Kosterlitz, H. W., and Smith, T. W. (1977) *Br. J. Pharmacol.* **61** (in press).
17. Jessel, T. M., and Iversen, L. L. (1977) *Nature* (*London*) **268,** 549–551.
18. Kosterlitz, H. W., and Hughes, J. (1975) *Life Sci.* **17,** 91–96.
19. Loh, H. H., Tseng, L. F., Wei, E., and Li, C. H. (1976) *Proc. Natl. Acad. Sci. U.S.A.* **73,** 2895–2898.
20. Loh, H. H., Brase, D. A., Sampath-Khanna, S., Mar, J. B., and Wei, E. (1976) *Nature* (*London*) **264,** 567–568.
21. Lord, J. A. H., Waterfield, A. A., Hughes, J., and Kosterlitz, H. W. (1977) *Nature* (*London*) **267,** 567–568.

22. Marks, N., Grynbaum, A., and Neidle, A. (1977) *Biochem. Biophys. Res. Commun.* **74,** 1552–1555.
23. Meek, J. L., Yang, H.-Y. T., and Costa, E. (1977) *Neuropharmacology* **16,** 151–154.
24. Meyerson, B. J., and Terenius, L. L. (1977) *Eur. J. Pharmacol.* **42,** 191–192.
25. Miller, R. J., K.-J. Chang, and Cuatrecasas, P. (1978) *In* "Centrally Acting Peptides" (J. Hughes, ed.), pp. 195–229. Macmillan, New York.
26. Minneman, K. P., and Iversen, L. L. (1976) *Nature (London)* **262,** 313–314.
27. Mroz, E. A., Brownstein, M. J., and Leeman, S. E. (1976) *Brain Res.* **113,** 597–599.
28. Nicol, R. A., Siggins, G. R., Ling, N., Bloom, F. E., and Guillemin, R. (1977) *Proc. Natl. Acad. Sci. U.S.A.* **74,** 2584–2588.
28a. Pert, C. B., Bowie, D. L., Fong, B. T. W., and Chang, J.-K. (1976) *In* "Opiates and Endogenous Opioid Peptides," pp. 79–86. (H. W. Kosterlitz, ed.) Elsevier /North Holland, Amsterdam.
29. Puig, M. M., Gascon, P., Craviso, G. L., and Musachio, J. M. (1977) *Science* **195,** 419–420.
29a. Ross, M., Su, T.-P. Cox, B. M., Goldstein, A. (1976) *In* "Opiates and Endogenous Opioid Peptides." (H. W. Kosterlitz, ed.), pp. 35–40. Elsevier/North Holland, Amsterdam.
30. Simantov, R., Snowman, A. M., and Snyder, S. H. (1976) *Brain Res.* **107,** 650–652.
31. Simantov, R., Kuhar, M. J., Uhl, G. R., and Snyder, S. H. (1977) *Proc. Natl. Acad. Sci. U.S.A.* **74,** 2167–2171.
31a. Smith, T. W., Hughes, J., Kosterlitz, H. W., and Sosa, R. P. (1976) *In* "Opiates and Endogenous Opioid Peptides." pp. 57–62. (H. W. Kosterlitz, ed.) Elsevier/ North Holland, Amsterdam.
32. Sosa, R. P., McKnight, A. T., Hughes, J., and Kosterlitz, H. W. (1977) *FEBS Lett.* **84,** 195–198.
33. Subramanian, N., Mitznegg, P., Sprugel, W., Domschke, S., Wünsch, E., and Demling, L. (1977) *Naunyn-Schmiedeberg's Arch. Pharmacol.* **299,** 163–165.
34. Taube, H. D., Borowski, E., Endo, T., and Starke, K. (1976) *Eur. J. Pharmacol.* **38,** 377–380.
35. Terenius, L., and Walhlström, A. (1978) *In* "Centrally Acting Peptides" (J. Hughes, ed.), pp. 161–178. Macmillan, New York.
36. Van Neuten, J. M., Janssen, P. A. J., and Fontaine, J. (1976) *Life Sci.* **18,** 803–808.
37. Yang, H.-Y. T., Hong, J. S., and Costa, E. (1977). *Neuropharmacology* **16,** 303–307.
38. Wahlström, A., Brandt, M., Moroder, L., Wünsch, E., Lindeberg, G., Ragnarsson, U., Terenius, L., and Hamprecht, B. (1977) *FEBS Lett.* **77,** 28–32.
39. Waterfield, A. A., and Kosterlitz, H. W. (1975) *Life Sci.* **16,** 1787–1792.
39a. Waterfield, A. A., Smokcum, R. W. J., Hughes, J., Kosterlitz, H. W., and Henderson, G. *Europ. J. Pharmac.* **43,** 107–116.
40. Zieglagansberger, W., Fry, J. P., Hertz, A., Moroder, L., and Wünsch, E. (1976) *Brain Res.* **115,** 160–164.

On the Physiologic Role of Endorphins

B. M. COX AND AVRAM GOLDSTEIN
Addiction Research Foundation
and Department of Pharmacology
Stanford University
Palo Alto, California

INTRODUCTION

The discovery of the pentapeptide enkephalins (1), and then of the larger pituitary and brain endorphins (2), aroused much interest because they met the criteria for endogenous ligands of the opiate receptors. In bioassays in which peptide degradation can be prevented, they exert pharmacologic actions indistinguishable from those of morphine and other opiates, and these effects are blocked and reversed by the specific opiate antagonist naloxone. In binding assays using radioactive opiate agonists or antagonists as primary ligands, the endorphins compete for stereospecific binding sites (3). In this chapter we consider the data presently available concerning endorphin function.

ENDORPHIN PHARMACOLOGY

The pharmacology of morphine is extremely complex, and its numerous and diverse actions have been the subject of pharmacologic study for decades (4). Among these effects are the production of analgesia; alteration of subjective state in man (euphoria) and of various behaviors in animals, inhibition or stimulation of release of various pituitary hormones, vomiting caused by stimulation of the chemoreceptor trigger zone, miosis due to stimulation of central parasympathic outflow, and inhibition of peristalsis due to central and peripheral (myenteric plexus) actions. Morphine effects are species

ISBN 0-12-398450-5

specific. For example, it causes a state of plastic rigidity (catalepsy) in rats, locomotor stimulation (running fit) in mice, manic hyperactivity and hallucinatory behavior in cats, and sedation in dogs and rabbits. Even the inhibitory effect on acetylcholine output from myenteric neurons, which has proved so useful for bioassay (5), is seen only in the guinea pig, not in several other species.

Given the circumstances of their discovery—the outcome of a deliberate search for endogenous *morphinelike* substances—it is hardly surprising that the endorphins should behave like morphine in all systems examined to date. Indeed, it would be most interesting and significant to discover any actions that differ from those of morphine. In our opinion, understanding of endorphin function is not advanced by rediscovering the pharmacology of morphine in one system after another. The fact that endorphins given intracerebrally produce catalepsy in rats (6) (as morphine does) permits no inference to be drawn about a role of endorphins in pathologic catalepsy in humans. And when it is shown (as it surely will be) that endorphins produce mania in cats (as morphine does), it should not be inferred that endorphins have something to do with pathologic mania or hallucinations in humans. The recent report that endorphin administered intracerebrally causes interference with mating behavior in male rats (7) (as morphine does) does not by itself justify any inference about a role of endorphin in sexual behavior in humans. Nor does the fact that rats will self-administer leucine enkephalin intracerebrally (8) (as they will morphine) permit one to deduce a role of enkephalin in normal drive-motivated behavior. In summary, the fact that endorphins can mimic a great variety of morphine actions merely confirms that these peptides fit the opiate receptors, but adds no new information concerning their physiologic role or pathologic malfunctions.

FUNCTIONAL EFFECTS OF NALOXONE

A potentially more informative approach to the study of endorphin function employs the specific antagonist naloxone, which combines in a highly specific manner with the endorphin (opiate) receptors. If the endorphin system is tonically active, the administration of naloxone should cause some change in physiologic state, since it will competitively replace endorphin molecules at the receptors. However, very few effects of naloxone by itself have been observed. One provocative finding by Holtzman (9), is that food-seeking behavior of hungry rats is suppressed by naloxone in a dose-related manner, and at very low doses.

Except for the above effects, naloxone, under ordinary conditions, and even at high doses, seems to be quite inert pharmacologically. One has to conclude that most of the endorphin receptors are unoccupied in the normal physiologic state. We suggest, therefore, that the endorphin system is ordinarily on a standby basis. To learn about the physiological role of endorphins, one has to apply stimuli of a kind and intensity that might reasonably occur in an animal's natural life. Nature developed the system of endorphins and endorphin (opiate) receptors as an advanced adaptation in the vertebrates (they are not present in invertebrates), and it has conserved this system over millions of years. Obviously, the endorphins have survival value. This means they must confer some advantage, however slight, before the end of an animal's reproductive period, in its ability to fight or flee from a predator, to obtain food, to find a mate, and so on. The ability to feel acute pain and to respond appropriately is obviously essential to survival. A system for suppressing acute pain would be counterproductive, unless the pain were so severe as to interfere with other behaviors essential to dealing with a life-threatening crisis.

Some kinds of artificial stimulation appear to be capable of releasing endorphins, as judged by the production of analgesia that can be blocked by naloxone. The first of these predates the discovery of the endorphins. Electrical stimulation in the mesencephalic periaqueductal gray produces analgesia to noxious stimuli applied to the paws or tail, and naloxone abolishes or prevents this analgesia (10). Recently, electroacupuncture has been shown to produce analgesia (or electrophysiologic concomitants of analgesia) in cats (11), mice (12), and man (13), which is completely or partially prevented by naloxone. Although these experiments are of great interest in indicating the presence of an endorphin mechanism that can be activated artificially, they do not necessarily show that endorphins are involved in a normal regulation of pain.

Akil *et al.* (14) have presented evidence indicating that repeated footshock in rats raises the threshold for response to a thermal stimulus to the tail. This effect was a rather modest one, but was antagonized by naloxone. The threshold increase was accompanied by a small increase in the total brain content of endorphins. Whether increase in brain endorphin represents decreased release or increased synthesis or altered storage or modified reuptake is entirely unknown.

Jacob *et al.* (15) showed that naloxone has a hyperalgesic effect in mice left long enough on a hot plate so that they jump to escape the thermal stimulus. In the same experiment, in which threshold latency (4–5 sec to paw-licking) remained unchanged, naloxone reduced the much longer latency to jumping (90 sec) by about one-half. This effect occurred at very low naloxone doses. We confirmed these findings in all details (16). This positive result with mice suggests that intense and prolonged pain may be required to activate the endorphin system.

Negative results were obtained in a footshock experiment (17), in which the experimental animals were able to avoid prolonged exposure to a noxious stimulus. Rats trained to avoid footshock by jumping onto a pole showed no alteration in behavior with naloxone up to 25 mg/kg, the highest dose that did not interfere grossly with motor coordination. The shock threshold was unaffected, implying that endorphins were playing no modulatory role in the set-point of this threshold of response to a noxious stimulus. In the same system, low doses of morphine dramatically raised the threshold, and low doses of naloxone completely abolished the morphine effect.

Recently, Priscilla Grevert, in our laboratory, has been studying the effects of naloxone on experimental pain in human volunteers (18). After giving informed consent, the volunteers (males and females in equal numbers) were subjected to a painful stimulus at three sessions, 1 day apart. In the ischemic pain procedure, the arterial circulation to the forearm is occluded, a fixed amount of hand exercise is performed, and then pain is allowed to develop for a 10-min period. Subjective pain reports are given, on a 0 to 10 scale. After release of the tourniquet, a mood scale is administered. Then, on a double-blind basis, saline or 2 or 10 mg of naloxone hydrochloride is administered intravenously, and the entire pain procedure is repeated. Finally, the mood scale is administered again. The results of these experiments with ischemic pain were essentially negative. Naloxone had no measurable effect on pain or mood, with the single exception that at the end of the procedure, a significant ($P < 0.05$) drop in tension–anxiety was noted in the saline condition, but not after administration of naloxone. These experiments are being repeated with a different group of subjects to see if this single apparent effect of naloxone can be replicated, or if it was a chance occurrence.

In the cold-water pain procedure, subjects immersed the hand in cold water at 10°C for 5 min and reported subjective pain on a rating scale. A finger plethysmograph record permitted measurement of blood flow changes and of pulse rate. Mood scales were used again, including the Lexington MBG scale, which distinguishes the subjective effects of opiates from those of other drugs. As shown by Wolf and

Hardy (19), the sensation of pain increases for the first 2 min, then decreases. The digital pulse amplitude decreases, then increases. This apparently adaptive suppression of pain response made us hope that endorphin activation was responsible. However, there were no effects of naloxone (1 or 10 mg) on any variable measured in this procedure (P. Grevert and A. Goldstein, unpublished observations). Subjects were also unable to guess when they had saline and when they had naloxone.

These results with human subjects agree with those published by El-Sobky *et al.* (20), who used a much lower dose of naloxone. The naloxone dosage in our experiments can be placed in perspective by noting that a victim of heroin overdose, who is comatose and near death, can be revived, dramatically, by the intravenous injection of less than 1 mg of naloxone. Here we used a dose 10 times higher. One cannot reasonably argue that naloxone occupies the receptors competitively in the face of an otherwise saturating concentration of heroin (morphine) but is completely ineffective when endorphin is the ligand. Certainly, the *in vitro* bioassays and the binding assay show endorphins to display normal competitive behavior with respect to naloxone. Thus, we conclude that the painful stimulation used in our experiments was insufficient to activate the endorphin system.

ENDORPHIN STEADY-STATE LEVELS AND TURNOVER

The most reliable indications of the physiologic role(s) of endorphin are likely to come from measurements of endorphin steady-state levels and turnover in anatomically defined structures, and from the analysis of changes resulting from the application of defined physiologic stimuli. At least initially it is probable that experiments of this type will have to be performed in laboratory animals. For the enkephalins, techniques for the measurement of steady-state levels are already available, and it is probable that simple separation procedures yielding pure enkephalins for measurement of the rate of incorporation of radioactive precursor aminoacids (21) will soon be in use in turnover studies. For the larger endorphins, simple separation procedures yielding a pure product that can be identified with certainty as a particular peptide are not yet available. The development of a rapid procedure for the separation of small amounts of β-endorphin from other tissue constituents is a major priority.

In the case of the pituitary endorphins, indications of turnover rate might also be obtained by an alternative procedure. The presence of high endorphin concentration in an endocrine gland suggests that these peptides are probably released into the blood stream. The level of circulating pituitary endorphin will reflect the rate at which this material is released from the gland. Given information about the rate of loss of endorphins from blood, a measure of overall turnover rate could be obtained from measurements of the gland steady-state levels and the circulating levels of endorphin. Preliminary data obtained by T.-P. Su in our laboratory suggest that a material with many of the properties of pituitary endorphin is present in human and rodent blood. Experiments on factors affecting the levels of circulating endorphin are now in progress.

Some data on concentrations and amounts of endorphin in the separated anterior and posterior lobes of rat pituitary glands have already been obtained. Dissected lobes of individual pituitary glands were extracted by a modification of the acetone/glacial acetic acid procedure used in the initial demonstration of the presence of opioid material in the pituitary gland (22). The opioid activity in each extract was determined by estimation of its ability to displace ^{3}H-etorphine from opiate receptor sites in dispersed rat brain membranes. Highest concentrations of endorphin were found in the posterior lobe, although significant quantities were also present in the anterior lobe, particularly in female rats where the gland weight is higher than in males. This distribution is similar to that found in bovine pituitary glands (23). In experiments in which the posterior lobe of rat pituitary was dissected into pars intermedia and infundibular process (pars nervosa), almost all of the opioid activity was found in the pars intermedia in agreement with the immunocytochemical results of Bloom *et al.* (24). The low level found in the infundibular process may well result from incomplete removal of small fragments of pars intermedia tissue. β-Lipotropin, the precursor of β-endorphin, also shows this distribution (25). The apparent molecular weight of the major opioid component of extracts of rat pituitary glands (23) is close to the molecular weight of β-endorphin, suggesting that this peptide is probably responsible for most of the observed opioid activity.

We have found significant changes in both endorphin concentration per unit tissue weight and in gland endorphin content during the life span of albino rats. There was little change in the endorphin content during the first 5 weeks of life, but between the 5th and 10th week the level increased fivefold and remained at this elevated level at 25 weeks. The rise in pituitary endorphin content coincides with the onset of sexual maturity in these rats.

INDUCED CHANGES IN PITUITARY ENDORPHIN LEVELS

The precursor peptide of β-endorphin, β-lipotropin, also contains the aminoacid sequence of β-melanocyte stimulating hormone (β-MSH), and it has been suggested that β-lipotropin may serve as a prohormone for both β-MSH and β-endorphin (26–29). We have examined the possibility that stimuli which alter the pituitary content of MSH might also affect the levels of endorphin. Howe and Thody (30) have reported that the MSH content of the posterior lobe of rat pituitary was elevated following administration of hypertonic saline in place of drinking water. The pars intermedia receives an innervation from the supraoptic and paraventricular nuclei (31), and administration of hypertonic saline causes distinct morphological changes in these nuclei (32). We found that saline administration resulted in a decline in endorphin content of the pituitary in some, but not all treated rats (unpublished observations). Depletion of endorphin levels could result from an inhibition of synthesis, or a substantial enhancement of endorphin release from the pituitary. On the assumption that the endorphin is derived from β-lipotropin, inhibition of synthesis of β-endorphin would presumably be accompanied by a reduction in the levels of MSH, and not an elevation as observed by Howe and Thody (30). However, an enhanced release of β-endorphin, leading to an increase in the turnover of β-lipotropin, would generate increasing amounts of the amino-terminal fragment of β-lipotropin, and hence of β-MSH, which might be accumulated in the gland.

The paraventricular and supraoptic nuclei are also activated during parturition, and by suckling. We have measured endorphin levels in the pituitary glands of lactating rats shortly after parturition. The observed levels were not significantly different from levels in control female rat pituitaries (unpublished observations). It is possible therefore that hypertonic saline administration may act as a specific stimulus for endorphin release. Alternatively, hypertonic saline may be more stressful to rats than the physiological stimuli of parturition and lactation. E. R. Baizman in our laboratory is conducting experiments on the effects of different forms of stress on the pituitary levels of endorphin. Preliminary results indicate that prolonged footshock, or physical restraint, can lower the amounts of endorphin in the pituitary gland, but in this case the reduction occurred primarily in the anterior lobe of the pituitary.

The data we have reported here provide some background information relevant to the study of the physiologic role of the endorphins, but much further experimentation is required to establish such a role.

We have assumed as a working hypothesis that a reduction in the steady-state level of pituitary endorphin reflects an enhanced release of the peptide(s) into the blood stream, and not a reduced rate of synthesis. This assumption will become testable with the development of an assay for endorphin circulating in the blood. The target sites for endorphins released from the pituitary remain uncertain. It is possible that they can gain access to opiate receptors in spinal cord and brain and thus induce behavioral adaptations of value in stressful situations.

ACKNOWLEDGMENTS

We thank Drs. Priscilla Grevert, T.-P. Su, and E. R. Baizman for permission to describe unpublished work, and Rekha Padhya for skilled technical assistance. This work was supported by National Institute on Drug Abuse grant DA-1199.

REFERENCES

1. Hughes, J., Smith, T. W., Kosterlitz, H. W., Fothergill, L. A., Morgan, B. A., and Morris, H. R. (1975) *Nature (London)* **258**, 577–579.
2. Cox, B. M., Opheim, K. E., Teschemacher, H., and Goldstein, A. (1975) *Life Sci.* **16**, 1777–1782.
3. Goldstein, A. (1976) *Science* **193**, 1081–1086.
4. Goodman, L. S., and Gilman, A., eds. (1975) "The Pharmacological Basis of Therapeutics," 5th ed. Macmillan, New York.
5. Kosterlitz, H. W., Lord, J. A. H., and Watt, A. J. (1973) *In* "Agonist and Antagonist Actions of Narcotic Analgesic Drugs" (H. W. Kosterlitz, H. O. J. Collier, and J. E. Villarreal, eds.), pp. 45–61. Univ. Park Press, Baltimore, Maryland.
6. Bloom, F., Segal, D., Ling, N., and Guillemin, R. (1977) *Science* **194**, 630–632.
7. Meyerson, B. J., and Terenius, L. (1977) *Eur. J. Pharmacol.* **42**, 191–192.
8. Belluzzi, J. D., and Stein, L. (1977) *Nature (London)* **266**, 556–558.
9. Holtzman, S. G. (1974) *J. Pharmacol. Exp. Ther.* **189**, 51–60.
10. Akil, H., Mayer, D. J., and Liebeskind, J. C. (1976) *Science* **191**, 961–962.
11. Pomeranz, B., Cheng, R., and Law, P. (1977) *Exp. Neurol.* **54**, 172–178.
12. Pomeranz, B., and Chiu, D. (1976) *Life Sci.* **19**, 1757–1762.
13. Mayer, D. J., Price, D. D., and Rafii, A. (1977) *Brain Res.* **121**, 368–372.
14. Akil, H., Madden, J., Patrick, R. L., and Barchas, J. D. (1976) *In* "Opiates and Endogenous Opioid Peptides" (H. W. Kosterlitz, ed.), pp. 63–70. Elsevier, Amsterdam.
15. Jacob, J. J., Tremblay, E. C., and Colombel, M. C. (1974) *Psychopharmacologia* **37**, 217–223.
16. Grevert, P., and Goldstein, A. (1977) *Psychopharmacology* **53**, 111–113.
17. Goldstein, A., Pryor, G. T., Otis, L. S., and Larsen, F. (1976) *Life Sci.* **18**, 599–604.
18. Grevert, P., and Goldstein, A. (1977) *Proc. Natl. Acad. Sci. U.S.A.* **74**, 1291–1294.
19. Wolf, S., and Hardy, J. D. (1943) *Res. Publ., Assoc. Res. Nerv. Ment. Dis.* **23**, 123–142.

20. El-Sobky, A., Dostrovsky, J. O., and Wall, P. D. (1976) *Nature (London)* **263**, 783–784.
21. Clouet, D. H., and Ratner, M. (1976) *In* "Opiates and Endogenous Opioid Peptides" (H. W. Kosterlitz, ed.), pp. 71–78. Elsevier, Amsterdam.
22. Teschemacher, H., Opheim, K. E., Cox, B. M., and Goldstein, A. (1975) *Life Sci.* **16**, 1771–1776.
23. Ross, M., Dingledine, R., Cox, B. M., and Goldstein, A. (1977) *Brain Res.* **124**, 523–532.
24. Bloom, F., Battenberg, E., Rossier, J., Ling, N., Leppaluoto, J., Vargo, T. M., and Guillemin, R. (1977) *Life Sci.* **20**, 43–48.
25. Dessy, C., Herlant, M., and Chrétien, M. (1973) *C. R. Hebd. Seances Acad. Sci.* **276**, 335–338.
26. Bradbury, A. F., Smyth, D. G., and Snell, C. R. (1976) *Biochem. Biophys. Res. Commun.* **69**, 950–956.
27. Graf, L., Rónai, A. Z., Bajusz, S., Cséh, G., and Székely, J. (1976) *FEBS Lett.* **64**, 181–184.
28. Lazarus, L. H., Ling, N., and Guillemin, R. (1976) *Proc. Natl. Acad. Sci. U.S.A.* **73**, 2156–2159.
29. Seidah, N. G., Lis, M., Gianoulakis, C., Routheir, R., Benjannet, S., Schiller, P. W., and Chrétien, M. (1977) *Can. J. Biochem.* **55**, 35–40.
30. Howe, A., and Thody, A. J. (1970) *J. Endocrinol.* **46**, 201–208.
31. Howe, A. (1973) *J. Endocrinol.* **59**, 385–409.
32. Stutinsky, F. (1974) *In* "Neurosecretion: The Final Neuroendocrine Pathway" (F. Knowles and L. Vollrath, eds.), pp. 15–23. Springer-Verlag, Berlin and New York.

Discovery and Function of the Endorphins

L. TERENIUS
Department of Medical Pharmacology
University of Uppsala
Uppsala, Sweden

INTRODUCTION

A specific opiate receptor was observed in neural tissue around 1973 (1–3). This receptor shows selective affinity for opiates and has virtually negligible affinity for conventional neurotransmitters, neuromodulators, and other agents with effects on the central nervous system. It was therefore tested, in the following years, whether this receptor could have a natural substrate. This hypothesis appeared to be true (4,5) and a group of substances collectively called endorphins, were isolated from neural and pituitary tissue (6–9). This communication will summarize some of the working hypotheses that were followed and tested during the author's work in this area.

ENDORPHINS AND MORPHINE—CHEMICAL COMPARISONS

Chemical work and structure–activity studies in various biological systems led to the assumption that there must exist a complementary receptor binding area, "the opiate receptor" (10). Despite the fact that quite a large variety of compounds with seemingly different structures possess morphinelike activity, certain common structural features were present. It was therefore postulated that also the unknown ligands, if they existed, should share these structural features. In the preliminary screening of differently prepared brain extracts, an extrac-

ISBN 0-12-398450-5

tion procedure which would also have had extracted morphine (and its congeners) was included (5). These extracts were negative when tested for opiate receptor affinity. On the other hand, processing the original extract in other ways gave evidence for very water-soluble ligands with opiate receptor affinity. These ligands were different from the opiate alkaloids in their physicochemical characteristics. When the structure of the first endorphins to be described were published (11) it was immediately evident that the structure was largely discordant, the endorphins being peptides with a very flexible structure. Attempts have been made to find overall dimensional similarities on molecular models between the simplest possible peptide fragments with opioid activity, Tyr–Gly–Gly–Phe–Met(Leu) (the enkephalins, 11), and morphine. Some similarities seem to exist (12). Despite these similarities it is obvious that the flexible nature of the peptides would make them more easily adaptable, and in fact, they seem to bind to two classes of opioid receptors with equal affinity, while opiate alkaloids show selectivity against one of these receptor populations (see below).

MULTIPLE ENDORPHIN SYSTEMS

The existence of endorphins was purely speculative a few years ago and their presence seemed very uncertain. For instance, the apparent inactivity of a narcotic antagonist like naloxone seemed to preclude their existence (13). It is therefore quite surprising that not just one but at least three apparently distinct systems may exist (Table I). In the brain both chemical analysis and immunohistochemical evidence

TABLE I
Characteristics of Various Endorphin Systems

System	Peptide	Localization	Metabolic degradation	Possible action profile
I	Enkephalins	Intraneuronally in specific CNS fibers, nerve plexi in gastrointestinal tract	Rapid	Neurotransmitterlike
II	β-Endorphin	Intraneuronally, mainly in fibers of the hypothalamus	Slow	Neuromodulatorlike
III	β-Endorphin	Pituitary, anterior lobe, pars intermedia	Slow	Hormonal

suggest that the enkephalins dominate quantitatively (14–16). Enkephalin fibers are distributed over wide areas in the CNS with high densities in the limbic system, the spinal trigeminal nucleus, and the substantia gelatinosa of the spinal cord. There seems to be a good correlation between the presence of these fibers and the presence of opiate receptors as measured in incubation experiments or by autoradiography (17–19). This close anatomical association between enkephalin fibers and opiate receptors may be taken as support for the hypothesis that enkephalins may be neurotransmitters. Experiments where enkephalins (or morphine) are applied directly onto a neuron by microiontophoresis indicate that they are inhibitory in most areas (20,21). Enkephalins are also present in nerve fibers in the gut (14) which is a classical target organ for morphinelike substances and has opiate receptors (1,22).

Besides the enkephalins, fragments corresponding to a sequence in the pituitary hormone β-lipotropin, notably β-endorphin, show opiate-like activity (6). β-Endorphin has 31 amino acids with the N-terminal pentapeptide sequence identical to that in Met-enkephalin (23,24). β-Endorphin and its shorter fragment α-endorphin are found in the brain but are localized in rather few fibers, mainly in the hypothalamus (25,26). Thus there is no overlap in the distribution of fibers with enkephalin and the longer endorphins, indicating that the systems are truly different, perhaps also in their biosynthetic origin. At the moment one can only speculate about the differential roles of these two systems. One possible difference might be in the resistance to metabolic breakdown, β-endorphin being very stable if introduced into the brain ventricles and producing long-lasting analgesia (27) while the enkephalins show weak, transient effects even if injected in fairly large amounts (28,29). If similar differences exist *in situ* one may expect the β-endorphin system to be very slow and poorly adaptable while the enkephalins would show similarities with the classical neurotransmitters in their short period of action.

In the pituitary, there is comparatively little enkephalin but massive amounts of β-endorphin (30). In rats, the β-endorphin seems to be stored in the same cells as ACTH and has been found to be released in parallel with and in equal molecular amounts as ACTH (31). This opens the possibility that pituitary β-endorphin is a stress-hormone-like ACTH. Intravenous injection of β-endorphin produces analgesia in the mouse (32) but it is not yet clear if this is true in other species. It is an interesting possibility that the paradoxical insensitivity to pain experienced in severe shock or trauma (33) might be related to a release of pituitary β-endorphin.

RECEPTORS FOR OPIOID ALKALOIDS AND FOR OPIOID PEPTIDES

One starting point for the search for endorphins was the existence of opiate receptors which seemed to be a strange coincidence if they would not be substrates for endogenous substances. Receptor binding techniques were also used in the early work on isolating endorphins (5). With the determination of the structure of the enkephalins (11) synthesis of them became possible and it was also possible to synthesize labeled enkephalins which could be used as radioligands in binding experiments. Quite surprisingly it was found that the enkephalins had a high affinity for sites which show a low affinity for opiate alkaloids (34–36). However, the enkephalins also show equal affinity for the classic alkaloid sites observed using labeled dihydromorphine or naloxone as radioligands. The function of the extra "enkephalin sites" is not clear at the moment. In some *in vitro* systems such as the guinea pig ileum, classical alkaloid receptors dominate (34), while in the mouse vas deferens (34) and in the mouse neuroblastoma x glioma cell hybrid system (37) the "enkephalin sites" are prevalent. One characteristic of these "enkephalin sites" is their insensitivity to naloxone, which makes it difficult to study their importance. The existence of heterogeneity in opioid receptor populations suggests that more selective drugs may be produced in the future.

ENDORPHINS AND OPIATES—ACTIONS OTHER THAN ANALGESIA

It has been shown repeatedly that naloxone shows no or very little effect on pain thresholds in morphine-naïve animals (13,38) or in man (39,40). This suggests that under normal conditions the activity of the endorphin system is low and reaches a hardly detectable level of activity. However, it could well be that under conditions when the endorphin system is out of function or hyperactive that a pathological response may be observed. In order to evaluate this possibility we developed two different techniques which could be applied to studies of pathologic situations in the human, namely analysis of endorphins in the cerebrospinal fluid and administration of naloxone when hyperactivity might be present (41).

Analysis of endorphins in the cerebrospinal fluid has been done with a radioreceptor assay after a chromatographic separation. Two major fractions of activity are present and most significance is pres-

TABLE II
Distribution of Patients with Various Disorders with Respect to Fraction I Endorphin Levels in the Cerebrospinal Fluid

Patient category	Fraction I endorphin level			Reference
	<0.6	0.6–1.2	>1.2[a]	
Healthy volunteers	3	12	4	42
Chronic pain, somatic origin	20	4	5	43,44
Chronic pain, psychogenic origin	1	8	8	44
Schizophrenics	4	4	7	42
Manic-depression	0	0	4	42
Endogenous depression	2	0	10	45

[a] Expressed as if due to Met-enkephalin (pmole/ml).

ently being paid to the so-called fraction I. A summary of the correlation between levels of fraction I endorphins and some clinical diagnoses is given in Table II (42–45). The most striking findings are those of low levels in conditions of severe, chronic pain of organic, somatic origin (with clear neurologic case history) and high levels in several psychiatric disorders. Interestingly, cases of chronic pain where no somatic origin can be traced (for instance with diffuse pain) have high levels. In such patients the endorphin levels correlate with the degree of depression, the levels increasing with increasing depth of depression (44).

The high levels of endorphins in psychiatric disorders and considerations regarding the psychotomimetic effects of certain opiate derivatives led to clinical testing of naloxone in schizophrenia (46). The results of this pilot study were partly positive which warranted further investigation into the matter. Other trials of naloxone in schizophrenia were reported subsequently with confirmatory or negative results (47–49). The status of narcotic antagonist treatment in psychiatric disorders is therefore still uncertain.

SUMMARY

The discovery of the endorphins is one of those unexpected events in physiology. Their chemical nature, only remotely similar to that of opiate alkaloids, was also unexpected. The multiplicity of endorphin systems and the apparent diversity of opiate receptors suggest that endorphins act in several different contexts. In the normal, morphine-naïve individual it has so far been difficult to define a role for the endorphins. On the other hand, certain pathological conditions seem to be related to changes in endorphin homeostasis.

ACKNOWLEDGMENT

The author is supported by the Swedish Medical Research Council.

REFERENCES

1. Pert, C. B., and Snyder, S. H. (1973) *Science* **179,** 1011—9114.
2. Simon, E. J., Hiller, J. M., and Edelman, I. (1973) *Proc. Natl. Acad. Sci. U.S.A.* **70,** 1947–1949.
3. Terenius, L. (1973) *Act Pharmacol Toxicol.* **32,** 317–320.
4. Hughes, J. (1975) *Brain Res.* **88,** 295–308.
5. Terenius, L., and Wahlström, A. (1975) *Acta Physiol. Scand.* **94,** 74–81.
6. Goldstein, A. (1976) *Science* **193,** 1081–1086.
7. Hughes, J., and Kosterlitz, H. W. (1977) *Br. Med. Bull.* **33,** 157–161.
8. Frederickson, R. C. A. (1977) *Life Sci.* **21,** 23–42.
9. Terenius, L. (1978) *Annu. Rev. Pharmacol* **18,** 189–204.
10. Lewis, J. W., Bentley, K. W., and Cowan, A. (1971) *Annu. Rev. Pharmacol.* **11,** 241–270.
11. Hughes, J., Smith, T. W., Kosterlitz, H. W., Fothergill, L. A., Morgan, B. A., and Morris, H. R. (1975) *Nature (London)* **258,** 577–579.
12. Horn, A. S., and Rodgers, J. R. (1976) *J. Pharm. Pharmacol.* **29,** 257–265.
13. Martin, W. R. (1967) *Pharmacol. Rev.* **19,** 463–521.
14. Elde, R., Hökfelt, T., Johansson, O., and Terenius, L. (1976) *Neuroscience* **1,** 349–351.
15. Smith, T. W., Hughes, J., Kosterlitz, H. W., and Sosa, R. P. (1976) *In* "Opiates and Endogenous Opioid Peptides" (H. W. Kosterlitz, ed.), pp. 57–62. Elsevier, Amsterdam.
16. Simantov, R., Kuhar, M. J., Pasternak, G. W., and Snyder, S. H. (1976) *Brain Res.* **106,** 189–197.
17. Kuhar, M. J., Pert, C. B., and Snyder, S. H. (1973) *Nature (London)* **245,** 447–450.
18. Hiller, J. M., Pearson, J., and Simon, E. J. (1973) *Res. Commun. Chem. Pathol. Pharmacol.* **6,** 1052–1062.
19. Pert, C. B., Kuhar, M. J., and Snyder, S. H. (1976) *Proc. Natl. Acad. Sci. U.S.A.* **73,** 3729–3733.
20. Bradley, P. B., Briggs, I., Gayton, R. J., and Lambert, L. A. (1976) *Nature (London)* **261,** 425–426.
21. Frederickson, R. C. A., and Norris, F. H. (1976) *Science* **194,** 440–442.
22. Terenius, L. (1975) *Acta Pharmacol. Toxicol.* **37,** 211–221.
23. Bradbury, A. F., Smyth, D. G., and Snell, C. R. (1976) *Biochem. Biophys. Res. Commun.* **69,** 950–956.

24. Li, C. H., and Chung, D. (1976) *Proc. Natl. Acad. Sci. U.S.A.* **73,** 1145–1148.
25. Bloom, F., Rossier, J., Battenberg, E., Vargo, T., Minick, S., Ling, N., and Guillemin, R. (1977) *Neurosci. Abstr.* (in press).
26. Hökfelt, T., Terenius, L., and Elde, R. (1978) In preparation.
27. Loh, H. H., Tseng, L. F., Wei, E., and Li, C. H. (1976). *Proc. Natl. Acad. Sci. U.S.A.* **73,** 2895–2898.
28. Büscher, H. H., Hill, R. C., Römer, D., Cardinaux, F., Closse, F., Hauser, D., and Pless, J. (1976) *Nature (London)* **261,** 423–425.
29. Belluzzi, J. D., Grant, N., Garsky, V., Sarantakis, D., Wise, C. D., and Stein, L. (1976) *Nature (London)* **260,** 625–626.
30. Bloom, F., Battenberg, E., Rossier, J., Ling, N., Leppaluoto, J., Vargo, T. M., and Guillemin, R. (1977) *Life Sci.* **20,** 43–48.
31. Guillemin, R., Bloom, F., Rossier, J., Minick, S., Henriksen, S., Burgus, R., and Ling, N. (1977) *Proc. Am. Pept. Symp., 5th, 1978* (in press).
32. Tseng, L.-F., Loh, H. H., and Li, C. H. (1976) *Nature (London)* **263,** 230–240.
33. Melzack, R. (1973) "The Puzzle of Pain." Basic Books, New York.
34. Lord, J. A. H., Waterfield, A. A., Hughes, J., and Kosterlitz, H. W. (1977) *Nature (London)* **267,** 495–499.
35. Simantov, R., and Snyder, S. H. (1976) *Mol. Pharmacol.* **12,** 987–998.
36. Terenius, L. (1977) *Psychoneuroendocrinology* **2,** 53–58.
37. Wahlström, A., Brandt, M., Moroder, L., Wünsch, E., Lindeberg, G., Ragnarsson, U., Terenius, L., and Hamprecht, B. (1977) *FEBS Lett.* **77,** 28–32.
38. Jacob, J. J., Tremblay, E. C., and Colombel, M.-C. (1974) *Psychopharmacologica* **37,** 217–223.
39. El-Sobky, A., Dostrovsky, J. O., and Wall, P. D. (1976) *Nature (London)* **261,** 783–784.
40. Grevert, P., and Goldstein, A. (1977) *Proc. Natl. Acad. Sci. U.S.A.* **74,** 1291–1294.
41. Terenius, L., and Wahlström, A. (1977). *Proc. CINP Congr. 10th, 1976* (in press).
42. Lindström, L., Widerlöv, E., Gunne, L.-M., Wahlström, A., and Terenius, L. (1977) *Acta Psychiatr. Scand.* **57,** 153–164.
43. Sjölund, B., Terenius, L., and Eriksson, M. (1977) *Acta Physiol. Scand.* **100,** 382–384.
44. Almay, B. G. L., Johansson, F., von Knorring, L., and Terenius, L. (1978). *Pain* (In press).
45. Terenius, L., Wahlström, A., and Ågren, H. (1977) *Psychopharmacology* **54,** 31–33.
46. Gunne, L.-M., Lindström, L., and Terenius, L. (1977) *J. Neural Transm.* **40,** 13–19.
47. Volavka, J., Mallya, A., Baig, S., and Perez-Cruet, J. (1977) *Science* **196,** 1227–1228.
48. Davis, G. C., Bunney, W. E., Jr., De Fraites, E. G., Kleinman, J. E., van Kammen D. P., Post, R. M., and Wyatt, R. J. (1977) *Science* **197,** 74–76.
49. Emrich, H. M., Cording, C., Pirée, S., Kölling, A., von Zerssen, D., and Herz, A. (1978) *Neuropsychopharmakologie* (in press).

Recent Studies on Opiate Receptors and Analogs of Enkephalin

KENNETH A. BONNET
Department of Psychiatry
New York University Medical Center
New York, New York

JACOB M. HILLER AND ERIC J. SIMON
Department of Medicine
New York University School of Medicine
New York, New York

INTRODUCTION

The demonstration of stereospecific opiate receptors in the nervous system of all vertebrates studied (1–4) has provided powerful insights into the mode of action of acute opiate exposure and ultimately led to the discovery and description of naturally occurring endogenous opioid peptides the endorphins and of the smaller enkephalins (5,6). These opioid peptides have attracted considerable interest because of their putative role in central nervous system neuromodulation. The earliest identification of the Tyr–Gly–Gly–Phe–Met sequence of naturally occurring methionine enkephalin led to the identification of the possible parent prohormone β-lipotropin that contains the sequence of methionine enkephalin in residues 61–65 (6). Moreover, the entire C-terminal sequence (residues 61–91) is a naturally occurring opioid peptide that has a potency several times greater than the smaller enkephalins in the production of receptor-mediated effects in *in vivo* and *in vitro* test systems. This C-terminal sequence has been renamed β-endorphin.

The physiological role of the enkephalins is still in an early stage of investigation. It is clear that the enkephalins exert agonistic effects at

ISBN 0-12-398450-5

the opiate receptors and produce catalepsy and analgesia when injected intracerebrally (7–10). The enkephalins are rapidly degraded largely by exopeptidases (11). *In vivo,* the enkephalins show distinct regional localization in the central nervous system and appear to be stored in vesicular material and exhibit calcium-dependent release (12–15). The functional role of the enkephalins has been suggested to include the regulation of pain perception in the thalamus and spinal laminae, the modulation of visceral reflexes through the vagal nuclei of the medulla, and participation in the reward and euphoria responses mediated in the amygdala (16).

The activity of the opioid peptides appears to specifically require an N-terminal tyrosine containing a free hydroxyl group (17). Substitution of D-alanine for glycine^2 in the methionine^5-enkephalin sequence provides long-lasting enkephalin activity with no loss of affinity for the opiate receptor. The D-alanine^2-methionine^5-enkephalin is further protected from carboxypeptidase attack by modification of the carboxyl terminus to an amide moiety (17).

EFFECTS OF N-TERMINUS AND C-TERMINUS ALTERATIONS OF ENKEPHALIN

We were interested in the relative importance of aminopeptidase and carboxypeptidase activity in the breakdown of the opioid peptides. We have synthesized several peptides containing the methionine^5-enkephalin sequence with additions only on the N-terminus or the carboxyl terminus. These peptides were assayed for their receptor-binding affinity and their stability, and for their *in vivo* analgesic potency. The peptides are listed in Table I. Peptide A is the naturally occurring sequence of methionine^5-enkephalin. Peptides B, C, and D were synthesized to determine the contribution of peptidase activities, and peptides C and D were specifically designed to assess the necessity for a free amino group on the N-terminal tyrosine for opiate activity. Peptide E was given added residues on the N-terminus to attempt to confer greater stability yet retain the conformation of methionine^5-enkephalin.

Competition by these peptides for binding of ^{3}H-naloxone to receptors in rat brain homogenate is also shown in Table I. β-Endorphin was seven times as effective as morphine, whereas mentionine^5-enkephalin was equipotent with morphine. The addition of D-alanine to the carboxyl terminus (peptide B) did not alter receptor binding affinity. Addition of D-alanine to the N-terminus (peptide D) divested the peptide of nearly all binding activity but addition of L-alanine to the N-terminus (peptide C) retained binding and indicates

TABLE I
Structure–Activity Relationships in Receptor Binding and Relative Stability of Synthetic and Naturally Occurring Opioid Peptides[a]

Structure	IC_{50} (n*M*)	Stability
A. Tyr–Gly–Gly–Phe–Met	20	60
B. Tyr–Gly–Gly–Phe–Met–(D)Ala	30	67
C. Ala–Tyr–Gly–Gly–Phe–Met	185	87
D. (D)Ala–Ala–Tyr–Gly–Gly–Phe–Met	8,000	+
E. Tyr–Gly–Gly–Tyr–Gly–Gly–Phe–Met	230	116
α-Endorphin	35	∞ (no loss of activity)
β-Endorphin	3	—
Morphine	21	—

[a] IC_{50} determined by competitive binding with 10^{-9} *M* ^{3}H-naloxone, 25°C, 10 min. Stability determined by incubation with brain homogenate prior to binding assay. Times are approximate incubation times to lose 50% activity when preincubated at 25°C at concentrations from 300 n*M* to 10 μ*M*.

the probability that aminopeptidase activity in brain homogenate may cleave the L-alanine to yield sufficient methionine[5]-enkephalin to exhibit measurable binding activity. Similarly, the addition of a Tyr–Gly–Gly sequence to the N-terminus (peptide E) only reduced binding activity by about 50%, which suggests that some attachment to the tyrosine residues can be made with retention of measurable binding activity. It is also possible that binding activity in this peptide resulted from enzymatic cleavage of Tyr–Gly–Gly to yield methionine[5]-enkephalin.

The stability of these modified enkephalin peptides was assessed in rat brain homogenates at 25°C. Peptides A and B showed about a 50% loss of binding activity when preincubated in homogenates for 60 min. Peptides C and E showed greater stability; this may result from aminopeptidase activity in homogenates removing residues from the N-tyrosyl terminus to yield methionine[5]-enkephalin that subsequently degrades with the time course characteristic of peptide A. These effects generally suggest the predominance of aminopeptidase activity in brain homogenates. However, the relative amino- to carboxypeptidase activity in whole tissue or cerebrospinal fluid may not be the same as in the broken cell homogenates.

The *in vivo* analgesic effects of these peptides was assessed by microinjection in 1-μl volumes through indwelling cannulae in the cerebral aqueduct. Preadapted rats were tested by the jump-flinch procedure (18). Morphine (2.5 μg) effected an 88% increase in footshock threshold that persisted for 45 min (Fig. 1). Methionine [5]-enkephalin

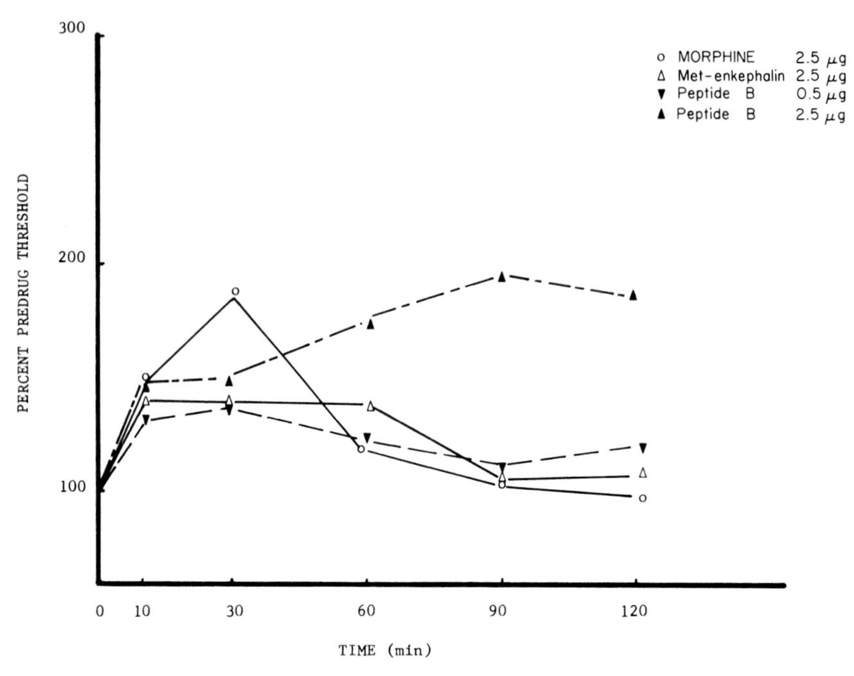

Fig. 1. The *in vivo* analgesic effects of various opioids. Each compound was injected in 1.0 μl volume into indwelling cannulae in the cerebral aqueduct of rats. Animals were tested for footshock thresholds before, and at various intervals after, the microinjection, as described in the text.

at 2.5 μg produced a 44% increase in threshold, with a similar duration of alangesia, and was thus twofold less effective than morphine on a molar basis in line with the three-fold lower dissociation constant for methionine^5-enkephalin. At 10 μg, methionine^5-enkephalin evidenced greater peak effect but a shorter duration than the lower dose. The analgesia seen with methionine^5-enkephalin is generally greater than that reported in microinjection studies from other laboratories (19). This is likely to be due to the relative lack of tissue damage in our studies as a result of injection into the aqueduct rather than into the periventricular gray tissue itself, and this should result in less release of degradative enzymes.

Peptide B is an effective analgesic at very low doses; 0.5 μg produced a 40% increase in footshock threshold with a duration of 30 min. Increased doses of 2.5 μg and 10 μg produced 120% and 170% increases in threshold, respectively, and proportional increases in duration of effects, as well. Analgesia was clearly evident at 10 min following microinjection, but appeared to increase and reach peak analgesic effect at 60–90 min.

Analgesia produced by these peptides was reversed by systemic administration of naloxone (Fig. 2). It was apparent from the effects of peptide B that the predominant degradative activity in the cerebral aqueduct was carboxypeptidase activity. We reasoned that the short duration of analgesia frequently reported from microinjection studies of methionine⁵-enkephalin might result from liberation of aminopeptidases from tissue damaged during microinjection directly into the periaqueductal gray matter. Injection of 10 μg methionine⁵-enkephalin into the aqueduct produced measureable analgesia,

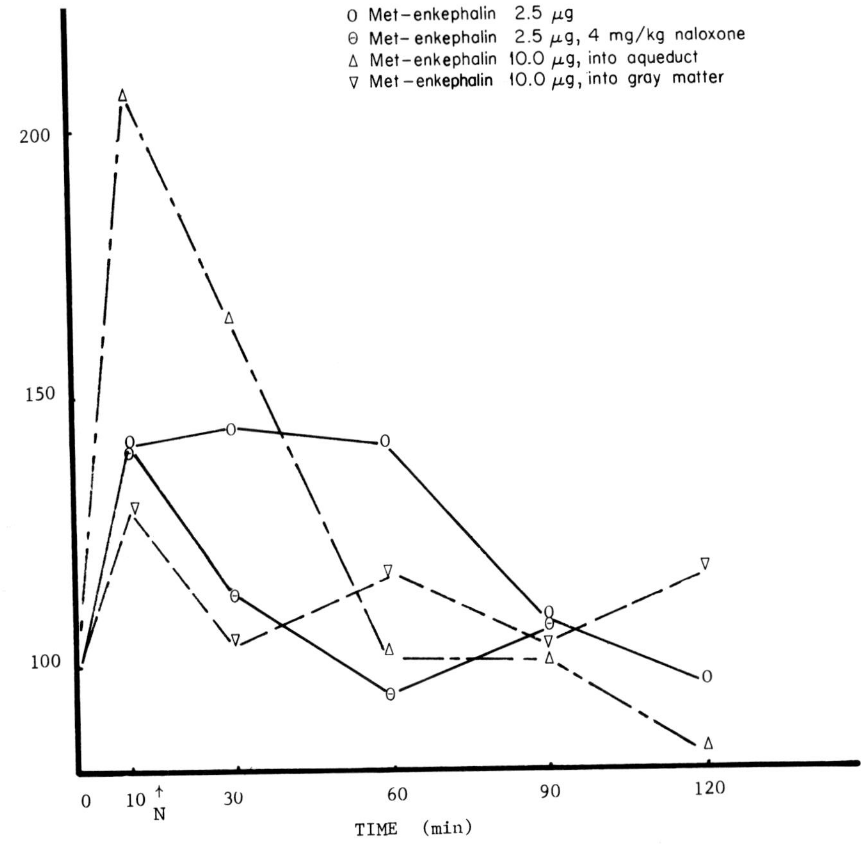

Fig. 2. The *in vivo* analgesic effects of methionine⁵-enkephalin after microinjection into the cerebral aqueduct as described in the text. Naloxone was systematically injected immediately after the 10-min test where indicated. Methionine⁵-enkephalin at 10 μg was injected into the cerebral aqueduct or into the grey matter in the floor of the aqueduct.

whereas injection into the floor of the aqueductal wall resulted in almost no detectable analgesic effect at these low doses.

EVIDENCE FOR LOCATION OF OPIATE RECEPTORS IN ORGANOTYPIC CULTURES

Organotypic cultures of central nervous tissue can provide valuable insights into problems related to the mode of action of opiates. The use of these cultures provides the advantages inherent in isolated systems. Such cultures derived from fetal spinal cords with attached dorsal root ganglia (20) have been found useful for studies of opiate action. Crain *et al.* (21) demonstrated that the sensory-evoked synaptic networks in the dorsal horn regions of these explants can be selectively depressed by exposure to analgesic concentrations of morphine and other opiates. These effects are reversed by naloxone.

Measurement of opiate receptor-binding levels in these spinal cord–dorsal root ganglion cultures as well as in cultures of isolated dorsal root ganglion and deafferented cord explants were made by Hiller *et al.* (22). Homogenates of these cultures were found to exhibit stereospecific binding of the potent antagonist diprenorphine. In these cultures profuse neuritic outgrowth develops, primarily due to the stimulation of the dorsal root ganglia by nerve growth factor, and these neurites extend for several millimeters beyond the explant zone. In some cases separate determinations of opiate binding were made on explant and outgrowth zones. It was apparent that the greatest amount of binding of diprenorphine was present in the neuritic outgrowth of both isolated dordal root ganglion cultures and cord–ganglion cultures. Depending on the number of days *in vitro*, 5 to 20 times more binding per milligram protein was seen in the neuritic outgrowth of the cultures than in the explant area.

Information from autoradiographic localization of opiate receptors in the adult rat spinal cord suggests the notion of the presynaptic presence of some opiate receptors (23). Experiments in rhesus monkeys have shown that stereospecific opiate binding in the dorsal horn of the spinal cord is reduced following deafferentation by dorsal rhizotomy (24). These authors have suggested that this may be due to degeneration of opiate receptor-bearing afferent terminals in the dorsal horn, consistent with a presynaptic location of receptors. They have pointed out, however, that their data could also be accounted for by transsynaptic effects on opiate receptors localized on presynaptic cord neurons.

The central afferent branches of the neuritic arborization from the dorsal root ganglion explant have been shown in cord–ganglion cultures to establish synaptic connections within the dorsal horn of the spinal cord explant. The high level of opiate receptors in the neuritic outgrowth of dorsal root ganglion cultures in the absence of postsynaptic cord neurons constitutes additional evidence for a presynaptic location of the receptors.

ACKNOWLEDGMENTS

This research was supported by grants to K. A. Bonnet (DA 1113) and to E. J. Simon (DA 00017) from National Institute on Drug Abuse.

REFERENCES

1. Simon, E. J., Hiller, J. M., and Edelman, I. (1973) *Proc. Natl. Acad. Sci. U.S.A.* **70,** 1947.
2. Terenius, L. (1973) *Acta Pharmacol. Toxicol.* **32,** 317.
3. Pert, C. B., and Snyder, S. H. (1973) *Science* **179,** 1011.
4. Pert, C. B., Aposhian, D., and Snyder, S. H. (1974) *Brain Res.* **75,** 356.
5. Terenius, L., and Wahlström, A. (1975) *Acta Physiol. Scand.* **94,** 74–81.
6. Hughes, J., Smith, T. W., Kosterlitz, H. W., Fothergill, L. A., Morgan, B. A., and Morris, H. R. (1975) *Nature (London)* **258,** 577–579.
7. Belluzzi, J. D., Grant, N., Garsky, V., Sarantakis, D., Wise, C. D., and Stein, L. (1976) *Nature (London)* **260,** 625–626.
8. Pert, C. B., Pert, A., Chang, J.-K., and Fong, B. T. W. (1976) *Science* **194,** 330–332.
9. Bloom, F., Segal, D., Ling, N., and Guillemin, R. (1976) *Science* **194,** 630–632.
10. Jacquet, Y. F., and Marks, N. (1976) *Science* **194,** 632–635.
11. Marks, N. (1977) *In* "Peptides in Neurobiology" (H. Gainer, ed.), pp. 221–258. Plenum, New York.
12. Elde, R., Hökfelt, T., Johansson, O., and Terenius, L. (1976) *Neuroscience* **1,** 349–351.
13. Atweh, S. F., and Kuhar, M. J. (1977) *Brain Res.* **129,** 1.
14. Simantov, R., Snowman, A., and Snyder, S. H. (1976) *Brain Res.* **107,** 650–657.
15. Smith, T. W., Hughes, J., Kosterlitz, H. W., and Sosa, R. P. (1976) *In* "Opiates and Endogenous Opioid Peptides" (H. W. Kosterlitz, ed.), pp. 57–62. Elsevier, Amsterdam.
16. Simantov, R., Kuhar, M. J., Uhl, G. R., and Snyder, S. H. (1977) *Proc. Natl. Acad. Sci. U.S.A.* **74,** 2167.
17. Pert, C. B., Pert, A., Chang, J.-K., and Fong, B. T. W. (1976) *Science* **194,** 330–332.
18. Bonnet, K. A., and Peterson, K. (1975) *Pharmacol. Biochem. Behav.* **3,** 47–55.
19. Buchser, H. H., Hill, R. C., Romer, D., Cardinaux, F., Closse, A., Hauser, D., and Pless, J. (1976) *Nature (London)* **261,** 423–425.

20. Crain, S. M., and Peterson, E. R. (1974) *Brain Res.* **79,** 145–152.
21. Crain, S. M., Peterson, E. R., Crain B., and Simon, E. J. (1977) *Brain Res.* **144,** 162–165.
22. Hiller, J. M., Simon, E. J., Crain, S. M., and Peterson, E. R. (1978) *Brain Res.* (in press).
23. Atweh, S. F., and Kuhar, M. J. (1977) *Brain Res.* **124,** 53–67.
24. Lamotte, C., Pert, C. B., and Snyder, S. H. (1976) *Brain Res.* **112,** 407–412.

PART V

CYCLIC NUCLEOTIDES

Regulation of Cyclic AMP Metabolism by Neural Hormones in Brain

THEODORE W. RALL
Department of Pharmacology
University of Virginia School of Medicine
Charlottesville, Virginia

INTRODUCTION

Adenosine 3′,5′-phosphate (cyclic AMP) was discovered in 1957 during the course of investigations on the mechanisms responsible for the hyperglycemic effects of epinephrine and glucagon (1,2). Cyclic AMP is formed from ATP by a membrane-bound enzyme complex (adenylate cyclase) (3) and is converted to 5′-AMP by a family of soluble and membrane-bound enzymes (cyclic ribonucleotide phosphodiesterases) (4,5). In these early studies the activity of adenylate cyclase was found to be stimulated by the hormones while that of phosphodiesterase was inhibited by methylxanthines. Initial studies using partially purified fractions of liver and muscle extracts showed that cyclic AMP promoted the accumulation of the more phosphorylated (and more active) species of glycogen phosphorylase. Subsequently, it was found that cyclic AMP interacted with a protein phosphotransferase causing activation (6) by dissociation of a catalytic subunit from an inhibitory subunit (7). One substrate for this enzyme is the less phosphorylated (and less active) form of another protein phosphotransferase, phosphorylase *b* kinase. The active form of this enzyme in turn phosphorylates the less active species of glycogen phosphorylase. Another substrate for the phosphotransferase interacting with cyclic AMP (cyclic AMP-dependent protein kinase) is the less phosphorylated but more active species of glycogen synthase (8).

ISBN 0-12-398450-5

Over the past 20 years, work in a number of laboratories has indicated that, with the exception of nonnucleated erythrocytes and certain mutant cell lines, all animal cells contain cyclic AMP (0.3 to 2 μM), adenylate cyclase, one or more species of soluble or membrane-bound cyclic ribonucleotide phosphodiesterase, soluble and particulate proteins capable of binding cyclic AMP with high affinity, and one or more species of soluble or particulate protein phosphotransferases whose activity is markedly stimulated by cyclic AMP (cyclic AMP-dependent protein kinases). Further, literally dozens of individual cell types have been found to respond to a specific array of blood-borne hormones, autocoids, or neurohormones by increased accumulation of cyclic AMP. In addition, the regulation of a wide variety of cellular processes by various peptide and biogenic amine hormones has been found to be correlated with the accumulation of cyclic AMP, to be potentiated by methylxanthines and other inhibitors of cyclic ribonucleotide phosphodiesterase and in a number of instances to be mimicked specifically by the use of cyclic AMP or its derivatives. These and other observations led Sutherland and his co-workers to put forth the generalized concept of "Second Messengers" in hormone action (9). It was proposed that nonpenetrating humoral regulatory substances ("First Messengers") interacted with tissue-specific receptors on the cell surface which in turn interacted with effector systems in the plasma membrane, resulting in the elaboration of intracellular mediators ("Second Messengers") common perhaps to all cells. These mediators would then go on to alter the rate of certain processes characteristic of the particular differentiated cell and located in a variety of subcellular organelles, ultimately leading to the recognizable hormone-induced effects. In the case of cyclic AMP, the crucial role of protein phosphorylation in the regulation of glycogen metabolism and the widespread occurrence of cyclic-AMP-dependent protein kinases led to the suggestion that all actions of cyclic AMP in animal tissues involve protein phosphorylation (10). Other potential "Second Messengers" include calcium ions (11,12) and cyclic GMP (13,14). The regulatory functions of cyclic GMP are still poorly understood and calcium ions interact with cyclic nucleotide function and metabolism in a complex fashion (15). At present, it appears that most of the actions of certain nonpenetrating hormones, notably insulin and growth hormones, cannot be explained adequately by the actions of cyclic AMP, cyclic GMP, and calcium ions, either singly or in combination. Thus, additional "Second Messengers" may be waiting for discovery.

In view of the observations discussed above, it has become obvious that the formation and subsequent action of cyclic AMP are crucial events in a multitude of hormone–tissue interactions involving the regulation of a wide variety of cellular processes. However, it is important to point out that the demonstration that cyclic AMP can influence a given cellular process does not necessarily mean that regulation of this process occurs exclusively via cyclic AMP (16). Neither does the demonstration that a given hormone-induced effect is mediated by cyclic AMP formation and action exclude the possibility that other effects produced by the same hormone in the same cell are mediated by different mechanisms. Nevertheless, the study of cyclic AMP metabolism and action has proven to be an extremely useful point of attack in the dissection of hormonal regulatory mechanisms.

ROLE OF CYCLIC AMP IN THE NERVOUS SYSTEM

The investigation of the role of cyclic AMP in neural tissue poses some very thorny problems. Most of the difficulty stems from the extreme heterogeneity and complex organization of neural tissue. In addition, our knowledge concerning the identity and function of potential "First Messengers" in the nervous system is fragmentary. Nervetheless, since the nervous system has the highest capacity to synthesize and degrade cyclic AMP of all animal tissues (17,18), it is reasonable to expect that this nucleotide plays important roles in the regulation of neural function. It is also reasonable to expect that each population of differentiated neurons that have been or will be characterized by their capacity to synthesize, elaborate, transport, or respond electrophysiologically to specific neurotransmitter substances will also be characterized by their ability to respond to a specific array of humoral substances in terms of increased accumulation of cyclic AMP. These humoral substances may be eventually classified as neuromodulators, trophic substances, or neurotransmitters. Thus, alteration of cyclic AMP is a potential assay tool in searching for endogenous regulatory substances; this idea will be developed further in a later section. In the meantime, some fairly direct clues as to the roles that cyclic AMP plays in the nervous system have been gathered.

The observations concerning the role of cyclic AMP in the nervous system fall into two broad categories: (1) those dealing with postjunctional events, and (2) those involving prejunctional processes. Historically, the first direct investigation of neural cyclic AMP function generated evidence that cyclic AMP mediated the response of cerebellar

Purkinje cells to norepinephrine (19–21). This evidence included the ability of cyclic AMP and its derivatives to mimic the characteristic decreased firing rate and increased membrane potential produced by norepinephrine. Subsequently, there have been a number of publications reporting that iontophoretic application of cyclic AMP and/or its derivatives decreased the discharge rate of neurons in the caudate nucleus, hippocampus, cerebral cortex, and limbic system as well as some disputing the validity of these observations (22). The latter publication also discusses the technical problems associated with the iontophoresis of cyclic nucleotides and provides plausible explanations for the discordant observations. The proposition that cyclic AMP functions in the generation of slow inhibitory postsynaptic potentials is also supported by observations made with mammalian sympathetic ganglia (23). Another potential postsynaptic role for cyclic AMP has to do with the increased accumulation of certain enzymes via protein synthesis ("transsynaptic induction"). Nathanson (24) has recently reviewed the status of the evidence relating cyclic AMP metabolism and the induction of tyrosine hydroxylase in mammalian sympathetic ganglia and adrenal glands as well as in various cultured cell systems. Despite the precedent for this type of function that has been established in liver (25), it seems clear that more work must be done before the controversy concerning the possible function of cyclic AMP in the transsynaptic induction of tryosine hydroxylase can be resolved.

A potential presynaptic role for cyclic AMP in the regulation of transmitter release was first suggested by the observation that theophylline augmented the facilitation of neuromuscular transmission induced by epinephrine (26). This was followed by reports that dibutyryl cyclic AMP and theophylline increased the frequency of miniature end plate potentials and the quantal content of end plate potentials in Mg^{2+}-blocked rat diaphragms (27). These observations were later shown to be due in part to effects of hypertonic conditions (28), and the augmentation of miniature end plate potential frequency by epinephrine and dibutyryl cyclic AMP required partial depolarization by K^+ ions in order to be visible under the conditions used (i.e., blockade of muscle action potentials with tetrodotoxin). Recently, it has been shown that dibutyryl cyclic AMP can induce repetitive firing of motor nerve terminals either spontaneously or after nerve stimulation in an *in situ* preparation of cat soleus muscle (29). Theophylline was observed to increase the frequency of miniature end plate potentials with or without elevated K^+ ions and to induce repetitive firing either with or without nerve stimulation. While the effects of theophylline have usually been ascribed to its ability to inhibit cyclic

AMP degradation, it is important to point out that adenosine has been shown to reduce the size and frequency of miniature and evoked end plate potentials (30) and that methylxanthines can block adenosine receptors in neural tissue (31). Thus, the effects of theophylline may reflect suppression of endogenous adenosine action more than preservation of cyclic AMP. In addition to the possibility that cyclic AMP mediates epinephrine-induced regulation of acetylcholine release, it has also been suggested that cyclic AMP formation and action are essential steps in the transmitter release produced by nerve action potentials at the neuromuscular junction (32). However, the evidence produced so far is not very convincing. Analogs of cyclic AMP have also been observed to increase the electrically induced release of norepinephrine and dopamine-β-hydroxylase from peripheral adrenergic nerves (33,34). It has been suggested that this is related to the β_2-adrenoreceptor-mediated facilitation of adrenergic transmission thought to function in response to circulating epinephrine (35). Since dibutyryl cyclic AMP has also been observed to augment the electrically induced release of ^{3}H-dopamine from rat striatal slices (36), it is possible that cyclic-AMP-mediated regulation of transmitter release is a general phenomenon in the nervous system. Another potential presynaptic role for cyclic AMP has to do with the regulation of neurotransmitter synthesis. Dibutyryl cyclic AMP increases the formation of dopamine from labeled tyrosine in slices of rat striatum (37), due to the activation of tyrosine hydroxylase, characterized by an increased affinity for the pteridine cofactor and a decreased affinity for the inhibitory end product, dopamine (38,39). This activation of tyrosine hydroxylase can be produced in soluble fractions of homogenates by addition of cyclic-AMP-dependent protein kinase and cyclic AMP (40). Thus it is possible that the activity of this enzyme is regulated via protein phosphorylation and dephosphorylation in a fashion analogous to glycogen phosphorylase or glycogen synthase. The relation of this mechanism and cyclic AMP metabolism to the alterations in enzyme activity produced by changes in impulse traffic is not clear at the present time (24).

REGULATION OF NEURAL CYCLIC AMP METABOLISM

The demonstrated importance of cyclic AMP in regulation of nonneural cell function along with the emerging roles and high metabolic capacity for cyclic AMP in the central nervous system have all provided impetus for the study of the regulation of cyclic AMP accumulation in brain tissue. Even though it is reasonable to expect that each differentiated cell type in the nervous system will respond to a characteristic set of "First Messengers" with increased accumulation of cyclic AMP, it is also quite possible that only a small proportion of cells will respond to any given agent. Furthermore, it is likely that the majority of neurotransmitters and other humoral regulatory substances functioning in the brain have yet to be identified. These considerations pose major experimental difficulties, yet at the same time they provide an opportunity to use cyclic AMP accumulation as an assay tool in searching for important endogenous regulatory substances. Such a search has been a major goal of the work carried out in this laboratory over the past decade.

The study of the regulation of neural cyclic AMP formation began in 1962 using catecholamines and broken-cell preparations from cat, sheep, and steer brains (41). However, the effects were small and varied considerably from preparation to preparation from the same source. Cerebellar preparations exhibited the most consistent and largest effects, up to a little more than a twofold stimulation of adenylate cyclase activity with β-adrenergic agonists. Since that time, successful use of broken-cell preparations for the examination of the effects of one or another putative neurotransmitter on cyclic AMP formation has been spotty and sometimes controversial. Some notable examples of success include the twofold stimulation of rat striatal preparations by dopamine (42) and by adenosine (43), and the twofold stimulation of guinea pig hippocampal preparations by histamine (44). In addition, small effects of norepinephrine and serotonin on preparations from rat cerebrum were visible if basal activity were reduced by EGTA (45). Histamine effects required the presence of GTP (44), perhaps another example of the important general role of guanine nucleotides in hormonal regulation of adenylate cyclase (46). Prémont *et al.* (43) showed that endogenous and assay-generated adenosine was sufficient to activate maximally their preparations and that the presence of adenosine deaminase was required to lower the basal enzymatic rates in order to observe effects of deaminase-insensitive adenosine analogs. Since the relatively enormous basal activity of brain adenylate cyclase preparations has probably been one important factor in the difficulty in observing hormonal stimulation, those maneuvers leading to decreased basal activity (e.g., EGTA, adenosine deaminase) should be of help in studying brain adenylate cyclase regulation in the future. However, the small effects observed to date and the unpredictability of the survival of hormone responses after cell disruption severely limit the usefulness of brain adenylate cyclase preparations in searching for unidentified humoral regulatory factors.

Studies on the regulation of cyclic AMP accumulation in brain slices were first reported in 1968 using rabbit tissues (47,48). These studies were otherwise notable because they (1) demonstrated that sometimes very large accumulations of cyclic AMP (up to 30-fold basal) could be induced, (2) provided the first evidence for the existence of specific histamine receptors in brain, and (3) showed that the relative effects of agonists (norepinephrine, histamine, and serotonin) varied widely depending upon the brain region examined. Large variations in patterns of responsiveness have subsequently been shown to be also a function of the species studied. For example, while guinea pig cerebral cortical tissue (49) produced results qualitatively similar to rabbit cerebrum (e.g., about twofold stimulation by norepinephrine and a large (more than eightfold) increase by histamine), in guinea pig cerebellar slices histamine was almost without effect (50) compared to the eight- to tenfold increases in cyclic AMP accumulation produced in rabbit tissue. On the other hand, in rat (51–53) and mouse (51,52) cerebral cortical slices, norepinephrine produced more than a fourfold increase in cyclic AMP while histamine was almost without effect. One response that apparently can be counted on is a relatively large effect of norepinephrine in cerebellar slices regardless of species. This species variability in patterns of responsiveness has prevented making even preliminary deductions linking function or a particular neurotransmitter with cyclic AMP. With regard to other putative neurotransmitters, these and other studies showed that serotonin occasionally produced small effects, while GABA, glutamate (1 m*M*), acetylcholine, and dopamine were without appreciable effect. The actions of higher concentrations of glutamate will be considered later.

The use of stimuli producing generalized depolarization of brain tissue has resulted in an even more highly variable pattern of effects upon cyclic AMP accumulation in brain slices. The effects of ouabain, veratridine, and batrachotoxin will not be discussed here beyond pointing out that both their absolute and relative effects upon cyclic AMP accumulation in cerebral cortical tissue vary markedly, depending upon the species used, and that their effects are reduced to different extents by the absence of Ca^{2+} ions or by the presence of tetrodotoxin or theophylline (53). For the purposes of this discussion, it will be sufficient to contrast and compare the effects of electrical pulses and elevated K^+ ions. It was observed that the application of electrical pulses to slices of guinea pig cerebral cortex increased cyclic AMP levels nearly tenfold within 5 min (49). These effects were paradoxically severely inhibited by the classical phosphodiesterase inhibitor, theophylline, and were augmented by the addition of maximal amounts of either norepinephrine or histamine. This led to the testing of brain extracts and culminated in the realization that adenine nucleotides and adenosine were powerful stimulants of cyclic AMP accumulation in guinea pig brain tissue (31). Adenosine was reasonably potent (EC_{50} = 30 μM) and was competitively inhibited by theophylline, complete inhibition occurring at about 20-fold molar excess. Subsequent studies have provided evidence for the existence of an "external" receptor in neural and certain other tissues responsive to adenosine and linked to adenylate cyclase so as to increase activity. Included in this evidence are (1) theophylline, while competitively inhibiting adenosine stimulation of cyclic AMP accumulation, does not reduce adenosine incorporation into the ATP of slices (31,54); (2) compounds inhibiting adenosine uptake into slices also potentiate the accumulation of cyclic AMP elicited by low concentrations of adenosine (54); (3) a restricted number of purine analogs of adenosine are effective agonists, while a restricted number of ribose analogs are antagonists (55); (4) the effects of adenine nucleotides, but not of certain adenosine analogs, are severely reduced in the presence of adenosine deaminase (56); (5) marked stimulatory effects of radioactive 2-chloroadenosine upon cyclic AMP accumulation in cultured VA-2 cells were not accompanied by significant formation of 2-chloro-ATP, 2-chloro cyclic AMP, or radioactive cyclic AMP (57); and (6) the demonstration that adenylate cyclase could be prepared from brain which was stimulated by low concentrations (1 μM) of adenosine or analogs and which stimulation was competitively antagonized by theophylline (43). The latter demonstration had been preceded by the observations of Haslam and Lynham on the platelet enzyme (58), of Blume and Foster on neuroblastoma adenylate cyclase (59,60), and of others. It should be pointed out that McKenzie and Bär (62) as well as others have observed inhibitory effects of adenosine at higher concentrations on adenylate cyclase activity. This may account for the hypersteep, bell-shaped dose–response curves observed in brain slices (31). In any event, adenosine has been found by many workers to be a very powerful stimulant of cyclic AMP accumulation in brain slices, producing increases of ten- to 50-fold in a variety of species and brain regions. The possible significance of this refreshing lack of variability will be considered later.

Another important and prominent feature of the effects of adenosine upon the accumulation of cyclic AMP in slices of guinea pig cerebral cortex was the potentiative interaction with norepinephrine and histamine (31). That is, the effect of a combination of adenosine and either norepinephrine or histamine was more than two- and 2.5-fold the sum of the effects of the agents acting individually, respectively. The synergism was even more dramatic at concentrations of adenosine below half-maximal (e.g., 10 μM). Again, marked regional and species variation in this phenomenon has been observed. For example, while the effects of a combination of adenosine and norepinephrine were between 1.5- and twofold the sum of the individual effects in slices of mouse and rat cerebral cortex, the small effects of histamine were not appreciably augmented in the presence of adenosine (52,61). On the other hand, the effect of the combination of norepinephrine and adenosine in slices of guinea pig cerebellum was almost exactly the sum of the large effects of the agents acting individually, while the small effect of histamine was augmented in the presence of adenosine (50). Furthermore, the effect of the combination of adenosine and histamine in slices of rabbit cerebral cortex was almost exactly the sum of the large effects of the agents acting individually, while the small effect of norepinephrine was augmented in the presence of adenosine (66). The mechanisms underlying these synergistic interactions are poorly understood and investigation of this phenomenon has been hampered by the fact that it has not been observed either in brain adenylate cyclase preparations, even those sensitive to adenosine (43), or in less heterogeneous intact-cell preparations, including cultured cell systems. The variability in the pattern of responses to combinations of adenosine and the amines would argue against mechanisms involving some general action of adenosine either to augment stimulatory effects of agonists on adenylate cyclase or to inhibit cyclic AMP breakdown. This conclusion is reinforced by the observation that the effect of a combination of norepinephrine and histamine increases cyclic AMP accumulation in guinea pig cerebral cortical slices more than twice the sum of the increases produced by the agents acting individually (63). Experiments such as the one depicted in Table I tend to eliminate the possibility that adenosine augments cyclic AMP accumulation in the presence of another agonist by somehow reducing cyclic AMP degradation even by a specific, receptor-mediated process. In this experiment, cyclic AMP levels are allowed to reach steady-state values in the presence of histamine in the absence and in the presence either of a mixture of phosphodiesterase inhibi-

TABLE I
Effects of Adenosine or Phosphodiesterase Inhibitors on Incorporation of ^{3}H-Adenine into Cyclic AMP in Brain Slices[a]

Additions	Cyclic AMP accumulation (pmole/mg protein)	Specific activity (cpm/nmole)		
		Cyclic AMP	ATP	Cyclic AMP/ATP
None (100 μM histamine only)	105	5950	2560	2.33
Theophylline + IBMX	263	4020	3460	1.16
Adenosine	350	6500	2630	2.48

[a] Approximately 300-mg portions of slices of cerebral cortex from adult Hartley guinea pigs were incubated for 50 min before being transferred to fresh medium containing histamine (100 μM) and the indicated additions. After 9.5 min, 100 μCi of ^{3}H-adenine were added and the incubation continued for 1.5 min. The slices were frozen and homogenized in methanolic HCl, and the homogenates were assayed for total cyclic AMP and protein (50). Cyclic AMP and ATP were isolated from deproteinized homogenates and their specific radioactivities were determined (52). When present, the concentration of adenosine was 10 μM, of theophylline was 500 μM, and of isobutylmethylxanthine (IBMX) was 500 μM.

tors or of a small amount of adenosine, before the addition of ^{3}H-adenine. It can be seen that, even though both adenosine and the phosphodiesterase inhibitors increase cyclic AMP accumulation to about the same extent, the specific radioactivity of cyclic AMP is reduced in the presence of the phosphodiesterase inhibitors and is maintained in the presence of adenosine. This indicates that adenosine increased the rate of cyclic AMP formation while increasing its accumulation. These and other data point to mechanisms involving regulation of adenylate cyclase. One hypothesis proposes the existence of "dependent" receptors; such receptors would require the simultaneous binding of two dissimilar agonists to two linked sites before appreciable regulation of adenylate cyclase could take place (64). In this view, the increased efficacy of norepinephrine and histamine in the presence of adenosine would reflect the recruitment of otherwise "silent" receptor–cyclase units. However, before this hypothesis can be taken seriously it will be necessary to show that receptors participating in a synergistic response reside on the same cell. This is a formidable task for the future.

Returning to the comparison of the effects of electrical pulses and elevated K^+ ions, it was observed that even though 40 mM KCl and electrical pulses produced about equivalent increased accumulation of cyclic AMP in slices of guinea pig cerebral cortex, the inclusion of theophylline could reduce the effects of electrical pulses by at least 85% but those of 40 m*M* KCl by no more than 50% (49,52). Furthermore, in the presence of maximal adenosine, electrical pulses had no significant additional effects in guinea pig cerebral cortical tissue while those of 40 m*M* KCl were augmented (50). The effects of electrical pulses were augmented by 14 m*M* Mg^{2+} ions and were slightly reduced by the omission of Ca^{2+} ions; either maneuver nearly obliterated the effects of 40 m*M* KCl. In slices of guinea pig cerebellum, electrical pulses also produced large (eightfold) increases in cyclic AMP accumulation that were inhibited by more than 85% by the theophylline (50). However, unlike the results in cerebral cortical tissue, 40 m*M* KCl failed to increase cyclic AMP accumulation; in the presence of maximal adenosine, electrical pulses produced about the same increment in cyclic AMP as in its absence while 40 m*M* KCl reduced the response to adenosine by about 35%. From this pattern of results it was concluded that the effect of electrical pulses in guinea pig cerebral cortical slices could be adequately explained by a calcium-independent release and action of adenosine while those of 40 m*M* KCl in part involved the calcium-dependent release and action of substances other than adenosine. We will return later to a discussion of the search for substances mediating the effects of K^+ ion depolarization of guinea pig cerebral cortical tissue. From these and other results it was also concluded that adenosine release and action could only partially account for the effects of electrical pulses in guinea pig cerebellar slices (50); the absence of a positive effect of 40 m*M* KCl on cyclic AMP accumulation either in the presence or absence of adenosine was taken to indicate the absence of a general facilititory effect of depolarization upon cyclic AMP formation and/or accumulation.

Current efforts are aimed at providing explanations for these puzzling effects of depolarizing agents, particularly of 40 m*M* KCl in guinea pig cerebral cortical tissue. At the moment we can only provide evidence excluding or limiting potential participation of known putative neurotransmitters. For example, the experiment depicted in Table II shows that phenoxybenzamine did not reduce the effect of 40 m*M* KCl in the presence of maximal adenosine while severely inhibiting the effects of histamine. Other experiments showed that under these conditions phenoxybenzamine would also nearly obliterate the effects of norepinephrine or a mixture of norepinephrine, histamine, dopamine, and serotonin. Shimizu and his collaborators have suggested that the release and action of glutamate could be important in the effects of K^+ ion depolarization in guinea pig cerebral cortical tissue (65). However, experiments such as the one summarized in

TABLE II
Lack of Effect of Phenoxybenzamine on Cyclic AMP Accumulation Produced by 40 m*M* KCl in the Presence of Adenosine[a]

Additions	Cyclic AMP accumulation (pmole/mg protein)
None (100 μ*M* adenosine only)	375 ± 26 (3)
Phenoxybenzamine (10 μ*M*)	349 ± 28 (3)
Histamine (50 μ*M*)	768 ± 38 (3)
KCl (40 m*M*)	665 ± 36 (4)
Histamine + phenoxybenzamine	428 ± 53 (3)
KCl + phenoxybenzamine	666 ± 18 (4)

[a] Approximately 100-mg portions of slices of guinea pig cerebral cortex were incubated for 50 min at 37°C in 20 ml of Krebs–Ringer bicarbonate glucose medium containing 100 μ*M* adenosine and continuously gassed with 95% O_2–5% CO_2. The slices were transferred to fresh medium containing the indicated additives as well as 100 *M* adenosine. After 10 min further incubation, the slices were frozen and homogenized in methanolic HCl, and the homogenates were assayed for cyclic AMP and protein (50). NaCl concentration was reduced by 35 m*M* when the KCl concentration was raised from 5 m*M* to 40 m*M*. Values are the mean ± SEM of the number of samples indicated in parenthesis.

Table III provide evidence of important distinctions between the actions of glutamate and 40 m*M* KCl: (1) maximal glutamate (6 m*M* or higher) is virtually without effect in the presence of theophylline while 40 m*M* KCl produces nearly a threefold increase in cyclic AMP; (2) in the presence of theophylline and norepinephrine glutamate increased cyclic AMP only about 30% while 40 m*M* KCl produced an effect almost twice the calculated sum of the individual effects; (3) while glutamate is capable of producing a response in the presence of theophylline and histamine qualitatively similar to that produced by 40 m*M* KCl (52), the response is much smaller; and (4) the consequence of combining glutamate with histamine plus norepinephrine yields a response which is only about 60% of the calculated sum of the responses to the three pairs of agents while 40 m*M* KCl and the amines produce an effect which is more than 90% of the calculated sum. Another way to look at this last item is to note that the combination of 40 m*M* KCl with the amines produced cyclic AMP levels more than twice those produced by the combination of glutamate and the amines. Thus, in the absence of added adenosine and in the presence of sufficient theophylline to block the effects of endogenously produced adenosine, only a portion of the effects of 40 m*M* KCl could possibly be accounted for by the release and concerted action of gluta-

TABLE III
Comparison of Glutamate and KCl: Interactions with Histamine and Norepinephrine in Adult Hartley Cerebral Cortical Slices[a]

Additions	Cyclic AMP accumulation (pmole/mg protein)
None (1 m*M* theophylline)	12.9 ± 0.42 (2)
Glutamate (6 m*M*)	16.3 ± 0.28 (2)
KCl (40 m*M*)	34.0 ± 2.8 (2)
Norepinephrine (100 μ*M*)	24.0 ± 2.5 (2)
plus glutamate (6 m*M*)	31.3 ± 2.4 (2)
plus KCl (40 m*M*)	74.9 ± 8.9 (4)
Histamine (100 μ*M*)	116 ± 25 (2)
plus glutamate (6 m*M*)	259 ± 30 (4)
plus KCl (40 m*M*)	475 ± 18 (4)
plus norepinephrine (100 μ*M*)	244 ± 22 (4)
plus norepinephrine + glutamate (6 m*M*)	321 ± 29 (4)
plus norepinephrine + KCl (40 m*M*)	702 ± 71 (4)

[a] After preincubation for 50 min in normal Krebs medium containing 0.8 m*M* $CaCl_2$, 40- to 100-mg portions of slices were transferred to fresh media containing 1 m*M* theophylline and the indicated addition (norepinephrine was added immediately after the tissue). Incubation was for 5 min and the tissue samples were processed as in Table II. Media containing 40 m*M* KCl had 35 m*M* less NaCl than normal media. Values are the mean ± SEM of the number of samples indicated in parenthesis.

mate, histamine, and norepinephrine. Clearly, we must search further either for the endogenous substances and receptors that mediate these effects or for some other explanation for these observations.

CONCLUDING REMARKS

One of the most notable consequences of the studies on the mechanisms responsible for the effects of depolarizing agents on brain cyclic AMP metabolism has been the discovery of the actions of adenosine, both by itself and in concert with other agents. This in turn led to the realization that methylxanthines were, among other things, effective blocking agents of the adenosine receptor. The fact that adenosine has proven to be a powerful stimulant to cyclic AMP accumulation in brain slices from all regions and species tested in contrast to the highly variable effectiveness of other agents may be an indication that glial elements in brain tissue may be the principal locus of the response to adenosine acting by itself. This possibility has received support from a recent ontogenetic study of cyclic AMP metabolism in guinea pig cerebral cortex wherein the response to adenosine by itself did not appear until after a major wave of glial proliferation and maturation had commenced (66). On the other hand, the potentiative interactions between norepinephrine, histamine, glutamate, and adenosine appeared earlier during a period of neuronal enlargement and maturation and diminished in intensity as the proportion of glial elements enlarged.

These and other observations discussed earlier have potentially important implications with regard to the possible functions of both adenosine and cyclic AMP and with regard to the pharmacological actions of caffeine and other methylxanthines in the central nervous system. First of all, adenosine formation would be expected to be promoted as a function of ATP utilization incited by depolarizing events, with the resultant influx of Na^+ ions and stimulation of Na^+–K^+ dependent ATPase in plasma membranes. This adenosine, acting in concert with otherwise excitatory neurotransmitters, might increase cyclic AMP in postjunctional neurons and thus tend to reduce firing rates in these cells. In addition, adenosine might decrease the release of excitatory neurotransmitters by actions on prejunctional receptors that either exerted a negative influence on cyclic AMP formation or had no relationship to cyclic AMP metabolism. In this way, adenosine might function as a general feedback regulator of synaptic activity serving to keep cellular activity in tune with the availability of oxygen. Furthermore, adenosine may regulate some as yet undefined restorative function of glial elements mediated at least in part by cyclic AMP. Finally, the well-known but vaguely defined "stimulatory" or "defatiguing" effects of methylxanthines in the central nervous system might be the result of inhibition of these actions of adenosine.

These speculations may prove to be incorrect at least with regard to their general validity. However, they do provide a useful framework for future investigation. It would appear to be profitable to search for endogenous substances capable of stimulating cyclic AMP accumulation in brain tissue, particularly in the presence of adenosine. These substances may turn out to be excitatory neurotransmitters, a category of neurohormone that is very underrepresented in the current catalog of putative transmitters. At least it would be reasonable to expect that any substance found to influence cyclic AMP metabolism might also have important regulatory functions that did not involve mediation by cyclic AMP. In any event it is clear that we have much to learn about neurohumoral regulation in the central nervous system and investigation of cyclic AMP metabolism and function should provide important clues in the future.

ACKNOWLEDGMENTS

The author acknowledges support by U.S. Public Health Service Grants NS 05716 and NS 12764.

REFERENCES

1. Rall, T. W., Sutherland, E. W., and Berthet, J. (1957) *J. Biol. Chem.* **224**, 463–475.
2. Sutherland, E. W., and Rall, T. W. (1957) *J. Am. Chem. Soc.* **79**, 3608–3609.
3. Rall, T. W., and Sutherland, E. W. (1962) *J. Biol. Chem.* **237**, 1228–1232.
4. Sutherland, E. W., and Rall, T. W. (1958) *J. Biol. Chem.* **232**, 1077–1091.
5. Appleman, M. M., Thompson, W. J., and Russell, T. R. (1973) *Adv. Cyclic Nucleotide Res.* **3**, 66–98.
6. Walsh, D. A., Perkins, J. P., and Krebs, E. G. (1968) *J. Biol. Chem.* **243**, 3763–3765.
7. Reiman, E. M., Walsh, D. A., and Krebs, E. G. (1971) *J. Biol. Chem.* **246**, 1986–1995.
8. Schlender, K. K., Wei, S. H., and Villar-Palasi, C. (1969) *Biochim. Biophys. Acta* **191**, 272–278.
9. Sutherland, E. W., Øye, I., and Butcher, R. W. (1965) *Recent Prog. Horm. Res.* **21**, 623–646.
10. Kuo, J. F., and Greengard, P. (1969) *Proc. Natl. Acad. Sci. U.S.A.* **64**, 1349–1355.
11. Rassmussen, H. (1970) *Science* **170**, 404–412.
12. Rasmussen, H., Jensen, P., Lake, W., Friedmann, N., and Goodman, D. B. P. (1975) *Adv. Cyclic Nucleotide Res.* **5**, 375–394.
13. Goldberg, N. D., O'Dea, R. F., and Haddox, M. K. (1973) *Adv. Cyclic Nucleotide Res.* **3**, 155–223.
14. Goldberg, N. D., Haddox, M. K., Nicol, S. E., Glass, D. B., Sanford, C. H., Keuhl, F. A., Jr., and Estensen, R. (1975) *Adv. Cyclic Nucleotide Res.* **5**, 307–330.
15. Berridge, M. J. (1975) *Adv. Cyclic Nucleotide Res.* **5**, 1–98.
16. Rall, T. W. (1975) *Metab. Clin. Exp.* **24**, 241–248.
17. Sutherland, E. W., Rall, T. W., and Menon, T. (1962) *J. Biol. Chem.* **237**, 1220–1227.
18. Butcher, R. W., and Sutherland, E. W. (1962) *J. Biol. Chem.* **237**, 1244–1250.
19. Siggins, G. R., Hoffer, B. J., and Bloom, F. E. (1969) *Science* **165**, 1018–1020.
20. Siggins, G. R. Hoffer, B. J., and Bloom, F. E. (1971) *Brain Res.* **25**, 535–553.
21. Siggins, G. R., Oliver, A. P., Hoffer, B. J., and Bloom, F. E. (1971) *Science* **171**, 192–194.
22. Bloom, F. E. (1975) *Ergeb. Physiol., Biol. Chem. Exp. Pharmakol.* **74**, 1–104.
23. Greengard, P., and Kebabian, J. W. (1974) *Fed. Proc., Fed. Am. Soc. Exp. Biol.* **33**, 1059–1067.
24. Nathanson, J. A. (1977) *Physiol. Rev.* **57**, 157–256.
25. Wicks, W. D. (1974) *Adv. Cyclic Nucleotide Res.* **4**, 335–438.
26. Breckenridge, B. M., Burn, J. H., and Matschinsky, F. M. (1967) *Proc. Natl. Acad. Sci. U.S.A.* **57**, 1893–1897.
27. Goldberg, A. L., and Singer, S. J. (1969) *Proc. Natl. Acad. Sci. U.S.A.* **64**, 134–141.
28. Miyamoto, M. D., and Breckenridge, B. M. (1974) *J. Gen. Physiol.* **63**, 609–624.
29. Standaert, F. G., Dretchen, K. L., Skirboll, L. R., and Morgenroth, V. H., III. (1976) *J. Pharmacol. Exp. Ther.* **199**, 544–552.
30. Ginsborg, B. L., and Hirst, G. D. S. (1972) *J. Physiol. (London)* **224**, 629–645.
31. Sattin, A., and Rall, T. W. (1970) *Mol. Pharmacol.* **6**, 13–23.

32. Standaert, F. G., Dretchen, K. L., Skirboll, L. R., and Morgenroth, V. H., III. (1976) *J. Pharmacol. Exp. Ther.* **199**, 553–564.
33. Wooten, G. F., Thoa, N. B., Kopin, I. J., and Axelrod, J. (1973) *Mol. Pharmacol.* **9**, 178–183.
34. Cubeddu, L., Barnes, E., and Weiner, N. (1975) *J. Pharmacol. Exp. Ther.* **193**, 105–127.
35. Westfall, T. C. (1977) *Physiol. Rev.* **57**, 659–728.
36. Westfall, T. C., Kitay, D., and Wahl, G. (1976) *J. Pharmacol. Exp. Ther.* **199**, 149–157.
37. Anagnoste, B., Shirron, C., Friedman, E., and Goldstein, M. (1974) *J. Pharmacol. Exp. Ther.* **191**, 370–376.
38. Ebstein, B., Roberge, C., Tabachnik, J., and Goldstein, M. (1974) *J. Pharm. Pharmacol.* **26**, 975–977.
39. Harris, J. E., Baldessarini, R. J., Morgenroth, V. H., III, and Roth, R. H. (1975) *Proc. Natl. Acad. Sci. U.S.A.* **72**, 787–793.
40. Morgenroth, V. H., III, Hegstrand, L. R., Roth, R. H., and Greengard, P. (1975) *J. Biol. Chem.* **250**, 1646–1648.
41. Klainer, L. M., Chi, Y.-M., Friedberg, S. L., Rall, T. W., and Sutherland, E. W. (1962) *J. Biol. Chem.* **237**, 1239–1243.
42. Kebabian, J. W., Petzold, G. L., and Greengard, P. (1972) *Proc. Natl. Acad. Sci. U.S.A.* **69**, 2145–2149.
43. Prémont, J., Perez, M., and Bochaert, J. (1977) *Mol. Pharmacol.* **13**, 662–670.
44. Hegstrand, L. R., Kanof, P. D., and Greengard, P. (1976) *Nature (London)* **260**, 163–164.
45. von Hungen, K., and Roberts, S. (1974) *Rev. Neurosci.* **1**, 231–281.
46. Rodbell, M., Lin, M. C., Salomon, Y., Londos, C., Harwood, J. P., Marton, B. R., Rendell, M., and Berman, M. (1975) *Adv. Cyclic Nucleotide Res.* **5**, 3–29.
47. Kakiuchi, S., and Rall, T. W. (1968) *Mol. Pharmacol.* **4**, 367–378.
48. Kakiuchi, S., and Rall, T. W. (1968) *Mol. Pharmacol.* **4**, 379–388.
49. Kakiuchi, S., Rall, T. W., and McIlwain, H. (1969) *J. Neurochem.* **16**, 485–491.
50. Zanella, J., and Rall, T. W. (1973) *J. Pharmacol. Exp. Ther.* **186**, 241–252.
51. Forn, J., and Krishna, G. (1971) *Pharmacology* **5**, 193–204.
52. Rall, T. W., and Sattin, A. (1970) *Adv. Biochem. Psychopharmacol.* **3**, 113–133.
53. Shimizu, H., Creveling, C. R., and Daly, J. W. (1970) *Adv. Biochem. Psychopharmacol.* **3**, 135–154.
54. Huang, M., and Daly, J. W. (1974) *Life Sci.* **14**, 489–502.
55. Huang, M., Shimizu, H., and Daly, J. W. (1972) *J. Med. Chem.* **15**, 462–466.
56. Mah, H. D., and Daly, J. W. (1976) *Pharmacol. Res. Commun.* **8**, 65–79.
57. Sturgill, T. W., Schrier, M. B. K., and Gilman, A. G. (1976) *J. Cyclic Nucleotide Res.* **1**, 21–30.
58. Haslam, R. J., and Lynham, J. A. (1972) *Life Sci.* **11**, Part II, 1143–1151.
59. Blume, A. J., and Foster, C. J. (1976) *J. Neurochem.* **26**, 305–312.
60. Blume, A. J., and Foster, C. J. (1976) *J. Biol. Chem.* **251**, 3399–3404.
61. Schultz, J., and Daly, J. W. (1973) *J. Neurochem.* **21**, 1319–1326.
62. McKenzie, S. G., and Bär, H. P. (1973) *Canad. J. Physiol. Pharmacol.* **51**, 190–196.
63. Huang, M., Shimizu, H., and Daly, J. W. (1971) *Mol. Pharmacol.* **7**, 155–162.
64. Sattin, A., Rall, T. W., and Zanella, J. (1975) *J. Pharmacol. Exp. Ther.* **192**, 22–32.
65. Shimizu, H., Ichishita, H., and Odagiri, H. (1974) *J. Biol. Chem.* **249**, 5944–5962.
66. Shonk, R. F., and Rall, T. W. (1978) *J. Neuro Chem.* (submitted for publication).

Electrophysiological Assessment of Mononucleotides and Nucleosides as First and Second Messengers in the Nervous System

G. R. SIGGINS
Arthur V. Davis Center for Behavioral Neurobiology
The Salk Institute
La Jolla, California

INTRODUCTION

Much has been written about the probable role of cyclic mononucleotides as Second Messengers in neuronal systems (1–3). This chapter will deal primarily with the electrophysiological evidence for such a role, while outlining other criteria that have been found useful for rigorously establishing an endogenous chemical as a Second Messenger. Criteria for characterizing endogenous substances as First Messengers (i.e., synaptic transmitters or "neuromodulators") are also presented for the sake of evaluating the evidence for purine nucleotides and nucleosides as First Messengers. Finally, mention is made of the possibility that uridine mononucleotides might also function as First or Second Messengers in certain neuronal systems.

FIRST MESSENGER CRITERIA

The molecular analysis of function in the nervous system labors against a frustratingly complex system of heterogeneous, intercon-

ISBN 0-12-398450-5

nected neurons and associated neuroglia. Therefore, the analysis of how nucleotides might participate in synaptic transmission must be undertaken along tactical lines in which the criteria for the identification of a synaptic transmitter intersect with the criteria for the mediation of that transmitter by a cyclic nucleotide.

The most important criteria for identification of a neurotransmitter as a First Messenger may be paraphrased and condensed from the several criteria previously suggested (4) for establishing a neurotransmitter:

1. Neuronal localization of the substance and its enzymes of synthesis and degradation.
2. Release of the substance upon selective activation of a specific neuronal pathway.
3. Identical physiological response to exogenously applied transmitter and to activation of the pathway.
4. Identical action of pharmacological agents (antagonists, etc.) on responses to pathway activation and to exogenous transmitter.

With regard to Second Messenger mediation by cyclic nucleotides, the central catecholamine-containing pathways merit consideration because they satisfy three practical requirements: (1) catecholamines meet most or all of the criteria above for a First Messenger as well as for a synaptic transmitter (5); (2) catecholamines are known to influence adenylate cyclase or cyclic AMP levels in various discrete regions of the nervous system by definable receptors (1,2); and (3) the source neurons and target neurons of the central catecholamine pathways have been sufficiently characterized so that their effects can be determined and related to the effects of cyclic nucleotides and related substances.

SECOND MESSENGER CRITERIA

The Second Messenger concept as currently applied to brain was originally derived from the mediator role of cyclic AMP in peripheral hormonal responses, as first suggested by the Sutherland group (6). As modified for neurons, this concept may be briefly summarized (Fig. 1) as follows. Synaptically released norepinephrine or dopamine would act at certain receptors to activate the synthesis of cyclic AMP within

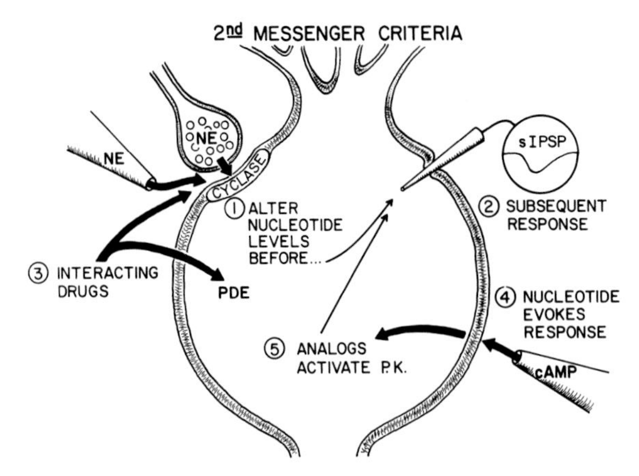

Fig. 1. Schematization of criteria for Second Messenger mediation, using cyclic AMP as an example of a Second Messenger mediating norepinephrine first messages postsynaptically.

the postsynaptic target neurons. Intracellular cAMP would then initiate subsequent enzymatic or molecular events, which, among other actions, would result in changes in membrane potential and cell discharge rate. How might we proceed with assurance that this sequence of synaptic transmission is mediated by an intracellular cyclic nucleotide Second Messenger? This question might be approached by stating the four major criteria, paraphrased from Sutherland's (6) criteria for hormones, to establish that the action of a transmitter was mediated by cyclic AMP (7).

1. Exogenous neurotransmitter substance and activation of the synaptic pathway both regulate intracellular levels of cyclic nucleotide in the postsynaptic cell population.
2. The change in intracellular cyclic nucleotide content should precede "the biological event" triggered by the transmitter or nerve pathway.
3. The effect of the transmitter or nerve pathway in eliciting the physiological event should be altered by drugs that specifically prevent the hormonal response on the nucleotide cyclase or that can inhibit the appropriate phosphodiesterase.
4. Exogenous cyclic nucleotides should elicit the biological event caused by the transmitter or nerve pathway.

These criteria are schematized in Fig. 1.

CENTRAL NOREPINEPHRINE AS A FIRST MESSENGER FOR CYCLIC AMP SECOND MESSAGES

As ably reviewed by Bloom (2) and Daly (1), considerable data exist for norepinephrine (NE) as a neurotransmitter in several brain regions, including but not limited to the cerebellum, hippocampus, and cerebral cortex. However, rigorously satisfying the Second Messenger criteria for central neurons meets with considerable technical obstacles (7), such as the indirect actions of systemic drugs, blood–brain barriers to systemic agents, difficulties in detecting cyclic AMP in single specific neurons *in situ*, slow nucleotide sampling and measurement times compared to fast synaptic events, and relative impermeability of cyclic nucleotides into target cells. Several of these obstacles can be partially overcome in the central nervous system by the techniques of microiontophoresis and electrophysiology, as they have been applied to several brain areas.

CEREBELLUM

To date the cerebellar Purkinje cell is the best candidate for a target neuron that receives a noradrenergic input from the nucleus locus coeruleus which is capable of generating cyclic AMP postsynaptically. The data reinforcing this notion have been reviewed in detail elsewhere (1–3), but may be summarized briefly as follows. (1) Catecholamines elevate cyclic AMP levels and increase adenylate cyclase activity in cerebellum *in vitro,* and exogenous NE and stimulation of the locus coeruleus (LC) increase cyclic AMP–histochemical immunoreactivity in Purkinje cells *in vivo.* (2) The increase in cyclic AMP immunoreactivity is detectable at least at the time when the electrophysiological effects of LC stimulation are apparent. (3) The inhibitory effects on Purkinje cells of LC stimulation or of iontophoresis of NE are potentiated by several phosphodiesterase inhibitors and antagonized by agents (e.g., PGE_1 and E_2, MJ-1999, fluphenazine) known to block NE-elevated cyclic AMP levels *in vitro.* (4) Effects of iontophoresis of cyclic AMP and several more potent synthetic analogs generally mimic the inhibitory hyperpolarizing action of iontophoretic NE and LC stimulation, as well as evoke the novel increases in membrane resistance usually seen with such noradrenergic stimuli.

Thus, the criteria listed above for Second Messenger mediation appear to be largely satisfied for the inhibitory NE input to Purkinje cells, except for the technical inability to detect postsynaptic increases in cyclic AMP at a time prior to the "biological event" triggered by exogenous or endogenous NE.

Although some disagreement exists as to the exact percentage of Purkinje cells inhibited by iontophoretic cyclic AMP (8,9), the inability to affect a large population of cells by the nucleotide can be explained by poor cell penetrability and other technical considerations (10–12). Moreover, iontophoresis of derivatives of cyclic AMP (e.g., 8-p-chlorophenyl-cyclic AMP) known to have a greater action on the protein kinase enzyme (the intracellular "receptor" for cyclic AMP) can depress the activity of up to 90% of Purkinje cells (11). In addition, the direct correlation between percentage of Purkinje cells depressed and the potency of several derivatives in activating protein kinase (11) argues for an involvement of cyclic-AMP-dependent protein kinase in the depressant responses.

HIPPOCAMPUS

Similar evidence exists for cyclic AMP mediation of the inhibitory norepinephrine input to hippocampal pyramidal cells (1–3,13). Here again, exogenous catecholamine elevates hippocampal cyclic AMP *in vitro*, the inhibitory effects of LC activation or NE iontophoresis are affected in a predictable way by drugs which interact with the cyclic AMP system, and iontophoresis of cyclic AMP (intracellularly as well as extracellularly) generally mimics the inhibitory action of LC stimulation and iontophoretic NE.

However, immunohistochemical methods for discrete *in vivo* localization of cyclic AMP to the pyramidal cells have not yet been applied to the hippocampus, nor has it been possible to detect cyclic AMP in hippocampus prior to the NE-induced biological event.

CEREBRAL CORTEX

Norepinephrine elevates cortical cyclic AMP levels *in vitro* (1). While it is known that the locus coeruleus sends NE-containing fibers to the cerebral cortex, the precise cellular targets for these fibers have not yet been identified electrophysiologically. Therefore, although a good correlation is now seen between those cortical pyramidal cells inhibited by iontophoretic NE and cyclic AMP (14,15), and these responses are potentiated by phosphodiesterase inhibitors (15), it is not proved that the same cells receiving an NE input from the LC are those responding similarly to cyclic AMP and exogenous NE. Therefore, a strict satisfaction of the Second Messenger criteria is not yet fulfilled at the cellular level.

DOPAMINE AS A FIRST MESSENGER FOR CYCLIC AMP

Although there are many similarities between the NE- and dopamine-regulated cyclic AMP systems *in vitro*, there are some important differences, including the involvement of different receptors (β-adrenergic versus dopamine receptors), and the greater sensitivity of the NE systems to homogenization (cf.1).

SYMPATHETIC GANGLIA

To date, the best neuronal model system for DA-activated cyclic nucleotides is the mammalian sympathetic ganglion, where input–output relationships are much simpler in comparison to brain. Fulfillment of Second Messenger criteria for DA–cyclic AMP relationships in the sympathetic ganglion, reviewed in depth by Greengard (16), is summarized briefly as follows. (1) Exogenous dopamine and stimulation of the preganglionic sympathetic trunk elevates cyclic AMP levels in ganglia in biochemical studies and increases the cyclic AMP immunoreactivity of principal sympathetic neurons in histochemical studies (17). (2) Increases in ganglionic cyclic AMP are detectable at least by the time the physiological response (slow IPSP) to preganglionic nerve stimulation is recorded. (3) Hyperpolarization to preganglionic stimulation (slow IPSP) or to exogenous DA is augmented by phosphodiesterase inhibitors and antagonized by agents (PGE_1, dopamine receptor blockers) which are known to antagonize DA-induced elevations in cyclic AMP. (4) Exogenous cyclic AMP evokes a weak hyperpolarization similar in time course to the slow IPSP (18).

Thus, considerable evidence exists for cyclic AMP mediation of the slow IPSP in mammalian ganglia, although the situation in amphibian sympathetic ganglia is much less certain because of difficulties in linking the slow IPSP either to DA (19) or to cyclic AMP (20).

CAUDATE NUCLEUS

Strict proof of cyclic nucleotide mediation of the profuse DA input to this structure (21) suffers from the present inability to selectively activate the nigrostriatal dopamine pathway (22). Thus, although exogenous DA (and apomorphine) elevates cyclic AMP levels in striatal homogenates (1,2), the effects of synaptically released DA are unknown. Likewise, immunohistochemical methods have not yet been applied to this structure. Electrophysiological proof of cyclic AMP mediation of DA effects here rests largely on iontophoresis and pharmacological experiments in rat showing: (1) blockade of the inhibitory effects of dopamine (but see Kitai *et al.*, 23) by phenothiazines, which block DA-induced cyclic AMP increases; (2) potentiation (24) of DA inhibitory responses by several phosphodiesterase inhibitors and PGE_1 (which elevates striatal cyclic AMP *in vitro*); and (3) the close mimicry between inhibitory responses to iontophoretic DA, apomorphine, cyclic AMP, and monobutyryl cyclic AMP (21,24). The fact that LSD elevates striatal cyclic AMP (e.g., 25–27) and also inhibits caudate neurons when applied by iontophoresis (G. R. Siggins and B. Jacobs, unpublished) also suggests cyclic AMP mediation in caudate.

Dopamine-containing fibers also project from ventral tegmental areas to certain cortical regions (28), where exogenous DA also inhibits neuronal activity (29) and elevates cyclic AMP levels (30). However, since electrophysiological analyses of the actions of iontophoretic cyclic AMP and of DA pathway stimulation in these areas are not yet forthcoming, criteria for cyclic AMP mediation here remain largely unfulfilled.

CYCLIC GMP AS A SECOND MESSENGER IN THE CNS

The putative role of cyclic GMP in central synaptic transmission is much more covert than that of cyclic AMP. This situation arises in part because of the insensitivity of guanylate cyclase to neurotransmitters in homogenates, and because of the great number of neurotransmitters which increase cyclic GMP levels in brain slice preparations (1,2). Moreover, early iontophoresis studies with cyclic GMP in rat cerebellum showed no differences between Purkinje cell responses to cyclic AMP and cyclic GMP and no clear-cut correlation with acetylcholine (ACh) effects (31). However, this finding was not surprising in view of the lack of evidence for cholinergic inputs to Purkinje cells.

A more encouraging relationship between ACh and cGMP has been reported for pyramidal cells of rat cerebral cortex, where there is better evidence for a cholinergic projection. In brief, Stone *et al.* (14,15) reported that those neurons responding to iontophoretic ACh with excitation generally respond equivalently to cyclic GMP. Further evidence for cGMP mediation of ACh effects is suggested by the fact that phosphodiesterase inhibitors potentiate excitations to both agents. However, rigorous proof of cGMP as a Second Messenger for cholinergic neurotransmission awaits fulfillment of the other Second Messenger criteria, such as localization and stimulation of the ACh pathway and immunohistochemical detection of increases in cyclic GMP in pyramidal cells after cholinergic stimulation and prior to the biological event.

A similar impasse exists for hippocampal pyramidal cells where a cholinergic input projects from the septal nucleus. Thus, in hippocampus *in situ* (32) and in intraocular transplants (see Hoffer *et al.*, this volume) both ACh and cyclic GMP are strongly excitatory, and may even cause paroxysmal discharges or frank seizures. Again, no biochemical or immunocytochemical studies have been done to detect or localize cGMP changes in the hippocampus with cholinergic stimulation, although some pharmacological data does exist for a link between ACh and cGMP excitations in hippocampus *in oculo* (33).

The fact that no specific agonists or antagonists of guanylate cyclase have been found may be significant in itself. It is possible that cGMP may increase as a result of, or be a mediator of, nonspecific membrane depolarization. This hypothesis is supported by studies showing dramatic increases in cGMP in cortical areas exhibiting penicillin-induced epileptiform seizures (N. Goldberg, personal communication). Although the increases in cerebellar cyclic GMP with harmaline treatment (34) are interpreted to implicate cGMP mediation of glutamate-transmitted climbing fiber responses, it also seems reasonable that cyclic GMP might increase as a result of nonspecific depolarization of Purkinje cells by any means. The answer to this dilemma hinges on whether the second criterion for cyclic nucleotide mediation, namely detection of cyclic GMP before depolarization, can be satisfied. Clearly, much more work is needed before conclusions can be drawn about cGMP mediation of synaptic transmission.

CENTRAL PURINES AS FIRST MESSENGERS FOR CYCLIC AMP SECOND MESSAGES

Adenine nucleotides and nucleosides have received attention as possible neurotransmitters in peripheral nervous systems (see the reviews of "purinergic" nerves by Burnstock, 35,36). The exact action of the purines is somewhat unclear, although they appear to be inhibitory in many peripheral sites (35–37). In smooth muscle of the taenia coli, the contractile inhibitions appear to be produced at low concentrations by suppression of spontaneous spikes and at higher concentrations by hyperpolarizations concomitant with an increase in membrane permeability, probably to K^+ ions (37).

In the central nervous system, the concept of purinergic neurotransmission gained support with the finding that exogenous adenosine and other adenine derivatives could evoke large increases in cyclic AMP levels in slices from several brain areas (38). Since this effect of the adenine derivatives is blocked (rather than potentiated) by methyl xanthines (38), and substitution of a chloro moiety at the 2′ position of adenosine (to prevent incorporation of adenosine directly into cyclic AMP itself) does not alter its cyclic-AMP-stimulating ability (39), it is thought that an "adenosine receptor" exists which is functionally linked to adenylate cyclase.

The concept of central adenosine (or some other purine) as a First Messenger acting at a discrete adenosine receptor has gained additional support from iontophoresis studies showing marked inhibition of neuronal activity by adenosine (similar to that produced by cyclic AMP) in the cerebellum (40,41), cerebral cortex (42), and caudate nucleus (21). In accordance with the biochemical studies, iontophoresis of 2-chloroadenosine also markedly depresses neuronal firing (21) and methylxanthines antagonize the depressant effects of iontophoretic adenosine (21).

The case for central 5′-AMP, 5′-ADP, and 5′-ATP as First Messengers for cyclic AMP is not so universal. Although iontophoresis of these nucleotides depresses cortical (42) and striatal (21) neurons in a manner sensitive to blockade by methylxanthines, the effect of the adenine mononucleotides on cerebellar Purkinje cells is still in dispute. Thus, ATP was originally reported to excite Purkinje cells and AMP was ineffective (43). Later, the Phillis group (41) reported only inhibition of discharge by these mononucleotides. In a recent reevaluation of this problem, Siggins *et al.* (20) confirmed the original finding of ATP excitatory actions. Thus, in the cerebellum the possibility exists that ATP and adenosine do not act at the same receptor.

Although the criteria for Second Messenger mediation of adenosine first messages are mostly satisfied (again except for detection of increased cyclic AMP prior to the biological effect), the case for adenosine and other purines as neurotransmitters confronts unique considerations. It is true that in peripheral systems (1) ATP and its associated enzymes are localized in nerves, as in all cells; (2) ATP can be released from tissue by activation of neuronal pathways; and (3) exogenous ATP and activation of the "purinergic" pathway have identical actions. However, strict proof of the hypothesis of purines as neurotransmitters requires the development of truly specific ATP antagonists. Furthermore, the ubiquitous distribution of ATP as an energy form in all cell types, and the possible presence of ATP (as a binding agent) in adrenergic storage granules, raise questions as to whether or not ATP release arises specifically from a discrete set of nerves containing only ATP as a neurotransmitter. The possibility exists that ATP might be released as a "cotransmitter" with some other substance such as NE or acetylcholine. The resultant biological response would then be the sum of the actions of the two substances, with modulating influences from possible synergisms, antagonisms, and differences in time course of action.

Similar considerations apply to purines as *central* neurotransmitters. ATP and its enzymes are present in the brain, and labeled purines are transported along specific nerve tracts (44) and released from brain slices with field stimulation (45) and from intact brain with specific pathway stimulation (44). However, no electrophysiological effect has yet been detected with nerve-released purines for comparison with the effect of exogenous purines. Moreover, the ubiquitous distribution of ATP in the brain complicates attempts to develop specific histochemical methods for localization of "purinergic" nerves. Although methylxanthines might be used as specific antagonists of adenosine (or possibly ATP) receptors, the lack of histochemically defined "purinergic" nerve tracts for electrophysiological activation nearly reduce this xanthine effect to a pharmacological curiosity. Thus, with the available evidence, adenosine and/or ATP might subserve a role as local neuromodulator (e.g., released on anaerobia, injury or under certain ionic conditions) or "cotransmitter" as easily as a discrete neurotransmitter.

MONONUCLEOTIDE EFFECTS IN CULTURED SYMPATHETIC GANGLIA

The question of purines as possible neurotransmitters might be more readily examined in a simpler system such as sympathetic ganglia, where advantage may also be taken of the large cell size (for intracellular recording) and ease of isolation for *in vitro* perfusion of drugs. Intracellular recording and drug superfusion is facilitated further by culturing explants of amphibian sympathetic ganglia from adult bullfrogs, since the principal neurons migrate out of the mass of cells and appear as "naked" cells apparently devoid of glial or fibroblast coverings (20,46).

Only one preliminary report (47) has utilized intracellular recording to study the effect of adenine nucleotides in neurons. However, the transmembrane neuronal effects of other purine and pyrimidine derivatives are not known. Therefore, we have recently examined the effect of such agents on intracellularly recorded sympathetic neurons from chronic explants of the adult bullfrog superior certical ganglion, visualized by Nomarski optics and impaled with glass micropipettes (8–40 $M\Omega$ impedance) filled with 3 *M* KCl or potassium acetate (20,46). Intracellular stimulation and estimation of input resistance were performed by a bridge method and current/voltage curves were constructed with a PDP-12 computer. The neurons ranged in size from 24 to 85 μm (long dimension) and displayed steady resting potentials of −35 to −58 mV with spike overshoots up to 30 mV or more.

Depolarization was the predominant response to all the nuclei acid components studied, whether applied by perfusion or iontophoresis. Occasionally a longer hyperpolarization followed the depolarizations. For a given purine or pyrimidine, the di- and triphosphonucleotides were equipotent; they were more potent than their 5′-monophosphates. In general, the nucleosides and the heterocyclic bases were ineffective at concentrations up to 1–2.5 m*M*.

Interestingly, of all nucleotides studied, 5′-uridine di- and triphosphate (UDP and UTP) were the most potent (Fig. 2) with thresholds for depolarization of 10^{-8} *M* to 5×10^{-8} *M*; 5×10^{-5} *M* produced depolarizations of 4 to 19 mV (mean = 10 mV). Thresholds for 5′-ATP and 5′-ADP were 10^{-6} to 10^{-7} *M*; 5×10^{-5} *M* depolarized an average of 5 and 6 mV, respectively. The di- and triphosphates of thymidine, guanosine, and inosine were roughly equipotent with ATP. UTP and UDP were also most potent when applied by iontophoresis, producing depolarizations up to 16 mV; ATP and ADP depolarized up to 10 mV with similar currents. Adenosine was ineffective. Of all the nucleotides tested only 5′-CTP and CDP were ineffective or weakly active at 5×10^{-5} *M*. Pyrophosphate, 2′-deoxy-ATP, uridine diphosphoglucose, and D-ribose-5′-phosphate were largely ineffective at concentrations (5×10^{-5} *M* to 10^{-4} *M*) maximally effective for the other mononucleotides.

Both the depolarizations and the occasional ensuing hyperpolarizations were generally accompanied by an increase or no change in input resistance, as measured by responses to hyperpolarizing intracellular stimulation (see Fig. 2) or by current/voltage curves. In addi-

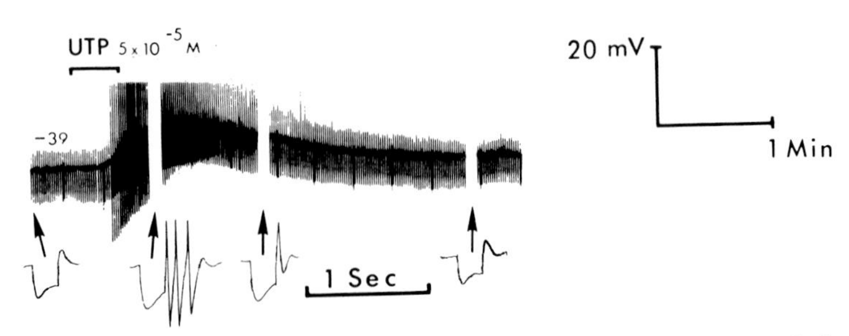

Fig. 2. Intracellular records of effects of UTP on membrane properties of a bullfrog sympathetic neuron in organ culture. Record shows membrane potential (heavy baseline) and response to hyperpolarizing constant current pulses of 0.05-nA, 200-msec duration delivered through a wheatstone bridge once every second (light deflections below and above the baseline potential). Underneath the record are four examples of individual responses to current at higher polygraph speed. Note that light lines above baseline consist of depolarizing responses to termination of current pulses (anodal break), which can trigger action potentials (spikes) at high currents or during increased membrane excitability. Heavy line descending below baseline at 20-sec intervals measures electrode resistance (1 MΩ/1 mV). Brackets above record indicate duration of drug administration. Note that UTP (5×10^{-5} *M*) produces depolarization with intense spiking. High-speed excerpts of responses to hyperpolarizing pulses taken from this record at times indicated by arrows and breaks in the record show multiple anodal-break spikes and a clear increase in neuronal input resistance during depolarization. Bar below record indicates time for high-speed records only.

tion, spiking increased during the initial phases of depolarization, although occasionally it decreased during the late phase. The nucleotides act like muscarine, which also depolarizes cultured sympathetic neurons with increased resistance and spiking.

It is unlikely that the nucleotides act by releasing endogenous acetylcholine (ACh), since atropine (3×10^{-6} to 1.3×10^{-5} *M*) had no effect on responses to the uridine and adenine nucleotides. Nicotine ($2.5–5 \times 10^{-5}$ *M*), *d*-tubocurare (1 m*M*), or high Mg^{2+} (10–20 m*M*) low Ca^{2+} levels (0.5 to 1 m*M*) have little effect on the nucleotide responses. That local application of UTP, UDP, ATP, and ADP by iontophoresis produces marked depolarization argues for a direct effect of the nucleotides. Furthermore, physostigmine (5×10^{-5} *M*, hexamethonium (0.5–2.5 m*M*), phentolamine (10^{-4} *M*), and MJ-1999 ($1–5 \times 10^{-4}$ *M*) do not alter responses to the nucleotides. Only quinidine (5×10^{-4} *M*) blocked UTP or ATP responses, although unselectively, since the effects of muscarine were also blocked (cf. 35,36). The nucleotide "receptor" is not equivalent to the adenosine receptor of brain (38) since methylxanthines (2.5 m*M*) do not block but often potentiate responses to mononucleotides. However, responses to exogenous cyclic AMP and cyclic GMP were weak and inconsistent. The nucleotide effect is not likely to result from Ca^{2+} chelation since such low concentrations (10^{-7} to 10^{-8} *M*) of the nucleotides are effective and since removal of Ca^{2+} from the Ringer's solution has little effect on the nucleotide responses.

The potent action of the nucleotides might indicate their role as neurotransmitters in "purinergic" nerves (35,36) or as "cotransmitters" released with ACh or norepinephrine from autonomic nerves. The generalized effectiveness of the purine and pyrimidine nucleotides, with uridine nucleotides being the most potent, suggests that the "purinergic" label is too restrictive. The postjunctional release of ATP by cholinergic stimulation in the electroplaque (48) also raises the possibility that postsynaptic release of a nucleotide could mediate the response to a neurotransmitter. The question still remains whether uridine nucleotides might be released from cells to play some role in neurotransmission, whether as a First or Second Messenger (see Fig. 3).

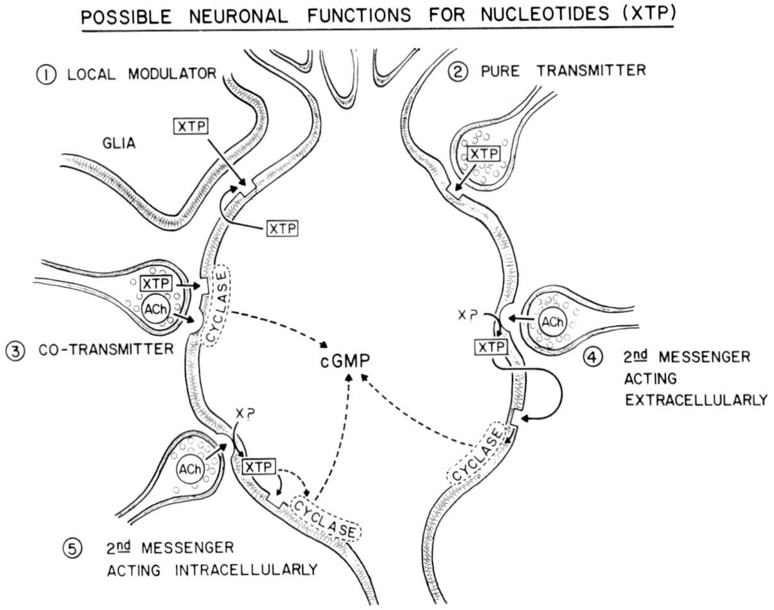

Fig. 3. Schematic of several hypothetical roles for noncyclic purine or pyrimidine nucleotides (XTP) in neurons, whether as First or Second Messengers. X might be any heterocyclic base. Dotted lines represent speculative roles for cyclic GMP (or cAMP) as a Second or Third Messenger for the nucleotide effects.

As a preliminary step in answering this question for the brain, UDP and UTP were applied iontophoretically to central neurons in rats under halothane (20). The spontaneous firing of 85–100% of cerebellar Purkinje cells and hippocampal pyramidal cells were increased by UDP and UTP. ATP also excited Purkinje cells, as previously reported (43). This action contrasts with the inhibitory effects of adenosine in Purkinje cells (40) and caudate neurons (21) and with depressions by a variety of adenine derivatives reported for cerebellum (41) and cerebral cortex (42,47). These findings reinforce the likelihood that ATP and adenosine receptors may not be identical for all neurons.

CONCLUSIONS AND SPECULATIONS

Results of electrophysiological tests, taken with biochemical and cytochemical data, satisfy most First Messenger or neurotransmitter criteria for norepinephrine and dopamine in brain. Studies summarized in this review also suggest that these two catecholamines may also serve as First Messengers for postsynaptic generation of a cyclic nucleotide Second Messenger, especially in the cerebellum, hippocampus, and mammalian sympathetic ganglia.

However, strict proof of a Second Messenger mediation in all catecholaminergic systems still awaits satisfaction of the criterion that increases in cyclic AMP occur prior to the physiological response. Future biochemical and immunohistochemical studies should be directed toward detecting cyclic AMP within the msec or tens-of-msec domain likely to represent the synaptic delay in central catecholaminergic neurotransmission (49).

To date, fulfillment of Second Messenger criteria for cyclic GMP has been difficult, principally owing to the paucity of pharmacological agents which interact with guanylate cyclase and the inability to localize and activate the central pathway(s) for endogenous release of the relevant First Messenger(s). Excluding these problems, the best candidates for cyclic GMP mediation in the CNS are the cholinergic excitations in identified hippocampal pyramidal cells and cerebral cortical pyramidal cells.

The concept of adenosine, and perhaps adenine nucleotides as well, as First Messengers for cyclic AMP second messages also seems likely, although the question of whether the purines function as distinct neurotransmitters or as local modulators remains to be explored. Since "adenosinergic" pathways have not been selectively localized and/or stimulated in brain, fulfillment of Second Messenger criteria for adenosine is incomplete.

Finally, several hypothetical issues, as schematized in Fig. 3, need future scrutiny. One such issue is the question of whether only cyclic nucleotides may be utilized as Second Messengers, since all mononucleotides possess the high energy levels presumably needed for catalytic reactions. A second issue is whether two or more sequential messages (for example, a primary neurotransmitter releasing a mononucleotide either pre- or postsynaptically) may precede the postsynaptic generation of a cyclic nucleotide. Another issue begging exploration is whether uridine nucleotides (or those of some other base) might function either as First or Second Messengers. In this regard it is interesting that uridine nucleotides free in brain attain levels of as much as one-third that of ATP (50).

In the final analysis, the concept of First and Second Messengers may be an oversimplification in neuronal systems, since the actual molecular consequences of neurotransmission might be represented as multileveled cascade of many sequential messages, including protein kinase activation and protein phosphorylation and/or dephosphorylation. Such a cascade in the nervous system would allow for an enormous amplification of the original first signal, such that a few neurotransmitter molecules could effect the opening or closing of a multitude of ionic gates, or the activation of many ionic carriers or pumps. The advantages of such an amplification could include reducing the need for axonal transport of many transmitter molecules (or their enzymes of synthesis) and the development of a high safety factor at the synaptic cleft. Obviously a great deal of research remains to delineate the functional significance of such a complexity of linkages.

REFERENCES

1. Daly, J. (1977) "Cyclic Nucleotides in the Nervous System." Plenum, New York.
2. Bloom, F. E. (1975) *Ergeb. Physiol., Biol. Chem. Exp. Pharmakol.* **74**, 1–103.
3. Siggins, G. R. (1977) *In* "Cyclic Nucleotides: Mechanisms of Action" (H. Cramer and J. Schultz, eds.), pp. 317–336. Wiley, New York.
4. Werman, R. (1966) *Comp. Biochem. Physiol.* **18**, 745–766.
5. Bloom, F. E. (1978) *In* "Psychopharmacology—A 20 Year Progress Report" (M. A. Lipton, A. DiMascio, and K. F. Killam, eds.), pp. 131–141. Raven New York.
6. Sutherland, E. W., Oye, I., and Butcher, R. W. (1965) *Recent Prog. Horm. Res.* **21**, 623–642.
7. Bloom, F. E. (1976) *Adv. Biochem. Pharmacol.* **15**, 272–282.

8. Godfraind, J. M., and Pumain, R. (1971) *Science* **174**, 1257.
9. Lake, N., and Jordan, L. M. (1974) *Science* **183**, 663–664.
10. Bloom, F. E., Siggins, G. R., and Hoffer, B. J. (1974) *Science* **185**, 627–629.
11. Siggins, G. R., and Henriksen, S. J. (1975) *Science* **189**, 559–561.
12. Shoemaker, W. J., Balentine, L. T., Siggins, G. R., Hoffer, B. J., Henriksen, S. J., and Bloom, F. E. (1975) *J. Cyclic Nucleotide Res.* **1**, 97–106.
13. Segal, M., and Bloom, F. E. (1974) *Brain Res.* **72**, 99–114.
14. Stone, T. W., Taylor, D. A., and Bloom, F. E. (1975) *Science* **187**, 845–847.
15. Stone, T. W., and Taylor, D. A. (1977) *J. Physiol. (London)* **266**, 523–543.
16. Greengard, P., and Kebabian, J. W. (1974) *Fed. Proc., Fed. Am. Soc. Exp. Biol.* **33**, 1059–1068.
17. Kebabian, J. W., Bloom, F. E., Steiner, A. L., and Greengard, P. (1975) *Science* **190**, 157–159.
18. McAfee, D. A., and Greengard, P. (1972) *Science* **178**, 310–312.
19. Weight, F. F., and Padjen, A. (1973) *Brain Res.* **55**, 255–228.
20. Siggins, G. R., Gruol, D., Padjen, A., and Forman, D. (1978) *In* "Iontophoresis and Transmitter Mechanisms in the Mammalian Central Nervous System" (R. Ryall and J. Kelley, eds.), pp. 435–455. Elsevier, Amsterdam.
21. Siggins, G. R., Hoffer, B. J., Bloom, F. E., and Ungerstedt, U. (1976) *In* "The Basal Ganglia" (M. D. Yahr, ed.), pp. 227–248. Raven, New York.
22. Siggins, G. R. (1978) *In* "Psychopharmacology—A 20 Year Progress Report" (M. A. Lipton, A. DiMascio, and K. F. Killam, eds.), pp. 143–157. Raven, New York.
23. Kitai, S. T., Sugimori, M., and Kocsis, J. D. (1976) *Exp. Brain Res.* **24**, 351–363.
24. Siggins, G. R., Hoffer, B. H., and Ungerstedt, U. (1974) *Life Sci.* **16**, 779–792.
25. Pieri, L., Pieri, M., and Haefely, W. (1974) *Nature (London)* **252**, 586–588.
26. von Hungen, K., Roberts, S., and Hill, D. F. (1974) *Nature (London)* **252**, 588–589.
27. Bockaert, J., Premont, J., Glowinski, J., Thierry, A. M., and Tassin, J. P. (1976) *Brain Res.* **107**, 303–315.
28. Fuxe, K., Hökfelt, T., Agnati, L. F., Johansson, O., Goldstein, M., Perez de la Mora, M., Possani, L., Tapia, R., Teran, L., and Palacios, R. (1978) *In* "Psychopharmacology—A 20 Year Progress Report" (M. A. Lipton, A. DiMascio, and K. F. Killam, eds.), pp. 67–94. Raven, New York.
29. Bunney, B. L., and G. K. Aghajanian (1978) *In* "Psychopharmacology—A 20 Year Progress Report" (M. A. Lipton, A. DiMascio, and K. F. Killam, eds.), pp. 159–169. Raven, New York.
30. von Hungen, H., and Roberts, S. (1973) *Eur. J. Biochem.* **36**, 391–401.
31. Hoffer, B. J., Siggins, G. R., Oliver, A. P., and Bloom, F. E. (1971) *Ann. N.Y. Acad. Sci.* **185**, 531–549.
32, Biscoe, T. J., and Straughn, D. W. (1966) *J. Physiol. (London)* **183**, 341–359.
33. Hoffer, B., Seiger, A., Freedman, R., Olson, L., and Taylor, D. (1977) *Brain Res.* **119**, 107–132.
34. Mao, C. C., Guidotti, A., and Costa, E. (1974) *Brain Res.* **83**, 526–529.
35. Burnstock, G. (1972) *Pharmacol. Rev.* **24**, 509–581.
36. Burnstock, G. (1975) *Handb. Psychopharmacol.* **5**, 131–194.
37. Tomita, T., and Watanabe, J. (1973) *J. Physiol. (London)* **231**, 167–177.
38. Sattin, A. and Rall, T. W. (1970) *Mol. Pharmacol.* **6**, 13–23.
39. Sturgill, T. W., Schrier, B. K., and Gilman, A. G. (1975) *J. Cyclic Nucleotide Res.* **1**, 21–30.
40. Bloom, F. E., Siggins, G. R., Hoffer, B. J., Segal, M., and Oliver, A. P. (1975) *Adv. Cyclic Nucleotide Res.* **5**, 603–618.
41. Kostopoulos, G. K., Limacher, J. J., and Phillis, J. W. (1975) *Brain Res.* **88**, 162–165.

42. Phillis, J. W., Kostopoulos, G. K., and Limacher, J. J. (1974) *Can. J. Physiol. Pharmacol.* **52**, 1227–1229.
43. Siggins, G. R., Hoffer, B. J., and Bloom, F. E. (1971) *Brain Res.* **25**, 535–553.
44. Schubert, P., Lee, K., West, M., Deadwyler, S., and Lynch, G. (1976) *Nature (London)* **260**, 541–542.
45. Pull, I., and McIlwain, H. (1972) *Biochem. J.* **130**, 975–981.
46. Siggins, G. R., Gruol, D., Padjen, A., and Forman, D. (1977) *Nature (London)* **270**, 263–265.
47. Phillis, J. W., and Edstrom, J. P. (1976) *Life Sci.* **19**, 1041–1054.
48. Israel, M., Lesbats, B., Mennier, F. M., and Stinnakre, J. (1976) *Proc. R. Soc. London, Ser. B* **193**, 461–468.
49. Siggins, G. R., Hoffer, B. J., Oliver, A. P., and Bloom, F. E. (1971) *Nature (London)* **233**, 481–483.
50. Tarr, M., Brada, D., and Sampson, F. E. (1962) *Am. J. Physiol.* **203**, 690.

PART VI

NEURONAL STRUCTURE AND DEVELOPMENT

Development of Peripheral Monoaminergic Neurons

MICHAEL D. GERSHON AND TAUBE P. ROTHMAN
Department of Anatomy
College of Physicians and Surgeons
Columbia University
New York, New York

HOWARD HOLTZER
Department of Anatomy
University of Pennsylvania School of Medicine
Philadelphia, Pennsylvania

INTRODUCTION

Events in the development of the autonomic innervation of a given peripheral organ include the differentiation of ganglion cells from precursors in the neural crest (or perhaps neural tube) (1,2), their migration to an appropriate location, and finally the extension of their axons to reach the relevant targets. While these events are occurring, the ganglion cells receive a preganglionic input and a proportion of the presumptive neurons die (3). In studying these events, it is important to have markers which permit detection of replicating presumptive neuroblasts and the definitive, postmitotic neuroblast or neuron. Most of the definitive, postmitotic, postganglionic sympathetic neurons synthesize the transmitter norepinephrine (NE), and they can be recognized by their content of large amounts of this transmitter (4) as well as by their high-affinity uptake mechanism for NE (5). Recently, we have obtained evidence for the existence of peripheral serotonergic neurons in the enteric plexuses (6). These neurons also can be recognized by their transmitter content (7) and their specific high affinity-uptake mechanism for 5-hydroxytryptamine (5-HT; 8). Formaldehyde-induced fluorescence provides a morphological means of studying the transmitter content of developing monoaminergic

ISBN 0-12-398450-5

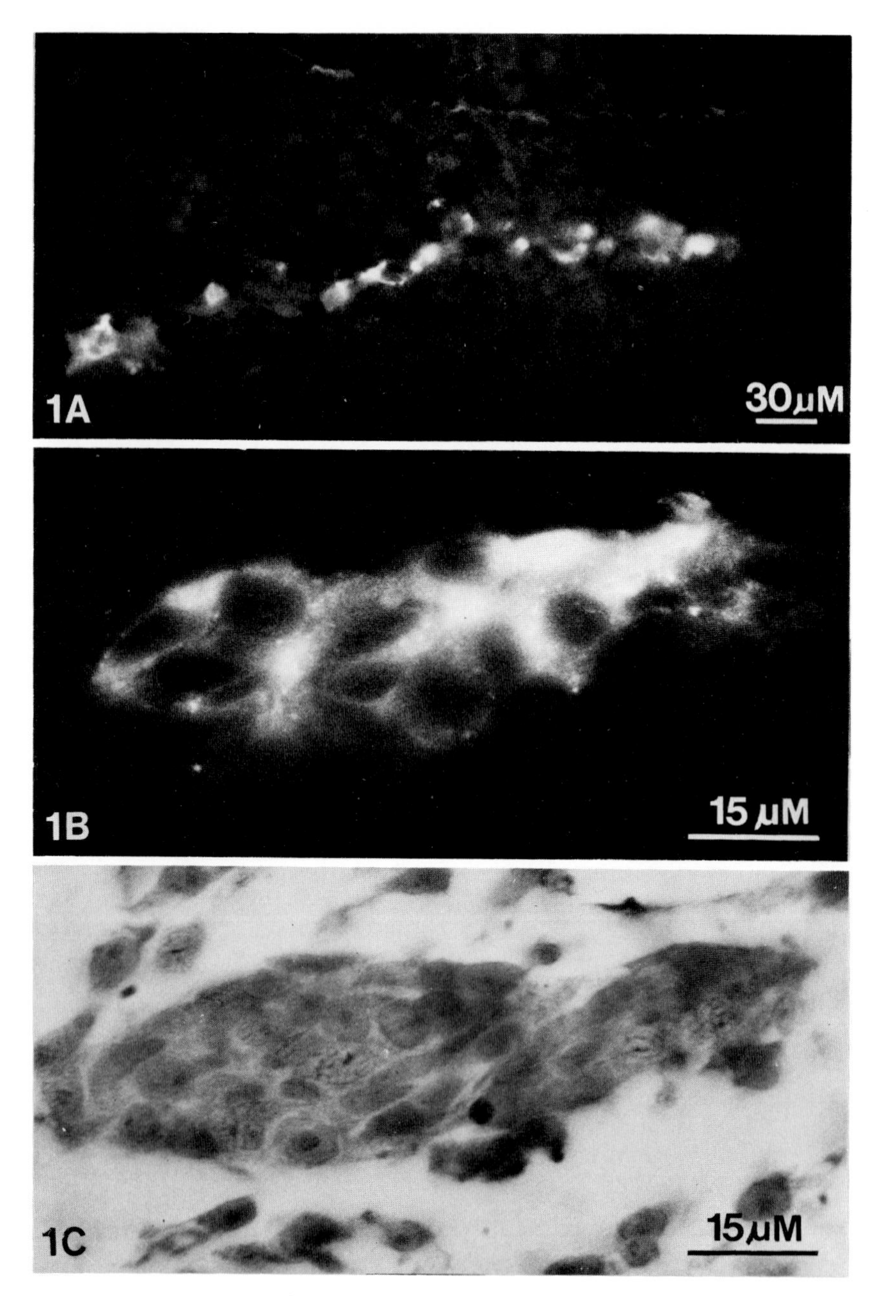

Fig. 1. Primary sympathetic ganglia from a chick embryo of 5 days incubation. (A) Longitudinal section of material prepared to show catecholamines by formaldehyde-

neurogenic cells (4). Radioautography provides a similar morphological tool for investigating monoamine uptake (9). In our studies we have asked whether some properties of the definitive, postmitotic, adrenergic neuroblasts are also present in their precursors, the replicating presumptive neuroblasts. We have also looked at a target organ, the gut, for the ingrowth of adrenergic axons in relation to the development of serotonergic neurons and in relation to the development of the mature functional characteristics of that organ. Adrenergic neurogenic cells normally migrate to a location distant from the gut in prevertebral ganglia and project axons to it (10) while serotonergic neurogenic cells provide an example of a system that migrates to locations within the gut itself (6,7,11).

DEVELOPMENT OF ADRENERGIC GANGLIA AND THE ADRENAL MEDULLA

Presumptive ganglion cells containing NE can first be detected by formaldehyde-induced fluorescence in chick embryos at 3.5 days of incubation (4). At this time the cells form the primary sympathetic ganglia and lie dorsolateral to the dorsal aorta. At first these ganglia consist of individual groups of cells but they soon connect longitudinally to form a primary sympathetic chain (Fig. 1). At 5 days of incubation the presumptive sympathetic neuroblasts migrate again, dorsally, to form the final, secondary, paravertebral ganglia, and ventrally, to form the splanchnic and aortic plexuses of prevertebral ganglia as well as the adrenal medulla. The gut receives its adrenergic innervation from these prevertebral ganglion cells. Thus, very early in their development, before they receive a preganglionic innervation, before they project their axons, and before they reach their final migratory destination, the presumptive sympathetic neuroblasts reveal themselves by expressing their transmitter.

The developing sympathetic neurogenic cells also express the high-affinity uptake mechanism for NE. We have demonstrated this uptake by radioautographic examination of embryonic tissues incubated with low concentrations (1 μM) of ^{3}H-NE and fixed in hyper-

induced fluorescence. At low power, the aggregates of fluorescent primary ganglion cells have fused to form a continuous chain. The faint outline of the notochord which displays only autofluorescence can be seen dorsal to the ganglia. (B) Transverse section of a primary ganglion at high power. Note that all of the ganglion cells are fluorescent; the fluorescence is confined to the cytoplasm. The nonfluorescent nuclei are readily distinguishable. (C) The same ganglion shown in (B), now stained with hematoxylin and eosin.

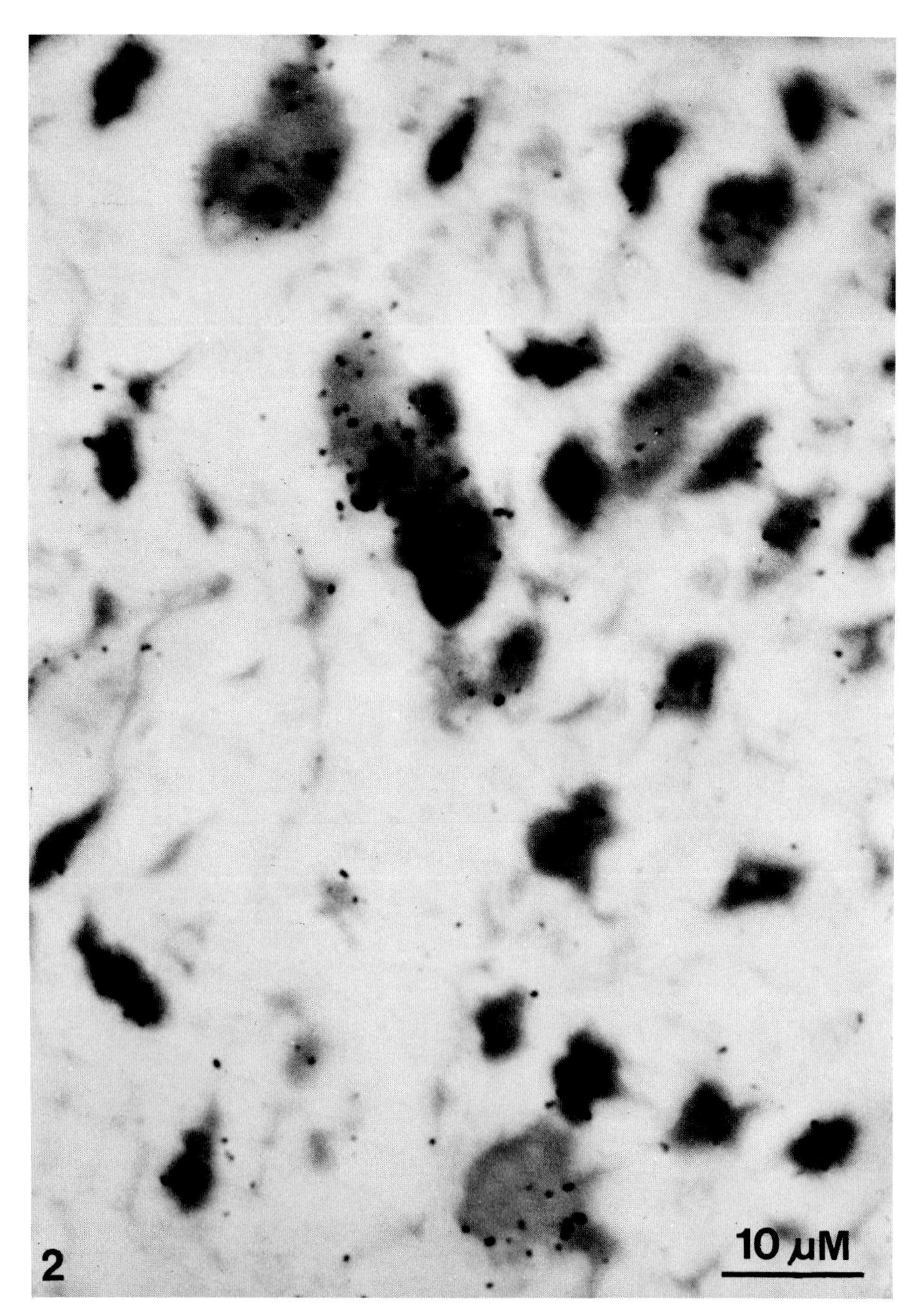
2
10 µM

tonic solutions of 2.5 % glutaraldehyde (Fig. 2). The uptake of NE is specific in these experiments because it is blocked by the inhibitor of neuronal catecholamine uptake, desmethylimipramine (10 μM). Uptake is first seen in scattered cells which have left the neural crest but have not yet aggregated to form primary ganglia. All of the neurons of the primary ganglia, when they do form, are labeled by ^{3}H-NE. However, it is important to note that there are far fewer adrenergic cells recognized either by fluorescence or radioautography at these early stages than are present at 5 days of incubation, when the primary ganglia migrate, or later in the final sympathetic ganglia (Fig. 3). Therefore, addition to the pool of definitive, postmitotic, adrenergic neurons must continue even after migration has been initiated and the neural crest has disappeared. The source of additional ganglion cells could be either (1) noncatecholamine containing precursor cells which yield postmitotic neuroblasts that then initiate the synthesis of catecholamines, or (2) the precursor neuroblasts, which, while replicating, synthesize catecholamines.

^{3}H-THYMIDINE INCORPORATION BY DEVELOPING ADRENERGIC GANGLION CELLS

Cohen (12) has presented preliminary evidence suggesting that replicating presumptive ganglion cells do synthesize, store, and incorporate catecholamines. To confirm this we adapted the technique, introduced by Okazaki and Holtzer (13), of double-labeling a single cell to study the developing adrenergic innervation. Chick embryos of 3–15 days of incubation were prepared for simultaneous demonstration of incorporation of ^{3}H-thymidine into DNA by radioautography and catecholamine content by histofluorescence. Tissues were freeze-dried and exposed for 1 hr to formaldehyde vapor generated at 80°C from paraformaldehyde previously equilibrated at 70% relative humidity. Dried tissues were embedded in Epon 812, cut at 2.0 μm, and coated for radioautography with Ilford L_4 emulsion. Epon is sufficiently impermeable to water so that the steps involved in radioautographic processing do not interfere with histofluorescence. Silver grains in the photographic emulsion were observed by transmitted-light dark-field microscopy and catecholamines were observed simultaneously by incident-light fluorescence microscopy. An orange filter

---

Fig. 2. Transverse section through the region of the primary ganglia incubated with ^{3}H-NE. Primary ganglia and scattered catecholamine-containing cells are moderately labeled.

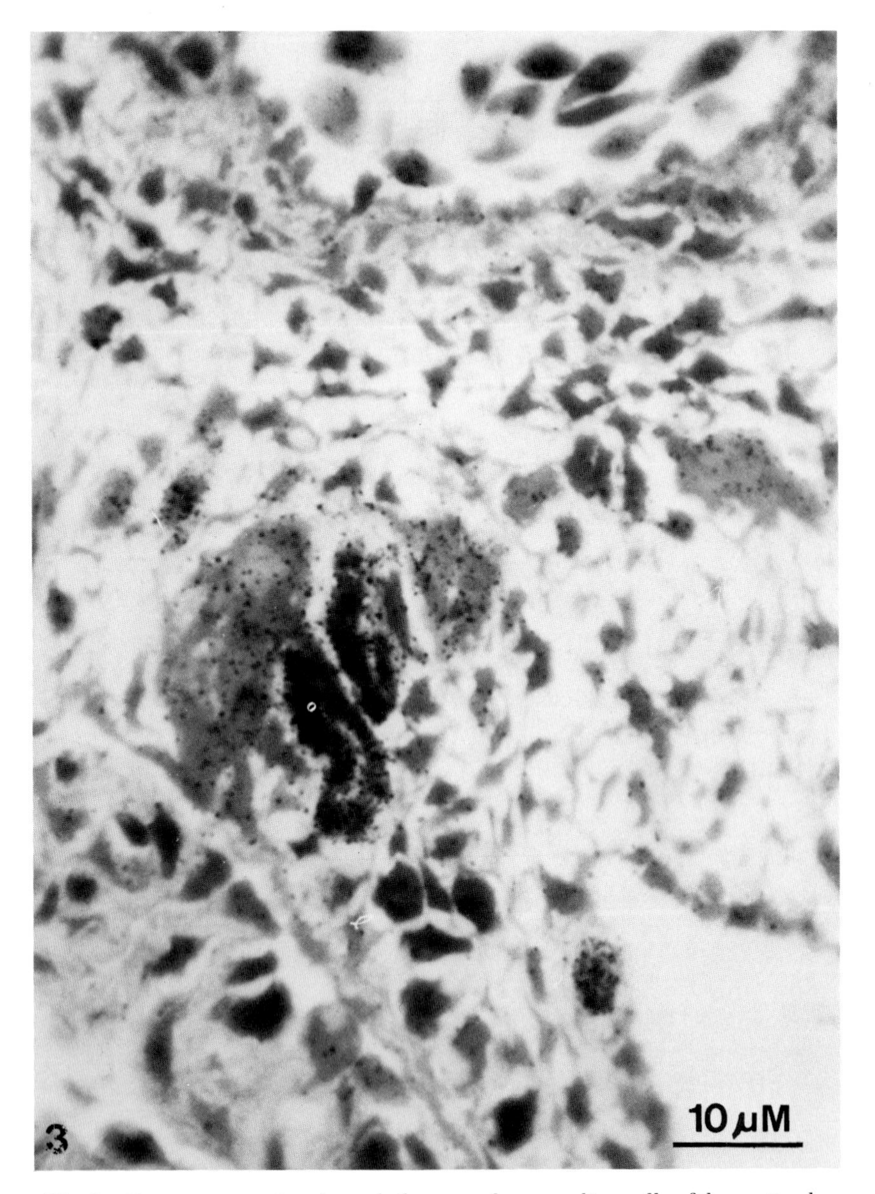

Fig. 3. Transverse section through the secondary ganglion cells of the aortic plexus of a 5-day chick embryo incubated with ^{3}H-NE.

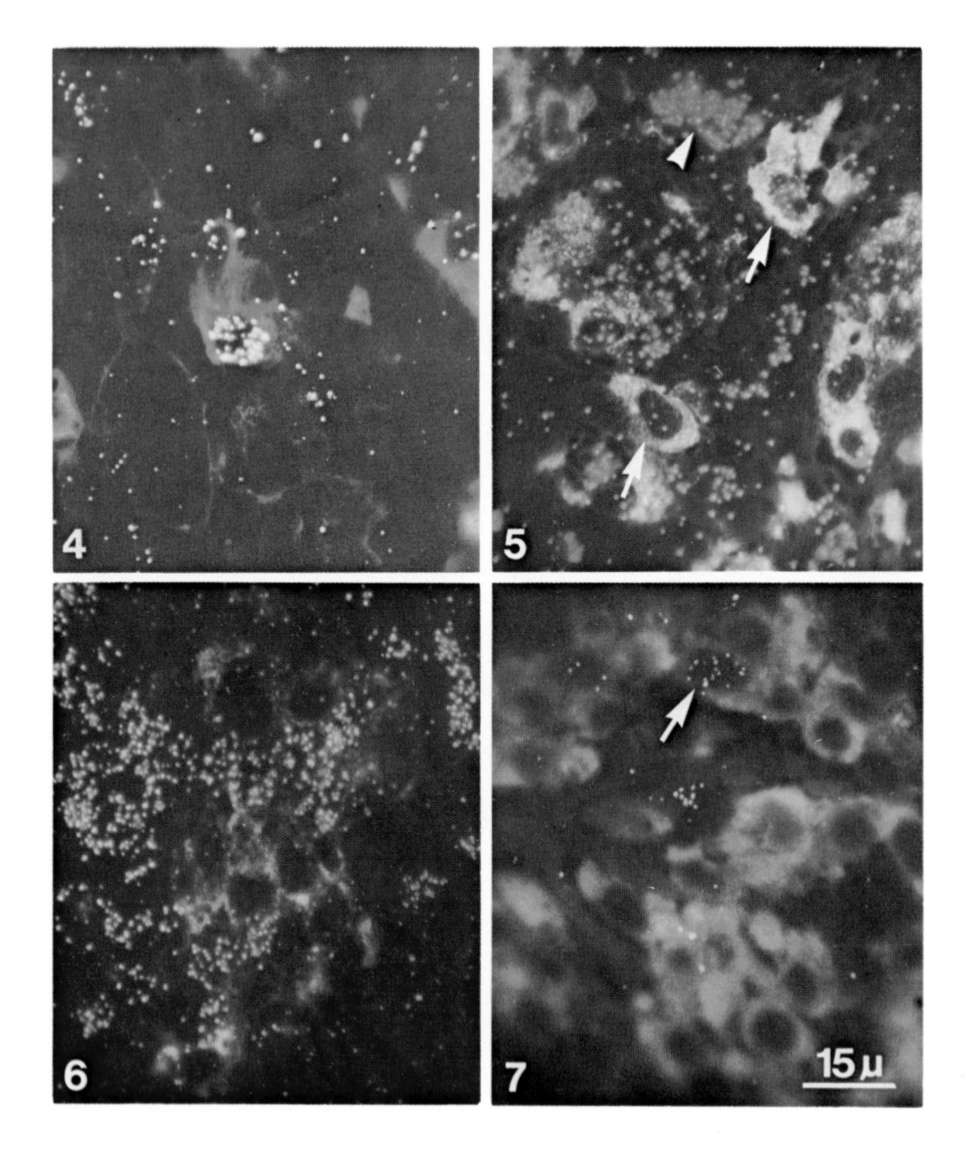
4
5
6
7
15 µ

was placed beneath the dark-field condenser so that the silver grains appeared orange while the catecholamine fluorescence appeared green. The thin sections precluded superimposition of cells (Fig. 4).

Labeling of catecholamine-containing cells by ^{3}H-thymidine was seen in primary, secondary, aortic, and splanchnic ganglia as well as in developing the adrenal medulla (Fig. 5). Experiments were done to determine whether the labeling was of cells which already contained catecholamine and were in the S phase of the cell cycle when ^{3}H-thymidine was injected, or whether cells became labeled and divided to yield catecholamine-containing postmitotic progeny. If the survival time following injection of ^{3}H-thymidine was reduced to 2 hr, a time inadequate to permit transit from S through G_2 and mitosis, catecholamine-containing cells were still labeled. These experiments are in complete agreement with the data and conclusions of Cohen (12).

Further experiments were done to determine when catecholamine-containing cells cease dividing. When eggs were chronically injected with ^{3}H-thymidine on days 3, 4, and 5 and the embryos were examined on day 6, most but not all catecholamine containing ganglion cells or adrenal medullary cells were labeled (Fig. 6). If injections of ^{3}H-thymidine were begun on day 2 instead of day 3 essentially all catecholamine-containing cells were now labeled. Therefore, although proliferation of catecholamine-containing cells continues, some cells of this population either withdraw from the mitotic cycle between days 2 and 3 or enter an extended pause. As development proceeds, similar experiments involving chronic administration of ^{3}H-

---

Fig. 4. A cluster of three fluorescent, catecholamine-containing cells from a 15-day chick embryo. One of these cells has been heavily labeled by ^{3}H-thymidine which was injected on the 9th day of incubation.

Fig. 5. Developing catecholamine-containing cells from the forming adrenal medulla. Within the field there are unlabeled cells which contain catecholamine as well as such cells labeled by ^{3}H-thymidine (arrows). Also seen are grain clusters marking the presence of labeled cells which do not contain catecholamine (arrowhead).

Fig. 6. A prevertebral sympathetic ganglion prepared for radioautography and formaldehyde-induced fluorescence. ^{3}H-Thymidine was injected on days 3, 4, and 5 and the embryo was fixed on day 6. Note the presence of unlabeled catecholamine-containing cells. The surrounding clusters of silver grains denote the presence of label in cells which do not contain catecholamine.

Fig. 7. A transverse section through a paravertebral ganglion of a late, 14-day chick embryo; formaldehyde-induced fluorescence for catecholamine and radioautography for ^{3}H-thymidine. ^{3}H-Thymidine was injected 4 hr prior to fixation to preclude the possibility of cell division intervening between injection and fixation. A labeled catecholamine-containing cell is shown (arrow). A cluster of silver grains marks the position of a labeled cell which does not contain catecholamines.

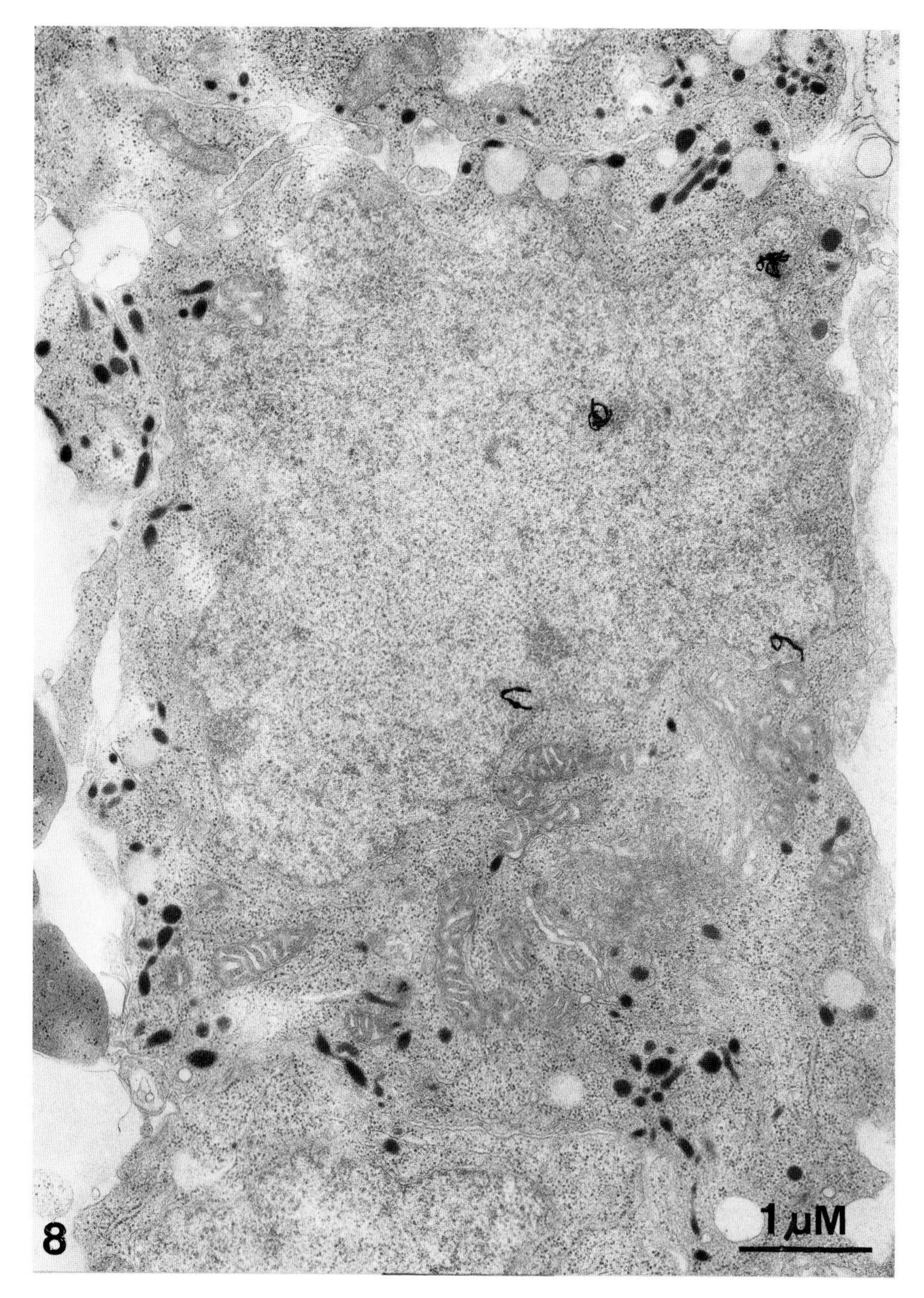
8
1 μM

thymidine, begun at later ages (Fig. 7), revealed a progressive increase in the proportion of catecholamine-containing cells withdrawing from the mitotic cycle. The latest age examined at which ^{3}H-thymidine injection produced labeled catecholamine-containing cells was hatching. Very few such labeled neurons were found in embryos injected at this time. Therefore, the sympathetic ganglion cells form a heterogeneous population. All neurons in the definitive ganglia contain catecholamine. When primary ganglia are examined by radioautography following incubation for 30 min with ^{3}H-NE, all of the ganglion cells are labeled. Nevertheless, some of the cells in this population continue to divide at least until hatching while an increasingly large proportion of the population is becoming postmitotic. We were unable to determine what if anything distinguishes those cells able to divide from those which cannot.

These conclusions were supported by electron microscopic examinations. Cells were found in primary ganglia which contained dense-cored vesicles and which were labeled with ^{3}H-thymidine (Fig. 8). Other such vesicle-containing cells were found in mitosis. These vesicles were electron opaque in material fixed with $KMnO_4$ and therefore, they probably contain catecholamine (14).

Since we have shown that the developing sympathetic cells take up NE, the possibility exists that these cells may not be able to synthesize the amine. Their store of the transmitter may be derived from circulating catecholamine which they have taken up. Yolk, for example, contains catecholamines (15). However, this possibility can be ruled out. Kirby has shown that inhibition of catecholamine uptake fails to deplete NE in developing sympathetic ganglion cells, while inhibition of tyrosine hydroxylase does deplete the transmitter (16). Therefore, synthesis as well as uptake of NE is a property of these neurons, and biosynthesis accounts for their NE store.

Thus we can conclude that the capacity of sympathetic cells to synthesize or incorporate catecholamines is not dependent on prior withdrawal from the cell cycle. In this respect, the early differentiating ganglion cells appear to be more similar, among other systems, to the early-forming red blood cells than to the later-developing skeletal muscle cells (17). In this case the final characteristic(s) which mark(s) the transition from precursor to mature sympathetic ganglion cell re-

Fig. 8. An electron microscopic radioautograph of a cell in the region of the developing adrenal medulla from an embryo of 5 days' incubation. ^{3}H-Thymidine was injected prior to fixation. A cell containing dense cored granules has taken up ^{3}H-thymidine and its nucleus is labeled.

main(s) to be determined. Sympathetic ganglion cells derived from the superior cervical ganglion can be induced to change their transmitter from NE to acetylcholine (ACh) or even to secrete both transmitters in culture (18,19). Perhaps the adrenergic nature of the dividing sympathetic ganglion cells is not yet fixed.

DEVELOPMENT OF THE MONOAMINERGIC INNERVATION OF THE GUT

Uptake of ^{3}H-NE can be used as a marker for processes of adrenergic neurons as well as a means to detect perikarya. In fact, this marker becomes more convenient when used at later embryonic stages than in the studies described above. This is because the notochords of early embryos take up ^{3}H-NE. Therefore, radioautography, not analysis of whole tissues, must be used to evaluate the uptake of ^{3}H-NE specifically by neurons while the notochord is intact. The notochord degenerates and loses its ability to take up ^{3}H-NE by 4 days of incubation. After this time, high-affinity uptake of ^{3}H-NE is restricted to adrenergic neurons. Therefore, uptake of ^{3}H-NE can be measured biochemically in whole tissues in older embryos and still be valid as an indicator of the presence in these tissues of adrenergic neurites. The uptake process is very sensitive as such an indicator. It appears to be more sensitive in this respect for growing axons than is the histofluorescent demonstration of the transmitter itself (5,20).

The maturation of neuromuscular function has been studied in one of the target organs of the autonomic nervous system, the gut. This is a multiply innervated structure. The enteric nervous system of the adult gut receives an adrenergic input of axons from prevertebral ganglia but, with isolated exceptions such as the guinea pig proximal colon (21), contains no adrenergic cell bodies. Cholinergic ganglion cells are intrinsic to both enteric plexuses, the myenteric and submucosal, and their existence has been known for years (22,23). Until recently ACh and NE were the only transmitters known to be present in the gut. However, the list of putative enteric neurotransmitter substances has now been considerably expanded. Included in this list are an inhibitory transmitter from intrinsic enteric neurons to smooth muscle which may be ATP (24), somatostatin (25), substance P (26), enkephalin (27), and 5-HT (6).

5-HT-containing neurites can be identified by their specific uptake of the transmitter substance. This uptake is a high-affinity process which persists after chemical sympathectomy and can be monitored either biochemically or by radioautography (Fig. 9) (8). Very slight changes in the 5-HT molecule greatly diminish uptake and the process persists in the face of high concentrations of NE (28). Therefore, since 5-HT neurons do not take up NE, 5-HT neurons will not interfere with the use of ^{3}H-NE as an adrenergic neuronal marker. Conversely, if an excess of nonradioactive NE is included in incubating media with ^{3}H-5-HT, uptake of 5-HT by adrenergic neurons will not interfere with detection of serotonergic neurites. 5-HT neurons have also been demonstrated by histofluorescence (7) and by immunocytochemical localization of tryptophan hydroxylase (6). If explants are removed from 17- to 18-day mouse fetuses and grown for 3 weeks in organotypic tissue culture, the extrinsic innervation of the gut, including the adrenergic innervation, degenerates while intrinsic neurons survive (7,29). Serotonergic neurons persist and can be detected in cultures by histofluorescence, radioautography with ^{3}H-5-HT, immunocytochemical localization of tryptophan hydroxylase and biosynthesis of 5-HT from L-tryptophan (6,7,11).

Uptake of amines was used to distinguish the development of the serotonergic and adrenergic innervation of the gut. Two processes of uptake of ^{3}H-5-HT by adult rabbit gut were detected (30). Only the high-affinity uptake was saturable and was detectable in fetal gut. Electron microscopic radioautography revealed that this process reflected uptake of ^{3}H-5-HT by axons, particularly terminal varicosities containing large dense cored vesicles and flattened membranous structures. The uptake in fetuses and in adults was temperature sensitive and was inhibited by ouabain and *p*-chloromethamphetamine. Specific uptake of ^{3}H-5-HT could first be detected at 16 days of gestation. In contrast, uptake of ^{3}H-NE could not be seen until 21–24 days of gestation. Again however, electron microscopic radioautography revealed that axons were responsible for taking up ^{3}H-NE. Therefore, the serotonergic innervation develops 5–8 days before the adrenergic innervation reaches the gut.

The early maturation of the enteric serotonergic innervation is marked by the early development of a specific 5-HT binding protein in the gut (31). This protein has properties which resemble those of the similar protein which has been found in raphe neurons of the CNS (32,33). No 5-HT-binding protein can be found at 15 days of gestation in the rabbit, 1 day before 5-HT uptake signals the development of the serotonergic innervation. However, by 21 days, when the enteric serotonergic innervation is well advanced (but the adrenergic innervation has not yet arrived), the 5-HT binding protein is already almost one-third that of the adult level (31).

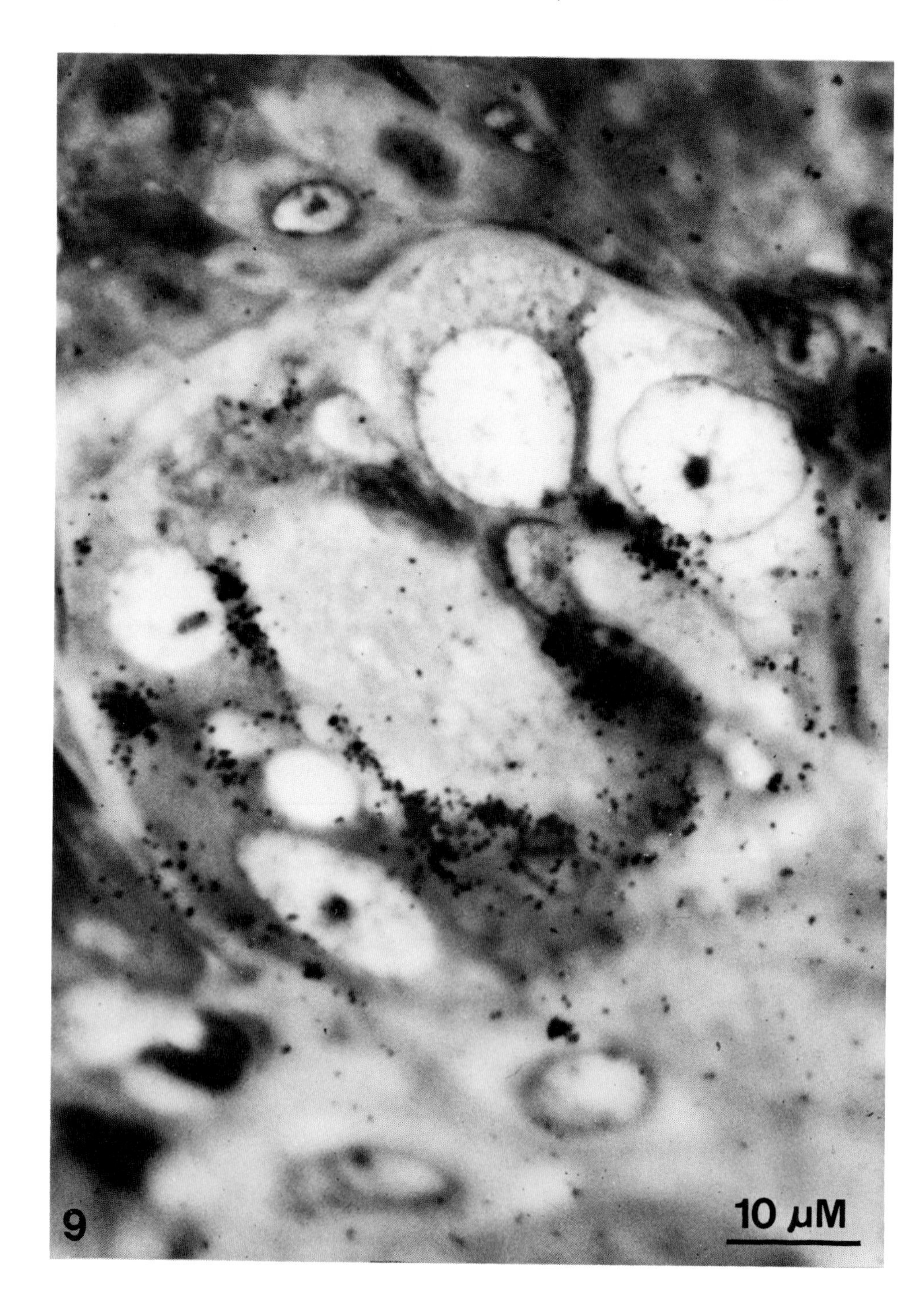
9
10 μM

Functional activity involving enteric neurons known to be activated by 5-HT can be detected as early as day 17. Both nerve-mediated excitation and relaxation of smooth muscle occur at this age (5). Thus, the targets of the 5-HT innervation, cholinergic and intrinsic inhibitory ganglion cells, mature after the 5-HT innervation. It is therefore possible that the 5-HT neurons may have a role in stimulating the maturation of these other neurons. Such a role would not be possible for NE. Since the intrinsic inhibitory innervation of the gut develops before adrenergic axons reach this organ, the nonadrenergic nature of the intrinsic neurons is confirmed.

CONCLUSIONS

In summary, we have used histofluorescence and transmitter uptake to study stages in the development of peripheral monoaminergic neurons. Adrenergic cells reveal their transmitter content and uptake mechanisms early, well before they develop axons or cease migrating. Many of these catecholamine-containing cells continue to replicate, but many probably become postmitotic even at these early stages. The proportion of postmitotic cells increases during development. It will be important to determine whether (1) the catecholamines synthesized by precursor adrenergic cells are identical to those synthesized by the definitive, postmitotic cells; and (2) whether the replicating, catecholamine-containing cells survive.

Both ^{3}H-5-HT and ^{3}H-NE are specifically taken up by developing fetal gut. Although serotonergic neuronal cell bodies are intrinsic and adrenergic cell bodies are extrinsic to the gut, uptake of both amines is primarily into axons. Therefore, it has not yet been possible to study the early stages in the development and migration of serotonergic cell bodies as was done with adrenergic neuroblasts. However, analysis of ^{3}H-5-HT and ^{3}H-NE uptake by the gut revealed that the serotonergic innervation of this organ develops before postganglionic intrinsic neurons, which act on smooth muscle, became functional and long before the gut receives an adrenergic innervation. A role for 5-HT in the development of the enteric nervous system is possible.

Fig. 9. A ganglion from the myenteric plexus of the intestine of a mouse, incubated for 20 min with ^{3}H-5-HT (10^{-7} *M*) in a medium that also contained nonradioactive NE (10^{-5} *M*) to prevent 5-HT uptake into adrenergic axons. The silver grains in this light microscopic radioautograph surround ganglion cells and suggest the presence of ^{3}H-5-HT in terminals abutting on these cells.

ACKNOWLEDGMENT

This work was supported by NIH grants, NS12969 and HD00030.

REFERENCES

1. Yntema, C. L., and Hammond, W. S. (1947) *Biol. Rev. Cambridge Philos. Soc.* **22,** 344–359.
2. Weston, J. A. (1970) *Adv. Morphog.* **8,** 41–114.
3. Landmesser, L., and Pilar, G. (1974) *J. Physiol. (London)* **241,** 737–749.
4. Enemar, A., Falck, B., and Håkanson, R. (1965) *Dev. Biol.* **11,** 268–283.
5. Gershon, M. D., and Thompson, E. B. (1973) *J. Physiol. (London)* **234,** 257–278.
6. Gershon, M. D., Dreyfus, C. F., Pickel, V. M., Joh, T. H., and Reis, D. J. (1977) *Proc. Natl. Acad. Sci. U.S.A.* **74,** 3086–3089.
7. Dreyfus, C. F., Bornstein, M. B., and Gershon, M. D. (1977) *Brain Res.* **128,** 125–139.
8. Gershon, M. D., Robinson, R. G., and Ross, L. L. (1976) *J. Pharmacol. Exp. Ther.* **198,** 548–561.
9. Wolfe, D. E., Axelrod, J., Potter, L. T., and Richardson, K. D. (1962) *Electron Microsc., Proc. Int. Congr., 5th, 1962* Vol. 2, Artic. L12.
10. Schofield, G. C. (1968) *Handb. Physiol., Sect. 6: Aliment. Canal,* **14,** 1579–1627.
11. Dreyfus, C. F., Sherman, D. L., and Gershon, M. D. (1977) *Brain Res.* **128,** 109–123.
12. Cohen, A. M. (1973) *Wenner-Gren Cent. Int. Symp. Ser.* **22,** 359–370.
13. Okazaki, K., and Holtzer, H. (1966) *Proc. Natl. Acad. Sci. U.S.A.* **56,** 1484–1490.
14. Hökfelt, T. (1971) *Prog. Brain Res.* **34,** 213–222.
15. Ignarro, L. J., and Shideman, F. E. (1968) *J. Pharmacol. Exp. Ther.* **159,** 49–58.
16. Kirby, M. L. *Brain Res.* (in press).
17. Holtzer, H., Rubinstein, N., Fellini, S., Yeoh, G., Chi, J., Birnbaum, J., and Okayama, M. (1975) *Q. Rev. Biophys.* **8,** 523–557.
18. Patterson, P. H., and Chun, L. L. Y. (1974) *Proc. Natl. Acad. Sci. U.S.A.* **71,** 3607–3610.
19. Furshpan, E. J., MacLeish, P. R., O'Lague, P. H., and Potter, D. D. (1976) *Proc. Natl. Acad. Sci. U.S.A.* **73,** 4225–4229.
20. Read, J. B., and Burnstock, G. (1969) *Histochemie* **20,** 197–200.
21. Costa, M., Furness, J. B., and Gabella, G. (1971) *Histochemie* **25,** 103–106.
22. Dale, H. H. (1906) *J. Mt. Sinai Hosp., N.Y.* **4,** 401–415.
23. Dale, H. H. (1906) *J. Mt. Sinai Hosp., N.Y.* **4,** 416–429.
24. Burnstock, G. (1972) *Pharmacol. Rev.* **24,** 509–581.
25. Hökfelt, T., Johansson, O., Efendic, S., Luft, R., and Arimura, A. (1975) *Experientia* **31,** 852–854.
26. Pearse, A. G. E., and Polak, J. M. (1975) *Histochemie* **41,** 373–375.
27. Hökfelt, T., personal communication.
28. Gershon, M. D., and Altman, R. F. (1971) *J. Pharmacol. Exp. Ther.* **179,** 29–41.
29. Cook, R. D., and Peterson, E. R. (1974) *J. Neurol. Sci.* **22,** 25–38.
30. Rothman, T. P., Ross, L. L., and Gershon, M. D. (1976) *Brain Res.* **115,** 437–456.
31. Jonakait, G. M., Tamir, H., Rapport, M. M., and Gershon, M. D. (1977) *J. Neurochem.* **28,** 277–284.
32. Tamir, H., and Huang, I. L. (1974) *Life Sci.* **14,** 83–93.
33. Tamir, H., and Kuhar, M. J. (1975) *Brain Res.* **83,** 169–172.

Characterization, Distribution, and Appearance of Surface Carbohydrates on Growing Neurites

KARL H. PFENNINGER
Department of Anatomy
College of Physicians and Surgeons
Columbia University
New York, New York

MARIE-FRANCE MAYLIÉ-PFENNINGER
Sloan-Kettering
Institute for Cancer Research
New York, New York

INTRODUCTION

The material presented in this chapter is concerned with problems of cellular differentiation in brain development. The complex series of differentiative steps that results eventually in the formation of the elaborate neuronal network comprising the brain (1), ultimately is governed by the sequential expression of selected portions of the genome in the participating cells (2). However, extrinsic signals are necessary to trigger various steps of this process. Perhaps the most prominent examples of this phenomenon are found in the course of formation of interneuronal connections. In this process, the neuron first stops mitotic activity and starts to form processes including an axon; a guidance mechanism leads the outgrowing axon to the appropriate target area; upon encounter of an appropriate target cell, a recognition mechanism triggers the onset of synaptogenesis, a process which involves localized differentiation of both future synaptic

ISBN 0-12-398450-5

membranes (3). There is no doubt that neuronal information transfer is a crucial ingredient in this sequence of events, well before synaptic transmission can occur. It is one of the goals of this chapter to develop a hypothesis on the nature of the signals that are exchanged between neurons during their development.

A steadily increasing body of evidence strongly suggests that membrane interactions are a requirement of cellular recognition phenomena; the specificity involved could lie in the membrane itself, i.e., in the properties of the cell surface, especially its carbohydrates (4–7). If, indeed, neuronal recognition is mediated by cell surface codes, this process (and probably neuritic guidance as well) is complicated by the fact that fast enlargement of the neuronal surface, i.e., membrane growth, occurs simultaneously. In other words, while the plasmalemma of the growing neurite is rapidly expanded, membrane properties suitable for recognition mechanisms have to be maintained. Hence it is important for our understanding of neuronal development both to analyze plasmalemmal properties of the nerve growth cone in search for a recognition code, and to study the mechanism of membrane expansion. We present here data from our work on surface carbohydrate composition of growing neurons. The following three questions will be discused: (1) What is the topographic distribution of specific saccharides on the surface of the growing neuron? (2) Are growing neurites from different types of neuron characterized by distinctive surface carbohydrate contents? (3) During growth of the neurite, where and by what mechanism do new carbohydrates appear on the neuritic surface? We attempt to answer these questions by labeling neuronal surfaces with lectins, proteins with a high and selective affinity for specific saccharides (8,9), which have been linked covalently to the electron-dense marker ferritin (10–12). The lectin–ferritin conjugates utilized in these studies have been characterized with regard to their binding properties and contain binding protein and ferritin in a 1:1 ratio. With these probes it is possible to quantitate electron microscopically lectin receptor sites, i.e., the density of lectin-accessible carbohydrate residues, on the plasma-lemmal surface of different cellular types and regions. In the order to be able to work on freely exposed cell surfaces, the analyses are carried out on 3- to 7-day-old cultures of explants or dissociated neurons from different nerve tissues of the fetal rat. After a few days *in vitro,* the neurons exhibit vigorous neuritic outgrowth. Prior to lectin labeling and aldehyde fixation, cultures always undergo extensive washing with a serum albumin medium for desorption of glycoproteins from cell surfaces. This method ensures labeling of true membrane components, rather than demonstration of glycoproteins adsorbed from the culture medium.

TOPOGRAPHIC DISTRIBUTION OF SURFACE CARBOHYDRATES ON GROWING NEURONS

Cultured neurons, isolated mechanically from rat superior cervical ganglia or enzymatically from rat spinal cords, are washed, fixed with glutaraldehyde, treated with glycine for quenching of remaining aldehyde residues, and then labeled with a series of lectin–ferritin conjugates including concanavalin A (Con A), wheat germ agglutinin (WGA), *Ricinus communis* agglutinin I (RCAI), and the agglutinin of *Ulex europeus* (UEA). The respective specifities of these lectins are glucose/mannose, *N*-acetylglucosamine, galactose, and fucose. As shown in Fig. 1, lectin–ferritin labeling results in a layer of electron-dense ferritin cores lined up at even distance from the electron-dense "tramlines" of the plasma membrane. In a control experiment, carried out in the presence of 0.2 *M* hapten sugar, virtually no binding can be detected. Figures 1A and B demonstrate furthermore that lectin receptors are uniformly distributed over the surfaces of growth cones, neuronal perikarya, and neuritic shafts (not shown). For a given type of neuron and the same lectin, binding sites occur at approximately the same density in the various topographic regions (12). Included in this uniformity of labeling are the vesicle-filled, moundlike protrusions which occur frequently on growing neurites, especially at the level of the growth cone (see Fig. 3A; cf. 13,14). The same result is obtained with all the lectins tested (however, there are quantitative differences; see below) and regardless of whether lectin labeling follows aldehyde fixation on precedes it (at 0°C).

This result indicates, at least as far as lectin-accessible residues are concerned, uniform surface carbohydrate composition of the neuron during the phase of neurite formation (12). This result is surprising in view of the fact that differences in membrane properties between growth cone and perikaryon have been discovered in freeze-fracture studies (15). The density of intramembranous particles is very low in the plasmalemma of the growth cone (approximately $110/\mu m^2$ for the two membrane leaflets combined), about one order of magnitude less than in the perikaryal membrane. Current evidence (for review, see

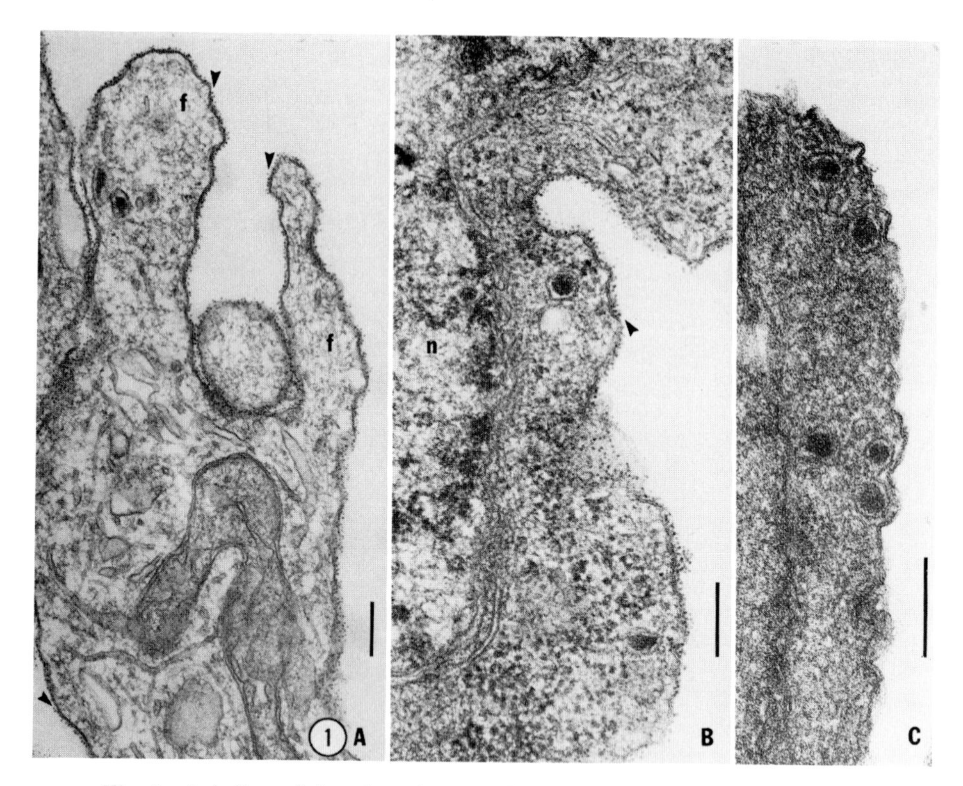

Fig. 1. Labeling of the plasmalemma of the growing neuron with ferritin–wheat germ agglutinin, specific for *N*-acetylglucosaminyl residues. The marker is used approximately at saturation level. (A) Part of a nerve growth cone from a superior cervical ganglion neuron. (B) Perikaryon of the same type of neuron. Note uniform distribution of the ferritin marker (arrowheads). (C) Control experiment; process of a superior cervical ganglion neuron labeled in the presence of 0.2 *M N*-acetylglucosamine. Absence of the ferritin marker in the control picture is evident. f, filopodia; n, nucleus. Magnification, ×46,600 (A), ×64,000 (B), ×85,500 (C). Calibration, 0.2 μm.

16) suggests that intramembranous particles are composed of a number of integral membrane proteins or glycoproteins. Thus it is tempting to infer that the high frequency of lectin receptors in the same membrane (at least $2000/\mu m^2$) may be determined to a large extent by the presence of glycolipids rather than of glycoproteins. But there is presently no evidence available which would support this conclusion. All we can say today is that, regardless of the uniform topographic distribution of lectin receptor sites on the developing neuron, growth cone plasmalemma is unique because of its very low particle content.

APPEARANCE AND MOVEMENT OF PLASMALEMMAL LECTIN RECEPTORS DURING MEMBRANE GROWTH

Studies on continued growth of severed neurites (17), on the movement of nerve growth cones relative to light microscopic surface markers or neuritic branch points (18,19), and on membrane structure in freeze-fractured growing neurites (3,6,15) have suggested that plasmalemmal expansion occurs by localized insertion of membrane components at distal sites, i.e., mainly at or near the growth cone. This hypothesis can be tested by analyzing, as a parameter of membrane growth, insertion of new lectin receptors into the membrane and lateral displacement of preexisting lectin binding sites (20). Uniform distribution of lectin receptors are reported above is a prerequisite for the successful execution of such experiments. It suggests, furthermore, that newly inserted membrane is furnished with the appropriate lectin receptors, especially if membrane addition is a localized phenomenon (cf. Fig. 2A). If plasmalemmal expansion is achieved by the insertion of membrane patches, e.g., by fusion of vesicles with the plasma membrane, preexisting lectin receptors should be displaced to the side (12,21,22). One should be able to observe this phenomenon in a single-label, pulse-chase experiment, in which live cultures are first labeled with ferritin–lectin conjugate, washed, allowed to survive for varied periods of time in the absence of the label, and then fixed and processed for electron microscopy (Fig. 2B). However, the result, as schematically illustrated in Fig. 2B, could also be interpreted as the consequence of growth-independent redistribution of cell surface markers by mechanisms similar to the ones leading to patching or capping in lymphocytes (23). The correct interpretation of the single-label experiment can be found in a double-label, pulse-chase experiment whose goal is the demonstration of newly inserted lectin receptors during the chase period (Fig. 2C). In this experiment, receptors for a specific lectin are first blocked with the native protein, which is invisible in the electron microscope. After 5 or 10 min of labeling, the lectin is washed off, and the neurites are allowed to continue to grow for periods ranging from 3 to 20 min before being fixed with aldehyde. After quenching of free aldehyde groups with glycine, the cultures are (re)labeled with ferritin–lectin conjugates to reveal lectin receptor sites which have appeared during the chase period (20).

The results of such experiments are illustrated in Fig. 3. It has become clear during these studies that the moundlike protrusions filled with 150-nm vesicles are structures of particular interest. Figure 3A

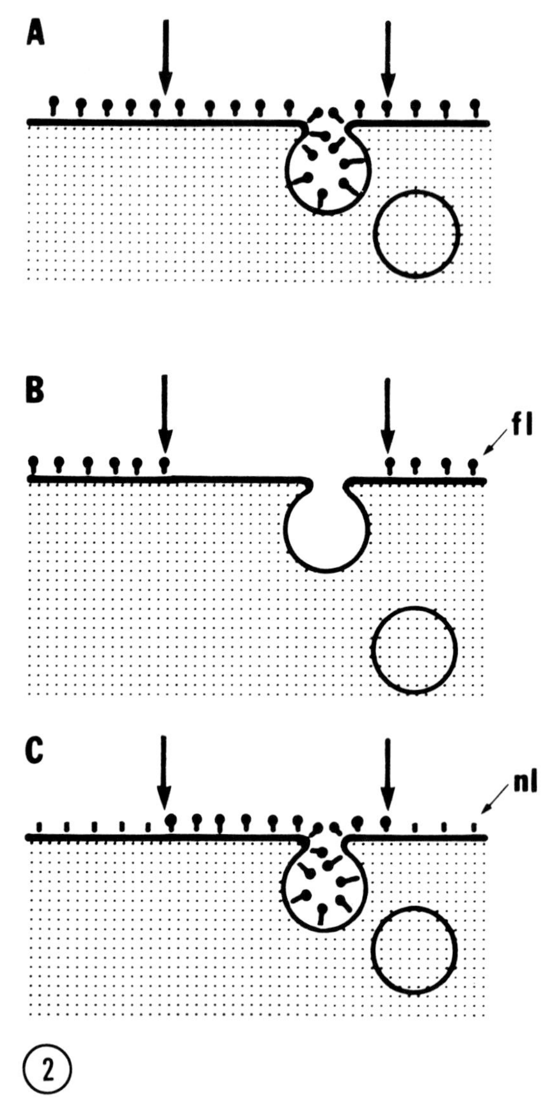

Fig. 2. Schematic representation of the studies on lectin receptor dynamics during neuritic growth. The plasmalemmal region between the arrows is a hypothetical site of localized insertion of preassembled membrane by fusion of vesicles. fl, ferritin-lectin conjugate; nl, native lectin. For further explanation, see text.

shows one of these mounds, prefixed with aldehyde and labeled with ferritin–wheat germ agglutinin. It is evident that the mound surface contains lectin receptors at approximately the same density as the surrounding plasmalemma. In a single-label, pulse-chase experiment, vesicle-filled mounds appear free of the surface marker after minutes of survival in the absence of the lectin conjugate. In the same experiment, it is also frequently observed that whole areas of the growth cone, especially filopodia, are free of the label. While pinocytosis of ferritin–lectin conjugates is regularly observed in areas outside the mound region, internalization of the marker into mound vesicles has never been found. This result is in disagreement with compartment tracer studies (24). However, the results from membrane labeling work are considered more reliable because redistribution of the marker by artifactual fusion of cellular compartments cannot occur. If the double-label, pulse-chase experiment is carried out in the cold, under conditions which exclude membrane expansion, no new lectin receptor is added during the chase period, and therefore, the amount of membrane-bound ferritin should be minimal. This observation can indeed be made, as shown in Fig. 3D. However, under growth conditions, at 36°C, dense patches of ferritin label appear on the mounds in experiments with chase periods of as little as 3 min. Quite frequently, the entire mound surface is covered with lectin–ferritin conjugate. Furthermore, the ferritin-conjugated label is also frequently seen on a sizeable fraction of the growth cone surface including many of the filopodia and on membrane regions near vesicle-filled mounds in more proximal segments of the growing neurite.

Although further evidence is still highly desirable, these data lend strong support to the hypothesis that membrane expansion in the growing neurite (and in other cell types containing the vesicle-filled mounds) is achieved by fusion of plasmalemmal precursor vesicles with the surface membrane of the mounds, i.e., by localized insertion of patches of preassembled membrane. Our experiments also demonstrate that the precursor membrane of the vesicles contains all the lectin receptors which are found on the growth cone plasmalemma and other parts of the neuronal surface membrane.

SURFACE CARBOHYDRATE COMPOSITION OF GROWTH CONES FROM DIFFERENT NEURON TYPES

If neuronal recognition is a cell surface phenomenon, i.e., if recognition clues are coded in the chemical composition of membrane com-

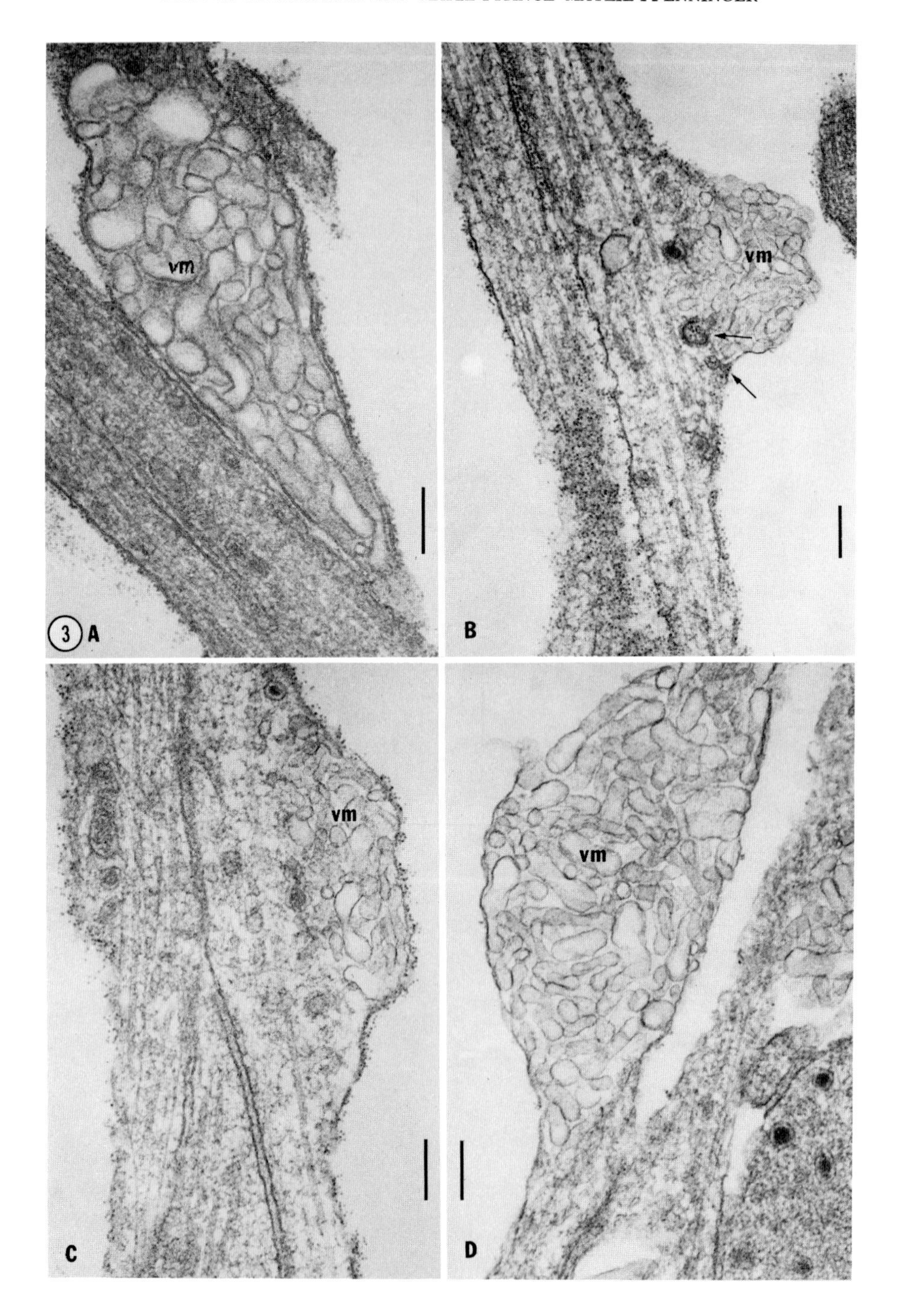
vm
3 A
vm
B
vm
C
vm
D

TABLE I
Lectin Receptor Densities on Developing Neurites of Different Origin[a,b,c]

	Con A glc/man	WGA glcNAc	RCA I gal	Neuramin. RCA I	SBA galNAc	LTA/UEA fucose
SCG	(1400)	2740	1440	nd	(1400)	0
DRG	(1800)	2220	(2200)	nd	—	0
SC	(800)	910	210	(2200)	0	0
CBL	—	530	560	2210	0	0
OB	(600)	1830	0	1950	—	0

[a] Binding sites/μm^2 of plasma membrane.
[b] *Key:* SCG, superior cervical ganglion; DRG, dorsal root ganglion; SC, spinal cord; CBL, cerebellum; OB, olfactory bulb (fetal rat tissues); Con A, concanavalin A; WGA, wheat germ agglutinin; RCA I, *Ricinus communis* agglutinin I; neuramin., neuraminidase treatment before labeling; SBA, soybean agglutinin; UEA, *Ulex europeus* agglutinin; LTA, *Lotus tetragonolobus* agglutinin.
[c] Preliminary data; figures in parentheses are estimated values; nd, not done.

ponents, such as the complex carbohydrates which extend into the extracellular space, it should be possible to detect differences in membrane surface chemistry when comparing growth cones stemming from different types of neuron. We have tested this hypothesis in a series of labeling studies utilizing a battery of lectin–ferritin conjugates with different binding specificities (25) (Table I), and carried out under identical conditions. The materials analyzed are growth cones and neuritic shafts in young explant cultures from fetal rat superior cervical and dorsal root ganglia, cerebellum (mainly Purkinje cell outgrowth), olfactory bulb (mainly mitral cell outgrowth), and ventral region of spinal cord (mainly motor neuron outgrowth). Within a

Fig. 3. Vesicle-filled mounds (vm) near nerve growth cones in lectin label pulse-chase experiments. (A) Aldehyde-prefixed element, labeled with ferritin–wheat germ agglutinin. Note uniform labeling of mound surface and nerve fiber shafts. (B) Single-label pulse-chase experiment (15 min chase) with ferritin–*Ricinus communis* agglutinin I (RCA I). While nerve fiber shafts are still uniformly labeled, the mound surface is free of the marker. No internalization into mound vesicles has occurred. One of the basal, open cisternae, typical of the mounds, and a coated vesicle are labeled (arrows). (C) Double-label, pulse-chase experiment with native RCA I, followed by 3 min chase, fixation, and postlabeling with ferritin–RCA I. Note the appearance of new lectin receptors mainly on the mound surface, less on nerve fiber shafts (compare perpendicularly sectioned membrane regions). (D) Double-label, pulse-chase experiment at 0°C with ferritin–RCA II (specific for *N*-acetylgalactosaminyl residues). Note the absence of ferritin label. Use of the different lectins yields comparable results in the various experiments. For further explanation, see text. Cultured rat superior cervical ganglion neurons. Magnifications: (A) ×62,100; (B) ×48,300; (C) ×55,300; (D) ×54,400. Calibration, 0.2 μm.

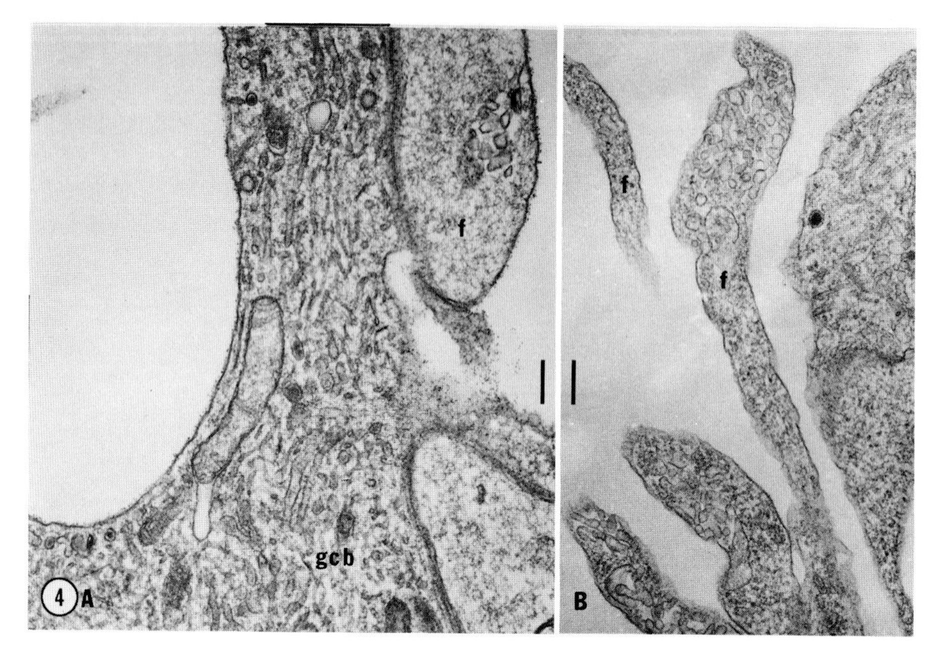

Fig. 4. Differential lectin labeling of nerve growth cones with ferritin–soybean agglutinin (specific for *N*-acetylgalactosaminyl residues). Note fairly dense label on the superior cervical ganglion growth cone (A) whereas the spinal cord growth cone elements in B exhibit no binding sites. gcb, growth cone body; f, filopodia. Fetal rat tissues. Magnification, (A) ×36,800; (B) ×37,000. Calibration, 0.2 μm.

certain range, the results seem independent of the fetal age at which the tissues were explanted and of the time in culture, so that the data presented here may hold for the entire phase during which these neurons exhibit neurite-forming capacity. As can be seen in Figs. 4 and 5 and in Table I, each of the growth cone types analyzed is characterized by its own specific number and combination of lectin receptor sites. This is particularly evident when comparing the binding of wheat germ agglutinin and *Ricinus communis* agglutinin I to the different types of growing neurite. In none of the growth cones analyzed are fucosyl residues detected with the lectins from *Lotus tetragonolobus* and from *Ulex europeus* seeds. A further important observation can be made in Table I: while dorsal root and superior cervical ganglion neurites are rich in binding sites for the various lectins, spinal cord-, olfactory bulb-, and cerebellum-derived growth cones generally exhibit much less labeling with the various lectins. The two classes of lectin binding correspond to the two main classes of nerve tissues stemming from neural crest and neural tube, respectively. However, paucity of

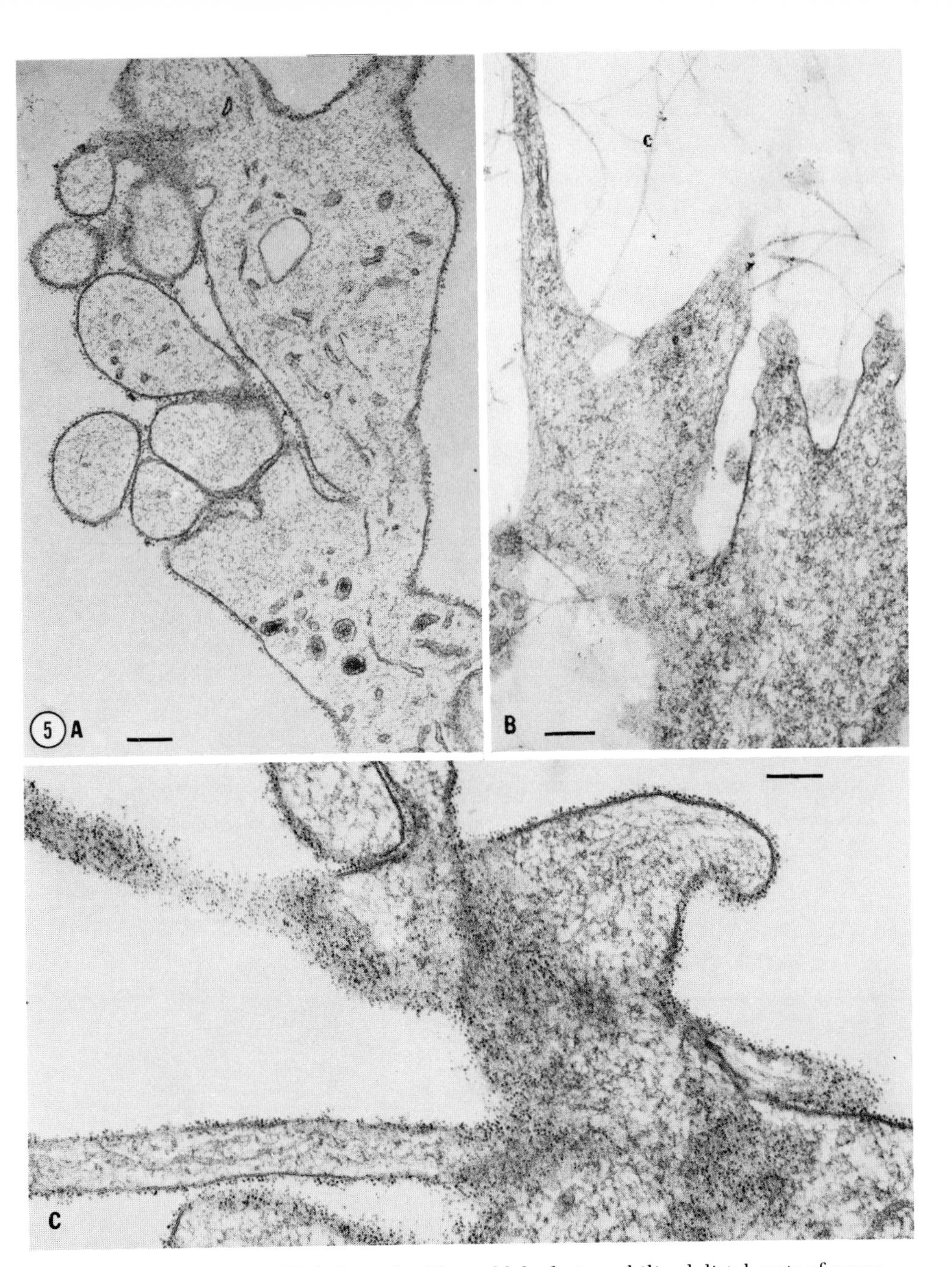

Fig. 5. Differential labeling of cold- or aldehyde-immobilized distal parts of nerve growth cones with *Ricinus communis* agglutinin I, specific for galactosyl residues. (A) rat superior cervical ganglion; (B) rat spinal cord; (C) rat spinal cord. Neurites were fixed with glutaraldehyde, neuraminidase treated, and then labeled. Note the striking differences in labeling between superior cervical ganglion and spinal cord, and between normal and neuraminidase-digested spinal cord. Magnifications, (A) ×42,600; (B) ×45,500; (C) ×54,500. Calibration, 0.2 μm.

certain lectin receptor sites on growth cones formed by tube-derived neurons does not imply paucity of carbohydrate residues on these cell surfaces. Indeed, if the same neurites are fixed with aldehyde, treated with neuraminidase (in the presence of bovine serum albumin for quenching of possible protease contaminants), and then labeled with ferritin-conjugated *Ricinus communis* agglutinin I, a high density of surface galactosyl residues can be demonstrated (Figs. 5B and C, Table I). This result suggests that the main difference in cell surface properties between neural-tube- and neural-crest-derived cells may lie in the amount of terminal sialic acid residues which mask other carbohydrate components present in deeper layers of the cell surface.

These studies demonstrate that, at least during the period of neurite-forming capacity, the neuronal cell surface exhibits a specific carbohydrate code which is distinctive for each neuron type and, furthermore, distinguishes at least two classes of neuron according to their embryonic origin. The presence of this type-specific cell surface signature lends strong support to the hypothesis that neuronal recognition is a cell-surface phenomenon, i.e., that this type of neuronal information transfer occurs via the interaction of complex carbohydrates on one membrane with specific carbohydrate-binding moieties on the surface of an adjacent cell. Indeed, there is increasing evidence for the existence of such carbohydrate receptors on cell surfaces, either in the form of lectinlike molecules (26–29) or in the form of glycosyltransferases (30).

SUMMARY AND CONCLUSIONS

These studies have shown that the nerve growth cone, which is the main recognizing structure in the developing nervous system besides the future postsynaptic element, exhibits specific plasmalemmal properties. Compared to the plasma membrane of its parent perikaryon, growth cone plasmalemma is unique because of its very low content of intramembranous particles combined with the usual high density of surface carbohydrate. These specific membrane properties, and the possible importance of glycolipids that they may imply, are likely to be relevant to the mechanism of neuronal recognition. Comparison of cell surface carbohydrate composition among growth cones formed by different neurons reveals type-specific coding provided by varied amounts and combinations of saccharide residues. This code also permits distinction of crest- and tube-derived nerve cells according to their surface properties, whereby the main difference may lie in the prevalence of terminal sialic acid residues in neurons stemming from the neural tube. It should be pointed out that the surface carbohydrate code that we have identified is not necessarily the recognition clue triggering synaptogenesis. There is no evidence available to decide whether this surface carbohydrate signature serves either neural morphogenesis, i.e., cellular migration and aggregation, or recognition in synapse formation, or both phenomena.

The studies on the appearance of new lectin receptors during membrane expansion strongly suggest localized insertion of patches of new membrane mainly at the level of the nerve growth cone. Besides it importance for our understanding of the processes involved in membrane biogenesis, this conclusion implies that growth cone plasmalemma consists of the most recently synthesized and added membrane and, therefore, is under very close control of perikaryal genetic and synthetic machinery. This dynamic aspect of surface properties of the growing neuron may be crucial to the normal functioning of neuronal recognition mechanisms. In fact, a striking analogy exists between neuronal information transfer in synaptic transmission, which is the main topic of this symposium, and information transfer in neuronal development. The mature neuron manufactures synaptic vesicles which are exported to the distal end of the axon, the nerve terminal, for exocytotic release of the signal substance, the neurotransmitter (31,32). Similarly, the growing neuron seems to manufacture vesicles consisting of plasmalemmal precursor membrane which are exported to the distal end of the growing neurite, the growth cone. There, the vesicles fuse with the plasmalemma for its expansion, and simultaneously expose their luminal surface bearing the carbohydrate code to the neuronal environment (cf. 33).

ACKNOWLEDGMENTS

This work is supported by USPHS grant NS13466, by grant BNS7618513 from the National Science Foundation, and a Career Scientist Award from the I.T. Hirschl Trust Fund awarded to K. H. Pfenninger.

REFERENCES

1. Cowan, W. M., and Hunt, R. K. (1978) *Neurosci. Res. Program, Bull.* (in press).
2. Holtzer, H., Rubinstein, N., Fellini, S., Yeoh, G., Chi, J., Birnbaum, J., and Okayama, M. (1975) *Q. Rev. Biophys.* **8**, 523–557.

3. Pfenninger, K. H. (1978) *In* "The Neurosciences: Fourth Study Program." MIT Press, Cambridge, Massachusetts (in press).
4. Moscona, A. A., ed. (1974) "The Cell Surface in Development." Wiley, New York.
5. Barondes, S. H., ed. (1976) "Neuronal Recognition." Plenum, New York.
6. Pfenninger, K. H., and Rees, R. P. (1976) *In* "Neuronal Recognition" (S. H. Barondes, ed.), pp. 131–178. Plenum, New York.
7. Fischbach, G. D., and Gottlieb, D. I. (1978) *Neurosci. Res. Program, Bull.*, (in press).
8. Sharon, N., and Lis, H. (1972) *Science* **177**, 949–959.
9. Lis, H., and Sharon, N. (1977) *In* "The Antigens" (M. Sela, ed.), Vol. 4, pp. 429–529. Academic Press, New York.
10. Maylié-Pfenninger, M.-F., Palade, G. E., and Jamieson, J. D. (1975) *J. Cell Biol.* **67**, 333a.
11. Maylié-Pfenninger, M.-F., and Jamieson, J. D., (1978). Submitted for publication.
12. Pfenninger, K. H., and Maylié-Pfenninger, M.-F. (1975) *J. Cell Biol.* **67**, 322a.
13. Yamada, K. M., Spooner, B. S., and Wessells, N. K. (1971). *J. Cell Biol.* **49**, 614–635.
14. Wessells, N. K., Nuttall, R. P., Wrenn, J. T., and Johnson, S. (1976) *Proc. Natl. Acad. Sci. U.S.A.* **73**, 4100–4104.
15. Pfenninger, K. H., and Bunge, R. P. (1974) *J. Cell Biol.* **63**, 180–196.
16. Pfenninger, K. (1978) *Annu. Rev. Neurosci.* **1**, 445–471.
17. Hughes, A. (1953) *J. Anat.* **87**, 150–163.
18. Bray, D., (1970) *Proc. Natl. Acad. Sci. U.S.A.* **65**, 905–910.
19. Bray, D., (1973) *J. Cell Biol.* **56**, 702–712.
20. Pfenninger, K. H., and Maylié-Pfenninger, M.-F. (1977) *J. Cell Biol.* **75**, 54a.
21. Abercrombie, M., Heaysman, J. E. M., and Pegrum, S. M. (1970) *Exp. Cell Res.* **62**, 389–398.
22. Brown, S. S., and Revel, J.-P. (1976) *J. Cell Biol.* **68**, 629–641.
23. Taylor, R. B., Duffus, P. H., Raff, M. C., and DePetris, S. (1971) *Nature (London), New Biol.* **233**, 225–229.
24. Bunge, M. B. (1977) *J. Neurocytol.* **6**, 407–439.
25. Pfenninger, K. H., and Maylié-Pfenninger, M.-F. (1976) *Neurosci. Abstr.* **2**, Part 1, 224.
26. Barondes, S. H., and Rosen, S. D. (1976) *In* "Neuronal Recognition" (S. H. Barondes, ed.), pp. 331–356. Plenum, New York.
27. DeWaard, A., Hickman, S., and Kornfeld, S. (1976) *J. Biol. Chem.* **251**, 7581–7587.
28. Nowak, T. P., Haywood, P. L., and Barondes, S. H. (1976) *Biochem. Biophys. Res. Commun.* **68**, 650–657.
29. Beyer, E. C., Kobiler, D., Mir, F., and Barondes, S. H. (1977) *J. Cell Biol.* **75**, 29a.
30. Roth, S., McGuire, E. J., and Roseman, S. (1971) *J. Cell Biol.* **51**, 536–547.
31. Holtzman, E. (1977) *Neuroscience* **2**, 327–355.
32. Pfenninger, K. H. (1977) *In* "Neurotransmitter Function" (W. S. Fields, ed.), pp. 27–57. Symposia Specialists, Miami, Florida.
33. Palade, G. E. (1975) *Science* **189**, 347–358.

Selective Synapse Suppression as a Mechanism Contributing to Specificity of Connections in the Nervous System

J. W. YIP AND M. J. DENNIS
Departments of Physiology and Biochemistry
University of California
San Francisco, California

Development of highly specific synaptic connections between individual elements of the nervous system is crucial for the precise integration of activity which characterizes that system as a whole. How these connections are established and how inappropriate ones are avoided during the course of normal development is as yet little understood, although considerable attention has been paid to the subject (for reviews, see 1–7). We would like to consider here the evidence for one particular mechanism which may contribute to the development of such specific connections, namely, that maladaptive synaptic contacts sometimes form but are subsequently suppressed in favor of functionally appropriate ones. Although this phenomenon does occur, at least in some systems, there is no pretense that it is the only organizing principle in development of the nervous system. Rather, there is clearly a set of organizational devices which act in concert to produce the exquisite system by which we are possessed.

The central question in this regard is how the nervous system develops during embryogenesis, but most of the relevant information obtained so far has come from study of denervation and reinnervation of adult tissue. The reason for this emphasis is simply a technical one: adult tissue is much more easily studied, whether by behavioral, physiological, anatomical, or biochemical methods. Since reinnervation of adult structures is obviously somewhat different from normal

ISBN 0-12-398450-5

development, we must maintain some caution in generalizing from one condition to the other. However, studies on mature animals do reveal some general principles which can then be tested in developing systems. In addition, most work so far has been concerned with the specificity of synaptic connections between nerve and muscle, even though eventually we would like to understand the formation of synapses between neurons in the central nervous system. Again, this emphasis has arisen as a consequence of the relative ease of investigation of peripheral synapses. Certainly, the philosophy of studying a simple system to gain understanding of more complex ones has stood in good stead in investigation of the physiology of normal synaptic transmission.

Most of the early speculation on the specificity of nerve–muscle interaction is derived from Weiss' behavioral observations of muscle function in limb transplants in lower vertebrates (1,2). In a series of careful experiments, Weiss (8–12) implanted supernumerary limbs adjacent to the normal forelimbs of larval and adult salamanders. These implanted limbs were innervated by branches of the brachial nerves, which also innervated the adjacent normal limb. Upon activation of movement Weiss observed that the supernumerary limbs showed "homologous responses" to those of the normal limbs; that is, corresponding muscles in both the normal and the supernumerary limbs were excited synchronously. This situation obtained regardless of orientation of the implanted limb; thus, even when the dorsal–ventral or anterior–posterior axis of the implant was reversed relative to the normal, the homologous muscles were still activated synchronously. On the basis of histological observations, Weiss concluded (10) that such homologous responses in an implant resulted if there was innervation of *any* of the brachial nerves.

In an effort to account for this apparent sufficiency of any brachial nerve to produce coordinated limb function, Weiss (13) proposed a Resonance Principle of neuromuscular development. According to this scheme, the innervation of the developing limb was random, with each nerve to the limb sending branches to *all* of the muscles. As a consequence, central excitation would be broadcast to all of the muscles simultaneously. To explain the observed coordination of muscle activity, Weiss further proposed that each muscle responded only to a specific and characteristic pattern of nerve activity, that pattern being different for each muscle. Thus, he envisioned constant activity in the nerve, with each muscle responding only when its particular pattern of activity appeared. This accounted for the homologous responses of implanted and normal limbs. However, this theory lost credibility when Wiersma (14) recorded the activity of individual muscles and their nerves in the frog, and found that muscle contraction was always associated with impulse activity in the nerve, regardless of the pattern of that activity.

In a further effort to explain his behavioral observations, Weiss (1) put forth a revised theory, that of Myotypic Modulation. His new postulate was that each muscle had its own specificity, which was intrinsic, and that this specific character "modulated" the properties of the neurons which formed connections with the muscle. Thus, the central organization of a motoneuron was modulated by the muscle which it contacted so as to adapt to the correct function of that muscle. This theory had a profound impact on subsequent studies of the development of neuromuscular coordination, and it was used for the next 30 years to explain the recovery of function which follows peripheral nerve lesions in lower vertebrates. It did not, however, adequately explain all available experimental observations of nerve regeneration (15).

The theory of myotypic modulation remained in vogue until the mid-1960's when it was shown that return of proper function following nerve lesion in teleost fin muscles (16) and extraocular muscles (17) required specific reinnervation by the appropriate nerve. When antagonistic muscles were carefully cross-innervated, inappropriate use of those muscles persisted. These results were inconsistent with the idea that the central organization of motoneurons was being changed under the influence of new and different target muscles. A more recent study by Grimm (18) further disposed of the notion of myotypic modulation. She cross-innervated flexor and extensor muscles of the axolotl forelimb and showed that, although there was improper use of the limb initially, this was followed by recovery of normal function. By means of electrical stimulation of individual nerves, she demonstrated that there had been reinnervation of the muscles by their original nerves. Thus, Grimm's results supported the notion of selectivity of muscle reinnervation in the salamander.

Another situation in which selectivity of muscular reinnervation has been demonstrated involves slow and fast skeletal muscle fibers. These two types of fiber differ in both physiological properties and in mode of innervation. In the frog and toad, some muscles, such as the pyriformis, contain both fast and slow fibers. When these are denervated the slow muscle fibers are initially reinnervated by fast motor nerves (19), but this innervation is subsequently replaced by the appropriate slow innervation (19,20). Cross innervation studies in toad (21) and chicken (22) muscles have also demonstrated that fast and slow muscle fibers show a strong tendency toward establishment of correct synaptic connections (i.e., fast nerve to fast muscle, and vice versa) in a situation of competitive reinnervation by both fast and slow nerves. These latter studies did not consider whether incorrect contacts were initially formed and subsequently replaced. The status of selective reinnervation of fast and slow muscle fibers in the rat is less clear, for there have been claims both for (23) and against (24) such a process.

Thus, the myotypic modulation hypothesis has been contradicted by considerable evidence that selective reinnervation does occur. In retrospect it is apparent that (1) Weiss' behavioral observations were not sufficiently sensitive to monitor the extent and the accuracy of reinnervation of the individual muscles in supernumerary limbs, and (2) he was incorrect in assuming that implantation of a single brachial nerve into a supernumerary limb necessarily prevented access of the normal variety of motor nerves to that limb (25).

It is of interest to consider how specific synaptic connections do form during development. One mechanism which is obviously involved is a high degree of accuracy in the initial outgrowth of axons to their appropriate targets, as was recognized by Ramón y Cajal (26) from histological studies. Landmesser and Morris (27) and Morris (this volume) obtained physiological evidence that the motor innervation of muscles in developing chick leg is very precise at the earliest time that individual muscle masses can be identified. They showed that each ventral root contributing to the lumbar plexus projects to a characteristic region of muscle in a highly reproducible manner, as judged by stimulus evoked contraction. It is not clear, however, whether minor inaccuracies in the initial innervation pattern would have been revealed by this technique.

Despite the general accuracy of the projection of motor nerves, there is some alteration in synaptic connections subsequent to their initial formation. Mammalian skeletal muscle fibers are multiply innervated at birth, yet all but one of the synapses on each fiber are eliminated within the subsequent 2 weeks (28–31). The mechanisms underlying this synapse elimination are not known, although it is not due to death of motor neurons (30). Clearly, there is not an exact, one-to-one specificity in the initial formation of nerve–muscle synapses.

Another process which may also be involved in establishing the precise wiring of the mature nervous system is the elimination of any inappropriate synaptic connections, subsequent to establishment of the correct connections. The original proposal of suppression of incorrect synapses came from Mark and his collaborators (32,33). In adult carp they denervated the superior oblique muscle, removed the inferior oblique muscle, and implanted its nerve (cranial nerve III) into the superior oblique muscle. By monitoring the extraocular reflex responses to body tilt they judged the state of cross innervation of the superior oblique muscle. Initially the reflexes were inappropriate, as would be expected if successful cross-innervation by the foreign (IIId) nerve of the superior muscle had occurred. Later this inappropriate reflex disappeared in some fish; this, they concluded, was due to suppression of function of the foreign synapses upon reinnervation of the superior oblique by its correct nerve (cranial nerve IV). On the basis of these behavioral observations Mark and associates assumed that the foreign synapses had ceased transmitting, due to suppression of function upon return of the correct nerve. At this time when the correct extraocular reflexes were returning, that is, when correct reinnervation was occurring, they looked for and failed to find morphological evidence of nerve terminal degeneration (34,35). From this it was concluded that suppressed foreign synapses were morphologically normal but silent.

Scott (36) repeated the experimental procedure followed by Mark and observed the same change in pattern of the extraocular reflexes. However, she observed that even after return of the appropriate reflex, the superior muscle still contracted in response to tetanic stimulation of the foreign nerve. In addition, she was able to record foreign (IIId cranial nerve) synaptic potentials in fibers of the superior oblique muscle after they had been reinnervated by their correct nerve. For these reasons, Scott came to the conclusion that suppression of foreign synapses did not occur in the carp eye muscles as had been proposed by Mark. She believed, instead, that the loss of the inappropriate reflex resulted from regeneration of the inferior oblique muscle, which had been removed initially. Unfortunately, Scott's work suffers from some of the same weakness as Mark's, namely, that she did not determine the efficacy of foreign synaptic transmission as a function of time after correct reinnervation. It is conceivable, and not excluded by her work, that the amount of transmitter released from foreign terminals does decline even if it is not completely eliminated; this would still constitute suppression of function. Thus, a definitive statement about the presence or absence of foreign synapse suppression in goldfish extraocular muscle awaits further electrophysiological examination. Such an examination has been conducted to another fish muscle; Frank and Jansen (37) experimentally induced and studied the fate of foreign synapses on gill muscles of the perch. In that system reinnervation by the correct nerve caused no change in efficacy of transmission by foreign nerve.

In amphibia, several studies, including that of Grimm (18) and those of the fast versus slow muscle fiber reinnervation discussed above, indicate a selective preference for correct reinnervation of muscle fibers. Cass *et al.* (38) examined the competition between correct and foreign nerves for reinnervation of hindleg muscle in axolotl, using primarily evoked twitch as a monitor of the state of innervation. For this system, they again proposed that foreign synapses were suppressed upon reestablishment of correct innervation, and again claimed that suppressed foreign synapses retained their morphological integrity. Fangboner and Vanable (39) denervated the superior oblique muscle of *Xenopus* larvae and from histology combined with observation of evoked contraction showed that it was spontaneously reinnervated by both its correct (IVth cranial) nerve and fibers from the IIId cranial nerve (incorrect). These incorrect nerve sprouts were subsequently withdrawn in a manner which suggested that competition with the correct nerve was responsible for their displacement. The fact that the number of incorrect (N III) sprouts in the muscle declined with time was an indication against the retention of silent synapses after their suppression, as had been proposed by Mark and associates.

Given the significance of such a process of synapse suppression and the lack of relevant physiological information at the cellular level, we decided to reexamine foreign–correct synapse competition in salamanders in more detail, making use of both intracellular recording and selective labeling of synapses for electron microscopy. Our experimental procedure and observations (40,41) were as follows: in forelimbs of adult salamanders (*Notopthalamus viridescens*) the flexor nerve was implanted into extensor muscle. This "foreign" nerve developed functional synapses when the correct nerve to the extensor muscle was cut. Evoked foreign synaptic potentials, recorded intracellularly, were at first small, but increased to suprathreshold amplitude within several weeks, in the absence of reinnervation by the correct nerve. When the correct nerve did return to its muscle, the efficacy of foreign synaptic transmission began to decline. The onset of this decline was correlated with the resumption of correct nerve transmission, and it required a month or more to come to completion. This suppression of foreign transmission involved a reduction in quantal content of transmitter release with no apparent change in postsynaptic transmitter sensitivity. Before the return of the correct nerve 97% of the extensor muscle fibers were functionally innervated by the foreign nerve, while 4 to 6 months after correct nerve return only 35% of the fibers retained foreign synapses, with weak transmission. Thus, suppression of foreign synapses was sufficiently thorough that most, but not all, ceased transmitting. In this regard, our observations agree with and extend the findings of Cass *et al.* (38).

In disagreement with that previous work, we produced two lines of evidence which indicated that suppressed foreign synapses are lost from the muscle fibers. First, a repeated lesion of the correct nerve 6 to 8 months after the initial denervation produced no significant increase in the proportion of fibers with foreign transmission (36%). Second, to distinguish active correct synapses from putative silent foreign synapses, muscles which showed complete suppression of foreign transmission were bathed in medium containing horseradish peroxidase (HRP) and the correct nerve was stimulated repetitively. Subsequent histochemical staining for HRP and examination of synapses with an electron microscope showed that 94% of the axon terminals had HRP incorporated into vesicles. Thus, at least that percentage of identifiable synapses were made by correct nerve terminals. We conclude, therefore, that suppressed foreign synapses are physically eliminated from the muscle, either by withdrawal or degeneration. Unfortunately, the morphological technique used did not permit us to distinguish whether synapse elimination occurs concomitantly with or subsequent to suppression of function.

The earlier conclusion of Mark and his collaborators that suppressed synapses were structurally intact (34,35,38) was based on two lines of evidence: (1) the absence of degenerating synapses during correct reinnervation, and (2) the presence of both degenerating and structurally normal synapses several days after a second lesion of the correct nerve. We feel that these observations can be accounted for without invoking the presence of silent synapses. Upon suppression of foreign transmission, the terminals may retract without leaving recognizable degeneration products, as has been indicated in the elimination of polyneuronal innervation of neonatal rat skeletal muscle (42). Thus the absence of degeneration products need not necessarily imply the continued presence of synapses. Furthermore, the morphologically normal terminals in cross-innervated goldfish fibers seen after the correct nerve was recut (35) may well have been those of functional foreign synapses; the behavioral test used by those investigators would not have revealed subthreshold foreign transmission.

Given that foreign synapses are suppressed upon return of the correct nerve, at least in salamanders, the next question which arises is how such suppression is initiated. One possible mechanism would involve contact between foreign and correct axon terminals in the end plate region, with direct interaction triggering foreign terminal inactivation and/or withdrawal. An alternative possibility is that the competing terminals do not come into contact on the muscle. In this latter configuration it would be possible either that the signal for foreign terminal withdrawal is communicated by way of the muscle fiber, or that some feedback loop from muscle stretch receptors to motoneurons would indicate maladaptive connections by the "foreign" neurons, and somehow initiate their withdrawal. At the present time we have little information which pertains to this question.

The next level of inquiry regarding this process is directed at the actual cause of suppression of the transmitter release machinery in the foreign terminals. Again, we have little relevant information at the present time. It has been proposed on the basis of indirect evidence (43) that suppression of release involves a disruption of the entry of calcium into the axon terminal, which is required for normal secretion. Clearly our present lack of information indicates the need for more worthwhile results rather than more speculation.

In contrast to the situation in adult salamanders, adult mammals do not have the capacity to reject foreign innervation of skeletal muscle (30,44,45). Even though correct reinnervation may occur subsequent to foreign nerve implantation, the foreign transmission persists. This failure to restore the original pattern of nerve–muscle connections is consistent with clinical and behavioral (46) observations that coordinated use does not return following reinnervation of skeletal muscle of adult mammals.

Why is it that adult salamanders, and perhaps other lower vertebrates as well, have the ability to distinguish correct from incorrect motor innervation and suppress the latter, while adult mammals are unable to do so? An appealing explanation is that this capacity is one which is common to all embryos and is used in the genesis of the nervous system to assure accuracy in establishment of connections, but which is lost during maturation in higher vertebrates. This possibility is consistent with the fact that salamanders retain certain embryonic characteristics in adulthood, such as tails and the ability to regenerate limbs. We propose that another such neotenous characteristic is the ability to suppress incorrect synapses. If this interpretation is correct, one would expect to find examples during embryonic development of higher vertebrates of the formation and subsequent suppression of inappropriate synapses. This expectation is strengthened by the observation of Ramón y Cajal (26) that

. . . scholars have not paid sufficient attention to the truly remarkable number of developmental errors found both in central as well as peripheral terminations. We have presented numerous examples of these in embryonic spinal ganglia, spinal cord, medulla oblongata, cerebellum, retina, and in the regeneration of nerves, ganglia and spinal cord.

We have considered here the evidence for a process whereby improper synaptic connections in the nervous system can be detected and eliminated. Certainly such a phenomenon does occur in adult salamanders, and it may be more general during development. Perhaps it represents one of the mechanisms which give rise to the high degree of accuracy that exists in the structure of the mature nervous system. Clearly there are other processes which also contribute to this accuracy, such as directed outgrowth of cell processes and selective cell death. No one mechanism alone can account for the genesis of the sophistication and complexity of the nervous system, but together the processes give rise to a marvelous product.

REFERENCES

1. Weiss, P. (1936) *Biol. Rev. Cambridge Philos. Soc.* **11**, 494–531.
2. Weiss, P. (1941) *Comp. Psychol. Monogr.* **17**, 1–96.
3. Sperry, R. W. (1951) *In* "Handbook of Experimental Psychology" (S. S. Stevens, ed.), pp. 236–280. Wiley, New York.
4. Gaze, R. M. (1970) "The Formation of Nerve Connections." Academic Press, New York.
5. Jacobson, M. (1970) "Developmental Neurobiology." Holt, New York.
6. Harris, A. J. (1974) *Annu. Rev. Physiol.* **36**, 251–305.
7. Purves, D. (1976) *In* "Review of Physiology" (R. Porter, ed.), Vol. 10, pp. 125–178. Univ. Park Press, Baltimore, Maryland.
8. Weiss, P. (1922) *Angew. Akad. Wiss. Wien,* **59**, 199–201.
9. Weiss, P. (1937) *J. Comp. Neurol.* **66**, 181–209.
10. Weiss, P. (1937) *J. Comp. Neurol.* **66**, 481–535.
11. Weiss, P. (1937) *J. Comp. Neurol.* **66**, 537–548.
12. Weiss, P. (1937) *J. Comp. Neurol.* **67**, 269–315.
13. Weiss, P. (1926) *J. Comp. Neurol.* **40**, 241–251.
14. Wiersma, C. A. G. (1931) *Arch. Neerl. Physiol.* **16**, 337–345.
15. Arora, H. L., and Sperry, R. W. (1957) *J. Embryol. Exp. Morphol.* **5**, 256–263.
16. Mark, R. F. (1965) *Exp. Neurol.* **12**, 292–302.
17. Sperry, R. W., and Deupree, N. (1956) *J. Comp. Neurol.* **106**, 143–161.
18. Grimm, L. M. (1971) *J. Exp. Zool.* **178**, 419–496.
19. Elul, R., Miledi, R., and Stefani, E. (1970) *Acta Physiol. Lat.* **20**, 194–226.
20. Schmidt, H., and Stefani, E. (1976) *J. Physiol. (London)* **258**, 99–123.
21. Hoh, J. F. Y. (1971) *Exp. Neurol.* **30**, 263–276.
22. Feng, T. P., Wu, W. Y., and Yang, F. Y. (1965) *Sci. Sin.* **14**, 1717–1720.
23. Hoh, J.F.Y. (1975) *J. Physiol. (London)* **251**, 791–801.

24. Miledi, R., and Stefani, E. (1969) *Nature (London)* **222**, 569–571.
25. Székely, G., and Czéh, G. (1967) *Acta Physiol. Acad. Sci. Hung* **32**, 3–18.
26. Ramón y Cajal, S. (1929) "Studies on Vertebrate Neurogenesis" (L. Guth, transl.). Thomas, Springfield, Illinois.
27. Landmesser, L., and Morris, D. G. (1975) *J. Physiol. (London)* **249**, 301–326.
28. Redfern, P. A. (1970) *J. Physiol. (London)* **209**, 701–709.
29. Bagust, J., Lewis, D. M., and Westerman, R. A. (1973) *J. Physiol. (London)* **229**, 241–255.
30. Brown, M. C., Jansen, J. K. S., and Van Essen, D. (1976) *J. Physiol. (London)* **261**, 387–422.
31. Rosenthal, J. L., and Taraskevich, P. S. (1977) *J. Physiol. (London)* **270**, 299–310.
32. Marotte, L. R., and Mark, R. F. (1970) *Brain Res.* **19**, 41–53.
33. Mark, R. F., and Marotte, L. R. (1972) *Brain Res.* **46**, 131–148.
34. Marotte, L. R., and Mark, R. F. (1970) *Brain Res.* **19**, 53–62.
35. Mark, R. F., Marotte, L. R., and Mart, P. E. (1972) *Brain Res.* **46**, 149–157.
36. Scott, S. A. (1975) *Science* **189**, 644–646.
37. Frank, E., and Jansen, J. K. S. (1976) *J. Neurophysiol.* **39**, 84–90.
38. Cass, D. T., Sutton, T. J., and Mark, R. F. (1973) *Nature (London)* **243**, 201–203.
39. Fangboner, R. F., and Vanable, J. W. (1974) *J. Comp. Neurol.* **157**, 391–406.
40. Yip, J. W., and Dennis, M. J. (1976) *Nature (London)* **260**, 350–352.
41. Dennis, M. J., and Yip, J. W. (1978) *J. Physiol. (London)* **274**, 299–310.
42. Korneliussen, H., and Jansen, J. K. S. (1976) *J. Neurocytol.* **5**, 591–604.
43. Harris, A. J., Wigston, D., and Ziskind, L. (1977) *Nature (London)* **268**, 265–267.
44. Bernstein, J. J., and Guth, L. (1961) *Exp. Neurol.* **4**, 262–275.
45. Frank, E., Jansen, J. K. S., Lømo, T., and Westgaard, R. H. (1975) *J. Physiol. (London)* **247**, 725–743.
46. Sperry, R. W. (1945) *Q. Rev. Biol.* **26**, 314–363.

The Functional Motor Innervation of Supernumerary Hind Limbs in the Chick Embryo

DEBORAH G. MORRIS
Department of Physiology
Harvard Medical School
Boston, Massachusetts

INTRODUCTION

The existing data indicate that the hind limbs of mammals and amphibia are innervated by specific columns of motoneurons with characteristic positions in the spinal cord (Romanes, 1,2; Cruce, 3; Székely and Czéh, 4; Burke *et al.*, 5). It is not known, however, how these motoneurons establish their appropriate peripheral connections during development.

Much of the recent literature in developmental neurobiology outlines three major hypotheses for the development of neuromuscular connections. They are (1) motoneurons are intrinsically "specified" (the tendency for a neuron to synapse invariably with a postsynaptic site) to make appropriate peripheral connections; (2) motoneurons make random peripheral connections and are then "specified" by individual muscles to receive appropriate central connections; and (3) motoneurons form appropriate peripheral connections by the matching of presynaptic cells to appropriate postsynaptic sites because of the target tissues' availability in time and/or space.

Initially it was important to determine if an innervation pattern could be detected at early developmental stages. An earlier study (Hughes and Prestige, 6) on the amphibian hind limb showed that the

ISBN 0-12-398450-5

first functional synapses, as demonstrated by spinal nerve stimulation and the subsequent observation of contraction of the embryonic limb musculature, formed a diffuse innervation pattern. This pattern became more precise at later developmental stages. Recently these findings were confirmed in a study in which HRP was injected to regions of the embryonic muscle mass (Lamb, 7).

Experiments similar to those performed by Hughes and Prestige (6) were used to test the initial functional motor innervation in the chick embryo hind limb (Landmesser and Morris, 8). Spinal nerve stimulation, visual observation of contraction in the embryonic musculature, tension recordings, and compound action potential recordings from muscle nerves demonstrated that the initial functional synapses (formed at Stages 27–28, 5.5 days) did not form a random or diffuse innervation pattern, but a specific pattern emerged at the onset. Figure

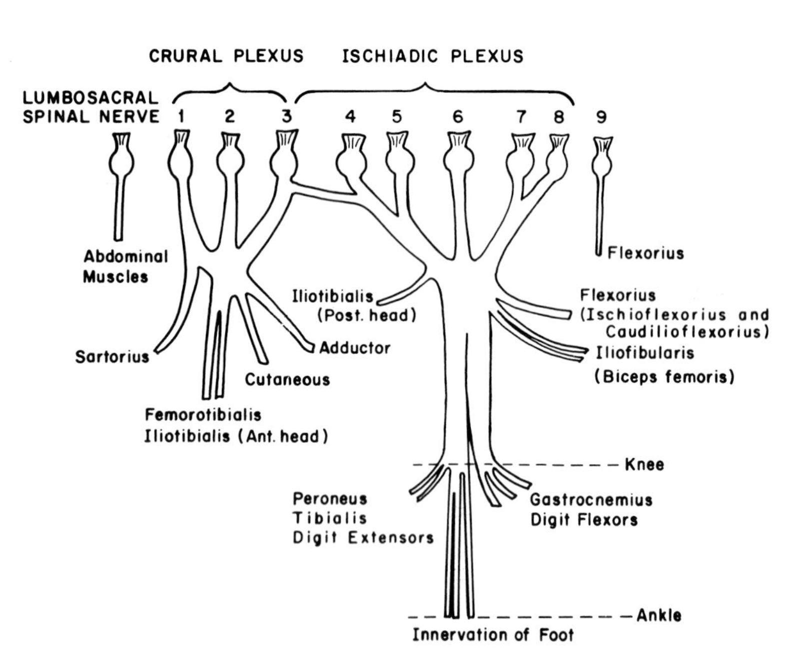

Fig. 1. (A) A schematic diagram of the innervation of the chick hind limb. Lumbosacral spinal nerves 1–9, corresponding to spinal ganglia 23–31 (14), contribute to the major muscle nerves represented here. (B) Lateral and medial views of the hind limb musculature of the chick as it appears at Stage 33 (top) and Stages 27–29 (opposite). At Stage 33 the hind limb is a miniature adult limb. The primitive muscle masses (dorsal and ventral) are shown below as they appear at Stages 27–29. The muscles that are derived from these masses are indicated.

1A shows spinal nerves innervating the chick hind limb musculature; and Fig. 1B shows the muscles studied. Following sequential spinal nerve stimulation of 100 animals and observation of limb muscles, the innervation pattern shown in Fig. 2 was apparent. The pattern was consistent throughout development.

When these findings were reviewed in light of the three major hypotheses for the formation of neuromuscular connections, they were inconsistent with random outgrowth and myotypic specification (Weiss, 9). In addition, the existing theories concerning the matching of a cranio–caudal gradient of maturation in the cord with the proximo–distal innervation of the limb (Hughes, 10; Jacobson, 11) did not explain the innervation pattern observed. However, the data were consistent with the theory of intrinsic specification.

The experiments on the normal development of motor innervation in the chick hind limb could not determine whether motoneurons were "intrinsically" (at a very early stage of development) specified for certain muscles, or whether they were specified at some later time, perhaps involving interaction with the periphery. In order to determine whether motoneurons of the chick exhibited any intrinsic dif-

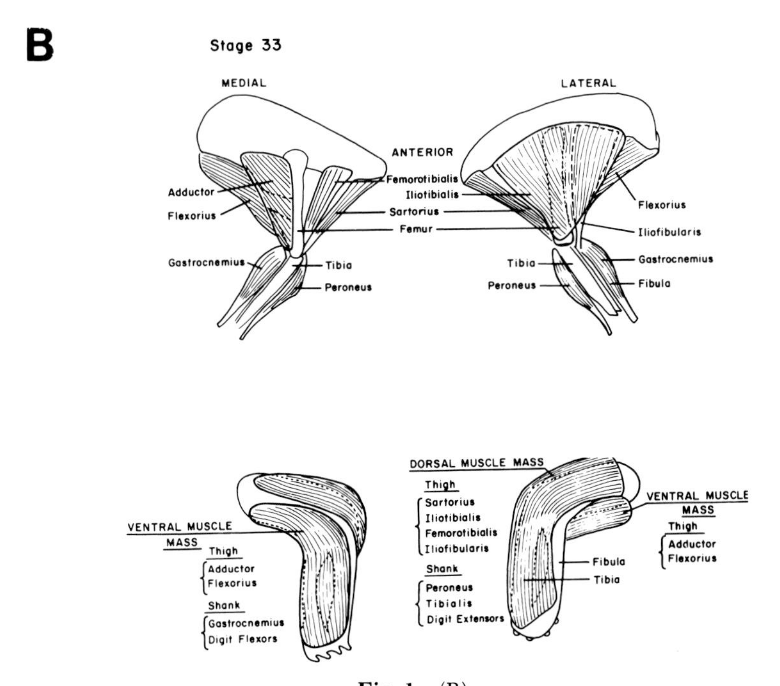

Fig. 1. (B)

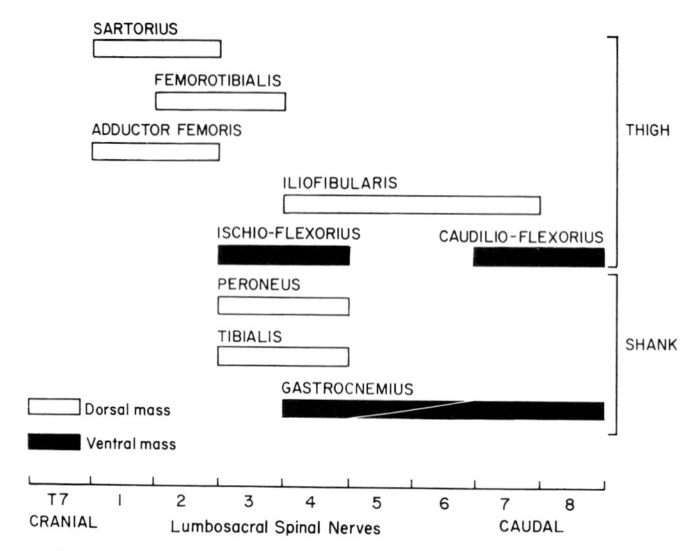

Fig. 2. The innervation pattern determined for selected muscles of the chick hind limb. This figure summarizes results obtained from movement, twitch tension, and compound action potential data. Each bar represents the contribution of the lumbosacral spinal nerves innervating a given muscle. Spinal nerves to the left are more cranial than those to the right. Open bars represent muscles derived from the embryonic dorsal muscle mass; filled bars, muscles from the ventral mass. The iliotibialis has been divided into anterior and posterior heads. The flexorius group has been divided into the ischioflexorius and caudilioflexorius. The gastrocnemius has been divided into its medial (left) and lateral (right) heads. This figure has been revised from Landmesser and Morris (8).

ferences with respect to the muscles they will come to innervate or whether the limb has any influence on motoneuron axon outgrowth and synapse formation, a study involving supernumerary limbs was undertaken (Morris, 12,13).

RESULTS

THE ANATOMICAL INNERVATION PATTERN OF SUPERNUMERARY HIND LIMBS

Hind limb buds from donor embryos (2–3 days; Stages 16–18) were transplanted to three general positions along the axis of the host embryos of the same age: (1) rostral, where they would receive only thoracic innervation; (2) slightly rostral to the normal limb where they would receive combined thoracic–lumbosacral innervation; and (3)

Fig. 3. A stage 40 embryo with a supernumerary hind limb in a thoracic–lumbosacral position. The transplanted limb musculature was innervated by thoracic spinal nerves 5, 6, 7 and lumbosacral nerves 1 and 2.

largely overlapping the normal limb, where the transplant would receive only lumbosacral innervation. The technique of chick limb bud transplantation in this series of experiments was similar to that previously described by Hamburger (14,15). An example of a late embryo used in the present series of experiments is shown in Fig. 3.

The anatomical innervation pattern was determined by dissection. While there was considerable variation in the number of spinal nerves entering the limb, the innervation pattern seen in supernumerary limbs was similar to that seen in normal limbs (Fig. 4).

The branching pattern of muscle nerves observed was similar from transplant to transplant and throughout development; however, dissection could not reveal which spinal nerves contributed to the innervation of any given muscle. Thus spinal nerves were stimulated and the contraction of individual muscles within the supernumerary was scored.

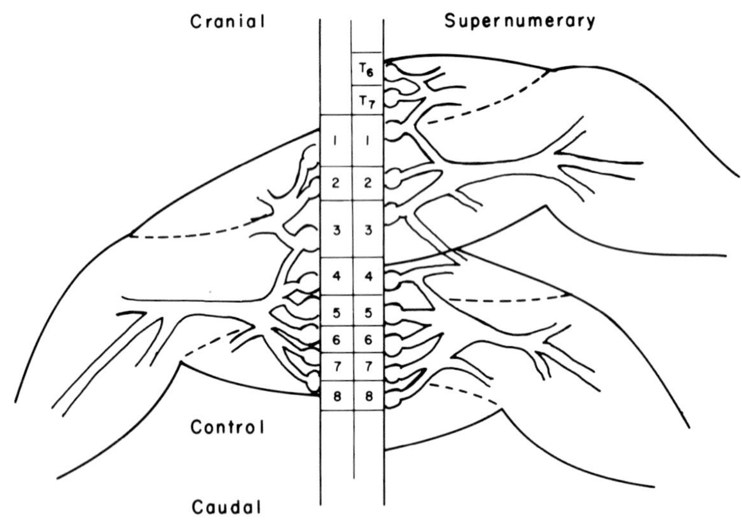

Fig. 4. Schematic diagram of the innervation pattern seen in the supernumerary (upper right), ipsilateral normal (lower right), and contralateral (left) hind limbs. In three cases limbs were transplanted near thoracic segments which formed the crural plexus, supplying primarily anterior thigh musculature. Lumbosacral spinal nerves 1–3 formed an ischiatic plexus and gave rise to a sciatic nerve which innervated posterior thigh muscles as well as the supernumerary shank and foot. The first contributing spinal nerve to the ipsilateral normal limb innervated some preaxial musculature. Lumbosacral spinal nerves 5–8 formed the sciatic nerve with a contribution from LS4 via a ramus. The branching pattern of muscle nerves innervating the supernumerary and ipsilateral normal hind limbs resembled that seen in the hind limbs of unoperated (control) animals.

CONTRACTION CAUSED BY SPINAL NERVE STIMULATION

Thoracic, lumbosacral, or thoracic and lumbosacral spinal nerves could contribute to the supernumerary limb. This variation in spinal nerve contribution depended upon the cranio–caudal placement of the limb bud at the time of transplantation. However, there was some variation in spinal nerve contribution even when limb buds were

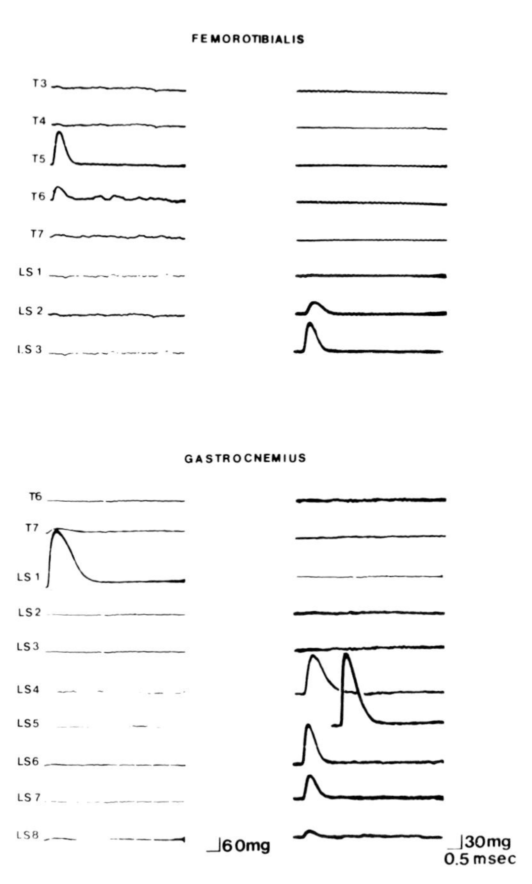

Fig. 5. Isometric twitch tension responses from the supernumerary femorotibialis (upper right) and gastrocnemius (lower right). Both supernumerary and control responses were elicited by sequentially stimulating spinal nerves with single shocks (0.5 msec duration) in Stage 40 embryos. Inappropriate spinal nerves T5 and T6 caused the supernumerary femorotibialis to contract, while only spinal nerves LS2 and LS3 caused contraction of the control femorotibialis. Inappropriate spinal nerves T7 and LS1 caused the supernumerary gastrocnemius (lateral and medial heads) to contract, while lumbosacral spinal nerves 4, 5, 6, 7, and 8 caused the lateral and medial heads of the control gastrocnemius to contract.

placed in the same general location; they had apparently healed somewhat differently.

The spinal nerves contributing to the innervation of a given muscle also varied with limb position. In order to quantify the relative contributions of different spinal nerves to a muscle twitch tension was measured. Tension records from the supernumerary femorotibialis and gastrocnemius muscles are shown in Fig. 5 for a St. 40 animal. Stimulation of spinal nerves T(thoracic)5 and T6 caused twitches of the femorotibialis; these spinal nerves never caused contraction of this muscle in normal animals (Landmesser and Morris, 8) and are referred to in this study as "inappropriate innervation." The supernumerary gastrocnemius in Fig. 5 was innervated by spinal nerves T7 and LS1. Results showing the variation in spinal nerve contribution for the femorotibialis and flexorius group (composed of the ischioflexorius which inserts on the tibia and the caudilioflexorius which inserts on both the femur and tibia) of three animals with supernumerary limbs are shown in Fig. 6. Here the spinal nerve producing the maximum twitch tension is said to produce 100% tension; other spinal nerve contributions are expressed as a fraction of this value. (Spinal nerve stimulation and tension recording techniques have been previously described, Landmesser and Morris, 8).

In order to determine whether or not there was a pattern matching certain spinal nerves to specific muscles, the variation of limb position and its effect on the spinal nerve contribution were normalized for, by designating the most cranial of the spinal nerves innervating the limb "normalized spinal nerve 1," while more caudal spinal nerves were assigned normalized spinal nerves 2 and 3, etc. This is shown in Fig. 7 for the femorotibialis. Similar normalized spinal nerves innervated a given muscle from preparation to preparation and throughout development. These results are summarized in Table I for animals Stages 35–41. Here the mean twitch tension (± S.D.) is presented. The standard deviation for some spinal nerve contributions was very large; this was due to the fact that the same normalized spinal nerve did not always contribute to the innervation of a given muscle. There was also considerable variation in the amount of tension produced by any normalized spinal nerve.

Table II summarizes the number of cases in which spinal nerve stimulation caused contraction (as scored visually) of eight muscles studied in supernumerary limbs in a thoracic–lumbosacral position. When the data from Tables I and II are compared with Fig. 2, it can be seen that the innervation pattern observed in supernumerary hindlimbs is similar to that seen in the hind limbs of normal animals.

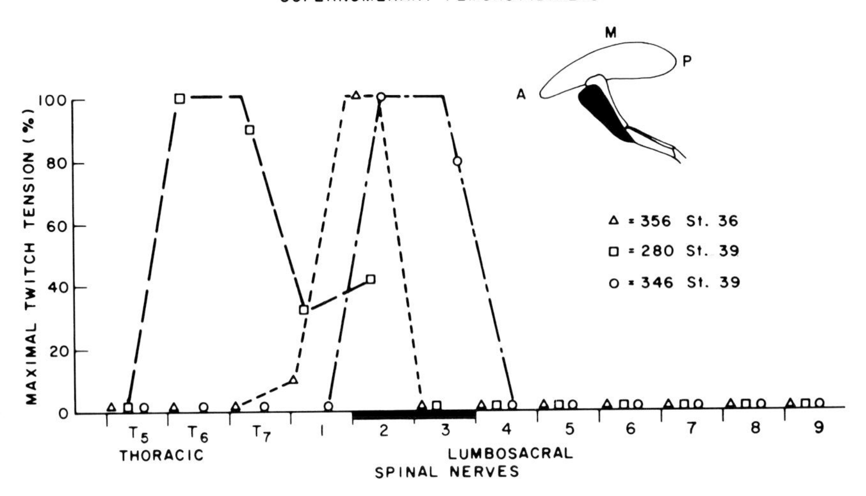

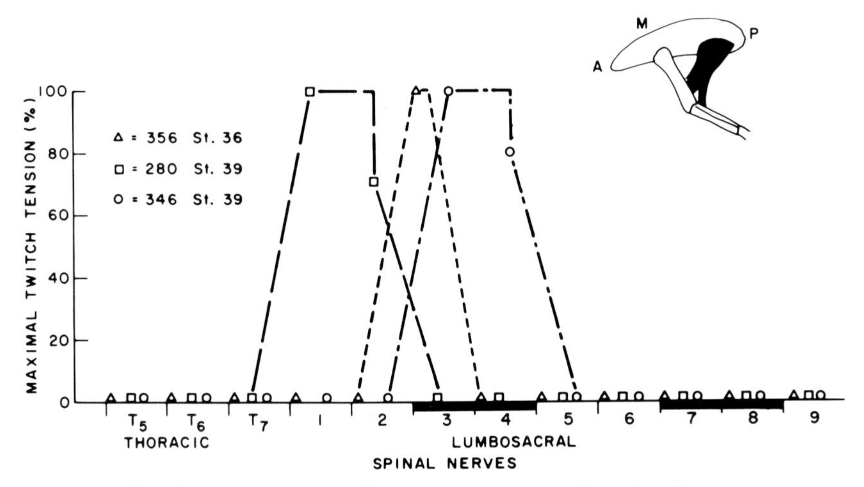

Fig. 6. The relative proportion of isometric tension produced in the supernumerary femorotibialis (top) and flexorius group (bottom) by sequential spinal nerve stimulation. The contribution of spinal nerves to the muscles varied with the position of the limb, as can be seen for the three cases shown. The spinal nerve producing maximal twitch tension was said to produce 100% tension and the contribution of other spinal nerves was expressed as a fraction of this. The spinal nerves which consistently contribute to the innervation of the femorotibialis in control animals have been underscored. The anatomical arrangement of the muscles is shown to the right. M represents the medial surface of the limb; A, anterior or preaxial surface; and P, posterior or postaxial.

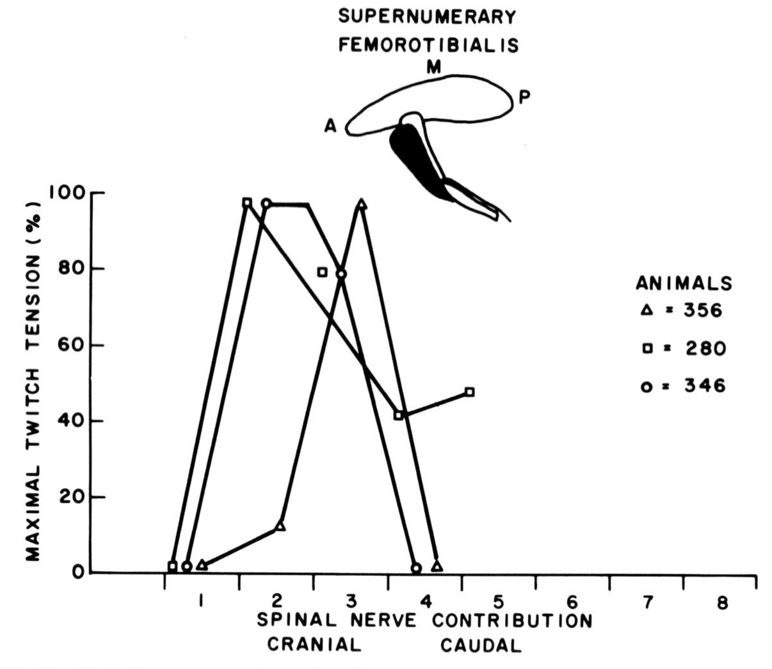

Fig. 7. Twitch tension produced in the supernumerary femorotibialis by sequential spinal nerve stimulation. Here the spinal nerve contribution has been normalized with respect to the most cranial of the contributing spinal nerves in the three cases shown. The normalized spinal nerve producing maximal tension was said to produce 100% tension; the contribution of other normalized spinal nerves was expressed as a percentage of this maximum. The anatomical arrangement of the femorotibialis is shown above.

The most cranial of the spinal nerves entering the limb (for thoracic–lumbosacral limbs these nerves were T5–T7) innervated the supernumerary sartorius and femorotibialis, although the femorotibialis is in turn innervated by more caudal segments than those contributing to the sartorius. The more caudal spinal nerves innervated muscles on the posterior surface of the thigh (posterior to the femur, see Fig. 1B) such as the flexorius group (ischioflexorius and caudilioflexorius) and iliofibularis, as occurs in the normal animal. Two muscles which have a similar origin (see Fig. 5B), the ischioflexorius and caudilioflexorius, also show an innervation pattern similar to normal; the ischioflexorius tends to receive spinal nerves from more cranial segments than the caudilioflexorius in normal and in transplanted limbs (compare Table I with Fig. 2). The differences in the innervation pattern of these two muscles in the supernumerary limb is not as marked as in the normal.

TABLE I
Percent Contribution (Mean ± S.D.) of Spinal Nerves to the Twitch Tension Normalized Thoracic–Lumbosacral Spinal Nerve Contribution

1	2	3	4	5	Number of observations
			Sartorius		
76 ± 48	50 ± 58	0	0	0	4
			Femorotibialis		
80 ± 4	74 ± 24	6 ± 14	8 ± 18	0	5
			Flexorius Group		
0	0	50 ± 71	86 ± 21	0	2
			Peroneus		
0	0	100	50 ± 71	0	2
			Tibialis		
0	0	56 ± 52	50 ± 58	16 ± 32	4
			Lateral and Medial Gastrocnemius		
0	0	60 ± 44	85 ± 37	17 ± 41	6

In the normal limbs there is not a strict matching of cranial spinal nerves with preaxial muscles (anterior to the femur or tibia) and postaxial muscles (posterior to the femur and tibia) by more caudal motoneurons. The adductor is a clear exception to this trend (see Fig. 2). Supernumerary limbs in the thoracic–lumbosacral position did not clearly follow this pattern. In one-half of the cases studied the supernumerary adductor receives from more caudal segments than strict adherence to the normal pattern would predict. In other cases, the supernumerary adductor was innervated by normalized spinal nerve 1, which resembles the normal trend (see Fig. 2).

In the shank, the supernumerary peroneus and tibialis, on the preaxial surface, are innervated by more caudal spinal nerves than those innervating the preaxial thigh musculature as in the normal limb. The supernumerary peroneus is innervated by more cranial spinal nerves than those innervating the gastrocnemius. In general, there is more overlap in the contribution of spinal nerves to individual muscles in the supernumerary limb; this is expected since there are fewer spinal nerves contributing to the limb (generally five instead of eight).

Although the innervation pattern seen in these supernumerary limbs resembled that of normal limbs, it was clear that there was no tendency for spinal cord segments to innervate the same muscles that they normally would have. In 70% of the cases studied the sartorius

TABLE II
Percent of Cases Where Movement Was Elicited by Stimulation of Individual Spinal Nerves
Normalized Thoracic–Lumbosacral Spinal Nerve Contribution

1	2	3	4	5	6	Number of observations
			Sartorius			
100	64	0	0	0	0	11
			Femorotibialis			
92	92	8	8	0	0	13
			Adductor			
50	0	50	0	0	0	4
			Flexorius–Ischioflexorius			
0	0	67	44	0	0	9
			Flexorius–Caudilioflexorius			
0	0	40	50	10	0	10
			Iliofibularis			
0	20	80	20	20	0	5
			Peroneus			
0	20	80	60	20	0	5
			Tibialis			
0	0	83	50	16	0	6
			Lateral and Medial Gastrocnemius			
0	25	67	50	17	8	12

was innervated by thoracic (nonlimb) segments; this was true in 60% of the cases for the femorotibialis. The more cranial of the lumbosacral segments which normally innervated these muscles contributed to the innervation of the limb in all cases; however, in only a few cases did they innervate their appropriate muscle. In addition, inappropriate spinal nerves could also elicit contraction from supernumerary muscles innervated by their own spinal nerves.

The tendency for certain "normalized" spinal nerves to innervate a given muscle was seen when the supernumerary limb was transplanted to overlap extensively with the normal limb or was placed in a thoracic region. This is seen in Tables III–V. However, when only lumbosacral spinal nerves contributed to the transplanted limb, spinal nerves did not innervate the same muscles that they would in the normal embryo. The femorotibialis, which was normally never innervated by LSl, was caused to contract by this spinal nerve in 93% of the cases studied. The ischioflexorius was innervated by inappropriate

TABLE III
Percent of Cases Where Movement Was Elicited by Stimulation of Individual Spinal Nerves
Normalized Lumbosacral Spinal Nerve Contribution

1	2	3	4	Number of observations
			Sartorius	
100	7	0	0	14
			Femorotibialis	
93	38	0	0	14
			Adductor	
14	100	14	0	7
			Flexorius–Ischioflexorius	
10	60	70	20	10
			Flexorius–Caudilioflexorius	
0	18	73	45	11
			Iliofibularis	
0	0	100	100	3
			Tibialis	
6	75	56	19	16
			Lateral and Medial Gastrocnemius	
0	50	64	29	14

TABLE IV
Percent Contribution (Mean ± S.D.) of Spinal Nerves to the Twitch Tension
Normalized Lumbosacral Spinal Nerve Contribution

1	2	3	4	5	Number of observations
			Sartorius		
92 ± 20	17 ± 41	0	0	0	6
			Femorotibialis		
80 ± 33	48 ± 51	0	0	0	8
			Flexorius		
0	43 ± 36	93 ± 11	19 ± 40	0	6
			Tibialis		
11.5 ± 29	68 ± 45	44 ± 46	25 ± 46	0	8
			Lateral and Medial Gastrocnemius		
0	77 ± 44	58 ± 42	18 ± 27	3 ± 8	9

TABLE V
Percent of Cases Where Movement Was Elicited by Stimulation of Individual Spinal Nerves
Normalized Thoracic Spinal Nerve Contribution

1	2	3	4	5	Number of observations
			Sartorius		
92 ± 20	17 ± 41	0	0	0	6
			Femorotibialis		
80 ± 33	48 ± 51	0	0	0	8
			Flexorius		
0	43 ± 36	93 ± 11	19 ± 40	0	6
			Tibialis		
11.5 + 29	68 ± 45	44 ± 46	25 ± 46	0	8
		Lateral and Medial Gastrocnemius			
0	77 ± 44	58 ± 42	18 ± 27	3 ± 8	9

			Sartorius			
80	40	0	0	0	0	10
			Femorotibialis			
63	100	13	13	0	0	8
		Flexorius Group (Ischioflexorius and Caudilioflexorius)				
0	17	66	66	33	33	6
			Iliofibularis			
0	25	75	25	25	0	4
			Peroneus			
0	40	60	60	20	0	5
		Lateral and Medial Gastrocnemius				
0	0	20	80	40	0	5

spinal nerves in 60% of the cases; the caudilioflexorius in 100% of cases; adductor in 14% of cases; iliofibularis in 80% of cases; tibialis in 79% of cases; and the gastrocnemius in 86% of cases.

COMPOUND ACTION POTENTIAL RECORDINGS

Compound action potentials were recorded from individual muscle nerves to supernumerary limbs in thoracic–lumbosacral and lumbosacral positions. A similar pattern was obtained from nerve recordings as was previously seen for tension measurements (Table VI). These results indicate that motoneurons did not send axons to muscles of the supernumerary limb and then fail to form synapses to any great extent.

TABLE VI
Percent Contribution (Mean ± S.D.) of Spinal Nerves to Muscle–Nerve Compound Action Potentials Normalized Thoracic–Lumbosacral and Lumbrosacral

1	2	3	4	5	Number of observations
			Sartorius		
100	90 ± 14	0	0	0	2
			Femorotibialis		
49.6 ± 50	57.8 ± 43	0	0	0	5
			Flexorius–Ischioflexorius		
0	0	66.6 ± 58	11.7 ± 20	0	3
			Flexorius–Caudilioflexorius		
0	0	40 ± 55	64 ± 50	0	5
			Peroneus		
0	33.3 ± 58	74.3 ± 44	0	0	3
			Lateral and Medial Gastrocnemius		
0	21 ± 44	49.4 ± 47	40 ± 55	1.2 ± 3	5

The data also suggest that movement and tension recordings were sensitive indications of the spinal nerve contribution. If spinal nerve stimulation produced many subthreshold postsynaptic potentials that were subliminal for contraction, a different pattern may have been detected by nerve recordings.

THE INNERVATION OF ANTERIOR–POSTERIOR REVERSED LIMBS

The innervation pattern observed in all of the previous experiments using supernumerary limbs suggested that the limb could influence the growth of axons so that a fairly normal innervation pattern would result. Furthermore, lumbosacral motoneurons when entering the limb from abnormal positions did not appear to grow to their own muscles. In order to test this possibility further, the anatomical disparity between spinal cord segment and the muscles they would normally have come to innervate was increased by transplanting limbs with the anterior–posterior axis reversed.

At the time of limb bud transplantation the anterior portion of the limb bud, which gives rise to preaxial musculature, was placed adjacent to caudal spinal cord segments, while the posterior portion was placed adjacent to cranial cord segments. The left limb bud was trans-

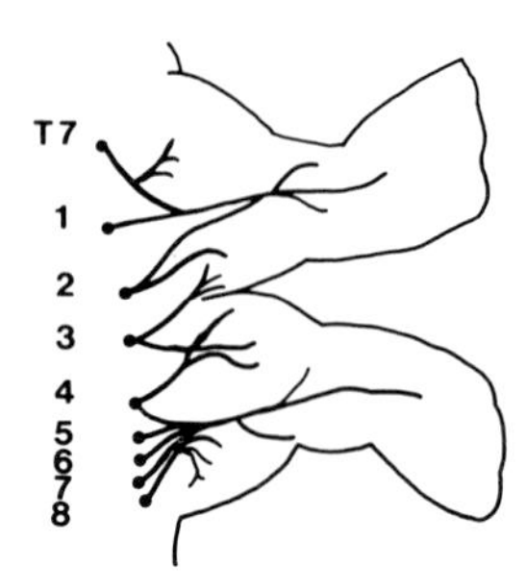

Fig. 8. (A) The innervation pattern seen in anterior–posterior reversed supernumerary limb (top) and the ipsilateral normal limb (bottom). The pattern was reconstructed from 15 μm longitudinal sections of the limbs stained by the method of Cajal and De Castro. (B) Longitudinal sections through the normal and supernumerary limbs of a Stage 28 embryo with a thoracic–lumbosacral limb which was reversed along the anterior–posterior axis. The bar in the top figure represents 0.5 mm; in the bottom figure, 0.1 mm. s, represents supernumerary; n, normal.

planted to the right side of the animal such that the dorso–ventral axis remained the same as that of normal limbs (Fig. 8).

Table VII summarizes results for animals (Stages 30–40) with reversed supernumerary limbs. As can be seen the innervation pattern observed is reversed from that seen in normal limbs (see Fig. 2) and supernumerary limbs with a normal orientation (see Table III). The most caudal of the contributing spinal nerves innervated muscles on the preaxial surface of the thigh, while the most cranial segments innervated muscles on the postaxial surface. In addition, the sartorius was innervated by more caudal segments than those innervating the femorotibialis. The ischioflexorius similarly receives innervation from segments more caudal to those innervating the caudilioflexorius, although both muscles are now innervated by the most cranial of the contributing segments. The adductor, while in anatomical proximity to these muscles on the posterior surface of the thigh, receives innervation from the more caudal segments that innervate the sartorius. A similar reversed pattern of innervation was seen in the shank for the peroneus, tibialis, and gastrocnemius. Thus the relative positions of muscles as they are represented in the cord is conserved but in reversed order.

B

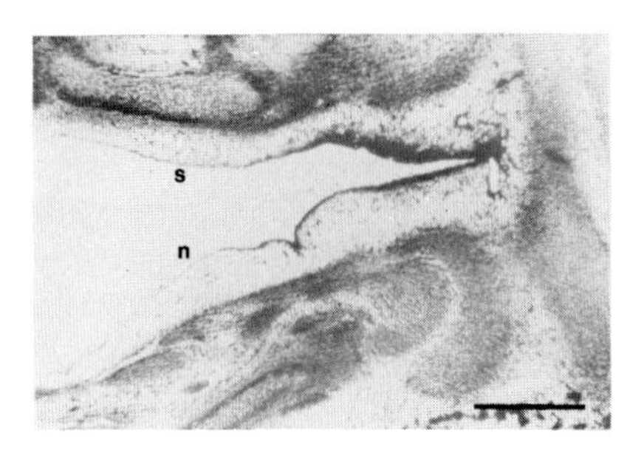

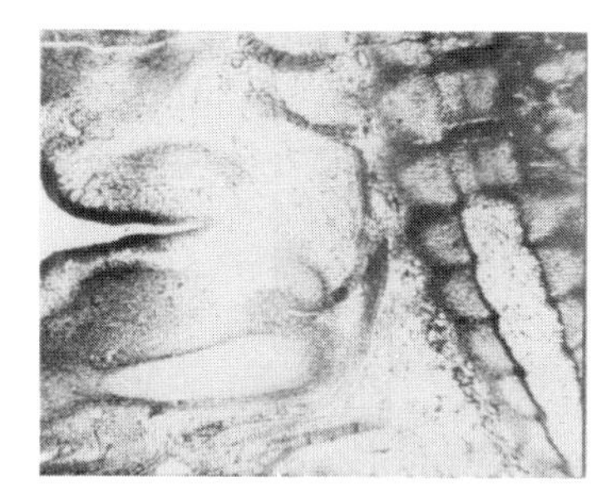

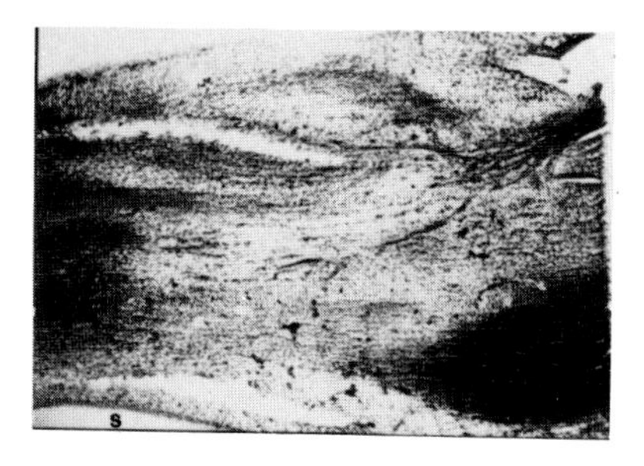

Fig. 8 (B)

One additional observation is that distal limb muscles are now innervated by more cranial motoneurons, indicating that there need not be a strict coincidence between the cranial–caudal axis in the cord and the proximo–distal axis in the limb, as has often been proposed (Romanes, 16,17; Roncali, 18).

TABLE VII
Percent of Cases in Which Individual Spinal Nerve Stimulation Caused Contraction of Muscles in A–P Reversed Limbs Normalized Spinal Nerve Contribution

1	2	3	4	Number of observations
		Sartorius		
0	0	44%	55%	9
		Femorotibialis		
0	30%	70%	20%	10
		Adductor		
8	38%	75%	25%	8
		Flexorius–Ischioflexorius		
25%	75%	25%	0	4
		Flexorius–Caudilioflexorius		
100%	33%	0	0	9
		Iliofibularis		
75%	25%	25%	0	4
		Peroneus		
0	75%	50%	0	4
		Tibialis		
0	33%	89%	0	9
		Lateral and Medial Gastrocnemius		
55%	64%	27%	0	11

When the data from Table III (the innervation pattern of lumbosacral limbs in a normal (a–p) orientation) and Table VIII(thoracic–lumbosacral and lumbosacral limbs in a reversed a–p orientation) were compared using Pearson correlation coefficients the results in Table VIII were obtained. It can be seen that the muscles innervated by spinal nerve 1 in supernumerary limbs of normal orientation were similar to the innervation pattern observed for spinal nerve 4, for animals in which the limb was reversed; as can be seen, the correlation coefficient derived when the percentage contribution of these two spinal nerves was compared is large and positive. In addition, other mirror image spinal nerves were also correlated.

THE POSITION OF MOTONEURON CELL BODIES INNERVATING THE SUPERNUMERARY LIMB

Although a considerable amount of evidence from silver-stained sections of the spinal cord (Ramón y Cajal, 19; Windle and Orr, 20)

TABLE VIII
Pearson Correlations between Spinal Nerves Innervating A–P Reversed Supernumerary Limbs and Supernumerary Limbs in the Normal Orientation

Spinal nerves to the supernumerary limb of normal orientation	vs.	Spinal nerves to the supernumerary limb of reversed orientation	r
1		4	0.84[a]
2		3	0.65[a]
3		2	0.56
4		1	0.63[a]

[a] Correlation coefficients are significant at $p > 0.05$.

and more recently from horseradish peroxidase (HRP) backfilling of cat motoneurons (Burke *et al.*, 5) suggests that in normal animals motoneurons send their axons out through the closest spinal nerve, this situation might be altered by surgical transplantation.

All of the preceding experiments have relied on spinal nerve stimulation to determine the innervation pattern of supernumerary limbs. The data reflected the innervation pattern of spinal nerves rather than the actual position of motoneuron cell bodies in the cord. In order to determine whether the position of motoneurons was accurately represented by the spinal nerve stimulation, HRP backfilling of motoneurons was used.

The earliest stage in which HRP was used to determine motoneuron position was Stage 29. In three embryos with thoracic—lumbosacral limbs, the postaxial surface (presumptive flexorius group and gastrocnemius) was injected *in ovo* with HRP (according to techniques described by Oppenheim and Heaton, 21). The enzyme was successfully transported back to the motoneuron cell bodies; the embryonic spinal cord was sectioned, reacted, and subsequently visualized under the light microscope. A typical example of these results is shown in Fig. 9. Segments LS1–4 show motoneurons with the reaction product; HRP granules were not seen in the motoneurons of segments 5–8. Spinal nerves and limbs of the animals studied were severed from the cord, and placed in oxygenated avain tyrode, before the cords were fixed. Only spinal nerves from the same segments that were later shown to contain peroxidase-labeled motoneurons caused postaxial limb musculature to contract.

At later developmental Stages 34–42, injections into individual muscles of the supernumerary and control (unoperated) limbs fol-

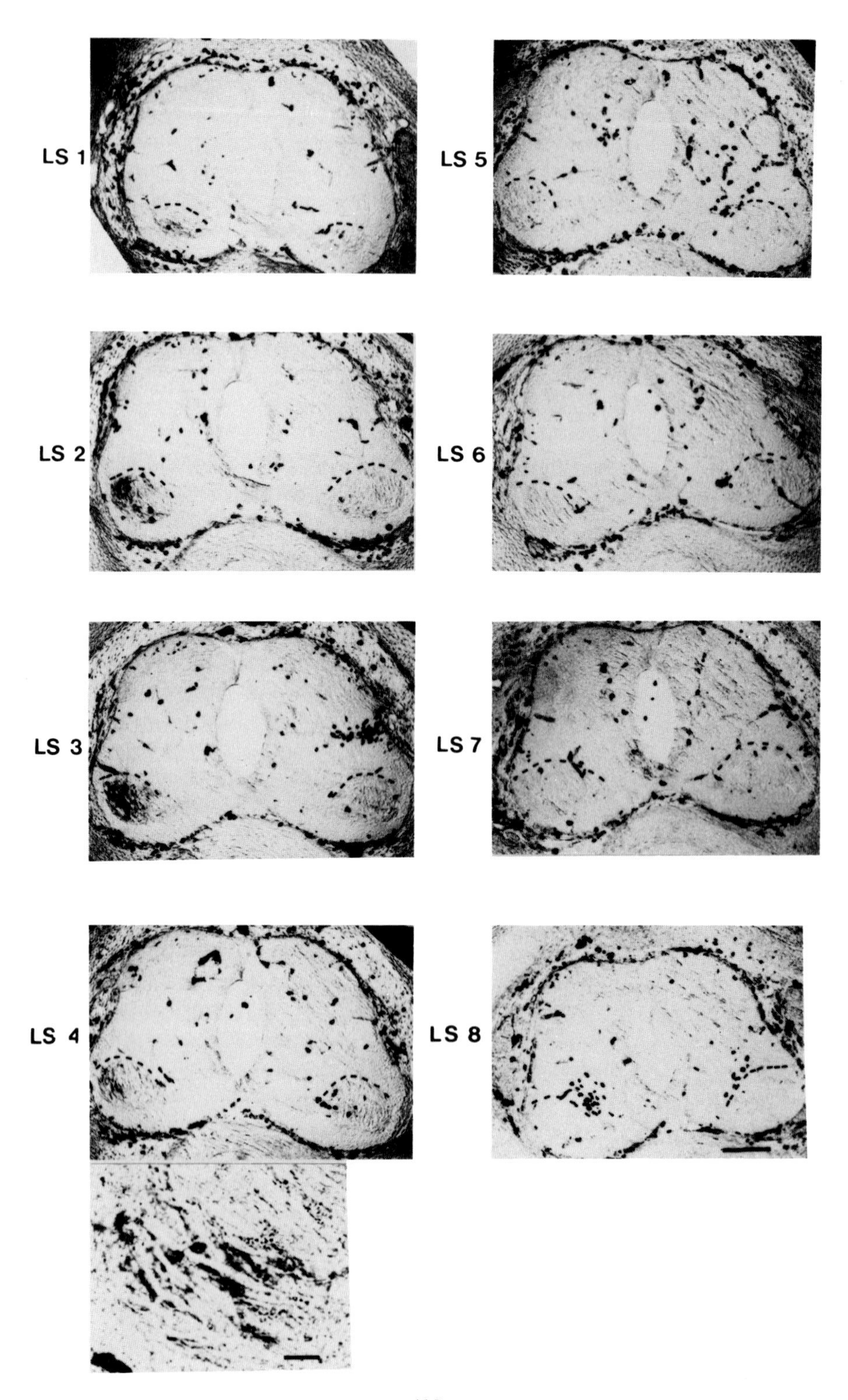
LS 1
LS 2
LS 3
LS 4
LS 5
LS 6
LS 7
LS 8

lowed by spinal nerve stimulation demonstrated a close correlation between the position of the motoneuron cell body and the spinal nerve from which it emerged (Fig. 10). In addition, when individual muscles in normal and supernumerary limbs were injected with HRP and their motoneuron positions compared, it can be seen (Fig. 11) that the medial-to-lateral position of motoneuron cell bodies was similar, although their cranio–caudal positions were different.

Romanes (2) has shown that, in general, motoneurons innervating flexor muscles occupy the lateral portion of the ventral horn, while motoneurons innervating extensors are medial. A brief study reflex behavior in normal and supernumerary limbs (Morris, 13) has shown that the gastrocnemius acts as an extensor, while the iliofibularis acts as a flexor in normal and transplanted limbs. Thus motoneuron position was consistent with reflex behavior.

DISCUSSION

The present series of experiments have shown that at the time of limb bud transplanation (Stages 16–18) motoneurons are not rigidly specified to innervate their appropriate muscles. The data presented here illustrates that both totally nonlimb motoneurons, i.e., thoracic, and inappropriate lumbosacral motoneurons are capable of forming functional synapses with hind limb musculature. Furthermore, it is apparent from these experiments that muscles can be innervated by inappropriate thoracic and lumbosacral spinal nerves even when appropriate nerves enter the limb. Indeed, there was no tendency for appropriate motoneurons to seek out and innervate their own muscles when given a possible peripheral choice.

Other investigators have shown by exchanging regions of the spinal cord or interchanging fore- and hind limbs, that embryonic limbs can be innervated by inappropriate motoneurons from regions of the spinal cord not normally innervating the limb (Detwiler, 22; Wenger, 23; Straznicky, 24; Narayanan and Hamburger, 25). However, none of these studies has demonstrated that thoracic motoneurons can inner-

---

Fig. 9. Cross section through the spinal cord of a Stage 29 animal with a supernumerary limb placed in a lumbosacral position. The presumptive postaxial supernumerary limb musculature was injected with HRP granules. Sections through levels LS5–8 show that motoneurons are not labeled. The lateral motor column is outlined. Red blood cells have endogenous peroxidase activity, which accounts for the large, randomly distributed, oval structures in the figure. The bar at level LS8 represents 100 μm. Below LS4 is an enlargement of a section from this level; the bar represents 10 μm.

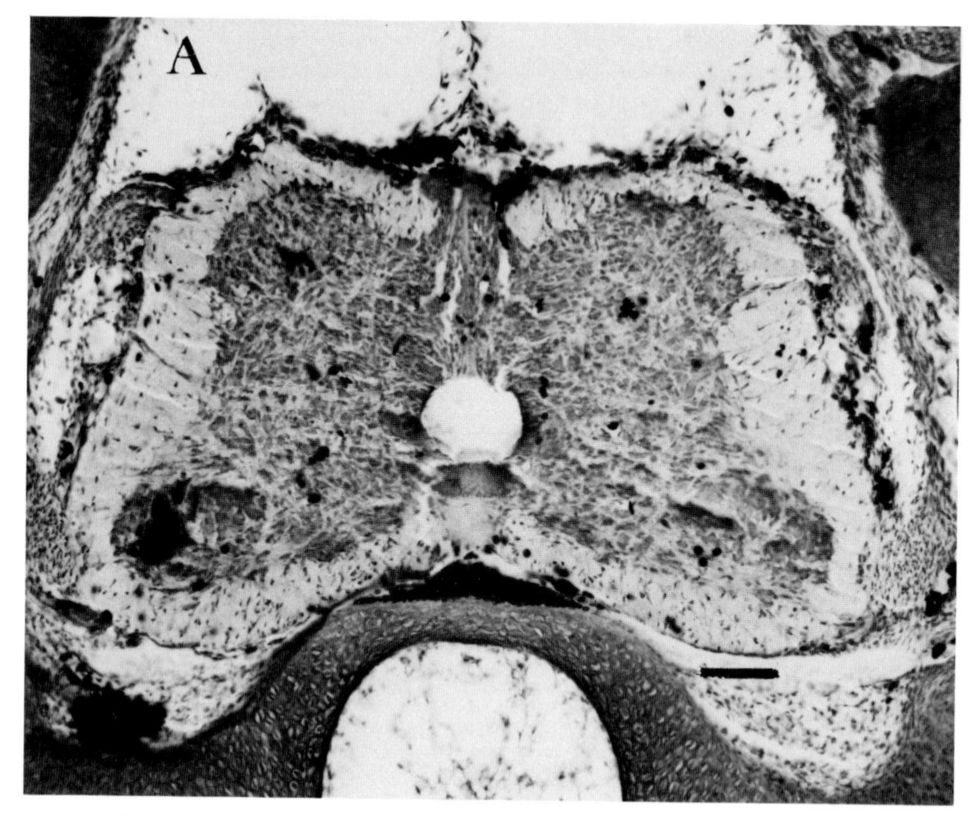

Fig. 10. (A) Cross section through the spinal cord of a Stage 35 embryo. The normal peroneus was injected with HRP and labeled motoneurons were present at levels LS3–5. The bar represents 200 μm. (B) Cross section through the spinal cord of a Stage 40 animal. The iliofibularis was injected with HRP and labeled motoneurons were present at levels LS4–7. The bar represents 50 μm.

vate limb muscles when lumbosacral motoneurons also enter the limb. In addition, it has never been shown that inappropriate lumbosacral motoneurons can innervate muscles whose appropriate motoneuron axons also enter the limb. Although similar experiments have been attempted in amphibia (Detwiler, 26; Székely, 27), there is such extensive overlap of motoneurons to different muscles in the amphibian spinal cord (Cruce, 3; Székely and Czéh, 4; Nicholas and Barron, 28) that any given lumbosacral spinal nerve in the amphibian has motoneurons for all the muscles of the limb. This makes it difficult to specify whether a muscle of a transplanted limb is innervated by appropriate or inappropriate motoneurons.

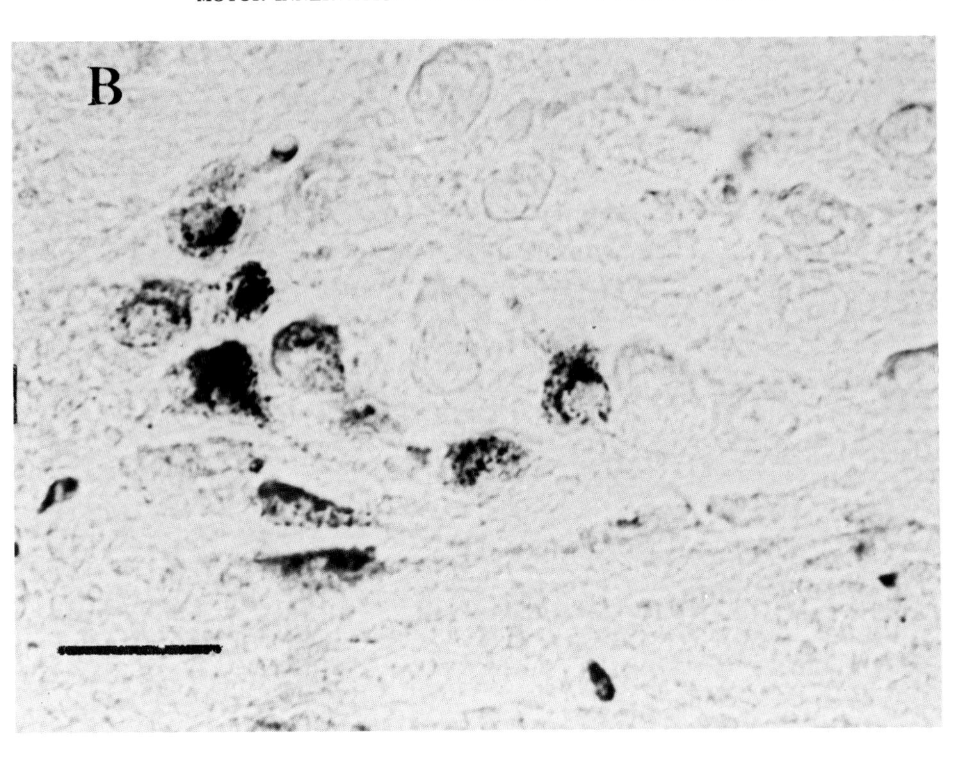

Fig. 10 (B)

Although there was no tendency for motoneurons to seek out their own muscles in the supernumerary limb, axon outgrowth in these limbs was not random. A distinct and generally normal anatomical pattern was observed by dissection and silver stained preparations of thoracic–lumbosacral and lumbosacral limbs as early as Stage 27 and this pattern was similar throughout development.

These results suggest that the limb may influence incoming nerve fibers by guiding axons without specifying them *per se*. It is possible that there may be substrate (i.e. glycoprotein) differences present in the early limb that may serve to guide axons. There may also be chemical gradients present in the developing limb (MacCabe and Parker, 29). These gradients may serve to guide axons to their proper targets. The results also suggest that the limb may actually confer specificity to motoneurons. At the time of limb bud transplantation, at Stages 16–18, lumbosacral motoneurons are beginning to withdraw from the mitotic cycle (Hollyday and Hamburger, 30). Neurons are said to be specified for their targets after they withdraw from the mitotic cycle in

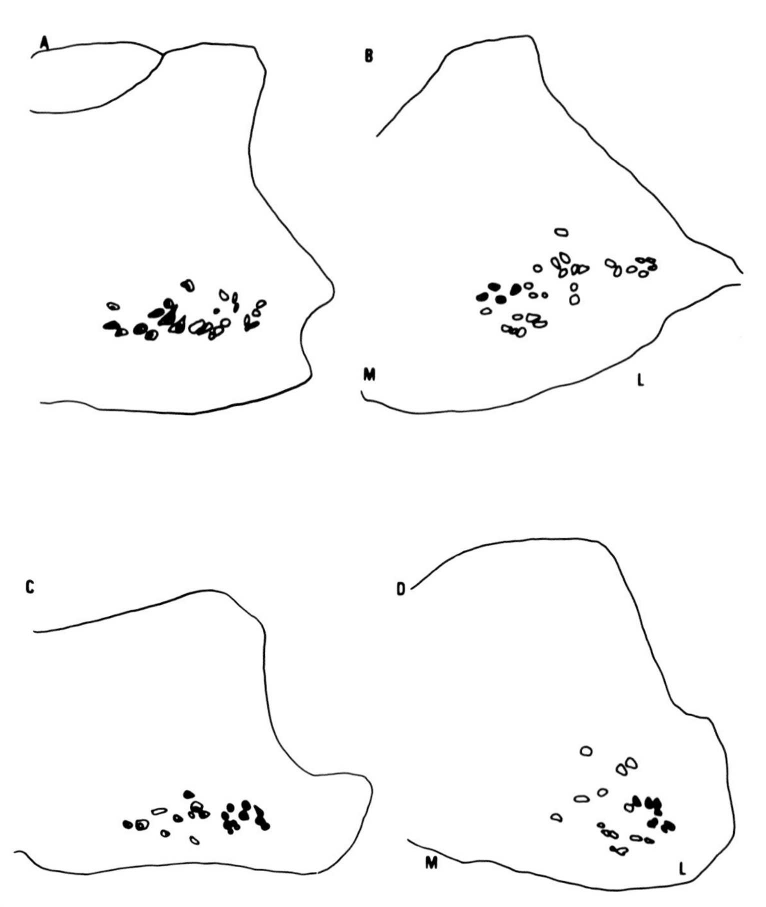

Fig. 11. (A) Camera lucida drawings of cross sections through the ventral horn of a Stage 40 (unoperated control) animal at LS6. The lateral gastrocnemius was injected with HRP; labeled motoneurons are stippled and occupy a medial position. (B) The supernumerary lateral gastrocnemius was injected with HRP; labeled motoneurons were found at level LS3 in a medial position. (C) Cross section through the ventral horn at LS7 of a Stage 40 control animal in which the iliofibularis was injected with HRP; lateral motoneurons were stained. (D) Cross section through the ventral horn at level LS2 of a Stage 40 animal with a supernumerary limb; the supernumerary iliofibularis was injected with HRP. Lateral motoneurons were labeled.

the visual system of amphibia (Hunt and Jacobson, 31–33) and birds (Crossland *et al.*, 4). However, chick motoneurons do not appear to be rigidly specified for specific targets at this stage. Transplantation at later stages has not been performed in this series of experiments. Perhaps at some later time during their differentiation, motoneurons demonstrate their specification by selectively seeking out their appropriate targets. Sterling (unpublished observations) has reported selective innervation of the muscles of abnormally placed wing segments at Stage 24. It is possible that some interaction with the limb before the time of surgery (St. 24) may confer specificity to motoneurons.

An observation which has suggested that the limb has the capacity to organize axon outgrowth is the reversal of the innervation pattern seen following limb reversals along the a–p axis. At the time of limb bud transplantation (Stages 16–18) the anterior–posterior axis of the limb had been laid down (Hamburger, 14; Chaube, 35). In addition, other experiments on the developing chick limb (Saunders and Gasseling, 36; MacCabe and Parker, 37; Tickle *et al.*, 38; Wolpert *et al.*, 39) have shown that the posterior margin of the limb bud near its margin with the body wall, the zone of polarizing activity (ZPA), has the capacity to induce anterior and posterior structures within the limb.

The ZPA may organize not only the anterior–posterior structures within the limb but the pattern of ingrowing nerve fibers as well. The ZPA or something like it may set up a chemical gradient which allows nerves to be guided to their targets.

ACKNOWLEDGMENTS

I would like to thank Dr. Lynn Landmesser for encouragement and advice during the course of this research and in the preparation of this manuscript. This research was supported by grant NS10666 from the National Institutes of Health to L. Landmesser, the Southern Fellowship Fund, and an NDEA fellowship.

REFERENCES

1. Romanes, G. J. (1951) *J. Comp. Neurol.* **94**, 313–363.
2. Romanes, G. J. (1964) *Prog. Brain Res.* **11**, 93–119.
3. Cruce, W. L. R. (1974) *J. Comp. Neurol.* **153**, 59–76.
4. Székely, G., and Czéh, G. (1967) *Acta Physiol. Acad. Sci. Hung.* **32**, 3–18.
5. Burke, R. E., Strick, P. L., Kanda, K., Kim, C. C., and Walmsley, B. (1977) *J. Neurophysiol.* **40**, 667–680.
6. Hughes, A., and Prestige, M. (1967) *J. Zool.* **152**, 347–359.
7. Lamb, A. (1976) *Dev. Biol.* **54**, 82–89.
8. Landmesser, L., and Morris, D. G. (1975) *J. Physiol.* (*London*) **249**, 301–326.
9. Weiss, P. (1947) *Yale J. Biol. Med.* **19**, 235–278.
10. Hughes, A. (1968) "Aspects of Neural Ontogeny." Academic Press, New York.
11. Jacobson, M. (1970) "Developmental Neurobiology." Holt, New York.
12. Morris, D. G. (1975) *Neurosci. Abstr.* **1**, 753.
13. Morris, D. G. (1976) Ph.D. Thesis, Yale University, New Haven, Connecticut.

14. Hamburger, V. (1938) *J. Exp. Zool.* **77**, 379–399.
15. Hamburger, V. (1939) *J. Exp. Zool.* **80**, 347–385.
16. Romanes, G. J. (1941) *J. Anat.* **76**, 112–130.
17. Romanes, G. J. (1946) *J. Anat.* **80**, 117–131.
18. Roncali, L. (1970) *Monit. Zool. Ital.* [N.S.] **4**, 81–98.
19. Ramón y Cajal, S. (1929) "Studies on Vertebrate Neurogenesis" Thomas, Springfield, Illinois (L. Gath, transl., 1960).
20. Windle, W. F., and Orr, D. W. (1934) *J. Comp. Neurol.* **60**, 287–303.
21. Oppenheim, R., and Heaton, M. (1975) *Brain Res.* **98**, 291–302.
22. Detwiler, S. R. (1923) *J. Exp. Zool.* **37**, 339–393.
23. Wenger, B. S. (1951) *J. Exp. Zool.* **116**, 123–163.
24. Straznicky, K. (1963) *Acta Biol. Acad. Sci. Hung.* **14**, 145–155.
25. Narayanan, D. H., and Hamburger, V. (1971) *J. Exp. Zool.* **178**, 415–432.
26. Detwiler, S. R. (1920) *J. Exp. Zool.* **31**, 117–169.
27. Székely, G. (1975) *In* "Aspects of Neurogenesis Studies on the Development of Behavior and the Nervous System (G. Gottlieb, ed.), Vol. 2, pp. 115–150.
28. Nicholas, J. S., and Barron, B. H. (1935) *J. Comp. Neurol.* **61**, 413–421.
29. MacCabe, J. A., and Parker, B. (1976) *Dev. Biol.* **54**, 297–303.
30. Hollyday, M., and Hamburger, V. (1975) *Neurosci. Abstr.* **1**, 779.
31. Hunt, R. K., and Jacobson, M. (1972) *Proc. Natl. Acad. Sci. U.S.A.* **69**, 780–783.
32. Hunt, R. K., and Jacobson, M. (1972) *Proc. Natl. Acad. Sci. U.S.A.* **69**, 2860–2864.
33. Hunt, R. K., and Jacobson, M. (1973) *Proc. Natl. Acad. Sci. U.S.A.* **70**, 507–511.
34. Crossland, W. J., Cowan, W. M., Rogers, L., and Kelly, J. (1974) *J. Comp. Neurol.* **155**, 127–164.
35. Chaube, S. (1959) *J. Exp. Zool.* **140**, 29–77.
36. Saunders, J. W., Jr., and Gasseling, M. (1968) *In* "Epithelial-Mesenchymal Interactions" (R. Fleischamjer and R. E. Billingham, eds.), pp. 78–97. Williams & Wilkins, Baltimore, Maryland.
37. MacCabe, J. A., and Parker, B. (1975) *Dev. Biol.* **45**, 349–357.
38. Tickle, C., and Summerbell, D., and Wolpert, L. (1975) *Nature (London)* **254**, 199–202.
39. Wolpert, L., Lewis, J., and Summerbell, D. (1975) *Cell Patterning, Ciba Found. Symp.* **29**, 95–130.

Cerebellar Maturation after Perinatal Alterations in Connectivity—Evidence for Intrinsic Determinism

BARRY J. HOFFER
Department of Pharmacology
University of Colorado
School of Medicine
Denver, Colorado

DONALD J. WOODWARD
Department of Cell Biology
Baylor College of Medicine
University of Texas Health Science Center
Dallas, Texas

LARS OLSAN AND ÅKE SEIGER

Department of Histology
Karolinska Institute
Stockholm, Sweden

INTRODUCTION

In this chapter we will present a series of studies on how the properties of the developing nervous system change when its maturation is subjected to systematic manipulations. The cerebellum in the rat is an ideal structure for such an analysis since the proliferation of the precursors of most interneurons and much of synaptogenesis occur perinatally, when the cerebellum is easily accessible for manipulation. Further, a considerable body of anatomical, physiological, and pharmacological information has accumulated concerning the structural and functional relations of the cerebellum in the adult and at var-

ISBN 0-12-398450-5

ious developmental ages (1–6). Two different types of cerebellar perturbations were utilized in the studies described here, neonatal X-irradiation *in situ* and prenatal homologous transplantation to the anterior eye chamber of adult recipients.

X-Irradiation permits a unique form of manipulation of development. Multiplying cells, as in the external germinating layer, are extremely sensitive (7) to ionizing radiation. Since mature, or even differentiating, cells are more radioresistant it is possible to selectively destroy the germinal cells of the external granular layer leaving intact the already matured Purkinje and Golgi cells, and cells of the underlying brain stem. Cells of the external granular layer can be subtotally eliminated by exposure at birth to a single dose of 150 R or 200 R X-ray, with no visible harm to the Purkinje cells as determined by light microscopic examination. A variable number of cells in the external germinal layer survive the treatment, divide rapidly, and are capable of reconstituting the germinal matrix (9,10). Successive doses of 150 R on alternate days can prevent such regeneration. The ultimate morphology of the cerebellum thus depends on (1) the time of initial exposure, since cells already differentiating become radioresistant; and (2) the number of successive exposures employed which delay or prevent regeneration of surviving cells. In this way, a wide variety of procedures are available (11) to control specific aspects of the development of the cerebellum.

Selected for this initial electrophysiological and pharmacological analysis were two radiation procedures having in common the most complete destruction of the cerebellar microneurons. In one group, doses were given beginning on the day of birth and on a sufficient number of successive days until regeneration of surviving cells was no longer possible. A detailed description of the morphological effects of this treatment has been given by Altman and Anderson (11), which should be consulted by the reader. In another group of animals, irradiation was begun on day 4 after birth; the morphological effects of this treatment are described by Altman and Anderson (12). When irradiation is begun at birth, the Purkinje cell bodies fail even to line up in a monolayer and remain scattered below the surface. Dendrites do grow and remain in the adult but in disorderly random directions due to the absence of the organizing matrix of parallel fibers. In another group of animals irradiation was begun at day 4. By this time the expansion of folia is normally sufficient so that the cell bodies are approximately in a monolayer. In both groups the nearly complete destruction of precursor cells of the external granular layer implies that further development of Purkinje cells must occur in the absence of the normal structural mileu of excitatory and inhibitory interneurons.

The central question of this study was the determination of what alterations of functional properties of Purkinje cells might occur due to the altered course of cerebellar development. Recordings of single action potentials were performed to determine the mean activity and firing patterns of Purkinje cells. Microiontophoretic application of drugs was performed to compare pharmacological properties of irradiated, transplanted, and normal Purkinje cells. Stimulation experiments were carried out to determine the presence of excitatory and inhibitory synaptic connections in the cerebellar cortex. Histological studies were used to characterize cerebellar structure.

METHODS

IRRADIATED ANIMALS

Radiation Procedure. Procedures for handling animals and their X-irradiation were described previously (11). Pups of Long–Evans hooded rats were reared in litters adjusted to six in number. The radiation source was a 300 kV X-ray unit. The distance between the source and the animals was 36 cm and a 1-mm copper sheet was used for filtration. Animals were immobilized in soft plastic tubes of 1-mm wall thickness which were placed in lucite blocks having holes of increasing diameter to accommodate growth. A slot between two movable, 16-mm thick lead sheaths was used to confine a variable width beam to the area of the head above the cerebellum. A Victoreen 250 R probe was used to measure exposure. The average error was ± 1 R. The heads of an entire litter were irradiated simultaneously at about 50 R/min.

One group of animals was given 200 R on days 0 and 1, then the exposure was reduced to 150 R on days 3, 5, 7, 9, 10, and 13. Radiation began on day 4 for another group of animals.

Rats were studied electrophysiologically 2 to 6 months after birth. At the end of an experiment the brain was perfused with 10% formalin, embedded in Paraplast, and sectioned at 10 μm. Figure 1 shows examples of the degree of degranulation achieved in the animals used in these experiments. Small numbers of interneurons typically survive in the animals irradiated from day 4 (12), but far fewer survive in those irradiated on day 0. There were few differences in results between the day 0 and day 4 animals so it is doubtful that a

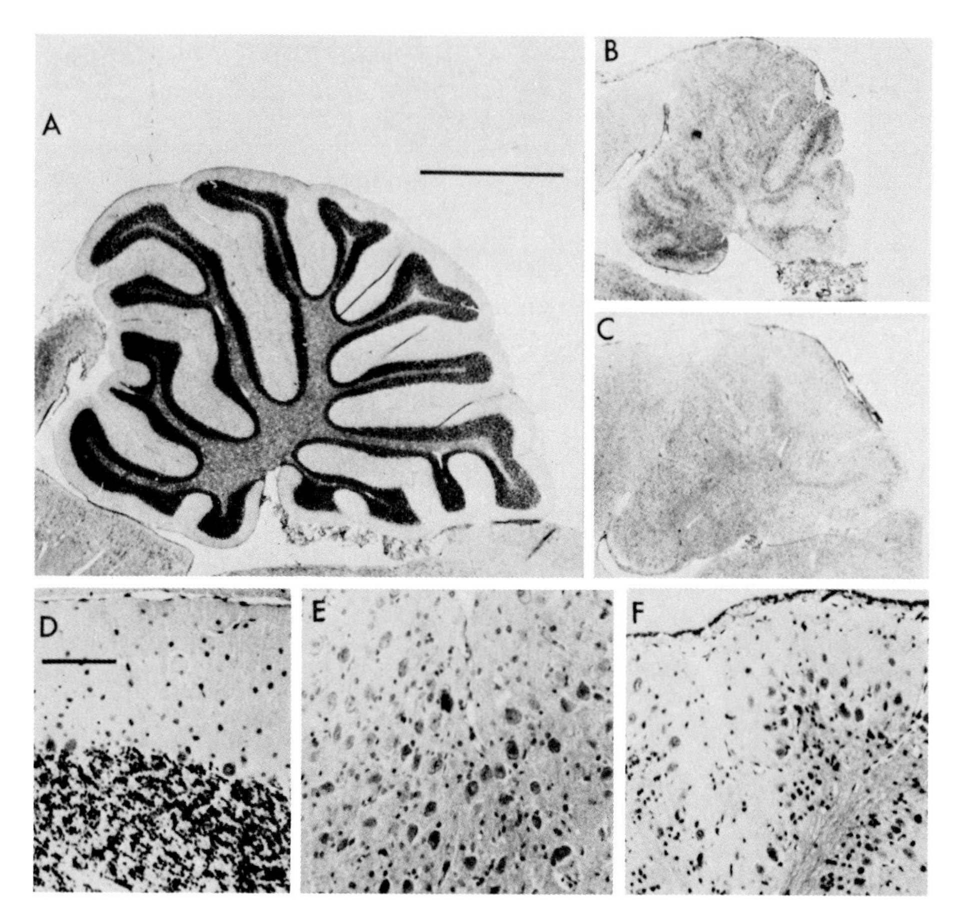

Fig. 1. Rat cerebellar cortex degranulated by X-irradiation. (A) Midsagittal section of normal rat cerebellum. (B) Corresponding section of cerebellum in adult rat irradiated beginning at postnatal day 4. (C) Cerebellum irradiated from day 0. (A), (B), and (C) have same scale. Bar in (A) is 2mm. (D), (E), and (F) show magnified views of the cortex in normal, 0-day, and 4-day animals, respectively. The line of Purkinje cell bodies in (D) separates the molecular layer from the densely cellular granular layer. In (E), cerebellum irradiated from day 0 is characterized by Purkinje cell bodies scattered in a multilayer. In (F) are shown foliations of cerebellum irradiated from day 4, in which Purkinje cell bodies approximate a monolayer but few interneurons remain in the granular layer. (D), (E), and (F) have same magnification; bar in (D) is 50 μm.

small contamination by surviving granule cells critically influences any conclusions drawn here.

Electrophysiological Methods. Animals were anesthetized and held in a stereotaxic device as described previously (13) for recording electrical activity from cerebellum. The skin and skull were removed and the cerebellum covered with warm 3% agar in saline. A pressure foot above the cerebellum damped movements. Use of 0.5 to 1% halothane allowed for the steady level of anesthesia essential for assaying and comparing mean firing rates. Glass micropipettes filled with 1 to 4 *M* NaCl were used for recording. When sampling activity, usually three to four units were encountered before data were taken on one judged both representative of the population and free from movement artifacts. Activity was photographed from an oscilloscope or recorded on tape for later analysis.

A PDP-12 computer (Digital Equipment Corp.) was used for computation of interval and poststimulus time histograms. The programs (14) employed process single events in the usual fashion, but also have the capacity to detect bursts generated by climbing fiber synaptic activity. The burst detection scheme involves an examination of successive interspike intervals and a declaration of a burst when an interval is encountered shorter than a specified constant, usually between 2 and 5 msec. Successive spikes are considered as within bursts until an interval is encountered longer than another specified long constant, usually 5 to 7 msec. Intervals between the initial spikes of successive bursts are summed and used to compute interburst interval histograms. This scheme proved quite useful when climbing fiber bursts consisted of discrete spike components, since the frequency of the initial spikes is distinctly greater than the background single spike discharge. Detection was also accurate when the bursts consisted of single full spike responses and an inactivation slow wave, provided the Schmitt trigger could be adjusted to detect the onset of the slow wave. In practice, constant visual and auditory monitoring of the computer burst detection was essential to ensure that the resulting burst histogram did not include artifacts produced by noise of multiple unit activity.

TRANSPLANTATIONS

Pieces of the developing cerebellar anlage were prepared from rat fetuses with crown–rump lengths (CRL) of between 14 and 40 mm, corresponding to gestational ages of between 15 and 22 days. At each side of the anlage, a cut was made parallel to the dorsal surface to obtain a transplant including roughly the dorsal half of the anlage. The

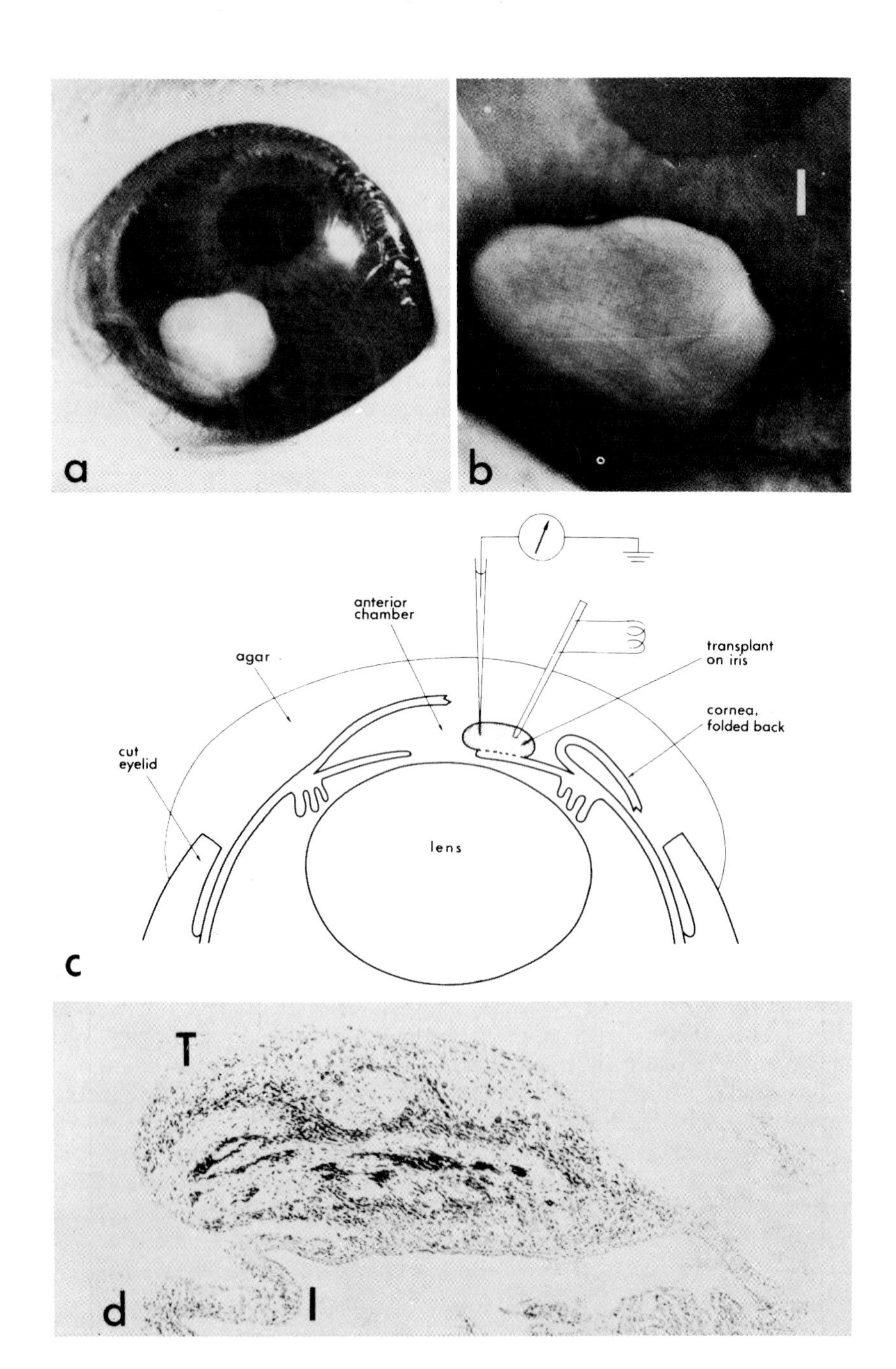
a
b
anterior chamber
agar
transplant on iris
cornea, folded back
cut eyelid
lens
c
T
d
I

pieces, totally free of any brain stem, were transplanted homologously and bilaterally to female recipients (Sprague–Dawley, 125–150 g) using the technique described earlier (15). In brief, transplants were injected into the anterior chamber of the eye through a slit in the cornea by means of a modified Pasteur pipette under microscopic inspection and using sterile instruments. The postoperative fate of the transplants was followed *in vivo* by repeated stereomicroscopic observations through the cornea of the lightly anesthetized animals (Fig. 2). In this way the percentage "successful takes" (i.e., well-vascularized, rounded transplants, diameter >1 mm) of approximately 347 transplants from various stages of development was determined and transplants suitable for electrophysiological recording and histological examination were chosen. All dating was from the time of grafting.

Electrophysiological Techniques. Rats with cerebellar transplants showing the most vigorous growth and vascularization were used. Animals were anesthetized with 1% halothane and the cornea removed (Fig. 2). Body temperature was maintained at 37°C. The transplants were then covered with 3% agar in Ringer's to prevent drying and minimize pulsations. Bioelectric potentials were recorded from single neurons using glass micropipettes filled with 3 *M* NaCl (2–4 MΩ resistance); all electrical activity below 200 Hz was filtered out. Units were excluded whose discharge suggested injury by the microelectrode or any relationship to cardiac or respiratory movements. The single action potentials were displayed on an oscilloscope, simultaneously separated from background noise by a window discriminator, and converted to pulses of constant amplitude. These pulses were then fed into a PDP-12 computer in order to construct interspike interval histograms and into a raster generator (16) to provide interspike and poststimulus interval dot displays.

Stimulation of the surface or base of the transplant was carried out by means of a fine, concentric, bipolar stimulating electrode (outer tip diameter, 0.2 mm). All stimuli were monophasic square waves, 0.1 msec in duration, and delivered at 0.2/sec, unless otherwise stated. Effective stimulation currents ranged from 50 to 400 μA. All conduc-

---

Fig. 2. Main stages in the experimental analyses of transplants. (a) Transplant in oculo as seen through a stereomicroscope in a living rat. Approximately $\times 10$. (b) Closeup of the same transplant as in (a). Note the very thin vascular network within the transplant (I, iris). Approximately $\times 25$. (c) Schematic representation of the arrangement for extracellular recordings and surface stimulation of the cerebellar transplants. Approximately $\times 10$. (d) Toluidine blue stained cross-section of a host iris (I) with its cerebellar transplant (T). Postoperative time, 27 days. Montage of microphotographs. Approximately $\times 84$.

tion velocities were calculated from response latency and the distance between stimulation and recording electrodes.

In experiments dealing with inhibition following stimulation, the noradrenergic terminals of the iris were either destroyed by ablation of the superior cervical ganglion 1 week prior to recording, or depleted of transmitter by injection of 2.5 mg/kg of reserpine 3 hr prior to recording. In either case, the efficacy of the treatment was confirmed by observation of formaldehyde-induced fluorescence in the iris (17–19) after recording from the transplant.

IONTOPHORETIC TECHNIQUES

Single units recorded extracellularly were tested with drugs administered at the site of recording by microelectrophoresis, using five-barrel micropipettes with 4–6-μm tip diameters (20). One barrel of the array was used to generate a balance current to minimize electrical fields around the electrode tips. In all cases, retaining currents were used to avoid undesirable diffusion of drugs from the pipette during periods between testing. The drugs studied and their concentrations in the micropipettes were as follows: 1.0 *M* γ-aminobutyric acid (Aldrich Chemical Co.); 1.0 *M* sodium glutamate (Gallard–Schlesinger); 0.5 *M* *dl*-norepinephrine (Mann Laboratories); 0.05 *M* serotonin creatinine sulfate (K and K Laboratories); 0.5 *M* acetylcholine–HCl (Calbiochem); 0.5 *M* adenosine 3′,5′-monophosphate (Calbiochem); 0.5 *M* MJ-1999 (Mead Johnson); and 0.1 *M* atropine sulfate (Calbiochem). All agents were dissolved in distilled water; pH was adjusted between 4 and 8.

The major artifacts complicating microiontophoretic studies are (1) direct effects of the iontophoretic current, (2) local anesthetic side effects of many of the drugs, and (3) effects secondary to the pH of the drug solutions. These possible artifacts were controlled for by techniques previously described (20).

Extracellular action potentials, mainly displaying a negative–positive spike configuration, were continuously monitored on an oscilloscope and recorded on magnetic tape. The action potentials were simultaneously separated from the background noise by a voltage gating circuit. The gated impulses were integrated over 1-sec intervals and the result displayed on one channel of a polygraph. The criteria of obtaining at least two drug responses, with subsequent recovery, were required before any given cell was considered to manifest a positive pharmacological effect.

RESULTS

IRRADIATED CEREBELLA

Spontaneous Activity of Purkinje Neurons. Microelectrodes inserted into the cerebellar cortex routinely encountered many active neurons (Table I). Extracellular unit recordings were found at all levels below the cortical surface in day 0 irradiated rats, consistent with the histological evidence of a multilayered arrangement of Purkinje cells. The population of neurons studied here undoubtedly consists mainly of Purkinje cells, because this is the dominant population left after the irradiation procedure. Correspondingly, recordings of cells in cerebellum radiated at day 4 were found at consistently similar depths which correlated with the remaining lamination. Typical streams of steady spontaneous activity are illustrated in Fig. 3.

Another type of firing activity, found more often in cerebellum irradiated from day 4, consisted of regularly appearing groups of spikes (three to four spikes per group) at 12/sec. Firing rates within groups were 100–200/sec (see Fig. 4A). This activity was not produced by injury since the pattern held steady indefinitely and was not affected by movements of the electrode. Interspike interval histograms of this activity resulted in two distinct peaks corresponding to the intervals within and between the groups (Fig. 4B). This discharge was interrupted occasionally by the more infrequent bursts (tentatively identified at this point as due to climbing fiber synaptic input) appearing randomly with respect to the regular rhythm. Considering frequency alone, it might be possible for repetitive climbing fiber activity to cause the bursts. Intracellular recording, discussed in detail later, however, revealed characteristic climbing fiber EPSP's to occur infrequently in groups and not at 10–12/sec rates.

TABLE I
Mean Firing Rate of Purkinje Cells

	N	(Spikes/sec)	± SEM[a]	± SD[a]
Rat irradiated from day 0	50	36.7	±2.2	±15.8
Rat irradiated from day 4	42	38.9	±2.8	±18.2
Normal rat[b]	43	34.3	±2.8	±18.3
6-OH-DA treated rat[b]	30	52.4	±5.3	±29.0
Transplants	58	31.7	±3.3	±19.1

[a] S.D. is the standard deviation and SEM the standard deviation of the mean.
[b] Data taken from Hoffer *et al.* (1971b).

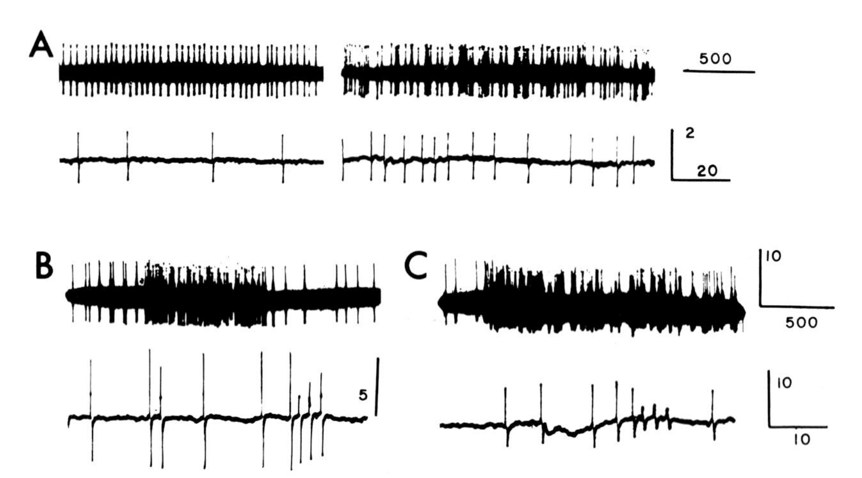

Fig. 3. Spontaneous activity of Purkinje cells recorded extracellularly in irradiated rat cerebellum. (A) Steady, single-spike activity shown (at left) at two sweep speeds. In (A) (at right) a period of climbing fiber bursting activity is shown consisting of extracellular spikes unchanged in amplitude. (B) Another cell illustrating single spiking interrupted by a period of bursting. In the lower trace in (B), the later spike components in typical bursts show partial inactivation. In (C), the bursting phase in another cell shows considerable inactivation of later spike components, more characteristic of normal Purkinje cells. Vertical scale is in mV and horizontal scale is in msec.

Activity of this oscillatory type was generally common within an area of cerebellar cortex, as all cells encountered would then display such groups of action potentials. When not recording from single cells, field potentials exhibiting 10–12 oscillations/sec indicated a synchronization within the population of surrounding cells.

Spontaneous "Climbing Fiber Bursts". In the cerebellum of normal rats, as in other animals, the ascending climbing fibers are known to have a powerful excitatory action on the Purkinje cell (3,13). Typical responses to climbing fibers observed extracellularly consist of a single large spike followed by a variable number of small, wavelike components. Such "complex spikes" normally occur at the rate of 1/sec, which clearly distinguishes the responses from the normal single spiking at 30–40/sec.

A striking difference, in the irradiated cerebellum, was that many cells did not demonstrate the characteristic "complex spikes" or "inactivation responses." Instead, cells exhibited all gradations between (1) a group of uniformly sized spikes in a distinct phase of supranormal rapid firing (see Fig. 3A), (2) distinct but partially inactivated spikes (see Fig. 3B), and (3) full sized initial spikes followed by more typical

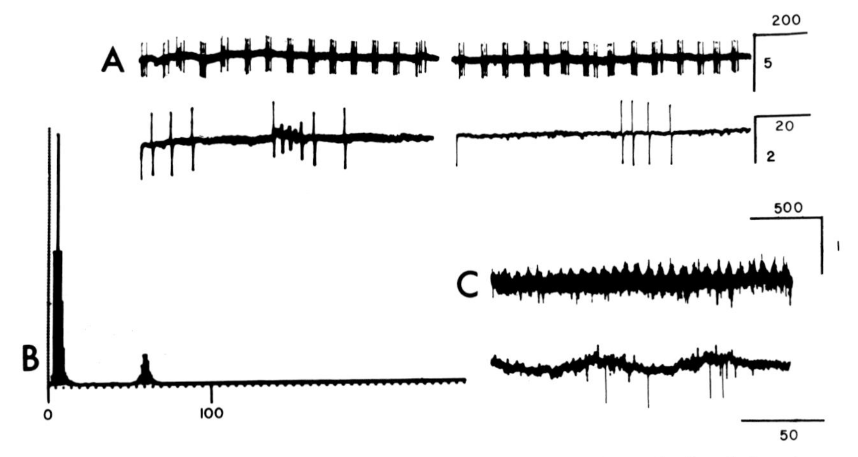

Fig. 4. Records from a Purkinje cell in irradiated cerebellum which exhibited regular, single-spike bursting activity not due to climbing fiber input. Slow upper sweep in (A) shows regular firing at 12/sec of groups of four spikes. Lower, faster sweeps were triggered on single spikes. At left is shown an inactivated burst due to climbing fibers, at right a group of normal sized spikes. In (B), an interspike interval histogram demonstrates the regularity in time of the short intervals within bursts and the fewer longer intervals between bursts. In (C) are shown slow and fast sweeps of regular field potential oscillations observed in a region exhibiting regular spike bursting activity; small spikes could be observed in the background.

inactivated spikes (see Fig. 3C). Most cells fired for a few seconds in a steady stream of single spikes which was then interrupted by a phase of frequent bursting (see Fig. 3A, B, C) presumed to be due to climbing fibers.

It appears likely that the distinct inactivation responses in normal Purkinje cells have been transformed into groups of more or less full-sized spikes. However, a problem arises in determining whether all or only some of the high-frequency spiking is derived from climbing fiber input. A primary method for examining this issue is to compare the temporal characteristics of the occurrence of the extracellular bursts with corresponding intracellularly recorded EPSP's.

Intracellular Correlates of Bursting. In a number of instances Purkinje cells were penetrated with a microelectrode in order to examine the transmembrane potentials correlated with the climbing fiber bursts. The periods of intense frequent bursting (but distinguished from the regular groups of spikes in Fig. 4) corresponded to a barrage of large unitary EPSP's. Faster sweep records, triggered on the leading edge of the EPSP (Fig. 5), revealed that the potentials con-

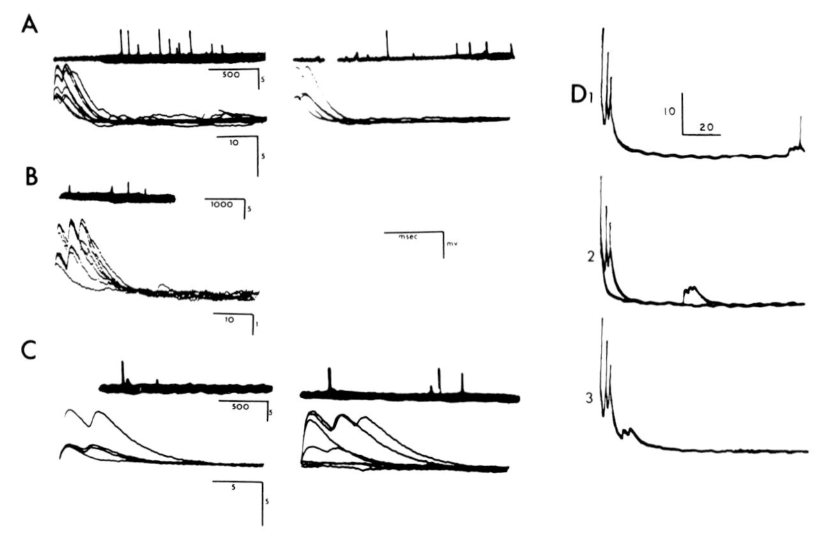

Fig. 5. Examples of spontaneous climbing fiber EPSP's in Purkinje cells of irradiated cerebellum. Upper slow sweeps in (A), (B), and (C) reveal activity consisting of large and small EPSP's. The faster sweeps in (A), (B), and (C) were triggered on the leading edge of the potentials and show that these EPSP's appear in discrete amplitudes. In (D1), (D2), and D3) the larger of two EPSP's caused spike generation. The smaller occurred independently of the larger, being superimposed on the falling phase in (D3).

sisted of single or multiple unitary components similar to normal climbing fiber EPSP's. Several properties suggest, however, that such potentials are generated by more than one climbing fiber firing independently and contacting different portions of the same Purkinje cell dendritic tree.

In contrast to normal animals, such potentials occurred usually in two, but sometimes in three or four, discretely different amplitudes. The large and small EPSP complexes appeared independently of one another. Instances could be found, during prolonged intracellular recordings, of large and small EPSP's only a few milliseconds apart or even partly superimposed (Fig. 5D3).

It was possible, in three cells, to construct interval histograms by detecting only the larger of two EPSP's. The minimum time between EPSP's was invariably greater than 30–50 msec, similar to the minimum interval between bursts in the normal cerebellum. In many cells where the discrete-sized EPSP's could be observed, the generalization held that different sized EPSP's occurred close together but those of the same size had a fixed refractory period. This phenomenon of different sized EPSP's has been seen in 57 cells in irradiated cerebella. All of 17 cells studied in one animal exhibited the EPSP's of different discrete sizes. Few cells in irradiated animals, in fact, could be shown with certainty to have only one unitary EPSP. Thus, most of the extracellular bursts or groups of spikes which appear in flurries at several-second intervals, are likely to have characteristic climbing fiber EPSP's as their synaptic origin.

Excitatory and Inhibitory Synaptic Actions. Surface stimulation was followed in many cases by no response of Purkinje cells in adjacent medial or lateral regions of the cerebellum. These results would be expected on the basis of the absence of parallel fibers which give rise to easily recognizable responses in normal animals (21).

An initial postulate was that simple destruction of parallel fibers would leave intact a single remaining climbing fiber excitatory afferent contact. Stimulation of afferents would then be capable only of an all-or-nothing excitatory response given a normal 1:1 relationship between a Purkinje cell and its climbing fiber. In fact, however, graded stimulation of the deeper regions near the cerebellar peduncle usually yielded clear evidence for a graded excitatory effect, as shown by an increasing number of spikes; this suggests that more than one excitatory synaptic afferent converged on a single Purkinje cell (Fig. 6). In a few cases, however, white-matter stimulation elicited a response (Fig. 6B) which remained constant over a considerable range of stimulus intensities. Surface stimulation also was effective at times in exciting Purkinje cells, particularly when both recording and stimulating electrodes were on the same side. In these cases, it appeared that the stimulation current was able to penetrate to the ascending afferent fibers which are closer to the surface, due to the absence of parallel fibers.

Two major possibilities could account for graded excitation; either more than one climbing fiber may contact a single Purkinje cell or mossy fibers may make direct connections. The graded excitation, when found, was quite substantial and of the magnitude of climbing fiber synaptic input. Hence it was unlikely to be produced by the very small number of remaining granule cells. Some relevant information was gained by recording intracellularly from Purkinje cells while stimulating the underlying white matter. Fifteen cells were recorded in which a characteristic climbing fiber EPSP response was evoked. In some cases, the climbing fiber response consisted of components of several amplitudes (Fig. 7), which provides further evidence for multiple climbing fiber innervation. Similarly, extracellular records

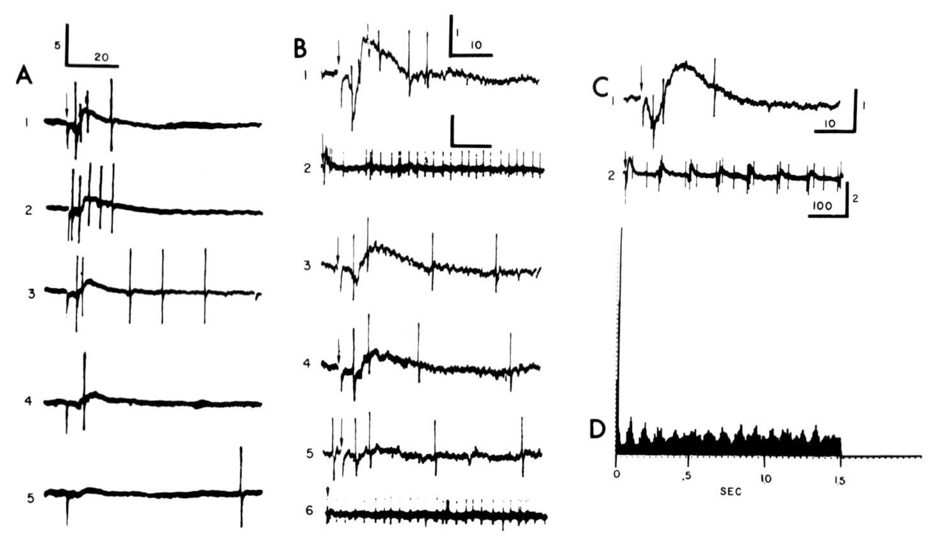

Fig. 6. Extracellular recordings of excitatory responses. In series (A), stimulation in a series of graded intensity to white matter in cerebellum irradiated from day 4 resulted in graded numbers of spikes. (A4) and (A5) at 9 V was just at threshold, (A3) at 10 V, (A2) at 15 V, and (A1) at 17.5 V. In series (B), stimulation given to white matter of an animal irradiated from day 0 resulted in graded spike responses. Stimulation was at threshold at 5 V in (B5) and (B6), 10 V in (B4), and 15 V in (B3). This range of increasing stimulus intensity caused an increase in amplitude of the field potential but evoked only two spikes at constant latency. The response increased abruptly to an inactivating burst response shown at 50 V in (B1) and (B2). (B2) shows a characteristic pause in spontaneous activity after strong excitatory activation. (C) shows a tendency in some cells for excitatory stimulation to provoke prolonged oscillation in spike and field potentials. In (D) a cell firing in regular single spike activity was entrained by white matter stimulation to produce periodicity in activity. The poststimulus time histogram shows a marked periodicity in the first 0.5 sec and a residual effect thereafter. Arrows denote stimuli in all records.

showing only one level of excitation might be accounted for by a similar threshold in all the excitatory afferents. The latency of these responses was between 5 and 10 msec, more characteristic of the "reflex" climbing fiber response than a direct stimulation.

A further question investigated was whether any form of short latency inhibition exists on these Purkinje cells, which could be mediated either by a few remaining inhibitory interneurons or by Purkinje cell recurrent collaterals. Any means of exciting Purkinje cells should activate the collaterals, whereas functioning of the former depends on the existence of excitatory contacts of climbing and mossy fibers with the inhibitory interneurons.

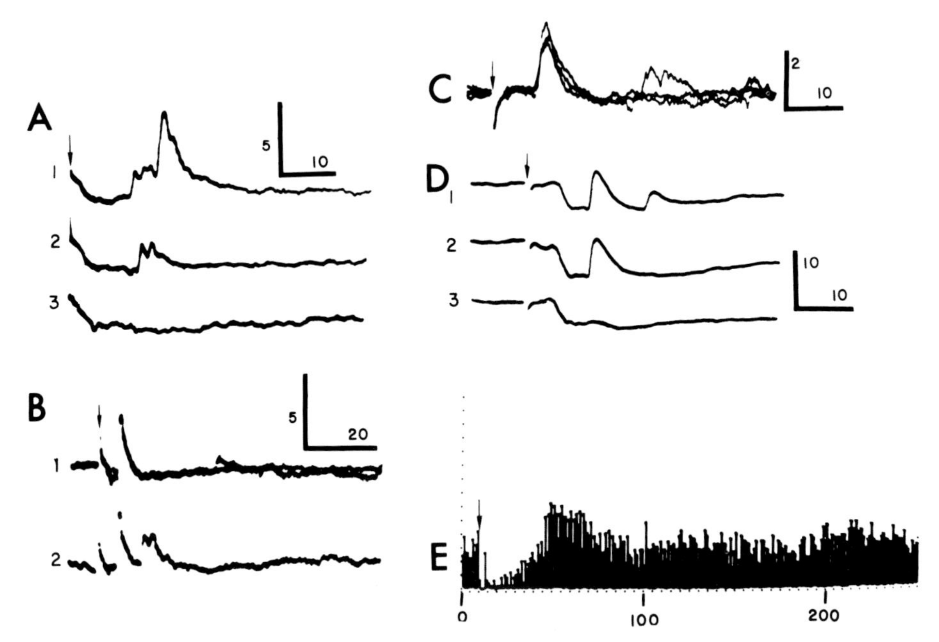

Fig. 7. Responses of Purkinje cells to white matter stimulation. In (A), stimulation of white matter at the same intensity could produce three possible responses. Both or either of two EPSP's of different amplitude appeared in all-or-nothing fashion partly superimposed. In (B), stimulation evoked two components which were temporally separated. (C) shows a consistent, apparent single response arising out of flat baseline. In (D), three sweeps show zero, one, or two EPSP's superimposed on a preceding hyperpolarization. The poststimulus time histogram of extracellular spike activity in another cell (E) shows a 50-msec period of inhibition beginning at 4 msec latency and without a prior excitatory phase.

In most cases, stimulation causing excitation of Purkinje cells resulted subsequently in a variable period of suppression of spontaneous activity (see Fig. 6B2,D). This suppression of activity cannot by itself be distinguished from a rebound depression of firing following an intense excitation, or a synchronizing effect on the resumption of spontaneous activity. Clear evidence for a form of inhibition could be shown in some cases by lowering the stimulation intensity to just below the threshold for excitation. An inhibitory pause could then be observed in poststimulus time histograms in the absence of an initial phase of excitation (Fig. 7E). Presumably, collaterals or interneurons in adjacent regions of the cortex were activated and spread inhibitory action to the area under study.

Intracellular recordings proved difficult to obtain in these animals due to the presence of a rather tough, fibrous interstitum between cells. However, recordings made while stimulating white matter did reveal hyperpolarizations in some cells which began at a minimum of 4 msec, a latency similar to that of the reduced discharge probability in the histograms (Fig. 7D).

Pharmacology. Iontophoretic application of a number of agents was performed to determine the membrane chemosensitivity of the Purkinje cell following the severe deafferentation.

Spontaneous discharge was used as a background upon which to examine the excitatory and inhibitory effects of the various drugs. Early in these experiments there was some ambiguity since the prominent bursts (see above), initially confused with injury, tended to overpower the usual excitatory and inhibitory influences of the drugs. As the underlying involvement of the climbing fiber in the bursting became better understood, it proved possible to obtain an appropriate range of responses provided periods of steady single spiking, relatively free from bursting, were present.

As summarized in Table II, the effects of drugs on discharge of Purkinje cells in irradiated cerebellum were generally similar to normal cerebellum. Most substances showed a predominantly inhibitory effect, norepinephrine (NE) and γ-aminobutyric acid (GABA) being very consistent in this respect. Glutamate, though not illustrated, was excitatory in all neurons. 5-OH-tryptamine (5-HT) was more consistently inhibitory (86% of cells) when compared with intact cerebellum (23), this being the only significant deviation from normal.

Specificity of the drug–receptor interactions was further tested by use of blocking agents (Fig. 8). The β-adrenergic antagonist, MJ-1999 (23), could be shown to selectively block the inhibitory action of nore-

TABLE II
Effects of Putative Neurotransmitters on Spontaneous Discharge Rate of Purkinje Cells in Postnatally Irradiated Rat Cerebellum[a]

	0	↑	↓
NE	1	1	48
5-HT	2	3	36
cAMP	8	3	31
GABA	0	0	10
ACH	5	6	21

[a] Indicated are numbers of cells which showed, respectively, ↑ = increased, ↓ = decreased, 0 = no change in firing rate.

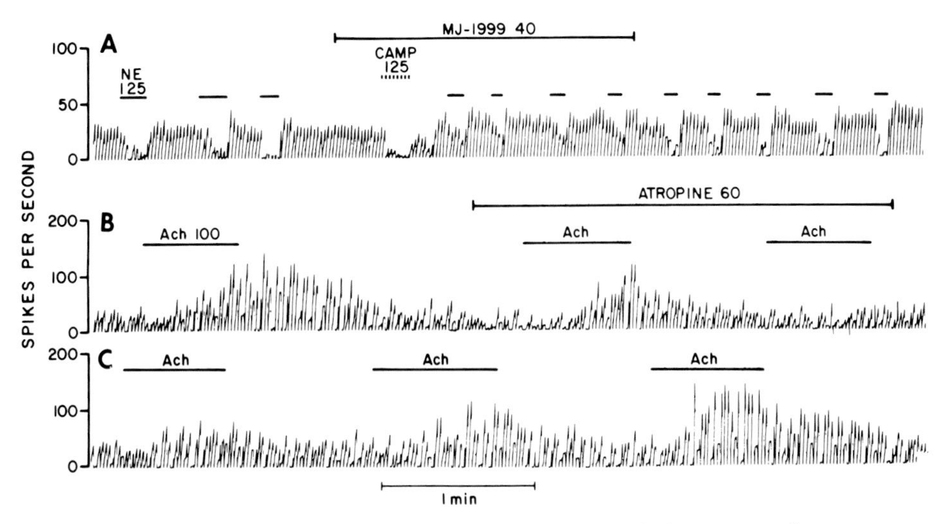

Fig. 8. Integrated spike activity of irradiated Purkinje cells during iontophoretic application of drugs. In (A) the inhibitory effect of NE but not that of cyclic AMP was specifically blocked by application of MJ-1999. Bars indicate the time of application of the drug; numbers denote the relative amount in nanoamperes of current. In (B), continued in time in (C), an excitatory effect of ACH is blocked for several minutes by local application of atropine.

pinephrine while leaving intact the inhibition due to cyclic AMP, as in normal cerebellum. Acetylcholine effects could be blocked by atropine (Fig. 8).

In summary, deafferentation by destruction of cerebellar interneurons yields no major alteration of sensitivity to drugs with the exception of a more consistent inhibitory action by serotonin.

TRANSPLANTED CEREBELLUM

The undifferentiated cerebellar bud that was transplanted grew and differentiated within the eye to reach a final stage of development where the light microscopic organization of cortical areas was similar to that of the normal adult trilaminar cerebellar cortex.

Despite rather marked differences in terms of size and geometry of the folia, the transplants also showed some macroorganizational features similar to those seen *in vivo.* Thus, the smooth or slightly lobulated upper surface of mature transplants often represented the molecular layer (Fig. 9c) of a superficial folium. Complementing this, there were almost always groups of large, multipolar neurons and myelinated fibers in the deep center and base of the transplants. These large

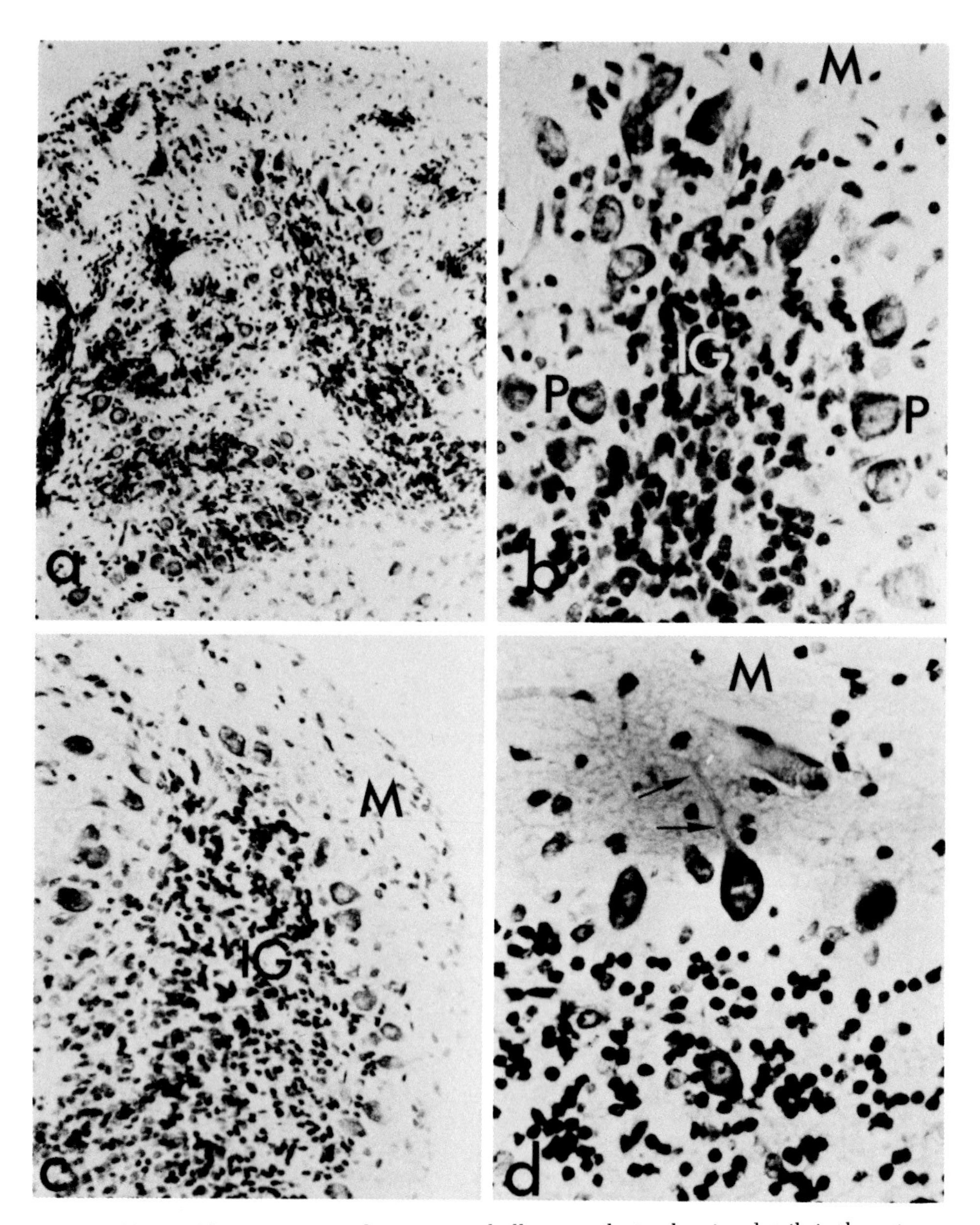

Fig. 9. Almost mature and mature cerebellar transplants, showing details in the pattern of organization. Microphotographs of toluidine-blue-stained 5-μm sections. (a) Transplant 27 days postoperatively with small, strongly stained "islands" of external

neurons in all probability constituted parts of the deep cerebellar nuclei. The correspondence between this area and the "juxtafastigial region" was also indicated by the electrophysiological experiments (see below).

In the fully developed transplants, Purkinje cells were spread out in one layer and their primary dendrites could often be seen to project into the molecular layer (Fig. 9). Slightly above the level of the Purkinje cell soma, lightly stained cells with prominent nucleoli were seen that clearly differed from the smaller, darkly stained internal granule cells, and which probably correspond to basket cells (4).

Electrophysiology

Spontaneous Activity in Transplants in oculo More Than 27–30 Days. Bioelectrical potentials characteristic of extracellularly recorded neuronal action potentials were readily seen in all older transplants studied. Such potentials were never seen when the micropipette tip was in the agar or in the iris adjacent to the transplant. Many neurons in these older transplants showed spontaneous activity. Several different types of patterns were seen. Of particular interest was a population of cells which showed large amplitude (>250 μV) negative–positive action potentials and a rapid discharge rate (see Table I). Recordings from these cells could often be maintained during 30–50-μm movements of the micropipettes, but were invariably lost after movements of > 100 μm, with or without antecedent "injury discharge." Neurons exhibiting this type of discharge were often found in a laminar orientation 150–250 μm below the surface of the transplant. The present study will focus on the electrophysiological characteristics of these particular neurons of the transplants.

In general, two types of discharge were characteristically recorded from these nerve cells. Most of the action potentials were single spikes about 0.5–1.0 msec in duration. However, 5–15% of the action potentials were in the form of high-frequency bursts; each burst consisted of two to five spikes over a 10–15 msec period. The spike fre-

---

granule cells (left). Purkinje cells in single rows are seen clearly bordered by a granule cell layer and a molecular layer; × 155. (b) Detail of (a). The large mature Purkinje cells (P) are oriented with their bases parallel to the granular layer (IG) and the apical dendrites pointing toward the molecular layer (M); ×435. (c) The surface of a transplant 27 days postoperatively, where the organization is very much the same as *in situ,* i.e., molecular layer (M) toward the surface, a single row of large Purkinje cells, and then the (internal) granule cell layer (IG); ×245. (d) Detail of a fully mature cerebellar transplant 43 days postoperatively. In the center, a large Purkinje cell is observed with the primary dendrite (arrows) projecting into the molecular layer (M); ×425.

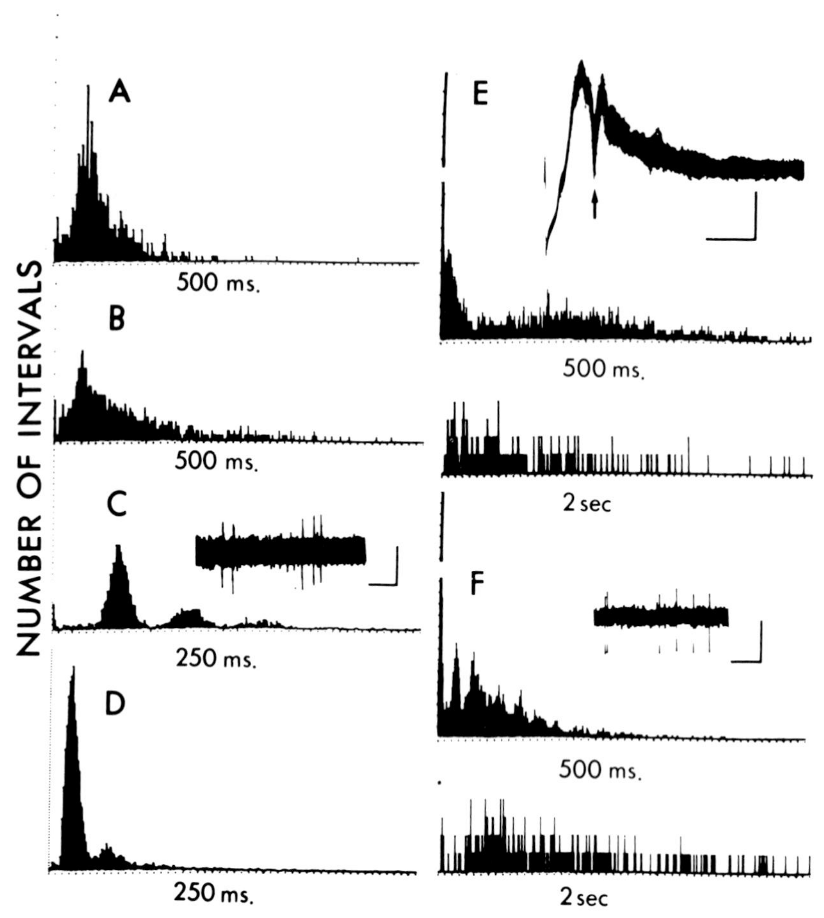

Fig. 10. Spontaneous discharge from neurons in older transplants. (A)–(D) show typical interspike interval histograms from four different cells. (E) and (F) show cells with a sufficient number of bursts to construct both interspike interval histograms (above) and interburst interval histograms (below). The interspike interval histograms in (A) and (B) are most typical, with a small burst peak at 2–5 msec, followed by a unitary, large, single-spike peak. The interspike interval histograms in (C), (D), and (F) show the multiple rhythmicities occasionally seen in some cells with several single spike peaks. Specimen record inset in (C) shows only single spikes, and in (F) shows a burst (two spikes) followed by a pause and four single spikes, respectively. Calibration 100 msec and 300 μV. Each dot on the vertical histogram ordinates is equal to 5 intervals. Time under abscissa represents the longest interspike intervals counted.

quency within the bursts was 200–450/sec. Bursts occurred at rates of 0.5–1.5/sec (overall average 0.9/sec) and were often followed by a 50–100-msec absence of spontaneous discharge.

Interspike interval histograms (IIH) were constructed for the majority of these neurons in order to obtain more precise information about discharge patterns. The histograms usually showed two characteristic peaks (Fig. 10A and B), one at 2–5 msec, corresponding to intervals within the burst, and a second somewhere between 10 and 150 msec, corresponding to the most probable single spike interval. A "tail" to the right of the single spike peak represents the population of pauses in discharge, which sometimes lasts up to several seconds (Fig. 10A). While many cells showed unimodal, single spike peaks (Fig. 10A and B), several cells had multiple peaks (Fig. 10C, D, and F) indicating multiple rhythmicities in single-spike discharge.

Excitation in Older Transplants. In order to determine if this population of neurons could be activated, either the surface or the base of the transplant was stimulated electrically while recording from cells 0.75–4.0 mm distant. Several classes of excitatory responses were observed. First, there was a short latency all-or-none single spike elicited in a few of the cells after stimulation of the base (Fig. 10E). This response readily followed up to 50/sec stimulation and the conduction velocities were 3–5 m/sec.

A second type of response, more commonly seen after surface stimulation, consisted of 1–3 driven spikes over a 5–10 msec period (Figs. 11 and 12). This excitatory response began to decrease at stimulation rates greater than 3/sec and practically disappeared at rates above 8/sec. The response was invariably graded (Fig. 11), rather than all-or-none, and had a conduction velocity of about 0.3–0.5 m/sec. Although the topological organization of the folia was not sufficiently

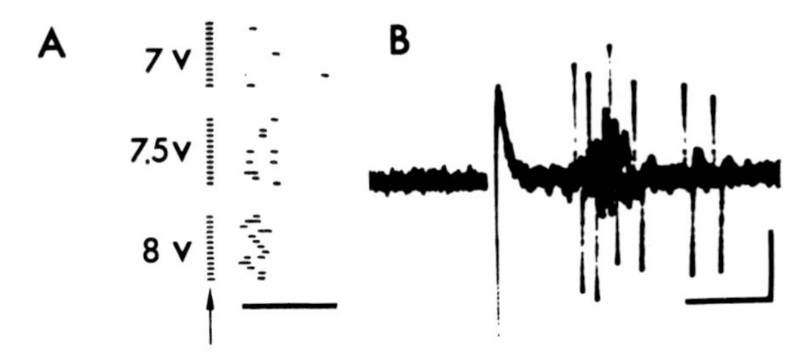

Fig. 11. Graded local excitation produced by surface stimulation in an older transplant. (A) Raster display showing graded nature of the response at three different stimulation strengths. Stimulation indicated by arrow. Calibration bar = 20 msec. (B) Specimen record showing three superimposed sweeps at 8 V stimulation strength. Calibration bar, 7 msec; 500 μV. Conduction velocity 0.4 mm/msec.

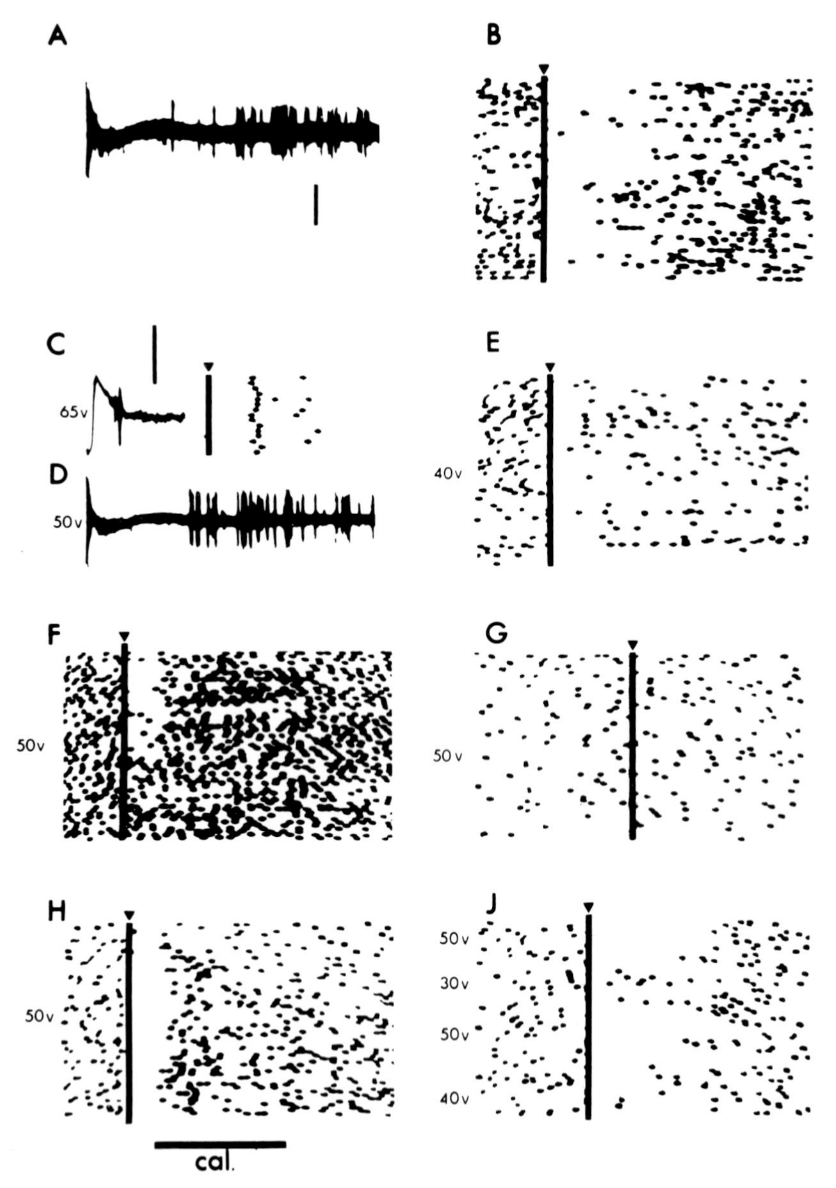

Fig. 12. Effects of changing stimulation strength and parenteral bicuculline on local inhibition. Animal pretreated with reserpine, 2 mg/kg, 3 hr prior to recording. (A) and (B) are from one cell, (C)–(J) are from a second cell. Surface stimulation at indicated intensity. All specimen records are superimposed sweeps with stimulus used to trigger oscilloscope sweep. Stimulus represented in rasters by solid vertical lines and inverted triangles. Cell shown in (A) and (B) manifested local inhibition without preexisting ex-

defined to determine the precise "on-beam," "off-beam" relationships between the stimulation and recording electrodes, it was frequently observed that small movements of the stimulating electrodes (0.5 mm) perpendicular to the stimulation–recording axis led to loss of response. The response usually returned with restoration of the original stimulation site. This graded excitatory response could be seen in transplants as young as 20 days. In almost all respects, these responses resembled those seen in older transplants, except for a slightly slower conduction velocity (0.2–0.3 m/sec).

Stimulation of the surface of the transplant also frequently produced a third type of response, namely, short latency inhibition of spontaneous discharge, lasting 40–120 msec (Fig. 12). This inhibition was also graded (Fig. 12J) and showed a marked dependence on the topological relationship of the stimulation and recording electrode similar to that described for the excitatory responses. The inhibition could be seen with or without antecedent excitation (Fig. 12).

In view of the well-known inhibitory action of norepinephrine on Purkinje neurons *in vivo* (23), it was important to determine if adrenergic fibers in the iris or transplant were involved in this inhibition. After destruction of adrenergic terminals by superior cervical ganglionectomy or depletion of adrenergic transmitter by parenteral reserpine (Fig. 12), this inhibition was still readily observed. Moreover, the inhibition was markedly antagonized by parenteral bicuculline, a potent GABA blocker (24), in all three cells tested pharmacologically (Fig. 12).

Overview of Iontophoretic Studies. A total of 57 cells from 12 mature transplants were suitable for analysis. It was quite difficult to record from most neurons in the transplants for times longer than 15–20 min with multibarreled micropipettes. Nevertheless, all pharmacological responses and interactions described here required at least two "positive" responses, with subsequent recovery, before inclusion in the data collection. The qualitative responses of the Pur-

---

citation. Calibration bar is 200 msec for (B) and 80 msec and 600 uV for (A). (C) Fast-sweep specimen record (left) and raster display (right) showing local excitation with one to three driven spikes at 65 V. Calibration bar, 16.5 msec, 1 mV. (D) and (E) At 50 and 40 V, respectively, this same cell showed local inhibition without preexisting excitation at these lower voltages. Bicuculline produced a speeding of discharge and subsequent disappearance of inhibition in (F) and (G). Two hours later (H) inhibition has returned. Raster (J) shows grading of the inhibitory response with change in stimulation intensity. Inhibition is strong at 50 V, less at 40 V, and minimal at 30 V. Comparison of (E) and (H) also shows this grading. Calibration bar for (D) and (G), 80 msec; (E), (F), (H), and (J), 200 msec.

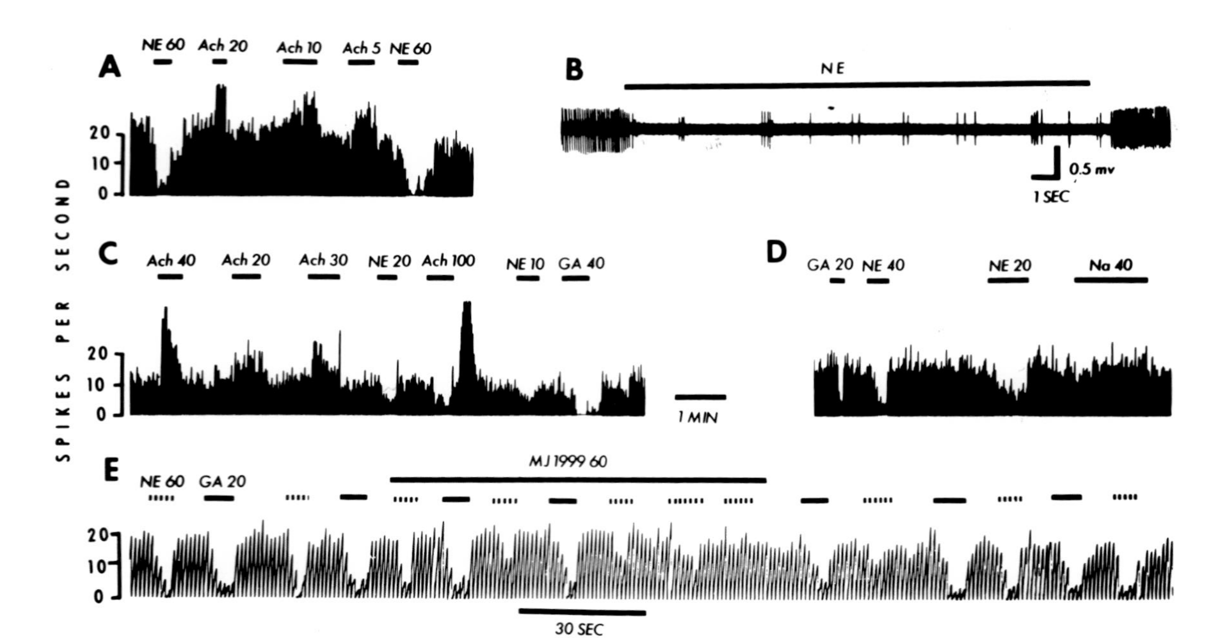

Fig. 13. Response of Purkinje cells in cerebellar transplants to putative neurotransmitters administered by microiontophoresis. (A) and (C)–(E) show polygraph records of the firing rate from four different cells. (B) An action potential record of the first norepinephrine (NE) response shown in (A). In this and all succeeding polygraph records from the iontophoretic experiments, the numbers after each drug refer to the ejection current in nanoamperes, and the bars show the duration of ejection. The 1-min calibration bar refers to (A), (C), and (D). The time calibration bars for (B) and (E) are underneath the respective records. Note the prompt and reversible selective blockade of NE by MJ-1999 in (E) at a dose which does not affect GABA (GA) responses. Responses to acetylcholine (ACH) are shown in (A) and (C). The usual response was a rapid, dose-dependent excitation. At higher doses, however, this was occasionally preceded by a slowing of discharge.

TABLE III
Responses of Purkinje Cell Spontaneous Discharge in Cerebellar Transplants to Putative Neurotransmitters

Neurotransmitter	Slows	Accelerates	No effects
NE	40	2	4
GABA	6	0	0
Glutamate	0	7	1

kinje cells (as identified by the criteria in Methods) to putative cerebellar transmitters are shown in Table III. Decreases in discharge were elicited by NE and GABA (Fig. 13), whereas glutamate increased the firing rate. Acetylcholine had both excitatory and inhibitory effects. At low doses, a short latency excitation was usually seen (Figs. 13A and C). An initial inhibition, with or without a subsequent elevation in discharge rate, could be produced by higher doses in some neurons (Fig. 13C).

Responses To Norepinephrine and Amphetamine. Norepinephrine produced an inhibition of spontaneous discharge in 40 of 46 neurons tested. The inhibitions were relatively prompt, usually maximal within 15 sec after the onset of the iontophoretic current, and were readily reversible after termination of the drug (Fig. 13). During NE inhibition, cells could readily be made to fire by application of the excitatory amino acid glutamate. Current controls were performed; these were usually negative (Fig. 13). The inhibitory responses to NE were antagonized by the β-blocker MJ-1999 in three of five cells, at doses which did not produce any inactivation of the spike-generating mechanism (Fig. 13).

DISCUSSION

After either neonatal X-irradiation or transplantation, the subsequent development of the cerebellar cortex and Purkinje neuron is marked by a retention of normal functional properties to the greatest extent possible. Thus, in both preparations, the Purkinje neurons fire spontaneously at rates approximating "normal" (Table I).

Previous studies on the effects of various other forms of deafferentation of Purkinje cells have also shown continuous activity to remain. A steady firing has been reported after deafferentation by remote lesions such as decerebration, which would be expected to diminish excitatory background activity (25), or by pedunculectomy (2). Isolated cerebellar folia also have been shown to exhibit sustained activity (26). In each of these cases the granule cell population remains intact and it can be argued that a spontaneous release of transmitter from the intact parallel fibers could drive the Purkinje cells to threshold.

Spontaneous activity is also maintained by Purkinje cells in tissue culture (27,28,29) where there is complete isolation from extracerebellar inputs and only sparse contacts from the few remaining interneurons. Activity in some cells has also been reported when such cultures are exposed to an elevated Mg^{2+} concentration expected to block synaptic activity. Moreover, a much slower but steady activity can be found in immature cerebellum before synapses are prevalent (13).

Similarly, Purkinje neurons in both the irradiated and transplanted cerebellum manifest normal pharmacological sensitivity to putative transmitters. The irradiated cerebellar cortex offers an unusual opportunity for the study of chemosensitivity of the postsynaptic membrane to putative neurotransmitters without presynaptic actions on parallel fibers and inhibitory interneuronal terminals. The only difference from normal Purkinje cell pharmacology was the consistent inhibition by serotonin in irradiated rats. A similar uniformity was found in immature Purkinje cells before parallel fiber contacts were made (13).

It has been previously reported that rat Purkinje cells exhibit their adult range of membrane chemosensitivity at least by the day of birth (13). At that time the population of cells is still migrating into a monolayer and has yet to form synapses. Thus, basic chemoreceptive properties appear early, are fully differentiated at the beginning of irradiation, and remain stable in spite of a most severely altered milieu for dendritic and synaptic growth.

In spite of the near-total destruction of interneurons, there is a possibility that some synapses employing each of the normal transmitters could be present. Climbing fiber synapses are present and may mediate effects by the same (although unknown) transmitter as parallel fibers. Excitatory transmitter may also be released from mossy fibers contacting with Purkinje cells. There is good evidence that basket and stellate inhibitory interneurons, as well as Purkinje cells, release GABA as their inhibitory transmitter (30,31). Purkinje collaterals are known to make extensive contact with other Purkinje cells in the young rat (32). These contacts may survive in large numbers in the irradiated cerebellum (11). Also, a few inhibitory interneurons may survive, and these could contact many Purkinje cells. Therefore, some GABA-mediated synapses may be present. Another Purkinje cell inhibitory transmitter, norepinephrine, is thought to be released onto Purkinje dendrites from fine, unmyelinated fibers originating in the locus coeruleus in the brain stem (33). Preliminary experiments on histochemical localization of norepinephrine-containing fibers by formaldehyde-induced fluorescence suggest that terminals appear in equal or greater than normal numbers, and hence could exert a substantial influence on activity.

In terms of excitatory and inhibitory input to the Purkinje neurons, it appears that any specific pathways that survive the initial perinatal disruption make appropriate synaptic connections. Thus, in the case of the transplant, climbing fibers are obviously destroyed during the initial grafting. However, parallel fibers and inhibitory interneurons survive.

The excitatory and inhibitory responses elicited by surface stimulation of the transplant correlate well with *in situ* parallel fiber excitation and basket–stellate cell inhibition (2,3,4), respectively. Both types of synaptic activity *in situ* are graded and critically dependent on the geometry of the stimulating and recording electrodes vis-à-vis beams of parallel fibers, as are the excitatory and inhibitory responses reported here. Moreover, the conduction velocities of these responses, 0.3–0.5 m/sec, correlate with known parallel fiber conduction velocities, as do the duration of excitatory (5–10 msec) and inhibitory (20–120 msec) effects (2,13).

Furthermore, the inhibitory action of surface stimulation is reversibly blocked by bicuculline, which has been reported to antagonize basket–stellate cell inhibition *in situ* (24). In view of the known specificity of this drug for GABA receptors, it is probable that also in the transplant, local inhibition is mediated by GABA. Light microscopic autoradiography of the transplants (35), after administration of ^{3}H-GABA, supports this hypothesis since labeling is prominent around Purkinje cells.

The opposite is true in the X-irradiated cerebella. Granule cells, parallel fibers, and inhibitory interneurons are largely absent, but a number of "appropriate" synaptic reorganizations occur at the level of the Purkinje neuron.

Evidence suggesting that more than one climbing fiber routinely activates a Purkinje cell in the irradiated cortex consists of (1) extracellular recordings revealing phases of frequent bursting with no refractory period between the bursts; (2) intracellular recording revealing large, unitary EPSP's similar to those in normal animals but with discretely different amplitudes; and (3) the EPSP's of different amplitudes occurring independently with effectively zero latency between them. The EPSP's of different sizes would be expected if different portions of the Purkinje cells were innervated by climbing fibers which make variable numbers of multiple small contacts. The phenomenon of zero latency between the bursts, or the EPSP's, would be expected if impulses from two or more afferents were to arrive independently. Such phenomena have not been observed by the authors in studies of several hundred Purkinje cells in normal rats. The only previous report of similar phenomena (22) described two of more than 100 Purkinje cells in normal feline cerebellum as having such multiple innervation.

The fact that the number of climbing fibers remains small, two to four at most, suggests that some normal tendency remains for this afferent to "capture" large portions of the potential postsynaptic receiving sites. The total number of postsynaptic sites may not be greater with the additional climbing fibers since each afferent by itself is often not able to generate an inactivation response.

Our assertion that more than one climbing fiber contacts a single Purkinje cell depends on the reasonable assumption that the EPSP's are in fact generated by climbing fibers, but this must still be subject to some scrutiny. One difficulty is that anatomical evidence for this form of multiple innervation has not yet been provided. Electrotonic connections between Purkinje cells could conceivably produce these phenomena, but electron microscopic studies do not favor this possibility (11). A further possibility is that these potentials are in fact produced by some mossy fibers respecified to behave somewhat like climbing fibers. This would require (1) an extensive anatomical reorganization toward multiple excitatory contacts with single Purkinje cells; (2) a decrease in spontaneous firing to 1/sec; and (3) the presence of a climbing fiber reflex response.

The possibility of direct mossy fiber contacts on Purkinje cells must be further investigated. Llinas *et al.* (36) have reported such contacts in the cerebellum of ferrets degranulated after infection with feline panleukopenia virus. Mossy fiber rosettes have also been observed in the cortex of irradiated cerebella in rats (11).

The inhibitory actions of Purkinje cells (see Fig. 7E) could be mediated by a few remaining interneurons (36), which would be excited by mossy fibers. Alternately, Purkinje cell recurrent collaterals may make contacts on other Purkinje cells (32) and mediate a substantial inhibition. This possibility is more likely since Altman and Anderson (11,12), using the Bodian silver technique, have observed the presence of fibers more numerous than the number of remaining interneurons in the irradiated cerebellar cortex. Positive evidence was obtained in one instance where a myelinated axon (which cannot be a basket cell terminal) formed an inconspicuous symmetrical synapse with a Purkinje cell soma. The 10–12/sec oscillatory bursting activity (see Fig. 4) conceivably might appear if a direct feedback inhibition were able to synchronize a population of Purkinje cells.

In conclusion, the data from both X-irradiated and transplanted cerebellum strongly support the primacy of inherent mechanisms in central neuronal development. Purkinje neuron spontaneous discharge, chemosensitivity to putative transmitters, and appropriate excitatory and inhibitory synaptic inputs are readily seen, despite severe alterations in the neurohormonal mileu. It remains for future research to determine if these electrophysiological properties are coded at the level of the genome and, if so, how the information is read out at the level of the neuronal membrane during maturation.

ACKNOWLEDGMENTS

This work was supported by NSPHS Grants NS09199(4) to BJH and NS09820 to DJW, and by Swedish MRC Grant 04X-03185 to LO.

REFERENCES

1. Addison, W. H. F. (1911) *J. Comp. Neurol.* **218,** 459–488.
2. Eccles, J. C., Ito, M. and Szentagothai, J. (1967) "The Cerebellum as a Neuronal Machine," Springer-Verlag, New York.
3. Llinas, R., ed. (1969) "Neurobiology of Cerebellular Evolution and Development." AMA Press, Chicago.
4. Altman, J. (1972a) *J. Comp. Neurol.* **145,** 353–398.
5. Altman, J. (1972b) *J. Comp. Neurol.* **145,** 399–464.
6. Altman, J. (1972c) *J. Comp. Neurol* **145,** 465–514.
7. Hicks, S. P., and D'Amato, C. J. (1966) *In* "Advances in Teratology," (D. H. M. Woollam, ed), Logos Press, London, pp. 195–250.
8. Altman, J., and Anderson, W. J. (1971) *Exp. Neurol.* **30,** 492–509.
9. Altman, J., Anderson, W. J., and Wright, K. A. (1969a) *Exp. Neurol.* **24,** 196–216.
10. Altman, J., Anderson, W. J., and Wright, K. A. (1969b) *Anat. Rec.* **163,** 453–472.
11. Altman, J., and Anderson, W. J. (1972) *J. Comp. Neurol.* **146,** 355–405.
12. Altman, J., and Anderson, W. J. (1973) *J. Comp. Neurol.* **149,** 123–152.
13. Woodward, D. J., Hoffer, B. J., Siggins, G. R., and Bloom, F. E. (1971a) *Brain Res.* **34,** 73–97.
14. Woodward, D. J. (1972) PISH-poststimulus time and interspike interval histogram. Digital Equipment Co. Users Society-Program Library, Decus No. 12-65, Maynard, Mass.
15. Olson, L., and Seiger, A. (1972) *Z. Zellforsh.* **135,** 175–194.
16. Wall, P. D. (1959) *J. Neurophysiol.*, **22,** 305–320.
17. Falck, B. (1962) *Acta physiol. scand.*, *56*, Suppl. **197,** 1–26.
18. Falck, B., Hillarp, N.-A., Thieme, G., and Throp. A. (1962) *J. Histochem. Cytochem.*, **10,** 348–354.
19. Malmfors, T. (1965) *Acta physiol. scand.*, Suppl. **248,** 1–93.

20. Salmoiraghi, G. C., and Weight, F. F. (1967) *Anesthesiology* **28,** 54–64.
21. Woodward, D. J., Hoffer, B. J., and Lapham, L. W. (1969a) *Exp. Neurol.* **23,** 120–139.
22. Eccles, J. C., Llinas, R., and Sasaki, K. (1966a) *J. Physiol.* **182,** 268–296.
23. Hoffer, B. J., Siggins, G. R., and Bloom, F. E. (1971a) *Brain Res.* **25,** 523–534.
24. Curtis, D. R., and Felix, D. (1971) *Brain Res.* **34,** 301–321.
25. Murphy, J. T., and Sabah, N. (1970) *Brain Res.* **17,** 515–519.
26. Snider, R. S., Teramoto, S., and Ban, J. (1967) *Exp. Neurol.* **19,** 443–454.
27. Gahwiler, B. H., Mamoon, A. M., and Tobias, C. A. (1973) *Brain Res.* **53,** 71–79.
28. Geller, H. and Woodward, D. J. (1974) *Brain Res.* **74,** 67–80.
29. Schlapfer, W. T., Mamoon, A., and Tobias, C. A. (1972) *Brain Res.* **45,** 345–363.
30. Obata, K., Ito, M., Ochi, R., and Sato, N. (1967) *Exp. Brain Res.* **4,** 43–57.
31. Woodward, D. J., Hoffer, B. J., Siggins, G. R., and Oliver, A. P. (1971b) *Brain Res.* **33,** 91–100.
32. Chan-Palay, V. (1971) *Z. Anat. Entwicklungs-gesch.* **134,** 200–234.
33. Olson, L. and Fuxe, K. (1971) *Brain Res.* **28,** 165–171.
34. Eccles, J. C., Llinas, R., and Sasaki, K. (1966) *Exp. Brain Res.,* **1,** 17–39.
35. Ljungdahl, A., Seiger, A., Hokfelt, T., and Olson, L. (1973) [^{3}H] GABA uptake in growing cerebellar tissue: Autoradiography of intraocular transplants. *Brain Res.* **61,** 379–384.
36. Llinas, R., Hillman, D. E., and Precht, W. (1973) *J. Neurobiol.* **4,** 69–94.

Index

C

D

V

W

X

A B 8 C 9 D 0 E 1 F 2 G 3 H 4 I 5 J 6